*Fundamental statistics
in psychology and
education*

McGraw-Hill Series in Psychology

Harry F. Harlow, Consulting Editor

Beach, Hebb, Morgan, and Nissen *The Neuropsychology of Lashley*
von Békésy *Experiments in Hearing*
Berkowitz *Aggression: A Social Psychological Analysis*
Berlyne *Conflict, Arousal, and Curiosity*
Blum *Psychoanalytic Theories of Personality*
Brown *The Motivation of Behavior*
Brown *The Psychodynamics of Abnormal Behavior*
Brown and Ghiselli *Scientific Method in Psychology*
Buckner and McGrath *Vigilance: A Symposium*
Cofer *Verbal Learning and Verbal Behavior*
Cofer and Musgrave *Verbal Behavior and Learning: Problems and Processes*
Crafts, Schneirla, Robinson, and Gilbert *Recent Experiments in Psychology*
Davitz *The Communication of Emotional Meaning*
Deese *The Psychology of Learning*
Dollard and Miller *Personality and Psychotherapy*
Dorcus and Jones *Handbook of Employee Selection*
Ellis *Handbook of Mental Deficiency*
Ferguson *Personality Measurement*
Ferguson *Statistical Analysis in Psychology and Education*
Ghiselli *Theory of Psychological Measurement*
Ghiselli and Brown *Personnel and Industrial Psychology*
Gilmer *Industrial Psychology*
Gray *Psychology Applied to Human Affairs*
Guilford *Fundamental Statistics in Psychology and Education*
Guilford *Personality*
Guilford *Psychometric Methods*
Guion *Personnel Testing*
Haire *Psychology in Management*
Hirsh *The Measurement of Hearing*
Hurlock *Adolescent Development*
Hurlock *Child Development*
Hurlock *Developmental Psychology*
Karn and Gilmer *Readings in Industrial and Business Psychology*

Krech and Crutchfield *Theory and Problems of Social Psychology*
Lazarus *Adjustment and Personality*
Lewin *A Dynamic Theory of Personality*
Lewin *Principles of Topological Psychology*
Lewis *Quantitative Methods in Psychology*
Maier and Schneirla *Principles of Animal Psychology*
Marx and Hillix *Systems and Theories in Psychology*
Messick and Brayfield *Decision and Choice: Contributions of Sidney Siegel*
Miller *Language and Communication*
Misiak and Staudt *Catholics in Psychology: A Historical Survey*
Morgan and Stellar *Psysiological Psychology*
Page *Abnormal Psychology*
Rethlingshafer *Motivation as Related to Personality*
Reymert *Feelings and Emotions*
Robinson and Robinson *The Mentally Retarded Child*
Scherer and Wertheimer *A Psycholinguistic Experiment on Foreign-language Teaching*
Seashore *Psychology of Music*
Shaffer and Lazarus *Fundamental Concepts in Clinical Psychology*
Siegel *Nonparametric Statistics for the Behavioral Sciences*
Stagner *Psychology of Personality*
Townsend *Introduction to Experimental Methods for Psychology and Social Science*
Vinacke *The Psychology of Thinking*
Wallen *Clinical Psychology: The Study of Persons*
Warren and Akert *The Frontal Granular Cortex and Behavior*
Waters, Rethlingshafer, and Caldwell *Principles of Comparative Psychology*
Winer *Statistical Principles in Experimental Design*
Zubek and Solberg *Human Development*

John F. Dashiell was Consulting Editor of this series from its inception in 1931 until January 1, 1950. Clifford T. Morgan was Consulting Editor of this series from January 1, 1950 until January 1, 1959.

Fundamental statistics in psychology and education

J. P. Guilford

Department of Psychology
University of Southern California

FOURTH EDITION

McGraw-Hill Book Company

NEW YORK   ST. LOUIS   SAN FRANCISCO
TORONTO   LONDON   SYDNEY

Preface

ABOUT ten years have passed since the preparation of the third edition of this volume. Those ten years have been as productive as almost any other recent decade in new developments in statistical methods and in changes in the relative importance of the various statistical procedures. Continued experience in teaching with this text has also indicated where further improvements in presentation could be effected. These statements summarize the reasons for a fourth edition.

As before, attention has been given to the "programing" of material to be covered, with an effort to see that information needed as a basis for the presentation of any topic shall have preceded that presentation. Within the limits of the application of this principle, of course, there is some leeway. Changes which have been aimed at this objective include the presentation of the introduction to the basic ideas and methods of correlation earlier (in Chapter 6 rather than in Chapter 8) and the introduction of a new chapter (Chapter 7) on Probability and Mathematical Distributions preparatory to the chapters on sampling statistics immediately following.

Additional new material includes the treatment of the basic definitions and theorems of probability in Chapter 7, the Kolmogorov-Smirnov nonparametric tests in what is now a separate chapter on nonparametric tests, and methods of item analysis, which have been restored to Chapter 18 on Validity of Measurements. Chapter 10 on Hypothesis Testing includes new treatment of errors of type II and power functions, as well as more attention to the problem of size of samples needed to meet certain testing requirements.

Some incidental additions have been made in the form of mathematical derivations of some of the more common formulas at various places in the text. This has been done to meet the questions of the mathematically interested students and to take further steps beyond the "cookbook" treatment; also, in recognition of the fact that students now entering courses on statistics have somewhat better mathematical backgrounds than formerly. The proofs given in Appendix A remain intact.

In line with the policy indicated in the preceding paragraph, a simple mathematical introduction is given for chi square and some further mathematical ideas basic to analysis of variance. A number of new formulas have been introduced to take care of special needs not previously met.

In order to keep this volume at about the same length, a number of omissions and condensations have been effected. The pages on rounding of numbers and significant digits have been eliminated. Chapters 3 through 6, on basic, descriptive statistics, have been materially shortened and streamlined. Chapter 14 of the third edition on Prediction of Attributes has been eliminated, with some of its more essential components now incorporated at the end of Chapter 15 on Prediction and Accuracy of Prediction.

Items of reorganization worthy of mention include the separation of the material on chi square and on nonparametric methods into two chapters, as already mentioned. Chapter 9 has also been divided into two new chapters, one on Statistical Estimations and Inferences and the other on Significance of Differences. In the latter small-sample statistical ideas are introduced.

Several tables in Appendix B have been improved. Table A now includes reciprocals of N and of the square root of N, in addition to squares and square roots, thanks to the University of Southern California Computer Center, where the new table was prepared. Table B is a much more complete listing of values associated with the unit normal distribution, thanks to the permission of Dr. Allen L. Edwards and Holt, Rinehart and Winston, Inc. Other tables have been extended to include additional values, and one new table has been added.

As usual, I am indebted to numerous individuals who have contributed to this revision, only a few of whom can be specifically mentioned. Mr. Stephen W. Brown has checked the accuracy of the answers given to problems in many of the chapters. I take full responsibility for any errors in answers which still remain. Mr. Henry Bedard rose to the occasion of typing most of the final manuscript under circumstances of almost emergency proportions. Above all, I am indebted to Dr. William B. Michael, who faithfully and generously gave time and counsel on many matters pertaining to teachability and to accuracy of statements. Any faults remaining are attributable to the author's decisions and oversights.

J. P. GUILFORD

Contents

Preface, vii

1. Introduction for students
1

2. Counting and measuring
11

Data in categories, 12

Measurements, 18

EXERCISES, 24

3. Frequency distributions
26

The class interval — its limits and frequencies, 26

Graphic representation of frequency distributions, 30

Cumulative frequencies and cumulative distributions, 36

EXERCISES, 40

4. Measures of central value
43

The arithmetic mean, 44

The median and centile values, 49

The mode, 55

When to employ the mean, median, and mode, 56

Means of means, percentages, and proportions, 63

EXERCISES, 64

5. Measures of variability
68

The total range, 68

The semi-interquartile range — Q, 69

The average deviation, 71

The standard deviation, 72

Descriptive use of statistics, 85

Uses and interrelationships of different measures of dispersion, 88

EXERCISES, 89

6. *Correlation*   91

   The meaning of correlation, 92
   How to compute a coefficient of correlation, 95
   Interpretations of a coefficient of correlation, 103
   Graphic representations of correlations, 106
   Assumptions underlying the product-moment correlation, 107
   Derivation of some correlation formulas, 108
   EXERCISES, 110

7. *Probability and mathematical distributions* 113

   The need for mathematical models, 113
   Principles of probability, 115
   Binomial distributions, 118
   The normal distribution, 124
   Areas under the normal-distribution curve, 127
   Other tests and other mathematical models, 132
   EXERCISES, 133

8. *Statistical estimation and inferences*   136

   Some principles of sampling, 137
   Inferences regarding averages, 142
   Inferences regarding other statistics, 158
   Some special problems of estimation, 164
   EXERCISES, 168

9. *Significance of differences*   171

   Differences between means, 173
   Differences between proportions and frequencies, 185
   Differences between coefficients of correlation, 189
   Differences between variances, 191
   Differences between changes, 194
   EXERCISES, 198

10. *Hypothesis testing*   200

   Some rules for statistical decisions, 200
   Errors in statistical decisions, 205
   Needed sample sizes, 214
   Testing hypotheses with the binomial model, 220
   EXERCISES, 224

11. *Chi square*   227

   General features of chi square, 227
   Chi square in a contingency table, 234
   Some special applications of chi square, 242
   EXERCISES, 250

12. Nonparametric or distribution-free statistics — 252

Tests of differences with correlated data, 253
Tests of differences with uncorrelated data, 257
Tests of similarity of frequency distributions, 260
EXERCISES, 266

13. Introduction to analysis of variance — 268

Analysis in a one-way classification problem, 269
Analysis in a two-way classification problem, 281
General comments on analysis of variance, 300
EXERCISES, 302

14. Special correlation methods and problems — 304

Spearman's rank-difference correlation method, 305
The correlation ratio, 308
The biserial coefficient of correlation, 317
Point-biserial correlation, 322
Tetrachoric correlation, 326
The phi coefficient, 333
Partial correlation, 339
Some special problems in correlation, 341
EXERCISES, 354

15. Prediction and accuracy of prediction — 356

Predicting measurements from attributes, 357
Predicting measurements from other measurements, 362
Regression equations, 366
The correlation coefficient and accuracy of prediction, 376
Prediction of attributes from measurements, 380
Prediction of attributes from other attributes, 386
EXERCISES, 389

16. Multiple prediction — 392

Multiple correlation, 392
Some principles of multiple correlation, 403
Multiple correlation with more than three variables, 408
Other combinations of measures, 416
Alternative summarizing methods, 428
EXERCISES, 435

17. Reliability of measurements — 438

Reliability theory, 438
Methods of estimating reliability, 445
Internal-consistency reliability, 453

Some special problems of reliability, 464
Derivation of the Spearman-Brown formula for the general case, 466
EXERCISES, 467

18. *Validity of measurements*   470
Problems of validity, 470
A brief introduction to factor theory, 473
Conditions upon which validity depends, 480
Item analysis, 493
EXERCISES, 506

19. *Test scales and norms*   510
Standard scores, 512
The T scale and T scaling of tests, 518
The C scale and C scaling, 524
Some norm and profile suggestions, 528
EXERCISES, 530

Appendix A   Some selected mathematical proofs
             and derivations, 533

Appendix B   Tables, 547

             Index, 599

*Fundamental statistics
in psychology and
education*

1 Introduction for students

WHY THE STUDENT NEEDS STATISTICS

Most seasoned workers in psychology or in education usually take the statistical methods for granted as an essential part of their routine, some more so and some less. The initiate may at first react to statistics as a frightful bogie whose mysteries loom forbiddingly before him, and he is likely to ask, "What is the good of them, anyway?" This is particularly true of one who feels he has always had trouble with numbers. Students who enter a first course in statistical methods in psychology or education, and probably in all related social sciences, range all the way from those who find mathematics in general easy and to their liking, to those at the other extreme who say they have difficulty in adding two and two. Somehow, all these must acquire what they can of a subject for which they are so unequally prepared.

Probably no other subject demonstrates so clearly that there are several kinds of intelligence. No less a person intellectually than Charles Darwin had trouble with statistics, as he is said to have frankly admitted. His almost equally illustrious cousin, Sir Francis Galton, who is believed to have had an IQ of about 200, and who had so much to do with introducing statistics into psychology, had to turn some of his mathematical problems over to others for aid.

There are different ways of understanding the same things. One student will grasp the new ideas offered by statistics in the way that a mathematician would understand them; another will appreciate the logical rules of thinking and the concepts provided as aids in thinking; still others will master rule-of-thumb operations and be able to carry through computations with a minimum grasp of what they are all about.

Learning without achieving insights and appreciations of the inner nature of things is learning without full motivation and enthusiasm and is not very satisfying. The average student will necessarily have to be content with levels of insight that fall short of those of the mathematician, remembering that even mathematicians have not by any means exhausted the meanings and ramifications of statistical ideas. On the other hand, each student should strive to inject as much meaning and significance, in his own way, as he can. The proper use and optimal use of statistical methods and statistical thinking require a certain minimal achievement of understanding. Clerks can be taught to carry out many of the computational procedures; it is not the primary purpose of this book or of those who teach with it to develop computational clerks. The purpose is to develop those who could be supervisors of clerks.

To be more specific, there are four simple, undeniable reasons why the student who takes a required course in statistics must develop some mastery of that subject.

1. *He must be able to read professional literature.* There is no questioning the fact that learning in any field comes largely through reading. The student never finishes the extension of his skill in the art of reading, if he is a thorough student. In any specialized field, reading is largely a matter of enlarging vocabulary. One cannot read much of the literature in any specialized field in the social sciences, particularly in the behavioral sciences, without encountering statistical symbols, concepts, and ideas on every hand. One could do as the young child does when he tackles reading matter that is somewhat beyond him – "skip over the hard places." But this is hardly excusable in the adult who is reading material that should not be beyond him and in which the "hard places" may, in fact, contain the crucial parts of the content. One who dodges such parts is likely to be dependent upon the conclusions of others for his own conclusions and opinions. This is hardly independent judgment or a symptom of mature scholarship. It is not necessary for every student to be able to sail through the "heavier" mathematical contributions of the specialist in statistics. It is severely limiting, however, for a person not to be able to read intelligently the average research paper in his field with some appreciation as to whether sound conclusions have been reached. The chances are that this appreciation will require familiarity with basic statistical ideas.

2. *He must master techniques needed in advanced courses.* Whether the advanced course is a laboratory course or a practicum, there are usually certain incidental techniques that are commonly used in the operations involved. In the laboratory course, results cannot be treated or reports written without at least minimal statistical operations. A field survey or the checking of a report also involves inevitable statistical steps.

3. *Statistics is an essential part of professional training.* The trained psychologist or educator likes to think of himself as a professional person. To some extent, statistical logic, statistical thinking,

and statistical operations are a necessary part of either profession. To the extent that he uses in his practice the common technical instruments, such as tests, the psychologist or educator will depend upon statistical background in their administration and in the interpretation of the results. Using tests without knowledge of the statistical reasoning upon which they depend is like the medical diagnostician's using clinical tests without a knowledge of physiology and pathology.

4. *Statistics are everywhere basic to research activities.* To the extent that either psychologist or educator intends to keep alive his research interests and research activities, he will necessarily lean upon his knowledge and skills in statistical methods. The relation of statistics to research will be elaborated upon in the next paragraphs. Here it is merely urged that in any professional fields where there are still so many unknowns as in the behavioral sciences, the advancement of those professions and of the competence of their members depends to a high degree upon the continued research attitude and research efforts of those members.

WHY STATISTICS ARE IMPORTANT IN RESEARCH

Briefly, the advantages of statistical thinking and operations in research are as follows:

1. *They permit the most exact kind of description.* When all is said and done, the goal of science is description of phenomena, description so complete and so accurate that it is useful to anyone who can understand it when he reads the symbols in terms of which those phenomena are described. Mathematics and statistics are a part of our descriptive language, an outgrowth of our verbal symbols, peculiarly adapted to the efficient kind of description that the scientist demands.

2. *They force us to be definite and exact in our procedures and in our thinking.* The writer once heard a prominent psychologist defend his rather vague conclusions by saying that he would rather be vague and right than be definite and wrong. But the alternatives are not to be either "vague and right" or "definite and wrong." One can also be definite and right, and it is the writer's contention that the odds for being right are overwhelmingly on the "definite" side of the matter.

3. *Statistics enable us to summarize our results in meaningful and convenient form.* Masses of observations taken by themselves are bewildering and almost meaningless. Before we can see the forest as well as the trees, order must be given to the data. Statistics provide an unrivaled device for bringing order out of chaos, of seeing the general picture in one's results.

4. *They enable us to draw general conclusions,* and the process of

extracting conclusions is carried out according to accepted rules. Furthermore, by means of statistical steps, we can say about how much faith should be placed in any conclusion and about how far we may extend our generalization.

5. *They enable us to make predictions* of "how much" of a thing will happen under conditions we know and have measured. For example, we can predict the probable mark a freshman will earn in college algebra if we know his score in a general academic-aptitude test, his score in a special algebra-aptitude test, his average mark in high-school mathematics, and perhaps the number of hours per week that he devotes to studying algebra. Our prediction may be somewhat in error because of other factors that we have not accounted for, but statistical methods will also tell us about how much margin of error to allow in making predictions. Thus not only can we make predictions but we know how much faith to place in them.

6. *They enable us to analyze some of the causal factors of complex and otherwise bewildering events.* It is generally true in the social sciences, and in psychology and education in common with them, that any event or outcome is a resultant of numerous causal factors. The reasons why a man fails in his business or in his profession, for example, are varied and many. Causal factors are usually best uncovered and proved by means of experimental method. If it could be shown that, all other factors being held constant, certain businessmen fail to the extent that they possess some defect in personality "*X*"—a trait—then it is probable that *X* is a cause of failure in this type of business.

Unfortunately for the social scientist, he cannot manage men and their affairs sufficiently to set up a good experiment of this type. The next best thing is to make a statistical study, taking businessmen as we find them, working under conditions as they normally do. The life-insurance expert does this when he follows the trail of all possible factors that influence the length of life and determines how important they are. On the basis of these statistical findings, he can predict about how long an individual of a certain type will probably live, and his insurance company can plan an insurance policy accordingly. Statistical methods are therefore often a necessary substitute for experiments. Even where experiments are possible, the experimental data must ordinarily receive appropriate statistical treatment. Statistical methods are hence the constant companions of experiments.

WHAT THIS VOLUME'S TREATMENT OF STATISTICS WILL INCLUDE

For the next few paragraphs we shall take a hasty overview of the things to come. The second chapter will give many more details of a general and preparatory nature. Here we shall try to look at the whole forest before we enter it.

Descriptive and sampling statistics.   It is common to make a broad distinction between *descriptive* and *sampling* statistics. This distinction refers to two important uses of statistics.

In the first place, statistics are used to describe. For example, averages tell us "how much" of certain quantities we have in a group of individuals or in a group of observations. An average (for example, *arithmetic mean, median,* or *mode*) is a general-level concept. That is, a single number tells how high one group, or sample, stands on a certain scale as compared with another.

Other statistics tell us how much variability, or scatter, the individuals of a group show. A statistic known as the *standard deviation* has been the almost universal indicator of the amount of variability in a set of individuals or observations, though there are other indicators.

A *coefficient of correlation* describes the closeness of relationship between two sets of measures of the same group of individuals or observations. Most of science is concerned with finding out what things go with what, and what things are independent of what. Correlation methods, in the social sciences at least, are the most useful devices to answer these questions of interrelationships. Averages and indices of dispersion and correlation are the basic and chief descriptive statistics.

Sampling statistics tell us how well the statistics we obtain from measurements of single samples probably represent the larger populations from which the samples were drawn. Almost every statistic has a *standard error*. A standard error is an index number that leads us to conclusions concerning how far the statistic derived from the sample probably differs from the value we would obtain if we had measured an entire population. A *population* is a well-defined group of individuals or of observations. For example, it could be one composed of Wistar-Institute albino rats between the ages of 30 and 60 days. Or it could be all possible reproductions a certain observer could make of a line 10 cm long under the same conditions of rest, time of day, and method of reproduction, for example, by drawing a line with a pencil. A sample in either case would be a limited number of observations out of the entire population. Arriving at conclusions that can be generalized to all members of a population depends upon reducing discrepancies between population values and sample values to as small a size as possible. This is probably best illustrated by public-opinion polling, in which the margin of error of voting outcome can be expressed in terms of a percentage of error.

In connection with sampling statistics, there is much in this volume on testing hypotheses. Scientific investigation proceeds from hypothesis to hypothesis. There are numerous hypotheses but relatively few established facts of a general nature. The sooner the research student realizes this point, the better for his clear thinking. Unfortunately, there are some investigators, many of them experienced, who do not make this distinction between a hypothesis and a fact; they mistake hypotheses for facts. For example, there is the hypothesis, stemming from Freudian psychology, that children suffering from asthma are of the "oral-dependent" type and that the breathing spasms are expressions of a cry for aid and love. The plausibility of the hypothesis, and its consistency with other hypotheses, may suffice to lead many a clinical or psychiatric investigator to act as if the problem were solved, as if the hypothesis were a fact. The properly skeptical investigator makes a study of a sample of asthmatic children and of their nonasthmatic siblings to see whether there is any greater incidence of dependency among the one group than among the other. The most fruitful scientific investigations, at least those that lead to dependable answers, or those that go beyond the exploratory stages, start by setting up a hypothesis, or several alternative hypotheses. Conditions are then arranged in such a way that if the results turn out one way, the hypothesis, or one of its alternatives, is supported and other hypotheses are rendered doubtful. The results must usually be cast in a statistical form, which makes possible a decision between hypotheses.

The simplest example of this is seen where we are studying the effects of one thing on another. Let us suppose that it is the effect of Benzedrine on ability to reason. We restrict our problem to two alternative and mutually exclusive hypotheses: (1) that Benzedrine will affect thinking output or efficiency or (2) that it will not. The first hypothesis can be subdivided into two: that thinking will be facilitated or that thinking will be hindered. The typical experimental operations would be somewhat as follows, briefly described. We develop or adapt a test of reasoning power. We select two groups of individuals of comparable age, education, and IQ, both of the same sex. We determine that the two groups are equal on a preliminary trial of the reasoning test. We administer the drug to one group and a control dose, or placebo, to the other. Neither group knows which has taken the drug. We administer another form of the reasoning test. We obtain two average scores, and there is some difference in a certain direction. The question is, does this difference support hypothesis one or could we still tolerate hypothesis two? Could the difference have occurred by chance? If not, it must have been due to the drug, for so far as we know there is no other difference between the two groups that could account for it. It requires a test of the statistical significance of the difference to permit us to reject hypothesis two and accept hypothesis one. Having rejected the idea that the difference was due to chance, we may accept the idea that it probably was due to the drug. Without the statistical test we would be helpless in reaching a dependable answer.

The normal distribution curve. Every student is familiar with the normal distribution curve; mention of it is ubiquitous in psychological and educational literature. There has been much use and abuse of it, and many erroneous things are said about it. The curve itself is a mathematical conception; it does not occur in nature; it is not a biological or a psychological curve. It is an ideal pattern or model that we can *apply* to useful purpose in many a situation. That there is a distinction between statistics and applied statistics (like that between mathematics and applied mathematics) must be kept in mind. Many fruitful applications of the normal distribution curve will be described in later chapters. Familiarity with the normal curve and its properties is therefore essential.

Prediction and statistics. Two chapters are organized under the heading of "prediction." Most elementary psychology textbooks start by saying that it is the purpose of psychology to predict and control human behavior. Dealing with the very complex and intricate set of phenomena that behavior of living organisms presents, and realizing the limitations to accurate predictions, it is appropriate for us to be modest on the subject. We should not feel guilty, however, about our failures to make predictions comparable with those in the physical sciences. We should make candid and realistic efforts to achieve the predictions that are possible, and we need not disparage results obtained under the limitations inherent in the subject matter.

The operation called *prediction* is actually made even when we do not realize it. The vocational counselor who tells a client that he should seriously consider vocations P, Q, and R and should shy away from vocations U, V, and W is tacitly predicting relative success in the one group and relative failure in the other. The clinician who diagnoses a person as having an anxiety neurosis is saying that he expects certain behavior of this individual. If he prescribes a certain program of therapy, he is predicting improvement under that treatment against lack of improvement if it is not applied. The promotion of a child to the next higher grade is a prediction that he will probably adjust better to that assignment than to reassignment to the same grade. Thus, almost all therapies and administrative decisions imply predictions, whether those who make those prescriptions would be willing to put themselves on record as making predictions or not.

Predictions in psychology and education are often called *actuarial*. That is, they are made on a statistical basis and with the knowledge that only "in the long run" will the practice represented by any prediction be better than other practices, based upon other predictions. Prediction of the single case is recognized as involving many chance elements. For the single case, the prediction is either correct or it is incorrect. In predicting in large numbers, there are certain probabilities of being right and being wrong which can be determined. Statistical methods provide the basis for choosing what prediction to make and also a basis for knowing what the odds are of being right or wrong. The various ways of making predictions and the ways of determining their degree of accuracy will be treated at length in Chaps. 15 and 16.

Test practice and statistics. Because tests play such an important role in psychology and education, considerable attention has been given to them in this volume. Recent investigations by statistical psychologists and educators have drastically changed our former understanding of tests as instruments of measurement. Many of these findings have been reflected in the chapters treating tests, particularly Chaps. 17 and 18. Certain ideas of reliability and validity of tests which have become securely entrenched in the thought and practice of test users are reexamined, and newer experiences have been used to advantage in the applications of statistics to test practice.

THE STUDENT'S AIMS IN HIS STUDY OF STATISTICS

With this overview of content and with a general idea of the advantages of statistics, what should the student, particularly the beginner, aim to do? In order to make his task more specific, the beginner's aims may be listed as follows.

1. *To master the vocabulary of statistics.* In order to read and understand a foreign language, there is always the necessity of building up an adequate vocabulary. To the beginner, statistics should be regarded as a foreign language, which, he should resolve, will not for long remain entirely foreign. The vocabulary consists of concepts that are symbolized by words and by letter symbols that are substituted for them. Along with mathematics in general, statistics shares the ordinary symbols for numerical operations. Thus, much of the vocabulary is already known to the student. As for the new concepts, their meanings will continue to grow the more the student uses them.

2. *To acquire, or to revive, and to extend skill in computation.* Although it was stated earlier that it is not an important aim for the student to become a statistical clerk, computation is important. For many people, the understanding of the concepts themselves comes largely through applying them in computing operations. The mere step-by-step activities with numbers, when certain goals are in mind, provide opportunities for new insights to occur. The average investigator always has a certain amount of computational work to do. Computational skill, and this includes application of formulas as well as planning efficient operations, like any skill, grows with practice.

3. *To learn to interpret statistical results correctly.* Statistical re-

sults can be useful only to the extent that they are correctly interpreted. With full and proper interpretations extracted from data,
statistical results are a most powerful source of meaning and significance. Inadequately interpreted, they may represent something
worse than wasted effort. Erroneously understood, they are worse
than useless. It is the latter eventuality that leads to the common
sour-grapish remark, "Anything can be proved by statistics." In the
hands of skilled operators, statistics make data "talk." It is therefore
very important that the implications of any statistical result be realized and that their proper meaning be made manifest. The average
reader is less able to interpret the result than the investigator should
be. Upon his shoulders rests the responsibility of telling the reader
what the conclusions should be and to include, also, some indication of
the limitations of those conclusions.

4. *To grasp the logic of statistics.* Statistics provides a way of thinking as well as a vocabulary and a language. It is a logical system, like
all mathematics, which is peculiarly adaptable to the handling of
scientific problems. This is hard to explain to the beginner. It is hoped
that it may become more apparent as later chapters, particularly
those dealing with sampling errors, hypotheses, predictions, and factor analysis, are encountered. The most efficient investigator is the
one who masters the logical aspects of his research problem before
he takes recourse to experiment or to field study. Proper formulation
of a research problem is more than half the battle. Too many inex-
perienced investigators think of a question or a problem and rush
to gather data before knowing what it is they really want to observe.
Because it is realized that data of some kind must be collected, much
time and effort are wasted in collecting them, without thinking
through the problem and coming to the proper decision as to just
what data are needed. Or, data are collected in such a manner that
no statistical operations now known are adequate to treat the data
so as to extract an answer. *Well-planned investigations always include in their design clear considerations of the specific statistical
operations to be employed.*

5. *To learn where to apply statistics and where not to.* While all
statistical devices can illuminate data, each has its limitations. It is
in this respect that the average student will probably suffer most
from lack of mathematical background, whether he realizes it or not.
Every statistic is developed as a purely mathematical idea. As such,
it rests upon certain assumptions. If those assumptions are true of
the particular data with which we have to deal, the statistic may be
appropriately applied. The student should note wherever a new statistic is introduced that there are likely to be mentioned certain assumptions or properties of the situation in which that statistic may

be utilized. Unfortunately, one can encounter masses of numbers that look as if they are candidates for the use of a certain statistic, for example, a biserial coefficient of correlation (see Chap. 14), when actually to apply that statistic would be meaningless if not misleading. The student without mathematical background will have to learn these exceptions by rote or be satisfied with common-sense reasons. He certainly will prefer to avoid making ridiculous applications, and when in doubt he should seek advice or refrain from doubtful applications.

6. *To understand the underlying mathematics of statistics.* This objective will not apply to all students. But it should apply to more than those with unusual previous mathematical training. Many an intelligent student who has not been introduced to analytical geometry or calculus can nevertheless grasp many of the mathematical relationships underlying statistics. This will give him a more than common-sense understanding of what goes on in the use of formulas. For the benefit of the student with mathematical background and for all others who wish to know more about the underlying basis of statistics, a number of the more readily understood proofs will be given in some of the chapters, and also in Appendix A. These proofs should help to make more intelligible and reasonable the operations by which certain statistics are computed and the reasons they are used. They should also help to avoid a purely "cookbook" presentation that leaves operations shrouded in mystery.[1]

[1]For more extensive proofs, the reader is referred to Peters, C. C., and Van Voorhis, W. R. *Statistical Procedures and Their Mathematical Bases.* New York: McGraw-Hill, 1940. Lewis, D. *Quantitative Methods in Psychology.* New York: McGraw-Hill, 1960. Hoel, P. G. *Introduction to Mathematical Statistics,* 3d ed. New York: Wiley, 1962.

2 Counting and measuring

TWO KINDS OF NUMERICAL DATA

Numerical data generally fall into two major kinds. Things are counted and this yields *frequencies*, or things are measured and this yields *metric values*, or *scale values*. Data of the first kind are often called *enumeration data*, and data of the second kind are called measurements, or *metric data*.

Statistical procedures deal with both kinds of data, which is the reason for this chapter. There are certain fundamental ideas about numbers and their use that it is well to have in mind before we go ahead. Perhaps it may seem strange to the reader, who has been counting and measuring as long as he can remember, that we should have to devote an entire chapter to these topics. The experts, who, we must admit, have had a great deal more experience with numbers and their use than most of us, never cease to report new ideas about the properties of the number system and its applications. It is well to keep in mind, incidentally, that there is a real difference between the number system, as such, and its application to counting and measuring. Much confused thinking has resulted from ignoring this fact. The world does not necessarily owe its existence to number and quantity. Numbers were invented by man as a symbolic system of internally consistent ideas which he can use effectively in describing the world as he knows it, thus gaining control over it.

DATA AND STATISTICS

Before we go further, there are some frequently used terms that should be defined. These words are *statistics* and *data*. The word *statistics* itself has several meanings. On the one hand it stands for a branch of mathematics which specializes in enumeration data and their relation to metric data. That is the meaning in the title of this book.

Another meaning, popular but not used by technical people, is implied in the mother's statement when she says, "Bobbie, stay out of the street, or you will become a vital statistic." Here the term in the singular refers to a fact of classification, which is a chief source of all statistics. What the mother meant is that Bobbie would change classification from the category "living" to the category "dead." This use of the term "statistics" is more common among those agencies that keep such records. The numerical records *are* the statistics. While this use of the term is recognized by teachers and writers who specialize in statistics, their use of the term and the use of it in this book will usually mean something else. In the textbook and the classroom, we are more inclined to use the word *data* in referring to details in the numerical records or reports. The fact that Bobbie is classified among either the living or the not-living is a *datum*. The word *data* is plural, always referring to more than one fact.

In the textbook and the classroom situation, too, the singular term *statistic* is most likely to mean a derived numerical value such as an average, a coefficient of correlation, or some other single descriptive concept. It may refer either to the *idea* of an average, a median, a standard deviation, etc., or to a particular value computed from a set of data. The reader can usually tell from the context which usage of these terms is meant.

Data in categories

Probably most social data are in the form of categorical frequencies, the numbers of cases in defined classes or categories. The number of births, marriages, and deaths constitutes the bulk of the so-called vital statistics. The number of accidents, fatal or otherwise; the number of arrests for different reasons; and the number of new cases of poliomyelitis constitute other important information by which social agencies keep a finger on the pulse of human affairs. Political and economic interests also have their "barometers" for keeping informed of the trend of events, though some of these depend upon measurements of variables as well as upon counting cases.

CLASSIFICATION

Before we count, in order to accumulate useful information, we must know what it is we count. We do not count indiscriminately. The frequency that we record refers to a particular class of objects or events, and this involves the process of classification. Classification is a basic psychological process which can be seen in rudimentary form even in the simplest conditioned response. Wherever discriminations are made, along with generalizations, classification of a sort occurs. Useful classifications for counting purposes, however, depend upon a high type of logical analysis. Much of science, following Aristotle, has been of the classificatory type. The classification of plant and animal life into species, genus, and order is the best example. Things thus become ordered and principles emerge.

As science progresses, it is likely to abstract *variables* from its data. Variables are continuous variations in single directions. Continuity gives opportunity for refined measurements. In spite of this general trend in a science, however, the classification of phenomena will probably never cease to be useful. Besides, there are some absolute categories that seem not reducible to continuous variables, such as living and dead, married and unmarried, male and female, and voter and nonvoter. Such discrete classes must be recognized and are usefully dealt with in research as well as in public affairs. Classification, then, is a very useful and necessary process in science as well as in practical life. It is the procedure by which objects become categorized for counting.

Some psychological categories.   Before specifying the way in which categories should be set up and utilized, it may be well to have in mind some examples of the more common kinds from the field of psychology. In experimental psychology, particularly in psychophysical studies, we have categories of judgment. The second of a pair of stimuli is judged as "greater than," "equal to," or "less than" the first. In public-opinion polling, responses are obtained in a small number of categories that are intended to be meaningful for interpretation purposes. In answer to the question, "Are you in favor of an atomic-test ban?" the response might be "Yes," "No," "I do not know what an atomic-test ban is," or "I know what the test ban is but I am undecided." In taking a vocational-interest test the examinee may be required to respond in one of three categories, "L" (for like), "I" (for indifferent), or "D" (for dislike), concerning the thing proposed. In a problem-solving experiment with rats, after preliminary observations, solutions might be categorized as falling among, say, four types. Clinical types in psychopathology are mostly categories having long-standing acceptance, e.g., neurotic versus psychotic; schizophrenic, manic-depressive, or paranoid, etc. And so one could continue. Many categories used in research are not static; they change as new light is thrown on the field of study. Some categories are invented for temporary duty as provisional scaffolding upon which to arrange data for better inspection.

There is not space here to give detailed instructions on how to choose or to construct useful categories. It may suffice to say, and it may seem trite to do so, that categories should be *well defined, mutually exclusive* (if possible), *univocal*, and *exhaustive*. The importance of good definitions cannot be overestimated. Making proper assignment of cases to classes depends upon it. Being understood by one's colleagues also depends upon it. A prime requirement of scientific findings is that they shall be communicable to others. Other investigators should be able, if they so desire, to repeat our operations to test our results. The requirement of mutual exclusiveness is perhaps the most difficult to achieve. Lack of it probably means something is missing in defining the basis of classification. Lack of it means some overlapping, interdependence, and loss of power to draw clear-cut conclusions. A set of univocal categories means that there is one and only one basis of classification. To group school children into three classes, boys, girls, and Mexicans, is to inject two principles or bases: sex difference and nationality difference. Perhaps anything so grossly absurd is easily avoided; it is the more subtle confusion of properties that causes trouble. By being exhaustive, a set of categories provides a place for all cases. If there are only two classes, such as delinquents and nondelinquents, and if they are well differentiated by objective criteria, then two categories can be exhaustive. In many a system, particularly when more than two classes are needed, there is often a necessity for one miscellaneous group. In this group are those cases which do not fall in any other category. These cases are often ignored, but if they are numerous it probably means biased sampling in other categories. It also probably means the classificatory system is inadequate as a whole.

Qualitative and quantitative categories. Most of the examples of categories given thus far have been what we call *qualitative*. The classes of objects are different in kind. There is no reason for saying that one is greater or less, higher or lower, better or worse than another. The basis is some qualitative attribute. There may be some intrinsic or external basis for thinking of the classes as being ordered on a scale of more or less, but, if so, we are unaware of it.

There are, however, many classifications in which the groups can be ordered according to quantity or amount. These are *quantitative* classifications. It may be that the cases vary continuously along a continuum that we recognize (such as degree of effort) but on which we cannot yet make refined measurements for lack of an instrument; we can only group in a gross manner. Ratings on a scale of five points (and even more) are examples of such categorizing. In such situations, the categories cannot be defined in terms of any differences in kind. Each one may be distinguishable merely by the fact that cases having a similar quantity of the attribute, such as effort, are in it, and these cases differ noticeably from members of other classes.

Another instance is where the variation of experimental conditions is in graded steps. Five groups of subjects receive different amounts of instruction of a certain kind. To cite another example, in selection by means of tests, examinees are categorized into the accepted and the rejected groups. Later, after the accepted examinees have been trained or have served on the job, there is a further classification between those who are satisfactory and those who are not. Experimental and technological practices are full of such examples. Later chapters will explain methods for dealing with them. The next chapter will show how continuously-graded measurements are most conveniently handled by somewhat arbitrary groupings in successive categories.

FREQUENCIES, PERCENTAGES, PROPORTIONS, RATIOS

A *frequency* has already been defined as the number of objects or events in a category. There are some other related concepts that, though common in advanced arithmetic, most students do not appreciate fully. They play an important role throughout this volume. We cannot review all the arithmetical features of these concepts here, but there are certain new uses of them that should be stressed and certain pitfalls to be pointed out.

Let us consider an example to illustrate the use of percentages. In Table 2.1 are given some original data in the form of frequencies in 12 categories. The categories are in a two-way classification, one qualitative and the other quantitative. The data pertain to the number of students in training and the number of these eliminated in each of four bombardier schools in the Army Air Force during the early part of World War II. In each school the students had been categorized in three levels as to aptitude. The categorization by schools is qualitative and that by aptitude is quantitative. Such a

*Table 2.1   Elimination rates for bombardier students of three levels of aptitude in four Army Air Force training schools**

School	Low			Moderate			High			All levels		
	No. in training	No. eliminated	% eliminated	No. in training	No. eliminated	% eliminated	No. in training	No. eliminated	% eliminated	No. in training	No. eliminated	% eliminated
A	62	26	41.9	340	105	30.9	162	29	17.9	564	160	28.4
B	69	23	33.3	274	51	18.6	125	10	8.0	468	84	17.9
C	69	20	29.0	334	43	12.9	166	15	9.0	569	78	13.7
D	139	21	15.1	274	19	6.9	149	9	6.0	562	49	8.7
All schools	339	90	26.5	1,222	218	17.8	602	63	10.5	2,163	371	17.2

*Aptitude was measured in terms of a composite score on psychological tests. The data were selected from results during the early months of World War II. (Adapted from unpublished data of the AAF Training Command. This will be true of other AAF data used in this volume unless otherwise specified.)

table would probably be set up to study the relation of elimination rate to aptitude and also to differences between schools. We can make comparisons both ways.

Percentage as a rate index. If we wanted to compare schools as to eliminations, the *number* eliminated in each school would be a poor index, particularly when our comparison is made at constant levels of aptitude. For example, at the low level of aptitude, the numbers of eliminations were not very different: 26, 23, 20, and 21. If we gave credence to such small differences, we should place the schools in the rank order *A*, *B*, *D*, and *C*, from most to least eliminations. Schools *A*, *B*, and *C* had comparable numbers in training, but school *D* had about twice as many. This makes us suspicious of the use of the mere number of those eliminated as the way to compare schools. To put the schools on a fair basis we need to find an index of elimination *rate*. We should ask what the elimination "scores" would have been if all schools had had equal numbers in training. If we assume that common number in training to be 100, the number eliminated per hundred is a familiar percentage. The percentages of eliminations for students of low aptitude are 41.9, 33.3, 29.0, and 15.1. Twenty-six is 41.9 per cent of 62; 23 is 33.3 per cent of 69; and so on. Now we see that there are larger differences (this is partly because three of the denominators, 62, 69, and 69, are less than 100) between schools, and the rank order is now *A*, *B*, *C*, and *D*. The inversion of the order of *C* and *D* is decisive; at least *D*'s position below *C* now seems decisive. The point of this illustration is that percentages are used to compare groups of objects on an equitable basis.

Some limitations to the use of percentages. Some precautions should be pointed out concerning the use of percentages. Ideally, a percentage of any number less than about 100 should be computed with hesitation. If the number is less than 100, a change, by chance, of only one case added to or removed from a category would mean a change of more than 1 per cent. If we ask what per cent 15 is of 25, the answer is 60. But if the frequency were to gain one, the percentage would be 64. If a lower limit must be mentioned as a total below which computation of percentages is unwise, it might be placed at 20. At this number, a change of one case would mean a corresponding change of 5 per cent. This is being quite liberal for the sake of applying a very useful index.

In line with the discussion above, it would seem to be not very meaningful to report percentages to any decimal places unless the total number of cases exceeds 100. When we want a percentage for use in further computations, however, it would be wise to retain at least one decimal place. Frequencies are "exact" numbers, and percentages based upon them are accurate to as many decimal places as we wish to use. They thus describe the sample in terms of *per hun-*

dred. It is when we become interested in letting an obtained percentage stand for a population value (see Chap. 8) that we must become conservative about reporting it. In Table 2.1 all percentages were reported to one decimal place because most of them were based upon totals greater than 100 and all were made consistent. Consistency of this sort carries some weight but should not be pushed too far.

When a percentage turns out to be less than 1.0 (for example, .2 per cent), it is not so meaningful as larger ones and, what is worse, it may be mistaken for a proportion (all proportions are less than, if not equal to, 1.0). In some social statistics a series of percentages may be this small. In this case it is common practice to change the base from 100 to 1,000 or even more, for example, to report 15 deaths per 100,000, 5 cases in 1,000, and the like. As percentages these would read .015 and .5, respectively. To avoid confusion with proportions, these should be written as 0.015 per cent and 0.5 per cent.

Proportions. Whereas with percentages the common base is 100, with proportions the base, or total, is 1.0. A proportion is a part, or fraction, of 1.0. A proportion is $^1/_{100}$ of a percentage, and a percentage is 100 times a proportion. Careless individuals often call a percentage a proportion and vice versa. By definition, and in all strictness, the two are different concepts. The symbol used for percentage is capital P; for proportion the symbol is a lowercase p. This should help to fix the idea of the relative sizes of the two. The *proportion* of eliminees among low-aptitude students at school A was .419 (see Table 2.1); for high-aptitude students at school B the proportion of eliminees was .080.

As compared with percentages, proportions have advantages as well as disadvantages. They are less familiar to nonmathematical individuals than are percentages. Whenever results are reported to the general reader, then, percentages are almost always to be preferred. Percentages have another advantage in that we can speak of percentage of gain or of loss. Proportions are always parts of something and can never exceed the total, which is 1.0. They have no place in expressing gain or loss, though presumably losses could be expressed in terms of proportions if we chose, for losses cannot exceed the total; but we never use a proportion for this purpose.

The advantages of proportions are best seen in later chapters. They are used more than percentages, in connection with the normal distribution curve, in connection with item analysis of tests, with certain correlation methods, and so on. It has already been said that percentages may be mistaken for proportions when they are less than 1.0. Since proportions can never be greater than 1.0, they are much less likely to be mistaken for percentages.

Probabilities. Another advantage of proportions is their relation to *probabilities.* Every probability can be expressed in the form of a proportion. We say that the probability of getting a head in tossing a coin is $\frac{1}{2}$ or 1 chance in 2. This is a more manageable figure if expressed as a probability of .5. We say that in throwing a die the probability of getting a six spot is 1 in 6. Expressed as a proportion this is .167. In general, for computation purposes, decimal fractions are much preferred to common fractions; they are much more easily manipulated in addition and subtraction and in finding squares and square roots. The interchangeability of proportions and probabilities will be found to be very common in the later chapters.[1]

Ratios.   A ratio is a fraction. The ratio of a to b is the fraction a/b. A proportion is a special ratio, the ratio of a part to a total. We may also have ratios of one part to another. For example, there were 69 low-aptitude students in training school B (Table 2.1), of whom 23 were eliminated and 46 were graduated. The ratio of graduates to eliminees was $^{46}/_{23}$, or 2 to 1. This ratio can also be expressed as 2.0. The ratio of eliminees to graduates was $^{23}/_{46}$, or .5. This could also be expressed as .5 to 1 but ordinarily is not. At any rate, in a ratio the base is 1.0, as it is in a proportion. The chief difference is that a proportion is restricted to the ratio of part to total, whereas ratios are not.[2]

Ratios are useful as *index numbers*, examples of which follow immediately. They describe rates and relationships. The IQ is an index number of rate of general mental growth — the ratio of mental age to chronological age (multiplied by 100). Comparisons of incomes of regions are made in terms of per capita — the ratio of total income to population. Costs of education are more meaningful if stated in terms of dollars per pupil per day attended rather than in terms of total expenditures. In dealing with index numbers one should keep in mind the operations by which they were derived. It sometimes makes a difference when they are used in computation, as in averaging them or in correlation problems (see pp. 64 and 351).

Measurements

SOME EXAMPLES OF PSYCHOLOGICAL MEASUREMENT

In order to make the discussion concrete and specific, let us consider some typical examples of measurements commonly made by psychologists. Perhaps the first examples that come to mind are scores on tests of mental ability. These are usually in terms of the number of correct responses to test items. A similar kind of measurement is

[1]At this point, it is suggested that readers who are not sure of their grasp of the concepts under discussion, and others who wish to test themselves, do Exercises 1 and 2 at the end of this chapter, then check their answers with those given following the exercises.
[2]See Exercise 3.

seen in scores on a personality questionnaire or a vocational-interest inventory. In these cases the score is not the number of "correct" responses but the number of responses indicating the same interest or trait, often weighted in proportion to their supposed diagnostic value. Also in the area of mental tests we find the frequent reference to "chronological age," "mental age," and that ratio between the two, the "intelligence quotient."

In the experimental laboratory as well as in the clinic, we frequently measure in terms of the time required to complete a specified test or task. In memory experiments, we measure learning efficiency in terms of the number of trials to attain a certain standard of performance or in terms of the "goodness" of performance at the end of a certain trial or time. We measure efficiency of retention in terms of the time required for relearning (overcoming the forgetting that has taken place) and the efficiency of recall in terms of association time or in terms of the number of items correctly recited.

In the sphere of motivation, we gauge the strength of drive in terms of the amount of punishment (electric shock) an organism (for example, a rat) will endure in order to reach his immediate goal or in terms of the number of times he will take a constant punishment in order to attain the same result. The difficulty of a task or test item can now be specified in quantitative terms, as can the affective value (degree of liking or disliking) for a color, a sound, or a pictorial design. In studies of sensory and perceptual powers, the threshold stimulus and the differential limen are given in terms of stimulus magnitudes.[1] The span of perception or of apprehension is given in terms of the average number of items that the observer can report correctly after momentary exposures. The galvanic skin response, the pupillary response, and the amount of salivation also serve as quantitative indicators of amounts of psychological happenings.

SOME EXAMPLES OF EDUCATIONAL MEASUREMENT

Many an educational problem is also a psychological problem, and its mode of measurement has been indicated in the preceding paragraphs. Achievement in any area of learning, like any mental ability, is measurable in terms of test scores. Marks, however obtained, have been the traditional mode of evaluating students in specific units of formal education. Attendance records and data on size of classes, on budgets, on supplies, and on other material aspects of the well-regulated school system compose another list of measurements in education. Outcomes of educational effort are often expressed quantitatively in terms of promotion statistics, achievement ratios, and

---

[1] A "threshold stimulus" is one so weak that it elicits a response a certain proportion of the time, and a "differential limen" is a stimulus increment that is observable a certain proportion of the time.

estimates of teaching success. Whether for purposes of research in education or for systematic and meaningful record keeping, statistical methods are indispensable.

BASIC KINDS OF MEASUREMENT SCALES

Philosophers and scientists have investigated the operations of measurement, and we shall take advantage of many of the results of their thinking. Conceptions of measurement are now much broader, with a more logical foundation than formerly. It is fairly well agreed that measurement should be defined as the *assignment of numbers to objects and events according to logically acceptable rules*. Beneath this simple-sounding statement lies a wealth of ideas; we cannot go into all of them, by any means.

The number system is highly logical, offering a multiplicity of possibilities for logical manipulations. If we can legitimately assign numbers in the describing of objects and events, we can then operate with those numbers in all permissible ways and emerge with conclusions that we can apply back to the observed phenomena that we measured. We are justified in describing real things with numbers provided there is a sufficient degree of *isomorphism* (similarity of properties or form) between those things and the number system. There are certain properties of numbers that must have parallels in the observed phenomena. For example, every number is unique; no other is exactly the same; a number has *identity*. Thus, any object or event to which a number is applied must also have identity. In the number system, numbers have the property of *order* or rank, one being greater than another. The objects to which they are applied must be orderable along some continuum, if the order of the numbers assigned to them is to lend description of order. Numbers also have the property of *additivity*, which means that the summing of a certain number with a certain other number must invariably yield a unique number. This property is the basis for almost all the more useful operations we can perform with numbers, for if we can add them we can also subtract (add negative numbers), multiply (add the same number to itself a number of times), or divide (produce successive subtractions).

It is not necessary that the phenomena to which we apply numbers have all the properties of identity, order, and additivity in order to measure those phenomena. But the usefulness of the numbers applied in measurement depends upon how many of those properties do apply. Several levels of measurement are dependent upon the number of those properties that do apply. We consider those levels of measurement next.

Nominal measurement and nominal scales.   The most limited type of measurement is the distinction of classes or categories—in other words, classification—about which much was said earlier in this chapter. Each group can be assigned a number to act as a distinguishing label, thus taking advantage of the property of identity. The assignment of numbers to classes is almost purely arbitrary, since one number would do as well as another—group 1, group 2, group 3, and so on. Having assigned the numerical labels, we must be logically consistent in identifying class members as group-1 cases, group-2 cases, and so on. Statistically, we may count the numbers of cases in each class, giving us frequencies. Many statistical methods are designed for dealing with categorical data, which fall under the heading of nominal measurement. But there is nothing that we can do meaningfully with the numbers used merely as labels for categories.

It may seem odd that we should refer to "nominal *scales*," when "scale" connotes for most of us the idea of a continuum of some kind. A continuum has the property of order, which does not apply to nominal scales. But the dictionary sometimes refers to a "scale" as "that which discriminates," a conception that justifies our use of the expression "nominal scale." The idea of discrimination or classification also extends to scales of higher types. Thus classification is the very basis of measurement of all kinds. The classification on scales of higher types is merely more refined; while keeping the property of identity, it adds others as well.

Ordinal measurement and ordinal scales. The nominal type of measurement just discussed corresponds to what was called "qualitative" classification earlier. Ordinal measurement corresponds to what was called "quantitative classification." The classes are ordered on some continuum; it can be said that one class is higher on the scale than another. There may be one member to a class, as when we give a complete rank order for observed phenomena, or each class may have a frequency greater than one.

Suppose that we place three boys, Charles, Robert, and David, in order of height, Charles tallest, and assign the three numbers 3, 2, and 1, respectively. All we have is information about serial arrangement. We cannot say that Charles is as much taller than Robert as Robert is taller than David, even though the three numbers assigned to them are equally spaced on the scale of measurement. We are not at liberty to operate with these three numbers by way of addition, subtraction, and so on, and expect to gain any information about the three boys. As with nominal measurements, we can find frequencies for the categories and operate with those numbers, and the fact that the class numbers are meaningful ranks offers us a few opportunities such as in correlations and in tests of significance that we shall investigate in later chapters.

Interval measurement and interval scales. If we actually apply a meter scale to the three boys and find their heights to be 195 cm, 180 cm, and 150 cm, respectively, then we have measurements on a scale of equal units: an interval scale. Now we can make some exact and meaningful inferences. We can say that Charles is 15 cm taller than Robert and 45 cm taller than David. We can say that the difference between Robert and David is twice that between Charles and Robert. We can, in fact, perform most of the useful numerical operations with these measurements. Almost all the statistical methods that we encounter later can be applied to such measurements.

Ratio measurement and ratio scales. The essential requirement for an interval scale is equality of units, which means the same numerical distance is associated with the same empirical distance on some real continuum, such as body height. Numerous scales, especially in the behavioral sciences, achieve or approximate this condition, but they lack an absolute zero point. For example, let us suppose that a mental-test score of some specified ability is on a scale that appears to have equal units. However, a score of zero on such a scale in all probability does not mean complete lack of that ability. All zero means is that the examinee just did not do any of the items correctly. On such a scale, we cannot say that a score of 50 is twice as high as one of 25, meaning that it represents twice the ability. If the scale is an interval scale, however, we could say that a score of 75 is as far above a score of 50 as 50 is above 25. If we were arbitrarily to move the zero point down to a point of -25, it would still be true that the new score of 100 (formerly 75) is as far above the new score of 75 (formerly 50) as 75 is above 50. But now the ratio would be $^{75}/_{50}$, where before it was $^{50}/_{25}$, which is obviously not the same.

In the highest type of measurement, a ratio scale has a meaningful, absolute zero point; zero actually means exactly nothing of the quantity being measured, whether it is a physical or a psychological variable that is concerned. Such scales are almost nonexistent in psychology, except in the area of psychophysical judgment. There are ratio-judgment methods, such as "this sound is twice as loud as that one" and "this pressure is 2.5 times as great as that one," that aim at deriving ratio scaling. Where ratio values can be obtained, we may legitimately multiply and divide by constants and obtain sensible results that can be verified.

There is almost nothing in the way of statistical methods that requires ratio scales of measurement of empirical quantities; interval-scale measurements will do for almost all purposes. It should be pointed out, however, that the enumeration we do in deriving frequencies does give us values on ratio scales. A zero frequency corresponds to the null condition. It can also be said that in statistical operations we create meaningful zero points, for example, at the mean of a distribution, or at a difference of zero. Deviations from these generated zero points can be treated as ratio-scale measurements, permitting the operations of multiplication, division, and the taking of square roots.

HOW NUMBERS SHOULD BE REGARDED IN MEASUREMENT

Most interval-scale measurements are taken to the nearest unit—nearest foot, inch, centimeter, or millimeter—depending upon the fineness of the measuring instrument and the accuracy we demand for the purposes at hand. In giving the height of a tree, measurement to the nearest foot—for example, 107 ft—would be adequate. In giving the height of a girl, we should resort to inches or perhaps centimeters as our practical unit. In giving the length of a needle, we should probably report in terms of millimeters, and in giving its diameter as seen under a micrometer, we should resort to some smaller unit. In any case, we may notice that our object does not contain an exact number of our chosen units. Our tree is more than 107 ft but is closer to 107 than it is to 108; our girl is not exactly 156 cm but is closer to 156 than to 155; etc. The result is that our report of 107 for the tree means anything between 106.5 and 107.5 ft, and our report for the girl means anything between 155.5 and 156.5 cm. Figure 2.1 shows a graphic illustration of units and their limits.[1]

And so it is with most psychological and educational measurements. A score of 48 is taken to mean from 47.5 to 48.5, and a score of 70 means from 69.5 to 70.5. We assume that a score is never a point on the scale but occupies an interval from a half unit below to a half unit above the given number. We can make this seem more reasonable by arguing that the person making a score of 48 actually might be just a fraction of a unit better than 47.5 at the moment, and being better than 47.5 is sufficient to give him a whole score of 48. Or our individual might just fail to be as good as 48.5 on the same test, but, not being quite good enough to achieve 49 items, he falls back to 48. Although our tests are probably never so refined as to cause an indi-

[1]To test yourself, see Exercise 6.

Fig. 2.1. *An illustration of two metric scales, showing selected units and their limits.*

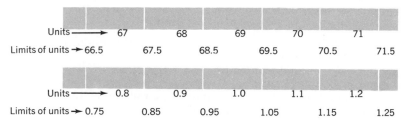

vidual to waver between fractions of a point (the margin of error is usually more than a whole point), this kind of argument rationalizes our procedure from one standpoint.

A more important practical consideration dictates *the taking of a score as occupying a whole interval on the scale,* as the student will appreciate later. If we did not do this, an average computed from a set of ungrouped measurements would not be consistent with one computed when the same measurements are grouped. Even in dealing with discrete measurements, as, for example, the number of children in a family, we customarily proceed *as if* 8 children meant anywhere from 7.5 to 8.5. The only notable exception to this general rule is in dealing with chronological age as given to the *last* birthday and the like. Then a twelve-year-old child is anywhere from 12.0 to 13.0. If ages are given *to the nearest birthday,* however, our rule again applies, and a twelve-year-old falls in the interval 11.5 to 12.5.

EXERCISES

1. In a certain school in a southwestern city, the fifth grade had 80 pupils, of whom 32 were of white, American-born stock, 20 were of Mexican, 12 of Japanese, and 16 of American-Indian stock. Complete the following table:

Stock	Frequency	Percentage	Proportion
American white	32		
Mexican		25.0	
Japanese			.15
American-Indian			

2. In selecting a child at random from the fifth-grade group, what is the probability of getting a Mexican? Of getting a Japanese? An Indian? Either a Mexican *or* an Indian?

3. What is the ratio of Mexicans to Indians? Of American white to Japanese? Of Indian to American white?

4. In the fourth grade in the same school, the following numbers of children appeared: American white, 47; Mexican, 27; Japanese, 11; and Indian, 15. In the third grade the numbers were: 66, 30, 6, and 18, respectively. Prepare a tabulation of the data in the three grades. State some conclusions drawn from the table.

5. For each of the following instances, state the highest level of measurement scale involved:
a. Numbers of men and women in a statistics class.
b. Number of pounds that a boy can lift.
c. The boy's guesses as to the number of pounds he is lifting, when weights of different heaviness are lifted by him.

d. Temperature on a Centigrade scale.
e. Numbers assigned consecutively to students as they complete writing an examination.
f. Number of items a student answers correctly in an examination containing ten items.
g. Numbers assigned to tickets sold in a raffle by boy scouts.

6. State the exact limits of the following scores or measurements: 57 sec; 150 kg; 65 points; 0 points; 14.5 cm; .125 sec; 15 years (to the last birthday).

ANSWERS
1. Frequencies: 32, 20, 12, 16.
   Percentages: 40.0, 25.0, 15.0, 20.0.
   Proportions: .40, .25, .15, .20.
2. Probabilities: $\frac{1}{4}$, $\frac{3}{20}$, $\frac{1}{4}$, $\frac{9}{20}$ ($\frac{20}{80}$ + $\frac{16}{80}$).
3. $\frac{5}{4}$, $\frac{8}{3}$, $\frac{1}{2}$.
5. *a.* ratio; *b.* ratio; *c.* ordinal; *d.* interval; *e.* ordinal; *f.* ordinal; *g.* nominal.
6. 56.5 to 57.5; 149.5 to 150.5; 64.5 to 65.5; −0.5 to +0.5; 14.45 to 14.55; .1245 to .1255; 15.0 to 15.99.

3 Frequency distributions

AFTER we obtain a set of measurements, the next customary step is to put them in systematic order by grouping them in classes. A set of individual measurements, taken as they come, as in the list in Table 3.1, does not convey much useful information to us. We have merely a vague, general conception of about how large they run numerically, but that is about all. The data in Table 3.1 are scores made by 50 students in an ink-blot test. Each score is the number of objects the student reported in observing 10 ink blots during a period of 10 min. Concerning such a set of data we usually want to know several things. One is what kind of score the average or typical student makes; another concerns the amount of variability there is in the group or how large the individual differences are; and a third is something about the shape of the distribution of scores, i.e., whether the students tend to bunch up at either end of the range or at the middle or whether they are about equally scattered over the entire range. The first steps in the direction of answering these questions require setting up a frequency distribution.

The class interval — its limits and frequencies

THE SIZE OF CLASS INTERVAL

We could begin by asking how many scores of 25 there are, of 26, 27, etc., but this would not give us an adequate picture, because in a group of only 50 individuals whose scores range from 10 to 55, many scores do not occur at all and others occur only once. We therefore combine the scores into a relatively small number of *class intervals*, each class interval covering the same range of score units on the scale of measurement.

The first thing to be decided is the size of the class interval. How many units shall it contain? This choice is dictated by two general customs to which experience has led us to agree. *One is the rule that we should prefer not fewer than* 10 *nor more than* 20 *class intervals.*

Although in some instances we find workers going outside those limits, the general tendency is to keep within the boundaries of 10 to 15. The advantage of a small number of groups lies in the fact that we often deal with small numbers of individuals in our measured sample and that a small number is more convenient. The advantage of a larger number lies in our desire for higher accuracy in computation, because the process of grouping introduces minor errors into the calculations, and the coarser the grouping, i.e., the smaller the number of classes, the greater is this tendency.

Some sizes preferred. *The second rule determining the choice of class interval is that certain ranges of units (scores) are preferred.* Those ranges are 1, 2, 3, 5, 10, and 20. These six intervals will be found to take care of almost all sets of data. To apply these rules to our data in Table 3.1, we need first to know that the lowest is 10, which gives us a total range of 45 points (we take the highest score minus the lowest). An interval of 3 points is the one that will give us the best number of classes, according to our first rule. It will be found that the range divided by the number of units in the class interval (in this case 45 divided by 3) ordinarily gives the total number of class intervals needed to cover the range. In this instance, we should therefore have 15 groups. If we chose 5 units as our class interval, we should have $^{45}/_5$, which is 9 groups. In view of the relatively small number of cases, and because an interval of 5 will give us a number next to the minimum of 10 groups, and because the sample is relatively small, we choose 5 as our class interval.[1]

WHERE TO START THE CLASS INTERVALS

It would be natural to start the intervals with their lowest scores at multiples of the size of the interval: when the interval is 3, to start with 9, 12, 15, 18, etc.; when the interval is 5, to start with 10, 15, 20, 25, 30, etc. This is by far the most common practice, though it is admit-

[1]Although the rules as just stated will be satisfactory for most purposes, some variations will be presented later in connection with grouping for graphic representation of distribution.

Table 3.1   **Scores in an ink-blot test**

25	33	35	37	55	27	40	33	39	28
34	29	44	36	22	51	29	21	28	29
33	42	15	36	41	20	25	38	47	32
15	27	27	33	46	10	16	34	18	14
46	21	19	26	19	17	24	21	27	16

tedly arbitrary. When the size of the interval is 3 or 5, there are advantages in starting intervals in such a way that the multiple of the size of interval is exactly in the middle of the group. By this approach, the grouping by threes gives groups like 8, 9, 10 and 14, 15, 16; etc.; by fives, it gives 8, 9, 10, 11, 12 and 18, 19, 20, 21, 22, etc. The midpoints would be multiples of 3 in the one case and of 5 in the second case. We use score limits so much more than we do midpoints, however, that the arguments seem mostly to favor beginning intervals consistently with the multiples of the size of interval, even when the size is three or five units.

Score limits of class intervals. We shall follow the usual practice here, placing in the lowest interval all scores of 10, 11, 12, 13, and 14; in the next higher interval, scores of 15, 16, 17, 18, and 19; etc. (see Table 3.2). Instead of writing out all the scores for each interval, we give only the bottom and top scores. Our intervals are then labeled 10 to 14, 15 to 19, 20 to 24, etc., or, more often, 10–14, 15–19, 20–24. The bottom and top scores for each interval represent what we call the *score limits* of the interval. They do not indicate exactly where each interval begins and ends on the scale of measurement. The score limits are useful mainly in tallying and labeling the intervals.

Exact limits of class intervals. We shall soon find that in computations we must think in terms of *exact limits.* Remember that a score of 10 actually means from 9.5 to 10.5, and that a score of 14 actually means from 13.5 to 14.5. This means that the interval containing scores 10 to 14 inclusive actually extends from 9.5 to 14.5 on the measurement scale. Likewise, the interval having score limits of 15 and 19 has exact limits of 14.5 and 19.5 on the scale. The interval labeled

Table 3.2   Frequency distribution of the ink-blot scores that were listed in Table 3.1

(1) Scores	(2) Tally marks	(3) Frequencies, f
55–59	/	1
50–54	/	1
45–49	///	3
40–44	////	4
35–39	7HH	6
30–34	7HH //	7
25–29	7HH 7HH //	12
20–24	7HH /	6
15–19	7HH ///	8
10–14	//	2

$$\Sigma f = 50 = N$$

55 to 59 actually extends from 54.5 to 59.5. The same principle holds no matter what the size of interval or where it begins. An interval labeled 14 to 16 includes scores 14, 15, and 16 and extends exactly from 13.5 to 16.5. An interval labeled 70 to 79 extends from 69.5 to 79.5. It will be seen that by following this principle each interval begins exactly where the one below leaves off, which is as it should be (see Fig. 3.1).[1,2]

TALLYING THE FREQUENCIES

Having decided upon the size of class interval and with what scores to start the intervals, we are ready to list them, as in Table 3.2. It is customary to place the highest measurements at the top of the list and the lowest at the bottom, as shown here. Space is left in the second column for the tallying process. Taking each score in Table 3.1 as we come to it, we locate it within its proper interval and write a tally mark in the row for that interval. Having completed the tallying, we count up the number of tally marks in each row to find the *frequency* (*f*), or total number of individuals falling within each group. The frequencies are listed in the third column of Table 3.2.

Checking the tallying. Next we sum the frequencies, and if our tallying has omitted none and duplicated none, the sum should equal the number of individuals. At the bottom of the column we find the

[1]Strictly speaking, limits such as 69.5 and 79.5 also stand for very small distances rather than points. Only in a *relative* sense are they division points between intervals. Some writers define an interval such as the one containing scores from 70 to 79 as being actually from 69.500 to 79.4999. One could extend the zeros and nines indefinitely. For practical purposes, the "exact" limits of 69.5 and 79.5 will serve very well when measurements are integers.
[2]To test your ability to choose class intervals and to state limits, see Exercise 1 at the end of this chapter.

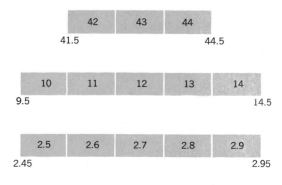

Fig. 3.1. *Exact limits of class intervals with different sizes of interval and of unit of measurement.*

symbol Σf, in which Σ (capital Greek sigma) stands for "the sum of" whatever follows it. Thus, Σf is "the sum of the frequencies." The total number of individuals or measurements in our sample is symbolized by the capital letter N, which stands for "number." If Σf does not equal N, there has been a mistake in tallying, and tallying should be repeated until this check is satisfied. Even if Σf does equal N, there could have been a tally or two placed in the wrong interval. There is no way of checking this kind of error except by doing the tallying twice. The moral is that great care should be taken to make the finding of frequencies correct at the first attempt.[1]

Graphic representation of frequency distributions

The frequency distribution in Table 3.2, particularly the array of tally marks, gives us a general picture of the group of individuals as a whole. We can see, for example, that the most frequent scores fall in the interval 25–29, that the very low and very high scores are more rare, and that the greatest bunching of scores comes in the lower half of the range. Much better pictures of this distribution are afforded in Figs. 3.2 and 3.3, however, where the general contour of the distribution is more accurately represented and the numbers

[1]See Exercises 2 and 3 at the end of this chapter.

Fig. 3.2. *A frequency polygon for the distribution of scores in the ink-blot test.*

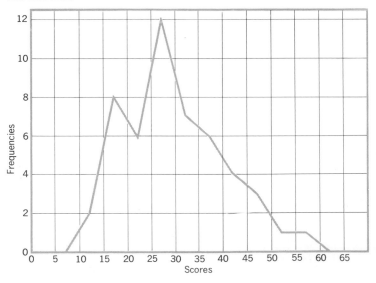

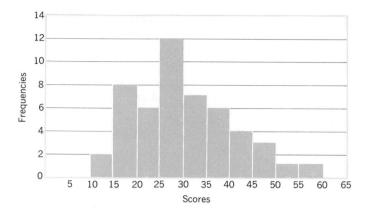

Fig. 3.3. *A histogram for the same distribution as in Fig. 3.2.*

of cases in the various intervals are more exactly shown. Figure 3.2 is of the type known as a *frequency polygon*, and Fig. 3.3 is of the type called a *histogram*, or sometimes, though less often, a *column diagram*.

THE FREQUENCY POLYGON AND HOW TO PLOT IT

A polygon is a many-sided figure, and thus the picture in Fig. 3.2 derives its name. There are a number of factors to be kept in mind in drawing such a figure.

The kind of graph paper.   First, it might be said that, in general, the most convenient type of cross-section paper is the type that is ruled into heavy lines 1 in. apart each way, subdivided into tenths of an inch more lightly drawn.

The width of the diagram.   Second, the question of the height and width of the entire figure arises. For the sake of easy readability, the width of the figure should be at least 5 in. We have altogether 10 class intervals in which there are frequencies, but, in drawing the diagram, we should allow for one more class interval at each end of the scale, making 12 in all. This is to permit bringing the ends of the polygon down to the base line (see Fig. 3.2).

Labeling the base line.   In deciding how many intervals to allow to the inch, it is well to remember that we are going to label the base line of the figure in terms of our measuring scale and hence should plan things so that $1/10$ in. will stand for an integral number of units on this original scale. In the ink-blot data, we have been dealing with a class interval of 5 units, and we are making room for 12 intervals on our base line—in other words, for 60 units. By allowing $1/10$ in. to each unit ($1/2$ in. to each class interval), our distribution will spread over an extent of 6 in., which is sufficiently large. On the base line, therefore, we label every fifth line with a multiple of 5, beginning with 5 at the left and ending with 65 at the right.

The height of the figure. The third important question is the relative height of the figure. For the sake of appearance and also for easy reading of the diagram, there is a general custom of making the maximum height of the distribution from 60 to 75 per cent of the total width. Our total width is 6 in., or $^{60}/_{10}$ in. Sixty per cent of this would be $^{36}/_{10}$ in., and 75 per cent would be $^{45}/_{10}$ in. Our highest frequency, as we see in Table 3.2, is 12. By allowing $^{3}/_{10}$ in. to the person, the height of $^{36}/_{10}$ would be attained, and by allowing $^{4}/_{10}$ in. to a person a height of $^{48}/_{10}$ in. would be reached. The former comes within our rule, and the latter does not; therefore we adopt $^{3}/_{10}$ in. as the unit on the vertical scale.

How to locate a midpoint. In order to plot a dot to represent the frequency in each class interval, we must next decide above what point on the base line the dot shall be. It is plotted exactly at the midpoint of the interval, and the midpoint is exactly midway between the *exact* lower and upper limits of the interval. A simple rule to find the midpoint is to average either exact or score limits of the interval. The interval containing scores 10 to 14 inclusive has exact limits of 9.5 and 14.5. The entire range is 5 units. Half this range is 2.5 units. Go this far above the lower limit, and you have 9.5 plus 2.5, or 12 exactly, as the midpoint. This could be written as 12.0. Or deduct 2.5 from the upper limit, 14.5 minus 2.5, and you also have exactly 12.0 as the midpoint; or the average of 10 and 14 is 12.0. The midpoint of the interval 55–59 is 57.0. When the class interval is 5 and the lowest score in each interval is a multiple of 5, as will be true in many instances met in psychology and education, the midpoints will end in 2 and 7 systematically. For the sake of a complete picture of the midpoints for the data in Table 3.2, we have given in Table 3.3 the full set of midpoints. For a general illustration of midpoints, see Fig. 3.4.

Plotting the points. Having determined the midpoints and knowing the frequencies corresponding to them, we are ready to plot the dots for the frequency polygon. For the two intervals at the ends of the distribution (see Table 3.3) we have frequencies of zero. Sometimes there are frequencies of zero *not* in the last two classes. When this occurs, we plot these dots also on the base line and bring the lines that connect the dots down to the base line at those places. That did not happen to be the case in these data. When the dots are placed at the midpoints, as directed, it may be noted that they do not appear directly above the midpoints of the marked places on the base line (5, 10, 15, 20, etc., in this case). Remember that these multiples of 5 are *not* the exact limits of the class intervals; they are merely convenient and meaningful reference points on our original scale. Had we begun

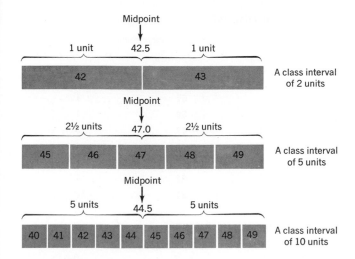

Fig. 3.4. *Midpoints of intervals with differing numbers of units.*

the class intervals at scores other than multiples of 5 — for example, at 11, 16, 21, 26, etc. — we should still plot at the midpoints of the intervals (now different than before) and should still label the reference points as multiples of 5, as in Fig. 3.2. The curve as drawn truly represents the shape of the distribution as we have grouped the scores.

THE HISTOGRAM AND HOW TO PLOT IT

Many of the facts learned in plotting the frequency polygon also apply in plotting the histogram. The choices of size, proportions, and units per square of graph paper all are the same. The only important difference is that, although we locate the height of each column or rectangle by placing a dot at the midpoint of each interval, we do not then connect dot to dot with straight diagonal lines. Instead, we draw a short horizontal line through each dot (see Fig. 3.3), extending it to the upper and lower *exact* limits of each class interval. Those exact limits are given in Table 3.3 for our data. Having done this, we erect vertical lines at each of these exact limits tall enough to form complete rectangles. Again it may be noticed that the rectangles seem to be misplaced a half unit with respect to the numbers on the base line, but this is correct; the choice of limits for our classes makes the exact limits come a half unit below the multiples of 5, i.e., at 4.5, 9.5, 14.5, 19.5, etc.

ADVANTAGES AND DISADVANTAGES OF THE TWO TYPES OF FIGURE

On the whole, the frequency polygon seems generally preferred to the histogram. For one thing, it gives a much better conception of the contour of the distribution; the transition from one interval to another is direct and probably describes the distribution more accu-

Table 3.3   **Class intervals and their midpoints**

Score limits	Exact limits	Midpoints	Frequencies
60 – 64	59.5 – 64.5	62	0
55 – 59	54.5 – 59.5	57	1
50 – 54	49.5 – 54.5	52	1
45 – 49	44.5 – 49.5	47	3
40 – 44	39.5 – 44.5	42	4
35 – 39	34.5 – 39.5	37	6
30 – 34	29.5 – 34.5	32	7
25 – 29	24.5 – 29.5	27	12
20 – 24	19.5 – 24.5	22	6
15 – 19	14.5 – 19.5	17	8
10 – 14	9.5 – 14.5	12	2
5 – 9	4.5 – 9.5	7	0

rately. The histogram gives a stepwise change from interval to interval, based upon the assumption that the cases falling within each interval are evenly distributed over the interval. The polygon gives the more correct impression that, on both sides of the highest point (directly above the mode),[1] the cases within an interval are more frequent on the side nearer the mode, except where there are inversions in the general trend (as between scores of 15 and 25 in Fig. 3.2).

On the other hand, the histogram gives a more readily grasped representation of the number of cases within each class interval; each measurement or individual occupies exactly the same amount of area. One more advantage of the polygon is that when we wish to plot two distributions overlapping on the same base line, as, for example, for two different age groups or the two sexes, the histogram gives a very confused picture, whereas the polygon type usually provides a clear comparison.[2]

PLOTTING TWO OR MORE DISTRIBUTIONS WHEN *N* DIFFERS

The comparison of two distributions graphically raises a new question when the numbers of individuals in the two groups differ. With large differences, naturally, there is the question of scale, or how much space to give the figure. If the smaller distribution is large enough to be clearly legible, the larger one may extend beyond reasonable

[1]As we see in the next chapter, the mode is that value on the measurement scale for which the frequency is greatest.
[2]See Exercise 4.

bounds. Furthermore, if it is general shapes and general levels on the measuring scale and dispersions or spreads that we wish to compare, the marked difference in size may make such comparisons very unsatisfactory. A common solution to this difficulty is to reduce both distributions to *percentage frequencies* instead of plotting the original frequencies. It is then as if we had two distributions, each of whose N's equals 100. This makes their two total areas approximately equal in the polygon form, and comparisons of shape, level, and dispersion are then quite satisfactory.

How to find percentage frequencies.   As an example of how to transform frequencies into percentages the data in Table 3.4 are presented. In each case, the frequencies in the distribution are each multiplied by 100, then divided by N. A shorter procedure would be to find the quotient $100/N$ to four or more decimal places, then multiply each frequency in turn by this ratio. In distribution I, the ratio is $100/51$, which equals 1.9608, and in distribution II it is $100/160$, which equals 0.6250. Multiplying each frequency f_1 by 1.9608, we obtain the list of percentages in column 4, and multiplying each frequency f_2 by 0.625, we obtain the list in column 5. Plotting these percentages above the corresponding midpoints of class intervals, we obtain the distribution curves in Fig. 3.5. Although it was apparent in Table 3.4 that the second group was higher on the scale than the first and that there was still considerable overlapping of scores between the two, these

Table 3.4   Frequency distributions of scores in a college-aptitude test for freshmen at two different colleges

(1) Scores	(2) f_1	(3) f_2	(4) P_1	(5) P_2
140–149		8		5.0
130–139		32		20.0
120–129		48		30.0
110–119	1	29	2.0	18.1
100–109	0	18	0.0	11.2
90–99	3	14	5.9	8.8
80–89	5	5	9.8	3.1
70–79	6	5	11.8	3.1
60–69	14	0	27.5	0.0
50–59	7	1	13.7	0.6
40–49	11		21.6	
30–39	4		7.8	
Sums	51	160	100.1	99.9

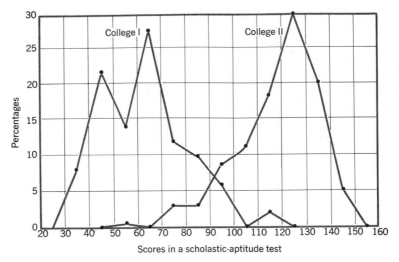

Fig. 3.5. *Distributions of scores in an aptitude test in two colleges. Frequencies have been reduced to a percentage basis.*

facts are more clearly brought out in graphic form. Also much clearer is the somewhat narrower dispersion in the second group as compared with the first.

SKEWED DISTRIBUTIONS

In addition, it is more clear that the first group bunches at the left in its own range and has relatively few high scores, whereas the second group bunches at the upper end of its range, with relatively few low scores. We describe the first distribution as being *positively skewed* (pointed end toward the right, or positive direction) and the second distribution as being *negatively skewed* (pointed end toward the left, or negative direction). It will help to note whether skewing is positive or negative by remembering that "skewing" comes from the same source as the word "skewer," a pointed stick used to hold roasts together. We shall see other references to skewed distributions in later chapters.

Cumulative frequencies and cumulative distributions

Many statistical procedures, particularly those applied to test scores and to psychophysical data, are based upon cumulative frequency distributions. In the preceding sections, we have had frequencies presented as belonging to certain score ranges or class intervals. In this section we are interested in the numbers of scores or other observations falling below certain points on the measuring scale. *The cumulative frequency corresponding to any class interval is the number of cases within that interval plus all those in intervals lower on the scale.*

HOW TO FIND CUMULATIVE FREQUENCIES

The cumulative frequencies are very readily found from the ordinary noncumulative frequencies by a process of successive additions. We use the familiar ink-blot-test scores (see Table 3.5). The scores for the intervals are listed in column 1 just as before, with high scores at the top. We next want a single score value to assign to each interval. Where before we used the midpoint of the interval, we now use the exact upper limit. The reason is that the frequency to be given corresponding to it includes all the cases *within* the class and *below* it. All those cases fall below the exact upper limit of the class interval. In column 3 are given the ordinary, noncumulative frequencies, merely because they are to be used in the cumulation process. The cumulation is started at the bottom of the list in column 3. Below the upper limit of the lowest interval (14.5) are two cases. Below the upper limit of the second interval (19.5) are these two plus the eight in the second interval, giving 10 as the cumulative frequency for the second interval. In the third interval we have six cases to add to what we already have, making 16 for the third interval. And so it goes, each cumulative frequency being the sum of the preceding one and the frequency in the class interval itself. This continues until the top interval is

Table 3.5   Cumulative frequency distribution for the ink-blot-test data

(1) Scores in the intervals	(2) Exact upper limit of the interval	(3) f Frequencies	(4) cf Cumulative frequencies
55–59	59.5	1	50
50–54	54.5	1	49
45–49	49.5	3	48
40–44	44.5	4	45
35–39	39.5	6	41
30–34	34.5	7	35
25–29	29.5	12	28
20–24	24.5	6	16
15–19	19.5	8	10
10–14	14.5	2	2

reached. The last cumulative frequency should be equal to N, which here is 50; if not, some error has been made.

PLOTTING THE CUMULATIVE DISTRIBUTION

In plotting the cumulative frequencies to show the trend in the relation of frequencies to the score scale, an ordinary histogram, which shows the frequency associated with each interval as a rectangle from the base line upward, is rather full of lines. But with a simple modification, we can represent each class frequency starting upward where the preceding one left off (see Fig. 3.6), to represent the summation process. We can also connect the points at which the neighboring rectangles touch, with straight lines, to produce a cumulated frequency polygon. These points of contact represent the cumulative frequencies at the exact upper limits of the intervals.

It will be noted that the general trend of the cumulative distribution curve is progressively rising; there are no inversions or setbacks. This is because all noncumulative frequencies are positive values, except for an occasional zero frequency. The upward rise is not a straight line. When the noncumulative distribution is symmetrical, the cumulative distribution is usually S-shaped. In Fig. 3.6, the upper branch approaches its limit (N) more gradually than the lower branch

Fig. 3.6. *A representation of the cumulative frequencies for the ink-blot-test score distribution. The rectangles show the frequencies for the intervals, each one beginning where the one below it ends. The diagonal lines connecting their corners constitute the most common way of drafting a cumulative curve.*

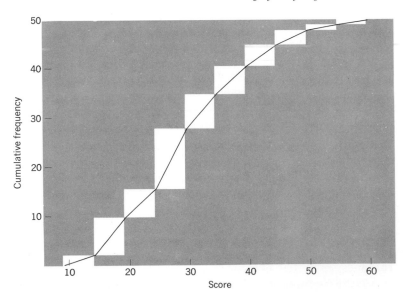

Table 3.6   Cumulative frequencies, percentages, and proportions for memory-test scores

(1)	(2)	(3)	(4)	(5) cP	(6)
Scores	X	f	cf	Cumulative %	cp
41–43	43.5	1	86	100.0	1.000
38–40	40.5	4	85	98.8	.988
35–37	37.5	5	81	94.2	.942
32–34	34.5	8	76	88.4	.884
29–31	31.5	14	68	79.1	.791
26–28	28.5	17	54	62.8	.628
23–25	25.5	9	37	43.0	.430
20–22	22.5	13	28	32.6	.326
17–19	19.5	8	15	17.4	.174
14–16	16.5	3	7	8.1	.081
11–13	13.5	4	4	4.7	.047
8–10	10.5	0	0	0.0	.000

approaches its limit of zero. This is because the noncumulative distribution is positively skewed. Thus, skewing shows up in the cumulative distribution, and it is in the direction of the tail that approaches its limit more gradually.

CUMULATIVE PERCENTAGES AND PROPORTIONS

Previously we had reason to transform frequencies into percentages for the sake of comparing two distributions where N differs (Fig. 3.5). The same reason, plus more important ones, prompts us more frequently to transform cumulative frequencies into percentages or into proportions. This, of course, standardizes the total of the frequencies at 100 or at 1.0, respectively.

In Table 3.6, another example of cumulative frequencies is given. They are obtained here, in column 4, just as before. We now wish to find what percentage of 86 each cumulative frequency is. The arithmetic is simply a matter of multiplying each cumulative frequency by $100/N$. This fraction, $100/86$, is equal to 1.1628. It is well here to keep as many as four decimal places so that there are three significant digits in the resulting values. To obtain the cumulative proportions we find the products of $1/N$ times cf, or .011628 cf, or divide the cumulative percentages by 100.

In Fig. 3.7, the cumulative percentages are plotted as points against

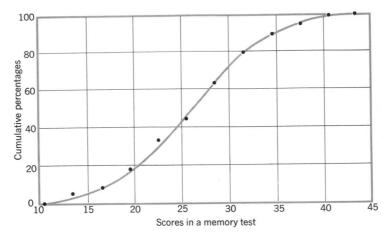

Fig. 3.7. *Smoothed cumulative distribution curve for the memory-test scores. Frequencies are in terms of percentages.*

the corresponding score points (exact upper limits of class intervals). Again, the S-shaped curve results, more clearly than in Fig. 3.6 because there is very little skew. In drawing the curve, some smoothing was done by inspection, since the points are so clearly in line. A cumulative percentage or proportion curve is often called an *ogive*. We shall encounter uses of cumulative distributions, including ogives, in various chapters in this volume.

EXERCISES

1. For each one of the following ranges of measurements, state your judgment of (1) the best size of class interval, (2) the score limits of the lowest class interval, (3) the exact limits of the same interval, and (4) its midpoint.
a. 83 to 197
b. 4 to 39
c. 17 to 32
d. 35 to 96
e. 0 to 188
f. −24 to +28
g. 0.141 to 0.205

2. Given the list of scores in a "nervousness" test in Data 3A and using a class interval of 5, set up a frequency distribution. In the first solution, begin the lowest class interval with a score of 35. List all exact limits of class intervals and also exact midpoints. In a second solution, start the lowest class interval with a score of 33. After finishing both solutions, write out a comparison of the two distributions and defend the choice of the one against the other.

3. Given a list of scores, each of which is the percentage of 400 words judged pleasant by an individual (Data 3B), set up a frequency distribution making the wisest choice of class interval and class limits.

4. Plot a frequency polygon and a histogram for Data 3*C*, group I. State your conclusions concerning these data as revealed by your plotted distribution.

Data 3A   **Scores in a nervousness inventory**

59	48	53	47	57	64	62	62	65	57	57	81	83
48	65	76	53	61	60	37	51	51	63	81	60	77
71	57	82	66	54	47	61	76	50	57	58	52	57
40	53	66	71	61	61	55	73	50	70	59	50	59
69	67	66	47	56	60	43	54	47	81	76	69	

Data 3B   **Affectivity ratios (all have been rounded to the nearest whole number)**

43	62	52	48	46	65	43	48	52	51	57	48	48
38	42	44	46	43	35	42	45	45	44	46	40	40
47	52	38	51	45	38	51	40	46	45	54	55	41
50	59	42	39	56	44	43	47	51	43	50	34	40
53	42	31	44	51	43	48	41	43	48	41	55	

Data 3C   **Distributions of chemistry-aptitude scores in two freshman chemistry courses, I and II**

Scores	Frequencies for group I	Frequencies for group II
90 – 94	4	2
85 – 89	10	0
80 – 84	14	0
75 – 79	19	0
70 – 74	32	2
65 – 69	31	4
60 – 64	40	5
55 – 59	28	12
50 – 54	29	13
45 – 49	21	21
40 – 44	18	21
35 – 39	10	19
30 – 34	6	20
25 – 29	1	14
20 – 24	3	1
Sums	266	134

5. Reduce distributions I and II (Data 3*C*) to percentage distributions and plot them on the same diagram. Make a descriptive comparison of the two distributions as drawn.

6. Carry through the following steps for the first distribution of chemistry-aptitude scores in Data 3*C*:
a. Find the cumulative frequencies and tabulate them.
b. Plot a cumulative distribution curve similar to Fig. 3.6.
c. Find the cumulative percentages and proportions and tabulate them.
d. Plot the ogive distribution, smoothing the curve.

ANSWERS
1.

i	*Score limits*	*Exact limits*	*Midpoints*
a. 10	80 to 89	79.5 to 89.5	84.5
b. 3	3 to 5	2.5 to 5.5	4.0
c. 1	17	16.5 to 17.5	17.0
d. 5	35 to 39	34.5 to 39.5	37.0
e. 20	0 to 19	−0.5 to 19.5	9.5
f. 5	−25 to −21	−25.5 to −20.5	−23.0
g. .005	0.140 to 0.144	0.1395 to 0.1445	142.0

2. Frequencies, first solution: 5, 4, 4, 8, 11, 12, 11, 6, 2, 1; second solution: 1, 4, 5, 5, 8, 13, 13, 8, 5, 1, 1.
3. Frequencies ($i = 3$, with lowest interval 30–32): 1, 1, 2, 4, 9, 8, 10, 15, 8, 3, 2, 1.
5. Percentages:
    I. 1.5, 3.8, 5.3, 7.1, 12.0, 11.6, 15.0, 10.5, 10.9, 7.9, 6.8, 3.8, 2.3, 0.4, 1.1.
    II. 1.5, 0.0, 0.0, 0.0, 1.5, 3.0, 3.7, 9.0, 9.7, 15.7, 15.7, 14.2, 14.9, 10.4, 0.8.
6. *a.* *cf*: 266, 262, 252, 238, 219, 187, 156, 116, 88, 59, 38, 20, 10, 4, 3.
    c. *cP*: 100.0, 98.5, 94.7, 89.5, 82.3, 70.3, 58.6, 43.6, 33.1, 22.2, 14.3, 7.5, 3.8, 1.5, 1.1.

4　Measures of central value

THIS chapter is about averages, of which there are several kinds. Three of them—the *arithmetic mean* (or *mean*), the *median*, and the *mode*—will be explained.

An *average* is a number indicating the central value of a group of observations or of individuals. To the question, "How good is a sixth-grade class in arithmetic?" the most reliable and meaningful kind of answer would be the mean or median in some acceptable test of arithmetical achievement. To the question, "What is the weakest tone to which this dog will respond?" the best kind of answer is to state the average result from a number of trials. In either case, a single score or a single measurement would be highly unreliable, for not all measurements, even from repeated observations of the same thing, have the same value. To answer those questions by reciting the long list of individual measurements would be highly uneconomical in the reporting and not very enlightening to the questioner.

The average, whether it be a mean, median, or mode, serves two important purposes. First, it is a shorthand *description* of a mass of quantitative data obtained from a sample. It is more meaningful and economical to let one number stand for a group than to try to note and remember all the particular numbers. An average is therefore descriptive of a sample obtained at a particular time in a particular way. Second, it also describes indirectly but with some accuracy the *population* from which the sample was drawn. If the sample of sixth-grade children is representative of all the sixth-grade children in the same school, in the same city, or even in the same county, then the average of their scores tells us much about the average that would be made by the population that they represent, be it school-wide, city-wide, or county-wide. If we examine the dog's hearing under a set of conditions that is characteristic of his general, day-to-day existence, the sample average will be very close to one that we could actually obtain by testing him day after day on many days.

It is only because sample averages are close estimates of larger population averages that we can generalize beyond particular samples at all and make predictions beyond the limits of a sample. This means considerable economy of effort, but, far more important, it makes possible all scientific investigation. We rarely or never know the average of a population; consequently we do not know by how much our obtained average has missed it, but if our sampling has been done in the proper manner we can estimate our approximate error, as will be shown in Chap. 8. In the present chapter we shall be concerned only with the methods of computing averages from sample data.

The arithmetic mean

THE MEAN OF UNGROUPED DATA

Most readers already know that to find the arithmetic mean (popularly called the *average*), we sum the measurements and then divide by the number of measurements or cases. In terms of a formula,

$$M = \frac{\Sigma X}{N} \qquad \text{(The arithmetic mean)[1]} \tag{4.1}$$

where M = arithmetic mean
$\quad\quad \Sigma$ = "the sum of"
$\quad\quad X$ = each of the measurements or scores in turn
$\quad\quad N$ = number of measurements or scores

In an experiment to determine the lowest frequency of vibration of a sound wave that would yield a tone for a human observer, 10 trials were given, with the following results: 13, 17, 15, 11, 13, 11, 17, 13, 11, 11 (cycles per second). The sum of these measurements is 132, and therefore the mean is 13.2 cycles per second. Note that in reporting a mean it is given in terms of the unit of measurement, which is specifically stated.

[1]To be completely explicit mathematically, we should designate a single observed measurement by the symbol X_i, which can stand for each of a series of measurements $X_1, X_2, X_3, \ldots X_n$, denoting the first, second, third, to the Nth measurement. The complete expression for formula (4.1) would read

$$M_x = \frac{\sum\limits_{i=1}^{n} X_i}{N}$$

where the symbols below and above the summation sign indicate that the things summed range from the first X_i to the last, or X_n. In most places in this text the limits of the summed items will not be written, since they will be readily understood from the nature of the formula and from the context. Formulas are generally much easier to read without such additional symbols.

As another example, the scores on the ink-blot test found in Table 3.1, when summed, give ΣX equal to 1,480. The mean, with the use of formula (4.1), is

$$M = \frac{\Sigma X}{N} = \frac{1,480}{50} = 29.60$$

The mean ink-blot score is 29.60 score units. In practice, it is customary in reporting a mean to round to one more figure at the right than the original measurements had—in this case, to keep one decimal place, where the original scores were whole numbers. We report the mean as 29.6 score units.

THE MEAN OF GROUPED DATA

When data come to us grouped, or when they are too lengthy for comfortable addition without the aid of a calculating machine, or when we are going to group them for other purposes anyway, we find it more convenient to apply another formula for the mean:

$$M = \frac{\Sigma f X_c}{N} \quad \text{(Arithmetic mean from grouped data)} \tag{4.2}$$

where the symbols N and Σ have the same meanings as before, $X_c =$ midpoint of a class interval, and $f =$ number of cases within the interval. The expression fX means the frequency times the X value for the interval. All such products must be found first, then summed.

The solution by way of this formula is illustrated in Table 4.1. Here we have only as many different X values as there are class intervals, instead of as many as there are original measurements. Each class interval has as its X value the midpoint of that interval, which is given the special symbol X_c. This practice assumes that the midpoint of the interval correctly represents all the scores within that interval. This will not be exactly true in some instances, but the discrepancy is small in any case and, in computing the mean, most of the discrepancies tend to counterbalance others, giving a mean that is essentially correct.[1]

In column 2 of Table 4.1, the midpoints of the intervals are given. We must add each midpoint into our total as many times as there are cases within that interval. This means finding for each interval the product of f times X_c, or fX_c. The fX_c products are listed in column 4. The sum of the fX_c products (ΣfX_c) is equal to 1,480. Dividing this by N, we find the mean to be 29.60, as it was for the same data ungrouped. As was indicated before, we should not be surprised to find a minor discrepancy between the means calculated from grouped and

[1] A discussion of "grouping errors" and their effects upon statistics will be found in the next chapter.

Table 4.1   **Computation of the mean in grouped data**

(1) Scores	(2) X_c Midpoint	(3) f	(4) fX_c
55–59	57	1	57
50–54	52	1	52
45–49	47	3	141
40–44	42	4	168
35–39	37	6	222
30–34	32	7	224
25–29	27	12	324
20–24	22	6	132
15–19	17	8	136
10–14	12	2	24
Sums		50	1,480
		N	ΣfX_c

$$\text{Mean} = \frac{\Sigma fX_c}{N} = \frac{1,480}{50} = 29.60$$

ungrouped data. It happened here that the discrepancy was zero. We may also expect trivial discrepancies in means when the same data are grouped differently, i.e., with different size of class interval or with different starting points for intervals of the same size.

THE MEAN COMPUTED FROM CODED VALUES

When the original measurements are relatively large numbers, particularly when the midpoints and the frequencies are large numbers, the method just described can well give way to a short-cut procedure that saves pencil-and-paper work. Even greater saving is appreciated when, as in the next chapter, a standard deviation is also to be computed. This procedure requires the use of "coded" values to replace the midpoint values.

The steps are illustrated in Table 4.2, including the coding process. In this table it can be seen that many of the actual midpoints would be four-digit numbers; for example, the highest interval has a midpoint of 154.5 (midway between 149.5 and 159.5). Consequently, the fX_c products would also be rather large. The coded values for the intervals, given in column 3, are called x'. They will now be explained.

The coding process. First, we select a new reference point, a par-

*Table 4.2   Computation of the mean in
grouped data by using the code method*

(1) Scores	(2) f	(3) x'	(4) fx'
150 – 159	2	+6	+12
140 – 149	2	+5	+10
130 – 139	4	+4	+16
120 – 129	1	+3	+ 3
110 – 119	5	+2	+10
100 – 109	5	+1	+ 5
			+56
90 – 99	12	0	0
80 – 89	10	−1	−10
70 – 79	12	−2	−24
60 – 69	10	−3	−30
50 – 59	1	−4	− 4
			−68
Sums	64		−12
	N		$\Sigma fx'$

$$M_{x'} = \frac{-12}{64} = -0.188$$

$$M_x = 10(-0.188) + 94.5 = 92.62$$

ticular X_c value that we arbitrarily choose to call zero. In order to obtain the greatest benefit from the coding method, it is well to choose this reference point near the center of the distribution. If there is an odd number of class intervals, the midpoint of the middle one is a good candidate for the origin. If there is an even number of class intervals, either of the two middle ones will do.

There are other considerations, however. When the distribution is rather skewed, as in the case of the data in Table 4.2, the middle of the data is not likely to be in the middle interval or intervals. Another solution is to select the midpoint of the interval containing the median. The median is in the interval 80–89.[1] This is farther from the

[1] The median, soon to be described, is the central value of X below which, and above which, half of the N measurements occur. Half of 64 (the N of Table 4.2) is 32. If we sum the frequencies from the bottom of the distribution upward, to reach 32 we have to enter the interval 80–89. This is as much as we need to know about the median for the purpose of selecting a central interval for using the coding method.

center of the range than we would ordinarily go to place the origin. A good compromise, then, seems to be the interval 90–99, with its midpoint of 94.5.

We could now find new midpoint values by subtracting 94.5 from the midpoint values X_c of all intervals represented in Table 4.2. These would range from −40.0 for the lowest interval to +60.0 for the highest interval, with a midpoint of 0.0 for the interval 90–99. The extreme values are still somewhat large; consequently, we proceed to make them smaller by dividing them all by 10, the size of the class interval. The result gives the x' values of column 3. We now have simple integers. Some of them are negative, which complicates things a bit, but this is the only price we pay for obtaining small code values with which to work.[1]

Let us proceed to find the mean of the coded values. The steps are much the same as those taken in Table 4.1. One difference is that some of the class values (x') are negative, and great care must be maintained to take this into account. The sum of the positive fx' products is +56, and the sum of the negative fx' products is −68. The algebraic sum of all the fx' products is $56 - 68$, which is −12. The $\Sigma fx'$ is therefore −12. The mean of the x' values is given by a formula like (4.2):

$$M_{x'} = \frac{\Sigma fx'}{N} \quad \text{(Mean of coded values)} \tag{4.3}$$

For the data of Table 4.2, $M_{x'} = -0.188$.

Uncoding the mean. To obtain from this value the mean of the original measurements we must go through the process of "uncoding." The coding process involved two steps—subtracting 94.5, then dividing by 10. We can describe this in general terms by the equation

$$x' = \frac{X_c - X_o}{i} \quad \text{(Coded values from midpoints of intervals)} \tag{4.4}$$

where X_o is the midpoint value chosen for the origin of the coded values and other symbols are as defined before. The uncoding proceeds in reverse. The two steps include multiplying by i, then adding X_o. In terms of an equation,

$$M_x = iM_{x'} + X_o \quad \begin{array}{l}\text{(Mean of measurements}\\\text{from mean of coded values)}\end{array} \tag{4.5}$$

Substituting the necessary values in formula (4.5),

$$M_x = 10(-0.188) + 94.5$$
$$= 92.62$$

[1]Mathematically, the coding process is a linear transformation of the X values (see Appendix A, Proofs 1–3).

A summary of the code solution of the mean. The steps involved in the code method of computing the mean may be summarized as follows:

Step 1. Set up the frequency distribution.

Step 2. Choose a temporary origin, X_o. This is the midpoint of the interval (1) near the center of the range, or (2) containing the median, or (3) a compromise between the two.

Step 3. Assign to the class intervals new small, integral values, starting with zero at the origin, with positive values above it and negative ones below. Call these new values x'.

Step 4. Find the fx' product for each interval, and record all such values in a column.

Step 5. Sum the fx' products algebraically. This is $\Sigma fx'$.

Step 6. Divide the sum of fx' products by N, giving $M_{x'}$, the mean of the coded values.

Step 7. Multiply this quotient by i, the size of class interval.

Step 8. Add this algebraically to X_o, which gives the mean M_x.

A single formula representing the last three steps is

$$M = X_o + i \left(\frac{\Sigma fx'}{N} \right)$$ (Arithmetic mean from grouped and coded data)   (4.6)

The median and centile values

The *median* is defined as that point on the scale of measurement above which are exactly half the cases and below which are the other half. Note that, in general, it is defined as a *point* and not as a score or any particular measurement. If this conception is kept clearly in mind, many difficulties will be forestalled.

THE MEDIAN FROM GROUPED DATA

It is probably easier to grasp the process of computing a median in grouped data. For a first illustration, consider Table 4.3. Here there are 28 cases, so the median is that point on the measuring scale above which there are 14 cases and below which there are 14. Counting frequencies from the bottom upward, we find that $4 + 1 + 1 + 10 = 16$ cases, or 2 more than we want. To make 14 cases exactly, we need 8 out of the 10. The median lies somewhere within the interval 15–19, whose *exact* limits are 14.5 and 19.5. We assume for the sake of computation that the 10 cases within this interval are evenly spread over the distance from 14.5 to 19.5 (see Fig. 4.1). We must interpolate within this range to find how far above 14.5 we need to go in order to in-

Table 4.3   Computation of the median size of class in a certain school, with the use of grouped data

Class size	f
40 – 44	1
35 – 39	0
30 – 34	3
25 – 29	5
20 – 24	3
15 – 19	10
10 – 14	1
5 – 9	1
0 – 4	4
	N = 28

12 = number of cases
above the interval
containing the median

6 = number of cases
below the interval
containing the median

$Mdn = 14.5 + {}^{8}/_{10} \times 5 = 14.5 + 4.0 = 18.5$

$Mdn = 19.5 - {}^{2}/_{10} \times 5 = 19.5 - 1.0 = 18.5$

clude the 8 cases we need below the median. We must go $^{8}/_{10}$ of the way, for 8 is the number we require, and 10 is the total number in the interval. The total distance is 5 units, and so on the scale of measurement we go $^{8}/_{10}$ of 5, or exactly 4.0 units. Adding this 4.0 to the lower limit of the class interval 14.5, we get 14.5 + 4.0 = 18.5 as the median.

We can check this by counting down from the top of the distribution until we include $N/2$ of the cases, 14 in this problem. Starting at the top, we find that

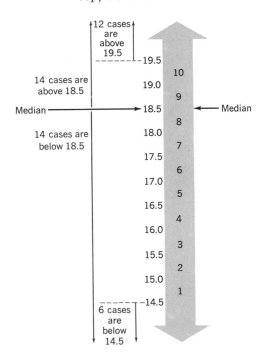

12 cases
are
above
19.5
----- 19.5

14 cases are
above 18.5

Median ────────→ 18.5 ←─── Median

14 cases are
below 18.5

6 cases
are
below
14.5

Fig. 4.1. *Showing how the 10 cases in the interval 14.5 to 19.5 are distributed. Each case is assumed to occupy a tenth of the interval, or one-half of a score unit. The eighth case extends up to the point 18.5, which is the median.*

$1 + 0 + 3 + 5 + 3 = 12$

We need 2 more cases out of the next group of 10. We must go $2/10$ of the way below the *upper* limit of the interval, i.e., below 19.5. This means $2/10$ of 5, or exactly 1.0 unit. The upper limit, 19.5 minus 1.0, gives us 18.5 for the median, which checks with the one obtained by counting up from below. It is well always to check the determination of a median in this manner, and to do so involves very little work. If the two estimates do not agree exactly, something is wrong.

To take another example with grouped data, consider Table 4.4, where N is an odd number. Here $N/2$ is 18.5, but the principle of interpolating within an interval for the exact median is just the same. Counting up from below, we find that $1 + 5 + 8 = 14$, which lacks 4.5 cases of including the lower half. In the next interval, we must go 4.5/8 of the way, or 4.5/8 times 2, which equals $9/8$, or 1.125. Adding this many units to the lower limit of the interval (22.5), we have 23.625 as the median; or dropping all but one decimal place, we report the median as 23.6 score units. Checking by counting down from the top, we find 15 cases above the point 24.5. Going 3.5/8 of the way down into the interval of 2 units, we find that we must deduct 0.875 from 24.5 to find the median. When rounded to one decimal place, the median is 23.6, as before. In terms of a formula, the interpolated median

Scores	f
37 – 38	1
35 – 36	2
33 – 34	0
31 – 32	1
29 – 30	0
27 – 28	6
25 – 26	5
23 – 24	8
21 – 22	8
19 – 20	5
17 – 18	1

Table 4.4   Computation of the median score in a sentence-construction test as given to 37 men

15 = number of cases above the interval containing the median

14 = number of cases below the interval containing the median

$$N = 37 \qquad \frac{N}{2} = 18.5$$

$$Mdn = 22.5 + \frac{4.5}{8} \times 2 = 22.5 + \frac{9}{8} = 22.5 + 1.125 = 23.6$$

$$Mdn = 24.5 - \frac{3.5}{8} \times 2 = 24.5 - \frac{7}{8} = 24.5 - .875 = 23.6$$

is found from below by

$$Mdn = l + \left(\frac{\frac{N}{2} - F_b}{f_p}\right)i \qquad \text{(Interpolation of a median from below)} \qquad (4.7a)$$

where l = exact lower limit of class interval containing the median, F_b = sum of all frequencies below l, f_p = frequency of the interval containing the Mdn, and N and i are defined as usual.

In terms of a similar formula, the median is found from above by

$$Mdn = u - \left(\frac{\frac{N}{2} - F_a}{f_p}\right)i \qquad \text{(Interpolation of a median from above)} \qquad (4.7b)$$

where u = exact upper limit of the interval containing the median and F_a = sum of all frequencies above u.

A summary of the steps for interpolating a median. The steps for computing a median from grouped data may be summarized as follows:

Step 1. Find $N/2$, or half the number of cases in the distribution.
Step 2. Count up from below until the interval containing the median is located.
Step 3. Determine how many cases are needed out of this interval to make $N/2$ cases.
Step 4. Divide this number needed by the number of cases within the interval.
Step 5. Multiply this by the size of class interval.
Step 6. Add this to the exact lower limit of the interval containing the median.
Step 7. Check by adding down from the top to find to what point the upper half of the cases extend in a manner analogous to that described in steps 2 to 5 inclusive.
Step 8. Deduct the number of score units found in step 7 from the exact upper limit of the interval containing the median.

SOME SPECIAL SITUATIONS

There are some instances in which things do not turn out just as they did in the two illustrative examples.

When the median falls between intervals. If it should happen, in adding up cases from below, that half the cases take in *all* the cases in the last interval, the median is then the exact upper limit of that interval. In counting down from above, it would be found that all the cases in the interval just above this one would also be required to make $N/2$, and so its exact bottom limit would be the median. This coincides with the exact upper limit of the interval below; thus, the median checks. As an example, note the following fictitious data:

Scores	20–24	25–29	30–34	35–39	40–44	45–49	50–54	55–59
f	2	7	10	15	18	8	3	5

Here $N/2$ is 34. This many cases takes us exactly through the interval 35–39. The median is 39.5. From above down, we are carried through the interval 40–44, whose lower limit is 39.5. Again the median is 39.5.

When there are no cases within the interval containing the median. Another question arises when the median falls within an interval where there are *no* cases. It is even possible that, in the region of the median, two or more intervals have frequencies of zero. If the range having no cases is one interval, the median may be taken as the midpoint of that interval, but this gives a very crude estimate unless the size of the interval is small—for example, not over three units. If that range covers two or more intervals, no good estimate can be made for the median.

Scores	5–7	8–10	11–13	14–16	17–19	20–22	23–25	26–28
f	1	7	9	0	6	7	2	2

In the data just preceding, the median is 15.0, which is midway between 13.5 (to which point the lower half of the cases extends) and 16.5 (to which point the upper half of the cases extends). Or it is the arithmetic mean of those two limits, for 16.5 + 13.5 divided by 2 is 15.0.

THE MEDIAN FROM UNGROUPED DATA

What we have learned in finding a median in grouped distributions should carry over almost intact to the use of ungrouped data. The median is a *point* on the measuring scale. In ungrouped data, each score or measurement is assumed to occupy a *range* of one unit. The median either falls within one of those units or somewhere between units. The first step is to arrange the measurements in order of their size. The list of 10 measurements of the threshold for pitch as given on p. 44, when placed in rank order, becomes

11, 11, 11, 11, 13, 13, 13, 15, 17, 17

As in the case of grouped data, it is assumed that the four 11's occupy the range from 10.5 to 11.5; the three 13's occupy the range from 12.5

to 13.5, etc. Counting from below to include five cases brings us to the first 13 that must be included among the five. We must therefore extend one-third of the way in the interval of 1 unit, or 0.33 unit into the interval, starting at 12.5. The median is 12.5 + 0.33, which equals 12.83, or, when rounded, 12.8. In checking from above, the median is found at 13.5 − 0.7, which also equals 12.8.

In the series of measurements

2, 5, 7, 8, 9, 10, 17

the median comes midway in the fourth one, which is 8. Since 8 occupies a range of 7.5 to 8.5, the median is the midpoint of this range, or exactly 8.0. In the series of measurements

7, 9, 10, 12, 13, 15, 18, 20

four are 13 or above, and four are 12 or below. The division between upper and lower halves comes at 12.5, which is the median in this case. In the array of scores

15, 17, 18, 20, 23, 24, 27, 30

the lower half extends up to 20.5, and the upper half extends down to 22.5. Midway between these two values is the point 21.5, or the average of the two.[1]

It is probably obvious that the median of so small a number of observations cannot be very reliable, and we should not place too much reliance upon it or carry the calculations to more than one decimal place (we might even report the nearest whole numbers); but in order to keep consistent certain principles of the median and the process of computing it, certain steps have been emphasized. Whenever there is doubt concerning special cases not covered by these illustrations, an application of these principles should take care of the matter.

OTHER INTERPOLATED VALUES – CENTILE POINTS

Although not in the category of averages, because they are computed in the same manner as medians, centile points may be mentioned here. Their importance will be seen mainly in Chap. 19, where the subject of test norms is treated.

Many test norms are given in terms of centile ranks. A centile rank is a position in a series of a hundred ranks, where higher rank numbers mean higher scale positions. A score value at the 95th centile rank exceeds 95 per cent of the population; a score value at the 15th centile rank exceeds the lowest 15 per cent, and so on. Corresponding

[1]Mathematically, there are an infinite number of points between 20.5 and 22.5, any one of which could be truthfully taken as a median. We do the reasonable thing and select 21.5 as the best estimate of the median.

to each *centile rank* is a point on the test-score scale, known as the *centile point*.

The median is at the centile point where the centile rank is 50. Just as the median is found by interpolation, so may any other centile point be found. For example, if we want to know where the 90th centile point is located in the distribution of scores for the test represented in Table 4.2, we first determine how many out of the 64 cases correspond to 90 per cent. Ninety per cent of 64 is 57.6 of the cases. Counting frequencies from below we find that 56 of them are below the interval with exact limits of 129.5 to 139.5. We need 1.6 more of the 4 cases within that interval to reach exactly 57.6. The amount of score interval to be added to the lower limit, 129.5, is 1.6/4 of 10, or 4.0. Added to the lower limit, this gives 133.5 as the estimate of the 90th centile point. The student may check this by interpolating from the upper end of the distribution. The interpolation at any other centile rank would follow the same principle.

The mode

The *mode* is defined as the *point on the scale of measurement with maximum frequency in a distribution.* When we have ungrouped data, the mode is that measurement that occurs most frequently. Usually it is somewhere near the center of the distribution, and in a strictly normal (Gaussian) distribution it coincides with the mean and the median.

THE CRUDE MODE

In a distribution of grouped data, the crude mode is the midpoint of that class interval having the greatest frequency. In Table 4.1, the highest frequency is 12, for the interval 25–29. The midpoint of this interval is 27, so the mode is taken to be 27.0. In Table 4.2, there are two intervals with the same maximum frequency of 12. If these two intervals had been separated by more than one intervening interval of lower frequency, we should be justified in saying that the distribution is *bimodal* (having two modes). But the single intervening frequency of 10 hardly gives us sufficient basis for this conclusion. The distribution is therefore probably really unimodal, but we are not able to decide upon its crude mode. A calculated mode can be estimated, as we shall soon see.

In Table 4.3, the crude mode is clearly 17.0. In Table 4.4, the maximum frequency is shared by two neighboring intervals. In a situation like this, we do the reasonable thing of assigning the crude mode to the dividing point between these intervals, which is 22.5. Unless the data are reasonably numerous, so that there is clearly an interval of highest frequency, we should not attempt to assign a modal value to the distribution. For example, the 10 measurements of threshold for pitch present an unusual situation, with the greatest frequency (four cases) at 11, which is at one end of the distribution. Following right behind is the measurement of 13, with three cases. Here it would be rather meaningless to say that the mode is 11 with the implication that it is a "central value."

THE MODE ESTIMATED FROM THE MEAN AND MEDIAN

Fortunately, because of certain mathematical relationships between the mode and the other two measures of central value, we can estimate the mode from them. A simple approximation formula is

$$Mo = 3Mdn - 2M \qquad \text{(Estimation of a mode from mean and median)} \qquad (4.8)$$

In other words, the mode equals three times the median minus two times the mean.

Applying this formula, we can now estimate the mode of the distribution in Table 4.2, in which we were unable to decide upon a crude mode. The median for this distribution is 88.5, and the mean is 92.6. Applying formula (4.8), the computed mode equals

$$(3 \times 88.5) - (2 \times 92.6) = 265.5 - 185.2 = 80.3$$

The estimated mode is 80.3. Reference to the distribution in Table 4.2 again will show that this point comes about midway among the four high frequencies. Had we done a very reasonable thing and placed the crude mode midway among these four intervals, it would have been at 79.5, which is less than one unit from the calculated estimate.

When to employ the mean, median, and mode

CERTAIN ADVANTAGES OF THE MEAN

The arithmetic mean is to be preferred whenever possible because of several desirable properties. First, it is generally the most reliable or accurate of the three measures of central value. By this we mean that, from sample to sample from the same population, the mean ordinarily fluctuates less widely than either the mode or the median. Second, the mean is better suited to further arithmetical computations. Deviations of single cases from the central value give important information about any distribution. Much is done with these deviations, as will be seen in the following chapter. It will also be found that we square those deviations, and we are really justified in doing this only when the deviations are taken from the mean. When distributions are reasonably symmetrical, we may almost always use the mean and should prefer it to the median and mode. On the other hand, there are instances, particularly when distributions are skewed and when the mean would lead to erroneous ideas about a distribution, in which other measures of central value are better used for descriptive purposes.

A COMPARISON OF THE MEAN WITH MEDIAN AND MODE

One property of the mean is that it is sensitive to the size of extreme measurements when they are not balanced by other extreme measurements on the other side of the middle. In the following set of measurements, the mean is 9 and the median is 9:

4, 5, 7, 9, 11, 13, 14

Now, if the 14 had been 23 instead of 14, the median would be unchanged, but the mean would become 10. There are still an equal number of cases above and below 9. So far as the median is concerned, the 11, 13, and 14 could have been 22, 23, and 28, and still the median would be 9. But in this rather unusual but not impossible event, the mean would become 14, where formerly it was only 9. The conclusion to be drawn is that when, in a small sample particularly, there are any very extreme measurements not balanced by other extreme measurements in the other direction, the median is to be preferred to the mean.

Some mathematical properties of the arithmetic mean and the median.   A better appreciation of the nature of the mean and of the median may be gained by noting some of their mathematical peculiarities. To illustrate, let us use the data presented in Table 4.5. There six scores are given for six individuals. The mean of these scores is 6.0 and the median is 4.5.

The first feature to be pointed out is that the mean is the *center of gravity* of the scores. In Fig. 4.2 we have the six scores represented on the measurement scale. Imagine that the six individuals are arranged in their proper places along this scale. Imagine that the scale itself is a rigid plank or bar. The six persons may be regarded as exactly the same in all respects except for their scores on this scale. Each "weighs" the same; his effect upon the tilting of the bar depends only upon his position on it. If we wish to rest the bar on a single fulcrum in such a position that the bar will be perfectly balanced, that position must coincide with the mean. The measurements in any sample are perfectly balanced about the arithmetic mean.

Each individual in this small distribution carries an effective weight in proportion to his distance from the mean. In the parlance of the physicist, each person's distance from the mean is called a *moment.* In statistics, also, we often speak of moments in a similar sense.

In column 3 of Table 4.5, each of the six "moments" for this small distribution is given. They are more commonly called *deviations from the mean*, or simply *deviations*. The size of each deviation indicates how much effective weight the moment carries, and its algebraic sign tells in what direction that weight is applied. The algebraic sum of these moments is zero, as it always is when the arithmetic mean and the deviations are correctly computed. This is simply another indication that the mean is a center of gravity, for the positive and negative moments about the mean are perfectly balanced.

The arithmetic mean is the only value in a distribution from which the deviations always sum algebraically to zero. This statement is easily proved, as follows:

A deviation from the mean, x, is equal to $X - M$, so that

$$\Sigma x = \Sigma (X - M)$$

Breaking up the sum on the right-hand side into two components,

$$\Sigma x = \Sigma X - \Sigma M$$

Since M is a constant, summing M N times is equivalent to the product NM, so that

$$\Sigma x = \Sigma X - NM$$

From formula (4.1), $M = \Sigma X / N$. Substituting the latter expression for M,

Table 4.5 Illustration of certain properties of the arithmetic mean and the median

(1)	(2)	(3) Deviations from the mean	(4) Deviations from the median	(5) Deviations from the mean, squared	(6) Deviations from the median, squared
Person	Score				
A	2	−4	−2.5	16	6.25
B	3	−3	−1.5	9	2.25
C	4	−2	−0.5	4	0.25
D	5	−1	+0.5	1	0.25
E	9	+3	+4.5	9	20.25
F	13	+7	+8.5	49	72.25
Sums	36	0	+9.0	88	101.50
Means	6.0	0.0	+1.5		
Median	4.5				

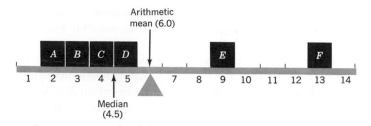

Fig. 4.2. *Illustration of the positions of six cases with respect to the arithmetic mean and with respect to the median. With all cases carrying equal weight, they are perfectly balanced when the fulcrum is placed at the arithmetic mean.*

$$\Sigma x = \Sigma X - N\Sigma X/N$$

From which

$$\Sigma x = \Sigma X - \Sigma X = 0$$

To show that the median does not qualify in this respect, let us find the deviations of the six scores from the median and sum them (see Table 4.5). The algebraic sum of the deviations from the median is 9.0. This means a net balance of nine units on the plus side. A fulcrum placed at the point 4.5 on the scale would be seriously overbalanced toward the end with the high scores. This comes from the fact that in computing a median we ignore the distance of each case from the central value. If we want the bar to balance when the fulcrum is placed at the median value, we shall have to rearrange the cases, treating all cases above the median as if they had the same value and all cases below the median as if they also had the same value and the deviation of all cases above the median equal to that of all cases below it.

Not only are the deviations from the mean balanced about it but they have another important property. If we square each deviation, we have the squared moments about the mean. The peculiarity of the mean is that the sum of the squared deviations about it is smaller than that for the squared deviations about any other value. In most of the following chapters we shall be concerned with squared deviations from the mean. For the present, it is significant to point out that when squared deviations are considered, the arithmetic mean is closest to the measurements of the sample as a whole. In Table 4.5 we can see that for this small sample the sum of squared deviations is much smaller when the reference point is the mean than when it is the median, the two sums being 88 and 101.5. The reader may verify the fact that 88 is the smallest possible sum of squared deviations in this sample by arbitrarily choosing other values as possible points of central value.

It is possible to give a proof for the principle that the sum of squares of deviations from the mean is a minimum.[1] Stated mathematically, what is to be proved is that $\Sigma(X - R)^2$ is a minimum when $R = M$ (the mean). Here X is each of the N observed values in turn and R is any constant quantity deducted from it. The first step is to expand the squared expression:

$$\Sigma(X - R)^2 = \Sigma(X^2 - 2XR + R^2)$$

Distributing the summation in the right-hand expression, we have

$$\Sigma X^2 - \Sigma 2XR + \Sigma R^2$$

Taking constants out from the summation, the expression becomes

$$\Sigma X^2 - 2R\Sigma X + NR^2$$

Next we apply a useful device of adding NM^2 and also $-NM^2$, which leaves the total value of the expression the same. Let us also substitute NM for ΣX, and we then have

$$\Sigma X^2 - NM^2 + NM^2 - 2RNM + NR^2$$

Combining the last three terms and factoring out N, we have

$$\Sigma X^2 - NM^2 + N(M^2 - 2MR + R^2)$$

which equals

$$\Sigma X^2 - NM^2 + N(M - R)^2$$

From the last term we see that the entire expression is a minimum when $M = R$, for then the last term equals zero.

CENTRAL VALUES IN SKEWED DISTRIBUTIONS

In skewed distributions, the mean is always pulled toward the skewed (pointed) end of the curve, as Fig. 4.3 shows. The arithmetic mean, as the center of gravity of the distribution, is weighed toward the extreme values, as was demonstrated above. The *sum* of the deviations on the one side of it equals the *sum* of the deviations on the other side. The median comes at a point that divides the *area* under the distribution curve into two equal parts. The *number* of scores on the one side of it equals the *number* of scores on the other. The interpretations of mean and median should be made accordingly. For example, for the data on class size in Table 4.3, the *median* of 18.5 tells us that half the

[1]Suggested by a proof given by Hammond, K. R., and Householder, J. E. *Introduction to the Statistical Method*. New York: Knopf, 1962.

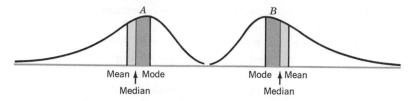

Fig. 4.3. *Two skewed distributions, (A) skewed negatively and (B) skewed positively, showing the relative positions of modes, medians, and means. Note that the mean is displaced farther from the mode toward the skewed end of the distribution and that the median is displaced two-thirds as far. The student should try to relate the latter fact to formula 4.8.*

classes had 19 or more students enrolled and half of them had 18 or less. The mean class size, which is 19.1, tells us that if all the enrolled students had been reapportioned so as to make all classes the same size, the enrollment in each class would have been 19.1, or 19, with a few students left over.

When the mean is misleading.   In some instances, reporting only the mean of a distribution is highly misleading. For example, in a study of class size in a certain university, among 62 classes, there were two classes having more than 200 students, and two having between 100 and 200 students, all the remaining classes except two being smaller than 60. The average size of the 62 classes was 34, but this was not very typical, because half of the classes had 20 or less (the median was 20.5). The most *typical* size of class would be given as the *mode*, which was 17 (crude mode). If our purpose happened to be to equalize the size of classes, assuming that this were practical, we could conclude that there should be 34 students per class. If we wanted to decide as a matter of educational policy whether or not there were too many small classes in general and if we had concluded beforehand that most teachers can successfully handle 30 students in a group, then the median would tell us, without knowing anything more about the distribution, that there were entirely too many small classes. The mean would not have told us this, because it was higher than 30. If we were piloting a visiting inspector about the buildings while classes were in session and wished to prepare him for the most likely size of class he would find at random, we should give him the mode, since this size would be more likely to occur than any other one size. If we were purchasing equipment to suit classes of various sizes, we should adapt it, if necessary, most often to classes of modal size, though in this case we should also want to know more about the entire frequency distribution.

Mean and median sometimes both reported.   In reporting central values of skewed distributions, it is sometimes desirable to state both the mean and the median, since each tells its own story, and from the difference between the two we can immediately infer in what direction the distribution is skewed and about how strongly. Although the mode is easily and quickly determined and will often serve until better averages can be computed, it should probably never be reported alone and need not be reported except when it is particularly meaningful to do so. When a distribution is symmetrical about the mode, the three averages will coincide, so only one of them, preferably the mean, need be reported.

WHEN THE MEDIAN IS ESPECIALLY CALLED FOR

There are one or two kinds of distribution in which the median is the only satisfactory average.

Distributions with indeterminate values. There are some distributions in which some of the extreme values are not accurately determined. We know that they lie out beyond a certain point on the scale but we do not know just how far. In certain time-scored tests, for example, some subjects would work on for unusual lengths of time if permitted to do so. Suppose that all those who work on a certain test up to 10 min are arbitrarily stopped. They are in the minority, and so a median can be found. Time spans up to 10 min may be classified, as usual, into chosen class intervals. From 10 min up, we find the laggards grouped together. We do not know just how long they might have kept working had we let them continue. An arithmetic mean cannot be determined here, but median and mode can still be utilized.

A SUMMARY OF WHEN TO USE THE THREE AVERAGES

In brief, the following rules will generally apply:
1. *Compute the arithmetic mean when*
    a. The greatest sampling stability is wanted. It usually varies less from sample to sample drawn from the same population.
    b. Other computations, such as finding measures of variability, are to follow.
    c. The distribution is symmetrical about the center.
    d. We wish to know the "center of gravity" of a sample.
2. *Compute the median when*
    a. There is not sufficient time to compute a mean.
    b. Distributions are markedly skewed. This is especially true when one or more very extreme measurements are at one side of the distribution.
    c. We are interested in whether cases fall within the upper or lower halves of the distribution and not particularly in how far they are from the central point.

    d. An incomplete distribution is given.
3. *Compute the mode when*
    a. The quickest estimate of central value is wanted.
    b. A very rough estimate of central value will do.
    c. We wish to know the most typical case.

Means of means, percentages, and proportions

The measures of central value described thus far will take care of the great majority of situations in which such statistics must be computed. There are some problems which, though rare, require other treatment. Two of these will be briefly mentioned: means of arithmetic means, and means of percentages (and proportions).

FINDING MEANS OF ARITHMETIC MEANS

When one has the means of several samples, presumably from the same population, on the same test or scale, he may wish to know the overall mean for the samples combined. At first thought, it might seem appropriate simply to average the several means just as one would average single observations. This would be proper procedure provided the samples are all of the same size. If the N's in the samples differ, however, the means are not equally reliable.

    In order to extract the best information about the central value of the composite sample, we should weight each mean according to the number of cases in the sample from which it was derived, for a mean's reliability is in proportion to the size of sample. This procedure is equivalent to pooling all the single measurements from the different samples and computing a single overall mean. We can accomplish the same end by computing a weighted mean of the means, which we already know. The general formula for computing a weighted mean is

$$_wM = \frac{\Sigma WX}{\Sigma W} \qquad \text{(A weighted arithmetic mean)} \qquad (4.9)$$

where $_wM$ = weighted mean
      W = weight
    ΣWX = sum of the values being averaged, each multiplied by its appropriate weight
      ΣW = sum of the weights

THE MEAN OF PERCENTAGES OR OF PROPORTIONS

The weighting procedure just described is even more important in determining the mean of a series of percentages or of proportions. Table 4.6 illustrates this point. The data in that table have to do with the percentage of pilot students eliminated in certain schools during

Table 4.6   Computation of an average percentage*

(1)	(2)	(3)	(4)
	No. enrolled	*No. eliminated*	*% eliminated*
School	N_i	$N_i P_i / 100$	P_i
G	243	55	22.6
H	63	7	11.1
K	196	43	21.9
L	61	2	3.3
S	125	34	27.2
Sums	$688 = \Sigma N_i$	$141 = \Sigma N_i P_i / 100$	$86.1 = \Sigma P_i$
Means	$137.6 = M_N$		$17.2 = M_p$†

*The data represent students enrolled in five AAF pilot schools selected to illustrate this procedure.
†The weighted mean of the percentages equals $14,100/688 = 20.5$. The value 17.2 is the unweighted mean.

one training period. Had the schools had the same enrollment, or even very nearly the same, the unweighted mean would suffice. Since the largest class is nearly four times as great as the smallest, however, and since elimination rates vary from 3.3 to 27.2, there is a marked difference between weighted and unweighted means. If we wished to know the overall elimination rate in order to make decisions for some administrative purpose, the unweighted mean would be misleading. Certainly, when the percentage or the proportion in a composite is wanted for further computations, the weighting procedure is essential, unless the sample N's are equal.

In terms of a formula, the weighted mean of a percentage is

$$_w M_p = \frac{\Sigma N_i P_i}{\Sigma N_i} \quad \text{(Mean of percentages where N's differ)} \quad (4.10)$$

where N_i = number in each sample
$\quad\quad P_i$ = percentage for each sample
$\quad \Sigma N_i P_i$ = sum of products of each percentage times its corresponding N
$\quad\quad \Sigma N_i$ = sum of the sample N's

For a weighted mean of proportions, simply substitute p_i for P_i in the formula.

EXERCISES

1. Compute the arithmetic mean of any or all of the distributions in Data 4A to 4F, inclusive, using the methods that seem most feasible.

Data 4A   **Scores in an English-usage examination**

Scores	f
52 – 53	1
50 – 51	0
48 – 49	5
46 – 47	10
44 – 45	9
42 – 43	14
40 – 41	7
38 – 39	8
36 – 37	6
34 – 35	5
32 – 33	3
Sum	**68**

Data 4B   **Affectivity scores (Per cent of 400 words marked "pleasant")**

Scores	f
95 – 99	6
90 – 94	11
85 – 89	16
80 – 84	7
75 – 79	9
70 – 74	8
65 – 69	2
60 – 64	3
55 – 59	2
50 – 54	1
Sum	**65**

Data 4C   **Scores made by graduates and eliminees in the Complex Coordination Test by student pilots**

Scores	Frequencies	
	Graduates	Eliminees
95 – 99	1	
90 – 94	1	
85 – 89	7	1
80 – 84	13	2
75 – 79	37	6
70 – 74	75	23
65 – 69	189	34
60 – 64	297	94
55 – 59	406	144
50 – 54	425	208
45 – 49	341	209
40 – 44	174	205
35 – 39	81	105
30 – 34	16	34
25 – 29	5	15
20 – 24	0	2
15 – 19	1	

Data 4D   **Scores in an adjustment inventory obtained from alcoholics and nonalcoholics of both sexes***

Scores	Frequencies			
	Males		Females	
	Alcoholics	Nonalcoholics	Alcoholics	Nonalcoholics
66 – 71	1			
60 – 65	6		3	
54 – 59	13	1	2	1
48 – 53	13	1	10	2
42 – 47	17	3	11	1
36 – 41	33	3	12	1
30 – 35	32	2	8	8
24 – 29	32	9	11	17
18 – 23	23	16	5	26
12 – 17	24	36	2	40
6 – 11	7	43	2	49
0 – 5	1	25		21

*Manson, M. P. A psychometric differentiation between alcoholics and nonalcoholics. *Quar. J. Stud. Alcohol.*, 1948, 9, 175 – 206.

Data 4E   **Ages of college freshmen**

Age at last birthday	Men	Women
31–35	1	2
26–30	3	6
25	7	6
24	6	7
23	11	7
22	20	6
21	23	16
20	40	13
19	88	48
18	117	67
17	69	57
16	2	6
Sums	**387**	**241**

Data 4F   **Aiming-test scores**
(In terms of average error in millimeters)

Score	Men	Women
8.0–8.4	1	
7.5–7.9	5	
7.0–7.4	2	
6.5–6.9	7	2
6.0–6.4	6	4
5.5–5.9	11	3
5.0–5.4	10	9
4.5–4.9	16	7
4.0–4.4	18	15
3.5–3.9	19	12
3.0–3.4	17	15
2.5–2.9	17	13
2.0–2.4	14	14
1.5–1.9	13	10
1.0–1.4	8	1
0.5–0.9	1	
Sums	**165**	**105**

In Data 4*E*, you will have to make some assumption regarding the cases in the two highest intervals. If means are computed for these distributions, state your assumptions.

2. Compute medians for any or all distributions in Data 4*A* to 4*F* inclusive. Why is the difficulty experienced with computation of the mean in Data 4*E* not also encountered in computing the median?

3. Give the crude modes for all distributions in Data 4*A* to 4*F*. Compute the estimated mode in distributions for which you know both mean and median.

4. Compute and list the means, medians, and crude modes (where possible) for the distributions in Data 4*G*.

Data 4G   **Some ungrouped data**
a. 8, 15, 13, 6, 10, 16, 7, 12, 11, 14, 9
b. 12, 10, 18, 13, 4, 8, 17, 15, 6, 14
c. 9, 8, 9, 15, 3, 9, 11, 9, 13
d. 12, 28, 19, 15, 15, 35, 14, 15
e. 7, 18, 20, 14, 27, 23, 13, 3

5. For each distribution in Data 4*G*, tell to which measure of central value you give first preference and to which, second. Give reasons.

6. For each distribution in Data 4A to 4F inclusive, tell which measure of central value you would prefer and which would be your second choice. Give reasons.

7. Find the weighted means of the four means: 15, 16, 18, and 21. These means were derived from samples in which the N's were 6, 10, 25, and 20, respectively. Compute the unweighted arithmetic mean of the four, for comparison. Interpret your result.

8. Find the weighted mean of the proportions .25, .30, .32, and .33. These proportions were based upon samples whose N's were 44, 32, 18, and 25, respectively. Compute an unweighted arithmetic mean of these proportions, for comparison. Interpret your results.

9. For the aiming-test scores for men, in Data 4F, find the centile-point values for the following centile ranks: 90, 75, 25, and 10.

ANSWERS
1, 2, and *3.*

Data	4A	4B	4C		4D				4E		4F	
Mean	41.2	81.7	54.8	49.3	32.8	13.9	37.2	15.3	19.6	19.7	3.91	3.57
Median	42.2	84.7	54.4	48.8	32.1	11.8	38.0	13.4	18.6	18.9	3.78	3.43
Mode	42.5	87	52	47	38.5	8.5	38.5	8.5	18.5	18.5	3.7	3.7

4.

	a	*b*	*c*	*d*	*e*
Mean	11.0	11.7	9.6	19.1	15.6
Median	11.0	12.5	9.1	15.2	
Mode			9	15	

7. 18.4; 17.5.
8. .291; .300.
9. Centile points: 6.33; 4.99; 2.60; 1.74.

5 *Measures of variability*

KNOWING the central value of a set of measurements tells us much, but it does not by any means give us the total picture of the sample we have measured. Two groups of six-year-old children may have the same average IQ of 105, from which we would conclude that, taken as a whole, each group is as bright as the other, and we might expect from the two the same average level of performance in school or out of school in areas of life where IQ is important.

Yet when we are told, in addition, that one group has no individuals with IQ's below 95 or above 115, whereas the other has individuals with IQ's ranging from 75 to 135, we recognize immediately that there is a decided difference between the two groups in variability or dispersion of brightness. The first group is decidedly more homogeneous with respect to IQ than the second. We should expect the first group to be much more teachable in that they will grasp new ideas at about the same rate and progress at about the same rate. We should expect the second group to show considerable disparity in speed of grasping new ideas. There will be extreme laggards at the one end of the distribution and others at the other end of the distribution who may be irked at the slow progress of the group. The distributions for two such groups, when plotted, resemble those in Fig. 5.1.

It is the purpose of this chapter to explain and to illustrate the methods of indicating degree of variability or dispersion by the use of single numbers, just as in the preceding chapter we saw how the central value of a distribution could be indicated by a single number. The four most customary values to indicate variability are (1) the total range, (2) the semi-interquartile range Q, (3) the average (or mean) deviation AD, and (4) the standard deviation σ.

The total range

The total range is the indicator of variability that is easiest and most quickly ascertained but is also the most unreliable; thus it is almost entirely limited to the purpose of preliminary inspection. In the illustration of the preceding paragraph, the range of the first

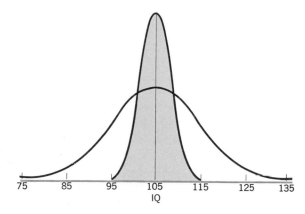

Fig. 5.1. *Two distributions with the same mean (IQ = 105) but with decidedly different ranges (dispersions).*

group (from an IQ of 95 to an IQ of 115) is 20 IQ points. The range of the second group is from 75 to 135 IQ points, 60 IQ points. The range is the distance given by highest score minus lowest score. The second group is considerably more variable than the first.

The semi-interquartile range — Q

The semi-interquartile range, Q, is *one-half* the range of the middle 50 per cent of the cases. First we find by interpolation the range of the middle 50 per cent, or interquartile range, then divide this range by 2. See Fig. 5.2 for a general picture of the relation of Q to a frequency distribution.

QUARTILES AND QUARTERS

When we count up from below to include the lowest, or first, quarter of the cases, we find the point called the *first quartile*, which is given the symbol Q_1. Counting down from above to include the highest, or fourth, quarter of the cases, we locate the third quartile, or Q_3. Incidentally, the median, which separates the second and third quarters of the distribution, is also called Q_2. Note that the quartiles Q_1, Q_2, and Q_3 are *points* on the measuring scale. They are division points between the *quarters*. We may say of an individual that he is *in* the highest *quarter* (or fourth quarter), and we may say of another that he is *at* the third *quartile*. We should never say of an individual that he is *in* a certain *quartile*.

Interpolation of Q_1 and Q_3. In the distribution of ink-blot scores again, we locate the third and first quartiles by interpolation (see Table 5.1). One-fourth of the cases ($N/4$) is 12.5. Counting up from the bottom to include 12.5 cases, we find that we need 2.5 out of the 6 cases in the third class interval. As in earlier solutions in connection with computing a median, 2.5/6 times 5 gives 2.08. Added to 19.5, this gives 21.58 as the position of Q_1. Counting down from the top, we find

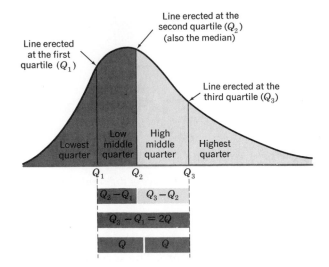

Fig. 5.2. *Illustration of the quartiles Q_1, Q_2, and Q_3, the interquartile and semi-interquartile ranges, and the quarters of the sample, in a slightly skewed distribution.*

that we need 3.5 cases out of 6 in the fifth class interval. Then 3.5/6 of 5 gives 2.92. Deducted from 39.5, this leaves 36.58 as our estimate of Q_3.

THE INTERQUARTILE RANGE AND Q

The interquartile range, or the distance from Q_1 to Q_3, is given by $Q_3 - Q_1$, or $36.58 - 21.58$, which equals 15.00.

The semi-interquartile range is one-half of this, or 7.5. In terms of a formula,

$$Q = \frac{Q_3 - Q_1}{2} \quad \text{(Semi-interquartile range)} \tag{5.1}$$

where Q_3 = third quartile and Q_1 = first quartile.

Table 5.1 **Determination of Q_3, Q_1, and Q (the semi-interquartile range) for the ink-blot-test scores**

Scores	f	
55–59	1	
50–54	1	
45–49	3	
40–44	4	
35–39	6	←Q_3 lies within this interval
30–34	7	
25–29	12	
20–24	6	←Q_1 lies within this interval
15–19	8	
10–14	2	
	$N = 50$	

$$Q_1 = 19.5 + \frac{2.5}{6} \times 5 = 19.5 + 2.08 = 21.58$$

$$Q_3 = 39.5 - \frac{3.5}{6} \times 5 = 39.5 - 2.92 = 36.58$$

$$Q = \frac{36.58 - 21.58}{2} = \frac{15.00}{2} = 7.5$$

HOW QUARTILES INDICATE SKEWNESS

It is of interest in passing to take note of the relative distances of Q_3 and Q_1 from the median, or Q_2, in a distribution. If the distribution is exactly symmetrical, the third and first quartiles will be the same distance from the median, and that distance is Q. When there is any skewness in the distribution, the two distances will be unequal. If the skewness is positive, the distance $Q_3 - Q_2$ will be greater than the distance $Q_2 - Q_1$. If the skewness is negative, the reverse will be true. In other words, skewness is:

positive when $(Q_3 - Q_2) > (Q_2 - Q_1)$
negative when $(Q_3 - Q_2) < (Q_2 - Q_1)$
and zero when $(Q_3 - Q_2) = (Q_2 - Q_1)$

The relative sizes of these two distances therefore tells much about the direction and the amount of skewness in the distribution. For the ink-blot scores, $Q_3 - Q_2$ is 8.4, and $Q_2 - Q_1$ is 6.6. Our inference is that the distribution is positively skewed to a moderate degree. In Fig. 5.2 the distribution is positively skewed and $(Q_3 - Q_2)$ is clearly greater than $(Q_2 - Q_1)$.

The average deviation

The average deviation, or AD, is the arithmetic mean of all the deviations when we disregard the algebraic signs. Every score or measurement in a distribution deviates from the mean in that it is a certain distance above or below the mean unless it happens to coincide with the mean, in which case the deviation is zero. Deviations above the mean are regarded as positive distances, those below the mean as negative distances. In terms of an algebraic definition,

$x = X - M$ (A deviation of a measurement from the mean)   (5.2)

where X = original score or measurement and M = arithmetic mean.

As pointed out in the preceding chapter, the deviations from the mean may be regarded as *moments* about a center of gravity. The sum of the deviations, taking into account algebraic signs, is zero, as demonstrated in Chap. 4. The average of the deviations would also be zero, for $\Sigma x / N = 0 / N = 0$. This kind of averaging tells us nothing about the size of the deviations. We want some indication of their overall size, in order to describe the amount of dispersion.

One solution is to disregard the algebraic signs of the deviations, thus ignoring their directions and taking into account only their sizes. Averaging absolute values gives us the kind of answer we need. The formula is

$$AD = \frac{\Sigma |x|}{N}$$ (The average deviation)

(5.3)

where $|x|$ (with the vertical bars embracing it) is the absolute value of x. The average deviation is now used so rarely that space will not be taken to illustrate how it is computed. The formula is actually very simply applied.

The standard deviation

The standard deviation is by far the most commonly used indicator of degree of dispersion and is the most dependable source of estimation of the variability in the total population from which the sample came. It also enters into hosts of other statistical formulas that we shall encounter later.

GENERAL FORMULA FOR THE STANDARD DEVIATION

Like the AD, the standard deviation is a kind of average of all the deviations about the mean of the sample, though not a simple arithmetic mean. The fundamental formula is

$$\sigma = \sqrt{\frac{\Sigma x^2}{N}} \quad \text{(The standard deviation)} \tag{5.4}$$

where x = deviation from the mean of the sample and N = size of sample.

As a general concept, the standard deviation is often symbolized by SD (sometimes S. D.). Some writers denote the SD of a sample by the single letter capital S. Many writers recommend that we compute the very similar statistic s, which is an estimate of the SD of the population from which the sample came. It is computed by using $N - 1$ in the denominator of formula (5.4) in place of N, for reasons that will be explained in Chap. 8. In this volume we shall use the symbol σ for the standard deviation of a sample and $\bar{\sigma}$, with a bar over it, to indicate the standard deviation of the population. Reasons for this will also be explained in Chap. 8.

Formula (5.4) calls for several steps in computation, in fixed order:

Step 1. Find each deviation from the mean (x).
Step 2. Square each deviation, finding x^2.
Step 3. Sum the squared deviations, finding Σx^2.
Step 4. Divide this sum by N, finding $\Sigma x^2/N$.
Step 5. Extract the square root of the result of step 4 (using Table A, in Appendix B). This is the standard deviation.

These steps are illustrated in Tables 5.2 and 5.3 and in Fig. 5.3.

VARIABILITY, VARIANCE, AND SUM OF SQUARES

Before proceeding to apply the formula, let us consider some important concepts. In verbal terms, a standard deviation is the square root of the arithmetic mean of the squared deviations of measurements from their mean. It has accordingly often been called the *root-mean-square deviation*. In this statement lies considerable meaning. Latent in the few steps enumerated above lie three statistical concepts that have had increasing importance and of which we shall see a great deal. At the end of step 3 we have the *sum of squares* (commonly symbolized as SS). At the end of step 4 we have the *mean square* (commonly symbolized as MS), which is also known as the variance of a sample. These ideas are best introduced by means of an illustration.

In Table 5.2 are listed seven fictitious scores representing a sample of seven individuals A to G inclusive. These are denoted by the usual symbol, X. The mean of these seven scores, as shown in column 2, is exactly 10.0. Column 3 shows the deviations of these scores from the mean. Their sum is zero and also their mean, as is to be expected. In column 4 we find the squared deviations. Their sum, 88, is the *sum of squares*. Their mean is equal to 12.57, which we have defined as the *variance*, in this sample. The square root of this is 3.55, the standard deviation. All this follows from formula (5.4) and from the steps and definitions given above. Let us see what this means in terms of a geometrical view of the problem.

A geometric picture of deviations, variance, and standard deviation. For a geometrical representation of these ideas, see Fig. 5.3. In the first diagram, the scale of measurement is shown, as usual, in the form of a straight line extending from left to right. Here, however, the original score values are not marked. The mean has been recognized as the main reference point and been called zero. This is what

Table 5.2   **Data illustrating sum of squares, variance, and standard deviation**

(1) *Person*	*(2)* *Score* *X*	*(3)* *Deviation* *x*	*(4)* *Deviation* *squared* *x^2*
A	15	+5	25
B	14	+4	16
C	11	+1	1
D	10	0	0
E	9	−1	1
F	7	−3	9
G	4	−6	36
Sums	$70 = \Sigma X$	$0 = \Sigma x$	$88 = \Sigma x^2$
Means	10.0	0.0	$12.57 = V$
Standard deviation			$3.55 = \sigma$

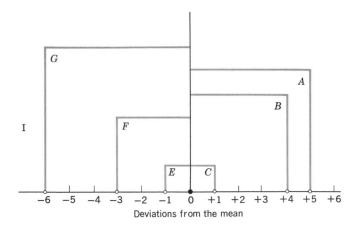

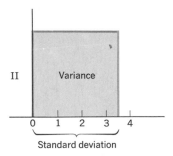

I

II   Variance

Deviations from the mean

Standard deviation

Fig. 5.3. *Illustration of deviations from the arithmetic mean, their squares, the mean of squared deviations (which is the variance), and the standard deviation (which measures the variability) in a sample of seven cases.*

happens when we derive deviations x from original scores X. All seven individuals still retain their relative positions, in correct rank order and at the same separations, as they had before. We have merely moved the zero point 10 units up the linear scale.

So much for representing deviations. It will be seen that the points on the line correspond exactly with the values in column 3 of Table 5.2. Consider now the squaring of the deviations. Where deviations themselves are represented by *linear* distances from a common reference point, squared deviations must be represented by *areas*, namely, squares. The squares belonging to the different individuals A to G are shown in Fig. 5.3. The areas of the squares are accurately represented numerically by the values given in column 4 of Table 5.2. It can be seen that the individuals come in the same rank order when we compare the squared deviations as when we compare x distances. It is also notable how large deviations, when squared, increase much more relatively than do small deviations. This point will be important to consider later.

The sum of the squares would be represented geometrically as an area equal to a composite of all the squares in Fig. 5.3 I. This could also be shown as a square or as a rectangle. Its dimensions could vary somewhat but its surface would contain 88 units, each unit equal in size to those representing persons C and E. Finding the arithmetic mean of this large area is equivalent to apportioning it equally among the seven individuals. It is the amount of area that each person would possess if each one of them were given the same amount. This is the variance, which we may represent in the form of a square as in Fig. 5.3 II. This square is shown on a base line like that in the first diagram. Its length of side is the square root of its area and represents the standard deviation.

Algebraic interrelationships of SS, V, and σ. Some important algebraic relationships, latent in formula (5.4), may be called to the attention of the reader. They are all important for general orientation toward this topic. They may be useful not only in thinking about the concepts of sums of squares, variances, and standard deviations but will be found to enter into computations of various kinds later. First, two more symbols need to be introduced. *V is used to stand for variance.* With this additional symbol given, we can state the following interrelationships:

$$\sigma = \sqrt{\frac{\Sigma x^2}{N}} = \sqrt{V} \tag{5.5}$$

$$V = \frac{\Sigma x^2}{N} = \sigma^2 \quad \text{(Interrelationships of } \Sigma x^2, V, \text{ and } \sigma) \tag{5.6}$$

$$\Sigma x^2 = NV = N\sigma^2 \tag{5.7}$$

Both V and σ, each in its own way, are indicators of amount of dispersion in a distribution. V is said to measure variance, σ to measure variability. When the sample is one of individuals measured on a common scale, either V or σ can become familiar indicators of the extent of the individual differences. To make these concepts more meaningful, then, it is well to think of them in terms of measures of amounts or degrees of individual differences.

Further interpretations of variance. Suppose, first, that we have a sample of only one case, with only one score. There is no possible basis for individual differences in such a sample, and therefore there is no variance or variability. Bring into the picture a second individual with his score in the same test or experiment. We now have one difference. Bring in a third case and we then have two additional differences, three altogether. Bring in a fourth, a fifth, and so on. There are as many differences as there are possible pairs of individuals. We could compute *all* these interpair differences and could average them to get a single, representative value. We could also square them and then average them. It is far more economical, however, to find a mean of all the scores and to use that value as a common reference point.

Each difference then becomes a deviation from that reference point, and there are only as many deviations as there are individuals. Either the variance or the standard deviation is a single representative value for all the individual differences when taken from a common reference point.

Consider the matter from a somewhat different point of view. Consider giving a certain test of n items to a group of persons. Before giving the first item to the group, so far as any information from this test is concerned the individuals are all alike. All have scores of zero. There is no variance. This may seem absurd, but it has a real bearing on what comes next. Next administer the first item in the test to all individuals in the group. Some will pass it and some will fail. Some will now have scores of 1 and some still have scores of zero. There are two groups of individuals. There is this much differentiation, this much variance. Give a second item. Of those who passed the first, some will pass the second and some will fail it, unless the two items are perfectly correlated. Of those who failed the first, some may pass the second and some may fail it. There are now three possible scores, 0, 1, and 2. More variance has been introduced. Carry the illustration further, adding item by item. The differences among scores will keep increasing, and so, by computation, also the variance and the variability, as indicated by V and by σ.

Psychological and educational testing depends almost entirely upon the phenomenon of individual differences and therefore upon variance. Probably less than 1 per cent of the tests commonly used yield scores on an absolute scale. The significance of any score is ordinarily its usefulness in placement of a person somewhere in the group. The greater the variance among the scores, other things being equal, the more accurately each person is placed.

In addition to the use of the variance and standard deviation in describing the spread or scatter of a certain sample, there is use, as we shall see in later chapters, in the evaluation of tests and test items in a number of ways (see Chap. 18). After this digression, let us return to the descriptive use of σ and its computation in a typical laboratory problem.

COMPUTATION AND INTERPRETATION OF A STANDARD DEVIATION

As an illustrative problem in computing σ by formula (5.4), let us take the 10 measurements of the threshold for pitch (see Table 5.3). Their mean we found to be 13.2. The deviations from the mean are given in column 2 and their squares in column 3. The sum of squares is 51.60. The mean of the squared deviations is 5.160. The standard deviation is the square root of this, or 2.27. This should not be reported to more

Table 5.3   Calculation of the standard deviation in ungrouped data

(1) Score X	(2) Deviation x	(3) x^2
13	−0.2	.04
17	+3.8	14.44
15	+1.8	3.24
11	−2.2	4.84
13	−0.2	.04
17	+3.8	14.44
13	−0.2	.04
11	−2.2	4.84
11	−2.2	4.84
11	−2.2	4.84
		51.60
		Σx^2

$$\sigma = \sqrt{\frac{51.60}{10}} = \sqrt{5.160} = 2.27, \text{ or } 2.3$$

than one decimal place. In terms of the unit of the measuring scale, this is 2.3 cycles per second.

The interpretation of a standard deviation.   The usual and most accepted interpretation of a standard deviation is in terms of the percentage of cases included within the range from one standard deviation below the mean to one standard deviation above the mean. This range on the scale of measurement includes about two-thirds of the cases in the distribution. In a normal distribution, the range approximately from -1σ (one standard deviation below the mean) to $+1\sigma$ (one standard deviation above) contains 68.27 per cent of the cases. Since most samples yield distributions that depart to some degree from normality, we say "about two-thirds," which is, of course, a little less than 68.27 per cent. Figure 5.4 illustrates the division of the area under a normal curve into regions marked off at -1σ and $+1\sigma$. With two-thirds of the surface *within* those limits, there is left one-third of the area to be divided between the two "tails" of the distribution — one-sixth below the point at -1σ and one-sixth above the point at $+1\sigma$.

In the problem just solved, where we found σ equal to 2.3, the distance from -1σ to $+1\sigma$ on the scale of measurement is 10.9 to 15.5

cycles; i.e., the mean 13.2 minus 2.3 is 10.9, and the mean plus 2.3 is 15.5 cycles. Within these limits are measurements of 11, 12, 13, 14, and 15. By actual count, there are four 11's, three 13's, and one 15, or 8 of the 10 measurements within these limits, whereas we should have expected 7. But, because of the small number of cases and the fact that the distribution is irregular, we should not be surprised at this result. In other problems this comparison serves as a rough check upon the accuracy of computation of σ. It will not catch all errors but will indicate gross errors if the sample is not too small and the distribution is fairly normal.

Grouping deviations as a short cut. Some saving in time and effort can be afforded in the solution of the standard deviation in data like those in Table 5.3, if we group them as in Table 5.4. Since the same measurement is repeated several times and its deviation from the mean is the same every time, as well as its deviation squared, we need to find the deviation and its square only once and multiply each x^2 by its frequency. The last column of Table 5.4 contains the fx^2 products, and their sum is again 51.60, from which the standard deviation will be the same as before. The formula for this reads

$$\sigma = \sqrt{\frac{\Sigma f x^2}{N}} \quad \text{(Standard deviation from grouped data)} \tag{5.8}$$

where the symbols are defined as before.

A similar treatment may be given all grouped data, in which we let the midpoint of each interval represent all cases within the interval, and this value (X_c) minus M gives the deviation of all cases within the interval. From here on, the procedure is the same as that in Table 5.4. We shall not illustrate the steps by means of a special problem, for there are more efficient methods of dealing with grouped data.

THE STANDARD DEVIATION BY THE CODE METHOD

The code method, which was employed in the preceding chapter to calculate a mean (Table 4.2), will now be extended in order to compute a standard deviation. The first steps are identical with those employed to compute a mean. The whole process of computing a standard

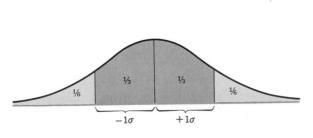

Fig. 5.4. *Approximate fractions of the area under a normal distribution curve (thus fractions of the N cases in a normally distributed sample) that lie within one standard deviation of the mean and also beyond the limits of one standard deviation, in either direction.*

*Table 5.4   Calculation of the
standard deviation in grouped data
with the use of actual deviations*

(1)	(2)	(3)	(4)	(5)
X	x	x^2	f	fx^2
17	+3.8	14.44	2	28.88
15	+1.8	3.24	1	3.24
13	−0.2	.04	3	.12
11	−2.2	4.84	4	19.36
				51.60
				Σfx^2

deviation by the code method can be carried through to the final step in terms of the coded values. That is, we can use the x' deviations from the temporary zero reference point (see p. 46). The main formula is[1]

$$\sigma = i\sqrt{\frac{\Sigma fx'^2}{N} - M^2_{x'}} = i\sqrt{\frac{\Sigma fx'^2}{N} - \left(\frac{\Sigma fx'}{N}\right)^2}$$ (Standard deviation from grouped   (5.9)
and coded values)

where i = size of class interval
x' = deviation from the origin of coded values
$M_{x'}$ = mean of the coded values
For convenience in computation, the formula may be modified to read

$$\sigma = \frac{i}{N}\sqrt{N\Sigma fx'^2 - (\Sigma fx')^2}$$ [Alternate for (5.9)]   (5.10)

The code method is illustrated in Table 5.5, which is similar to Table 4.2 through column 4. For all class intervals, we need to know the fx'^2 products, and these are given in column 5. In each row, the fx'^2 product is found by multiplying the corresponding numbers in columns 3 and 4; i.e., the first one, 25, is the product of 5×5; the second one is the product of 4×4; and the third, the product of 3×9; etc. This is because the product fx'^2 may be factored as $(fx')x'$. It is excellent checking procedure to do the multiplying also by the product $(f) \times (x'^2)$ for each interval.

[1]Proof bearing upon the effect of coding upon the standard deviation will be found in Appendix A (Proofs 4, 5, and 6). Briefly, it is demonstrated that adding (or deducting) a constant from all X values leaves the σ unchanged. Multiplying all X values by a constant C gives a σ C times as large. Such effects apply when both operations, adding a constant and multiplying by a constant, are applied, as in the coding process.

Table 5.5   Calculation of the standard deviation using the code method

(1) Score	(2) f	(3) x'	(4) fx'	(5) fx'²
55–59	1	+5	+ 5	25
50–54	1	+4	+ 4	16
45–49	3	+3	+ 9	27
40–44	4	+2	+ 8	16
35–39	6	+1	+ 6	6
30–34	7	0	0	0
25–29	12	−1	−12	12
20–24	6	−2	−12	24
15–19	8	−3	−24	72
10–14	2	−4	− 8	32
	50		−24	230
	N		$\Sigma fx'$	$\Sigma fx'^2$

$$M_{x'} = \frac{\Sigma fx'}{N} = \frac{-24}{50} = -0.48$$

Next we sum the fx'^2 products to obtain $\Sigma fx'^2$. In Table 5.5, this is 230. To find $M_{x'}$, we divide $\Sigma fx'$ by N. In this case, it is $-24/50$, which equals −0.48. We need $M^2_{x'}$, which is 0.2304. Now, to apply formula (5.10), we need next to divide $\Sigma fx'^2$ by N, or $230/50$, which equals 4.6. Deduct $M^2_{x'}$ from this, or 4.6 − 0.2304, and we have 4.3696. The square root of this is called for next, and this is 2.09. The last step is to multiply by i, the size of the class interval; 2.09 × 5 equals 10.45, which is the standard deviation we have been seeking.

We may now say that about two-thirds of the individuals should be expected between the mean minus 10.45 and the mean plus 10.45. Since the mean is 29.6, these limits are 19.2 and 40.0. Fortunately, for the sake of checking on this conclusion, these limits are close to the division points between class intervals (see Table 5.5). The four intervals included within these limits have in them 31 cases altogether, which are 62 per cent of the whole group. This is a little short of two-thirds but not unreasonably so.

Rough checks for a computed standard deviation. The kind of comparison just mentioned is a very rough check for the correct solution of the standard deviation. If the actual percentage of cases between $+1\sigma$ and -1σ deviates too far from 68 per cent, there is probably something wrong with the calculation, and a recalculation is in order. This check cannot always be satisfactorily applied with grouped data because the frequencies from -1σ to $+1\sigma$ cannot then be accurately determined.

Another rough check is to compare the standard deviation obtained with the total range of measurements. In large samples ($N = 500$ or more) the standard deviation is about one-sixth of the total range. Stated in other terms, the total range is about six standard deviations. In smaller samples, the ratio of range to standard deviation to be expected becomes smaller, as indicated in Table 5.6.

In the ink-blot data, since $N = 50$, we should expect the range to be 4.5 times the standard deviation. The standard deviation 10.45 times 4.5 gives us an expected range of about 47 points. Actually the range was 46 points, which checks so closely as to give us confidence that our standard deviation is at least not grossly in error.

It may seem strange that we use a less reliable statistic like range as a criterion of accuracy of a more reliable statistic like the standard deviation. The reasons are that (1) there can hardly be any error in computing such a simple thing as the range, whereas (2) there are chances of gross errors in calculating σ because of the many steps involved, for example, failing to make the final step of multiplying by i.

A summary of steps for computing the standard deviation. The steps necessary for the calculation of σ by the code method are as follows:

Step 1. Complete steps 1 through 6 already listed for finding the mean by the code method (see Table 4.2).

Step 2. Find for every class interval the fx'^2 product. The most efficient way is to compute the product of x' times fx' for each interval. These products will all be positive.

Table 5.6   **Ratios of the total range to the standard deviation in a distribution for different values of N***

N	Range/σ	N	Range/σ	N	Range/σ
5	2.3	40	4.3	400	5.9
10	3.1	50	4.5	500	6.1
15	3.5	100	5.0	700	6.3
20	3.7	200	5.5	1,000	6.5

*Adapted from Snedecor, G. W. *Statistical Methods*. Ames, Iowa: Collegiate, 1940. P. 85.

Step   3. Sum the fx'^2 products.

Step   4. Divide this sum by N, carrying to at least two decimal places.[1]

Step   5. Find $M^2_{x''}$, to at least two decimal places.

Step   6. Deduct the number found in step 5 from that found in step 4.

Step   7. Find the square root of the number found in step 6, keeping two decimal places.

Step   8. Multiply this number by the size of the class interval. If N is large, report two decimal places; if small, round to one decimal place.

Step   9. Interpret the standard deviation in terms of the two-thirds principle.

Step 10. Apply the rough check of comparing σ with the range and using the ratios of Table 5.6.

THE STANDARD DEVIATION FROM ORIGINAL MEASUREMENTS

If the number of measurements is not large, if the measurements themselves are small numbers, particularly when a good calculating machine is available, the best procedure for computing a standard deviation is by means of the formula

$$\sigma = \frac{1}{N} \sqrt{N\Sigma X^2 - (\Sigma X)^2} \qquad \text{(Standard deviation computed} \atop \text{without knowledge of deviations)} \qquad (5.11)$$

in which the essential steps are:

Step 1. Square each score or measurement.

Step 2. Sum the squared measurements to give ΣX^2.

Step 3. Multiply ΣX^2 by N to give $N\Sigma X^2$.

Step 4. Sum the X's to find ΣX.

Step 5. Square the ΣX to find $(\Sigma X)^2$.

Step 6. Find the difference $N\Sigma X - (\Sigma X)^2$.

Step 7. Find the square root of the number found in step 6.

Step 8. Divide the number found in step 7 by N (or multiply it by $1/N$).

On the calculating machine, the X's and the X^2's can be accumulated at the same time according to instructions provided with the machine. In tabular form, the solution of this kind is illustrated in Table 5.7.

[1]In this, and in the following steps, it is assumed that we are dealing with integral measurements. If they are in terms of decimal fractions or multiples of 10 or 100, this rule applies only after making the necessary allowance for the place of the decimal point.

X	X^2
13	169
17	289
15	225
11	121
13	169
17	289
11	121
13	169
11	121
11	121
ΣX 132	ΣX^2 1,794

Table 5.7   Calculation of the standard deviation from the original measurements and ungrouped data

$$\sigma = \frac{1}{10} \sqrt{10(1{,}794) - 132^2}$$
$$= \frac{1}{10} \sqrt{17{,}940 - 17{,}424}$$
$$= \frac{1}{10} \sqrt{516}$$
$$= \frac{22.7}{10}$$
$$= 2.27, \text{ or } 2.3$$

Derivation of formula (5.11).   Let us begin with the basic equation for the variance of a set of measurements X,

$$\sigma^2 = \frac{\Sigma x^2}{N} \tag{1}$$

the mean of the squared deviations. Each deviation equals $X - M$, so we may write (1) as

$$\sigma^2 = \frac{1}{N} \Sigma(X - M)^2$$

Expanding the squared term,

$$\sigma^2 = \frac{1}{N} \Sigma(X^2 - 2XM + M^2)$$

Distributing the summation,

$$\sigma^2 = \frac{1}{N} (\Sigma X^2 - \Sigma 2XM + \Sigma M^2)$$

Distributing $1/N$ and taking out constant terms,

$$\sigma^2 = \frac{1}{N} \Sigma X^2 - \frac{1}{N} 2M\Sigma X + \frac{1}{N} NM^2$$
$$= \frac{1}{N} \Sigma X^2 - 2M^2 + M^2$$
$$= \frac{1}{N} \Sigma X^2 - M^2$$
$$= \frac{1}{N} \Sigma X^2 - \left(\frac{\Sigma X}{N}\right)^2$$

Multiplying the entire expression on the right by N^2 and putting a $1/N^2$ term outside the brackets,

$$\sigma^2 = \frac{1}{N^2} \left[N \Sigma X^2 - (\Sigma X)^2 \right]$$

and, taking square roots,

$$\sigma = \frac{1}{N} \sqrt{N \Sigma X^2 - (\Sigma X)^2}$$

CORRECTION OF THE STANDARD DEVIATION FOR COARSE GROUPING

We are now ready to see more clearly why the number of class intervals should not be too small in grouping data or the class interval too large. Reference was previously made (p. 46) to a "grouping error." Let us see what the grouping error is and how it affects the standard deviation.

This phenomenon is illustrated in Fig. 5.5. There, a distribution is drawn with only five intervals. Our computations with grouped data thus far have assumed that all the values within an interval may be given a class value corresponding to the midpoint of the interval. In coarse grouping the midpoint value is not a very exact representative one in most intervals because the cases are not distributed evenly, or even symmetrically, within the interval. The exception to this is the interval that may happen to straddle the mean, in which case the midpoint and the average of the cases in the class may coincide.

In other intervals, note that the frequencies are greater toward the limit on the side nearer the middle of the distribution. If we computed an actual mean of the cases within each interval, we should find it nearer the mean of the entire sample than the midpoint is. The difference between the class mean and the midpoint of an interval is the grouping error in that interval. Above the sample mean the grouping errors are ordinarily positive (midpoint greater than the class mean) and below the sample mean the errors are ordinarily negative (midpoint less than the class mean). The effect of the grouping errors upon the computation of a mean is usually almost nil be-

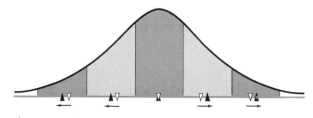

▲ Midpoints of class intervals

▽ Actual means of class values

Fig. 5.5. *Illustration of grouping errors resulting from letting the midpoint of each class interval represent all cases within the interval rather than using the mean of the values for that interval. The smaller the number of intervals the greater the errors.*

cause they are fairly well balanced. But their effect upon the average deviation, and especially upon the standard deviation, is often large enough to be concerned about. Grouping errors tend to enlarge the estimate of the standard deviation, and the coarser the grouping, the greater is this systematic error in σ.

Sheppard's correction.   When a correction in σ is necessary, Sheppard's formula, developed for this purpose, serves very well. When applied to a known standard deviation, it reads

$$_c\sigma = \sqrt{\sigma^2 - \frac{i^2}{12}} \qquad \text{(Sheppard's correction in } \sigma \\ \text{for coarse grouping)} \qquad (5.12)$$

where $_c\sigma$ = standard deviation corrected for errors of grouping
  σ = uncorrected standard deviation computed from data grouped in class intervals
  i = size of the class interval
To apply the correction earlier in the operations, as in connection with formula (5.9), we have

$$_c\sigma = i \sqrt{\frac{\Sigma fx'^2}{N} - \left(\frac{\Sigma fx'}{N}\right)^2 - .0833} \qquad \begin{array}{l}\text{(Solution of } \sigma \text{ with} \\ \text{Sheppard's correction} \\ \text{included)}\end{array} \qquad (5.13)$$

It has been stated that when the size of class interval, i, is equal to $.49\sigma$, Sheppard's correction amounts to only about 1 per cent. Such an error could be tolerated unless very precise calculations are going to be done with σ after it is computed. If an interval is about one-half σ (i.e., $.49\sigma$), as just stated, and if the sample is large, with a range of about six standard deviations, we should then have 12 class intervals. For large samples, then, 12 class intervals are a minimum for accurate computation of the standard deviation. If there are less than 12, for accurate work we should apply Sheppard's correction. Whether or not we apply this correction, therefore, depends upon the size of sample, the number of intervals, and the use we intend to make of σ.

Descriptive use of statistics

Thus far, the chief uses proposed for measures of central value and of dispersion have been as simple values descriptive of total distributions. This is best appreciated when we compare different samples. As an illustration of this, see Table 5.8, in which we have a few samples of Army General Classification Test data, each based upon a different civilian occupational group. We shall not concern ourselves at the moment with the question of how adequate these particular samples are either for size or for representativeness of the populations

Table 5.8 Statistics describing distributions of scores for selected occupational groups who took the Army General Classification Test during World War II*

Occupation	N	M	Mdn	σ	Range
Accountant	172	128.1	128.1	11.7	94–157
Lawyer	94	127.6	126.8	10.9	96–157
Reporter	45	124.5	125.7	11.7	100–157
Sales clerk	492	109.2	110.4	16.3	42–149
Plumber	128	102.7	104.8	16.0	56–139
Truck driver	817	96.2	97.8	19.7	16–149
Farm hand	817	91.4	94.0	20.7	24–141
Teamster	77	87.7	89.0	19.6	45–145

*From Harrell, T. W., and Harrell, M. S. Army General Classification Test scores for civilian occupations. *Educ. psychol. measmt.*, 1945, **5**, 229–240. By permission of the publisher.

from which they are purported to come. These considerations are, of course, important if we want to generalize our conclusions to those populations. Nevertheless, we can still compare samples as such.

Some general conclusions can be drawn from the inspection of Table 5.8.

When the means and medians are placed in rank order, the occupational groups are seen to fall into an approximate rank order for socioeconomic level. It is also apparent, as should have been expected, that occupations requiring more "headwork" are highest in the list. The test emphasized verbal, reasoning, and numerical facilities.

The importance of having both means and medians lies in the information they give concerning skewness. For the lower occupational groups, particularly, the medians are slightly higher than the means. This indicates slight negative skewing. This is a somewhat surprising result, for one would expect that the higher the mean, the greater the negative skewing, and the lower the mean, the greater the positive skewing. When a test of moderate difficulty is administered to a group of low average ability, scores tend to bunch at the lower end of the scale (positive skewing). When the same test is given to a group of high average ability, the bunching is expected near the upper end of the scale (negative skewing). Since in the data of Table 5.8 the skewing seems to be negative for most occupational groups and most marked for those of low average ability, some explanation is demanded. We can only speculate, which means we can suggest several hypotheses which would need further investigation in order to evaluate their worth. One hypothesis might be that in any occupational group, particularly among those of lower ability in the test, a minority of the more able examinees were very poorly motivated or took the test under adverse conditions so that they did not do full justice to themselves.

Two indices of dispersion are given: the standard deviation and the total range. Each tells its own story. Standard deviations are more meaningful here if it is remembered that for the *total* range of scores, all occupational groups combined, the standard deviation was approximately 20.0. The scaling that was utilized aimed at a standard deviation of 20.0 and a mean of 100. The mean in some forms of the test turned out to be somewhat above 100. We should expect dispersions within selected occupational groups to be smaller than the dispersions for all occupations combined. With three exceptions in Table 5.8, this is true. On the whole, the higher the occupational group and the higher the mean, the smaller the dispersion. The higher groups should not be expected to scatter so far from the mean, because the mean score approaches the highest scores made by individuals in *any* group. We might expect a similar curtailment for groups with lowest means. But a study of the ranges will show that this did not occur.

The ranges, as such, are surprisingly large for all groups. It is hard to imagine any individuals in the professional groups with scores below the general average, unless those scores were low because of poor motivation or because of advancing age, which is associated with slower rate of work. The test was a time-limit test. The lowest scores for the lower occupational groups are in line with expectations, but the maximum scores in those same groups are illuminating. Many a clerk or truck driver could evidently have successfully undertaken training for one of the professional occupations. In their prewar assignments for some reason they did not take full vocational advantage of their abilities. It is this fact and also the fact that men of very low academic abilities can engage successfully in the occupations like farm hand and teamster that are largely responsible for the unusually wide dispersions of scores in such occupational groups.

In this discussion we are not particularly interested in settling points concerning the relation of mental abilities to occupational level or success. The data are presented here merely as an illustration of the kind of inferences one may draw from a set of statistics and the hypotheses that may be set up for further investigation, possibly of a very fruitful nature. Such inferences and hypotheses would be impossible to make without this kind of inspection, and the inspection is made possible by having the statistical information.

Uses and interrelationships of
different measures of dispersion

CHOICE OF THE STATISTIC TO USE

Several considerations come into the picture when we decide what measure of variability to employ in any situation. One is the sampling stability of the statistic: its relative constancy in repeated samples. In this respect, when sampling is random, the statistics come in the order, from most reliable to least reliable: standard deviation, average deviation, semi-interquartile range, and total range. So far as quickness and ease of computation are concerned, the four are almost in reverse order to that just given. If further statistical computation is to be given the data, such as estimating the population mean and significance of differences between means, computing coefficients of correlation, regression equations, and the like, then the standard deviation is by all odds the one to employ.

As between standard deviation and average deviation, there is sometimes a choice. The standard deviation, because it derives from squared deviations, gives relatively more weight to extreme deviations from the mean. If a distribution should have an unusual number of extreme cases in one or both directions from the mean, some investigators prefer the average deviation to the standard deviation. This rule includes cases of markedly skewed distributions.

The semi-interquartile range gives even less importance to extreme deviations than does the average deviation and would sometimes be given preference to both standard and average deviations for this reason. It gives more importance to the central mass of cases. When the median is the measure of central value adopted, Q should naturally be the companion measure of variability. Both are based upon the same principles. When distributions are truncated, or have some indeterminate values, only Q can justifiably be used to indicate variability.

To recapitulate,

1. Use the range when
   a. The quickest possible index of dispersion is wanted.
   b. Information is wanted concerning extreme scores.
2. Use the semi-interquartile range, Q, when
   a. The median is the only statistic of central value reported.
   b. The distribution is truncated or incomplete at either end.
   c. There are a few very extreme scores or there is an extreme skewing.
   d. We want to know the actual score limits of the middle 50 per cent of the cases.

3. Use the average deviation when
   a. There are extreme deviations, which, when squared, would bias estimation of the standard deviation.
   b. A fairly reliable index of dispersion is wanted without the extra labor of computing a standard deviation.
   c. The distribution is nearly normal and we can therefore estimate σ from the AD [see formula (5.16)].
4. Use the standard deviation when
   a. Greatest dependability of the value is wanted.
   b. Further computations that depend upon it are likely to be needed.
   c. Interpretations related to the normal distribution curve are desired. It will be found in a later chapter that the standard deviation has a number of useful relationships to the normal curve and to other statistical ideas.

RELATIONSHIPS AMONG THE MEASURES OF DISPERSION

Previously, the standard deviation was related roughly to the range of measurements in a sample. In the general run of samples one meets in statistical work, the range varies from four to six times the standard deviation (see Table 5.6), depending upon the size of sample. If the distribution with which we deal is normal, or nearly normal, in form, we can use a number of other relationships. In a strictly normal distribution the following relationships hold:

$$Q = .845\text{AD} = .6745\sigma \qquad \text{(5.14)}$$
$$\text{AD} = 1.183Q = .798\sigma \qquad \text{(5.15)}$$
$$\sigma = 1.483Q = 1.253\text{AD} \qquad \text{(5.16)}$$

(Conversion of one measure of dispersion into another, assuming a normal distribution)

These equations are most useful for checking purposes when for some reason we have computed two or more of the statistics. They are also useful in estimating one measure of dispersion from another when we do not take the trouble to compute more than one. This should be done only with great caution, however, after having been assured both that the distribution is close to normal and that the one computed statistic is correct.

EXERCISES

1. Compute the interquartile and semi-interquartile ranges for the distributions in Data 4*A*, 4*B*, and 4*F*. Interpret your findings.

2. Compute the standard deviation for any or all of the distributions in Data 4*A* to 4*F* inclusive. Use any of the formulas that seem most convenient. Interpret your findings.

3. Compute the standard deviation in any or all of the distributions in Data 4*G*. Use any of the formulas that seem most convenient.

4. Decide which measure of variability is wisest to employ with each of the distributions in Data 4*A* to 4*F* inclusive and which is second best. Give reasons.

5. Compute the standard deviation for Data 5*A*, with and without Sheppard's correction.

Scores	Frequencies
70 – 79	1
60 – 69	4
50 – 59	10
40 – 49	15
30 – 39	8
20 – 29	2

Data 5A **Scores in a final examination**

ANSWERS
1. Q: 3.5; 7.7; 1.19.
2. 4.58; 10.86; 9.78; 9.75; 13.92; 10.42; 12.64; 9.97; 2.12; 2.77; 1.69; 1.30.
3. 3.2; 4.4; 3.2; 7.6; 7.5.
5. $_c\sigma = 10.68$; $\sigma = 11.07$.

6 Correlation

NO single statistical procedure has opened up so many new avenues of discovery in psychology, and the behavioral sciences in general, as that of correlation. This is understandable when we remember that scientific progress depends upon finding out what things are correlated and what things are not. A *coefficient of correlation* is a single number that tells us to what extent two things are related, to what extent variations in the one go with variations in the other. Without the knowledge of how one thing varies with another, it would be impossible to make predictions. And wherever causal relationships are involved, without knowledge of covariation, we should be unable to control one thing by manipulating another.

For example, when we know that the higher a girl's score in a clerical-aptitude test, the higher the average performance she is likely to exhibit after training, we can thereafter use scores on this test to predict level of proficiency. If the predictions are very accurate, we say that there is a high positive correlation between aptitude-test score and clerical success. We discover this fact by finding a coefficient of correlation between scores made by a number of girls and measures of clerical performance obtained later for the same girls. We cannot compute a coefficient of correlation from just two such measurements on one person alone, nor can we compute it without having made two sets of measurements on the same individuals, or on matched pairs of individuals.

In the same clerical-aptitude example, if we consider that the aptitude test has measured individual differences in some quality or qualities that lead to success, i.e., in the sense of a "cause" of clerical success, then we can not only predict future success for individuals but also promote high general efficiency in any group of clerks by selecting those with high scores. Thus studies leading to prediction and control of human affairs are promoted because correlation techniques are available. Without some device like this for checking up on a test, we can have only vague notions concerning its effectiveness, unless, indeed, its effectiveness is so obvious to direct observation as to require no inspection by correlation methods, a state of affairs that is highly unlikely.

The meaning of correlation

SOME EXAMPLES OF CORRELATION BETWEEN TWO VARIABLES

The coefficient of correlation is one of those summarizing numbers, like a mean or a standard deviation, which, though it is a single number, tells a story.[1] In different situations it can vary from a value of +1.00, which means perfect positive correlation, through zero, which means complete independence or no correlation whatever, on down to −1.00, which means perfect negative correlation.

A case of perfect positive correlation.   Figure 6.1 illustrates an instance of perfect positive correlation. It is a fictitious case, for such exact agreement between two things is rarely or never experienced, certainly not in psychology and other behavioral sciences. Here we have assumed two tests, X and Y. Ten individuals have received scores in the two tests. The pairs of scores are as follows:

Individual	A	B	C	D	E	F	G	H	I	J
Score in test X	2	4	5	6	7	8	9	10	12	13
Score in test Y	4	6	7	8	9	10	11	12	14	15

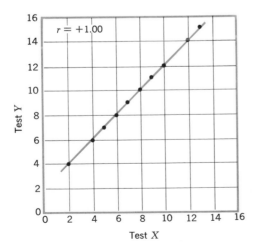

Fig. 6.1. *A simple correlation chart showing the kind of relationship between X and Y scores when the correlation is +1.00.*

[1]The comments in these next paragraphs pertain to the basic Pearson product-moment correlation.

Looking down the rows of scores, each pair made by one individual, we readily conclude that each person's score in Y is two points higher than his score in X. In terms of a simple equation, $Y = X + 2$. There are *no exceptions*, which makes the correlation perfect.

To take another instance:

Individual	A	B	C	D	E	F	G	H	I	J
Score in test P	1	3	4	5	7	8	9	11	12	15
Score in test Q	2	6	8	10	14	16	18	22	24	30

In this situation, each person's score in Q is two times that in P, again without exception; there is perfect agreement, and the coefficient of correlation would be +1.00. The equation for predicting Q from P is $Q = 2P$.

A case of high positive correlation. In Fig. 6.2, we have illustrated a case of correlation that is positive but less than +1.00. The graphic picture of the individuals shows that, *in general*, a person who is high in test X is also likely to be high in test Y, and one who is low in X is also likely to be low in Y. The actual scores for these 10 people are listed in the first two columns of Table 6.1. It will be seen that although the individuals are arranged in rank order for scores in X, there are some deviations from this rank order when we inspect their scores in Y. The coefficient of correlation by computation is equal to +.76. We shall soon see how this was obtained, but first simply note by comparison of Figs. 6.1 and 6.2 how the individuals are scattered in

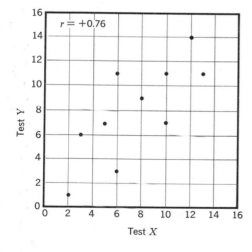

Fig. 6.2. *A correlation chart illustrating the kind of situation when the correlation is +.76.*

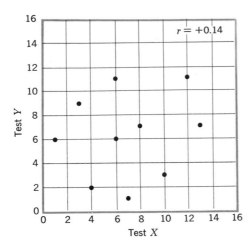

Fig. 6.3. *An example of a correlation chart when the correlation is only +.14.*

the two diagrams. In Fig. 6.1, they line up in perfect file from lowest to highest. In Fig. 6.2, they tend to fan out or to diverge from a strict lineup, but a definite *trend* of relationship can be observed. The amount of spreading in Fig. 6.2 as compared with that in Fig. 6.1 (in which there is, of course, none) illustrates the difference between correlations of +1.00 and +.76.

A case of low positive correlation. A third instance is shown in Fig. 6.3, in which the spreading effect is even greater. The coefficient of correlation here is +.14, in other words, close to zero. This being true, a person with a high score in X is likely to be almost anywhere within the total range in terms of his Y score. The three highest people in X, with scores of 10, 12, and 13, scatter all the way from 3 to 11 in test Y. The three lowest people in test X, with scores of 1, 3, and 4, scatter all the way from 2 to 9 in test Y. Although there is a trace of relationship between X scores and Y scores, it is very weak. The actual scores may be compared in Table 6.3.

A case of high negative correlation. The situation that obtains when there is a negative correlation is shown in Fig. 6.4. Here the coefficient is −.69. Compare this diagram with that in Fig. 6.2, and it will be apparent that the trend of the points is along the other diagonal now, from upper left to lower right. This illustrates the fact that persons making high scores in X are likely to make low scores in Y, and persons making low scores in X are likely to make high scores in Y. This inverse *order* of relationship is also apparent in the actual scores in the first two columns of Table 6.2. The numerical *size* of the coefficient (.69) is nearly the same as for the correlation in Fig. 6.2 (.76). It will be seen that the width of scatter of the points is about the same in the two cases. A perfect negative correlation would be

pictured as a line of dots like that in Fig. 6.1 but it would slant downward instead of upward from left to right. The algebraic sign of the
coefficient of correlation therefore merely has to do with the *direction*
of the relationship between two things, whether direct or inverse,
and the size of the coefficient (distance from zero) has to do with the
strength, or *closeness*, of the relationship.[1]

How to compute a coefficient of correlation

THE PRODUCT-MOMENT COEFFICIENT OF CORRELATION

The standard kind of coefficient of correlation and the one most commonly computed is Pearson's product-moment coefficient. The basic
formula is

$$r_{xy} = \frac{\Sigma xy}{N\sigma_x\sigma_y}$$ (Basic formula for a Pearson product-
moment coefficient of correlation)   (6.1)

where r_{xy} = correlation between X and Y
     x = deviation of any X score from the mean in test X
     y = deviation of the corresponding Y score from the mean in
          test Y
     Σxy = sum of all the products of deviations, each x deviation
          times its corresponding y deviation
     σ_x and σ_y = standard deviations of the distributions of X and Y
          scores

[1]For readers interested in the mathematical aspects of the coefficient of
correlation, a treatment of the relation of correlation to regression equations
is given in Chap. 15. A few proofs for certain formulas for computing r will be
given later in this chapter.

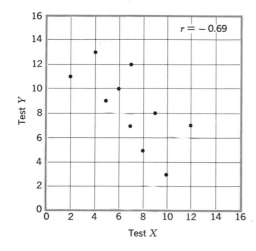

Fig. 6.4. *An example of a correlation chart
when the correlation is −.69.*

The steps necessary are illustrated in Table 6.1. They are enumerated here:

Step 1. List in parallel columns the paired X and Y scores, making sure that corresponding scores are together.

Step 2. Determine the two means M_x and M_y. In Table 6.1, these are 7.5 and 8.0, respectively.

Step 3. Determine for every pair of scores the two deviations x and y. Check them by finding algebraic sums, which should be zero.

Step 4. Square all the deviations, and list in two columns. This is for the purpose of computing σ_x and σ_y.

Step 5. Sum the squares of the deviations to obtain Σx^2 and Σy^2.

Step 6. From these values compute σ_x and σ_y.

Table 6.1   Correlation between two sets of measurements of the same individuals; ungrouped data; product-moment coefficient of correlation

	X	Y	x	y	x^2	y^2	xy
	13	11	+5.5	+3	30.25	9	+16.5
	12	14	+4.5	+6	20.25	36	+27.0
	10	11	+2.5	+3	6.25	9	+ 7.5
	10	7	+2.5	−1	6.25	1	− 2.5
	8	9	+0.5	+1	0.25	1	+ 0.5
	6	11	−1.5	+3	2.25	9	− 4.5
	6	3	−1.5	−5	2.25	25	+ 7.5
	5	7	−2.5	−1	6.25	1	+ 2.5
	3	6	−4.5	−2	20.25	4	+ 9.0
	2	1	−5.5	−7	30.25	49	+38.5
Sums	75	80	0.0	0	124.50	144	102.0
Means	7.5	8.0			Σx^2	Σy^2	Σxy

$$\sigma_x = \sqrt{\frac{124.50}{10}} = \sqrt{12.450} = 3.528$$

$$\sigma_y = \sqrt{144/10} = \sqrt{14.4} = 3.795-$$

$$r_{xy} = \frac{\Sigma xy}{N\sigma_x\sigma_y} = \frac{102.0}{(10)(3.53)(3.79)} = \frac{102.0}{133.90} = +.76$$

An alternative solution without computing the σ's:

$$r_{xy} = \frac{\Sigma xy}{\sqrt{(\Sigma x^2)(\Sigma y^2)}} = \frac{102.0}{\sqrt{(124.5)(144)}} = \frac{102.0}{\sqrt{17,928.0}} = \frac{102.0}{133.90} = +.76$$

Step 7. For every person, find his xy product (last column of Table 6.1). Sum these for Σxy.

Step 8. Finally, apply formula (6.1). In the illustrative problem, the arithmetic is given following Table 6.1.

A shorter solution. There is an alternative and shorter route that omits the computation of σ_x and σ_y, should they not be needed for any other purpose. The formula is[1]

$$r_{xy} = \frac{\Sigma xy}{\sqrt{(\Sigma x^2)(\Sigma y^2)}}$$ (Alternative formula for a Pearson r)   (6.2)

The solution with this formula is also given with Table 6.1, and it leads to the same coefficient. In both cases, two digits have been saved in r, for the reason that for so small a number of cases the sampling error in r is so relatively large that more than two digits would be very deceptive as to assumed accuracy.

Computing a negative coefficient. As another example of the computation of r, when the correlation is *negative*, Table 6.2 is presented. The operations are just the same, step by step. The only thing new is the care that must be taken with algebraic signs.

Computing r from original measurements. In both examples thus far, we have been dealing with a small number of observations and with ungrouped data. When the data are more numerous, we resort to grouping into class intervals. But first let us see another procedure with ungrouped data, which does not require the use of deviations. It deals entirely with original scores. When raw scores are small numbers or when a good calculating machine is available, this is the best procedure. The formula may look forbidding but is really easy to apply:[2]

$$r_{xy} = \frac{N\Sigma XY - (\Sigma X)(\Sigma Y)}{\sqrt{[N\Sigma X^2 - (\Sigma X)^2][N\Sigma Y^2 - (\Sigma Y)^2]}}$$ (A Pearson r computed from original data)   (6.3)

where X and Y are original scores in variables X and Y. Other symbols tell what is done with them. We follow the steps that are illustrated in Table 6.3.

Step 1. Square all X and Y measurements.
Step 2. Find the XY product for every pair of scores.
Step 3. Sum the X's, the Y's, the X^2's, the Y^2's, and the XY's.
Step 4. Apply formula (6.3).

[1]Proof for this formula is given at the end of this chapter.
[2]See the proof for this formula at the end of this chapter.

Table 6.2   *A negative correlation in ungrouped data by the*
product-moment method

	X	Y	x	y	x^2	y^2	xy
	12	7	+5	−1.5	25	2.25	− 7.5
	10	3	+3	−5.5	9	30.25	−16.5
	9	8	+2	−0.5	4	.25	− 1.0
	8	5	+1	−3.5	1	12.25	− 3.5
	7	7	0	−1.5	0	2.25	0.0
	7	12	0	+3.5	0	12.25	0.0
	6	10	−1	+1.5	1	2.25	− 1.5
	5	9	−2	+0.5	4	.25	− 1.0
	4	13	−3	+4.5	9	20.25	−13.5
	2	11	−5	+2.5	25	6.25	−12.5
Sums	70	85	0	0.0	78	88.50	−57.0
Means	7.0	8.5			Σx^2	Σy^2	Σxy

$$\sigma_x = \sqrt{78/10} = \sqrt{7.8} = 2.79$$

$$\sigma_y = \sqrt{\frac{88.5}{10}} = \sqrt{8.85} = 2.97$$

$$r_{xy} = \frac{-57.0}{(10)(2.79)(2.97)} = \frac{-57.0}{82.863}$$

$$= -.69$$

The author has found it more convenient, particularly when machine
work can be done, to compute r^2_{xy} first by the formula

$$r^2_{xy} = \frac{[N\Sigma XY - (\Sigma X)(\Sigma Y)]^2}{[N\Sigma X^2 - (\Sigma X)^2][N\Sigma Y^2 - (\Sigma Y)^2]} \tag{6.4}$$

and then finally extract the square root to find r_{xy}, as shown just below Table 6.3.

PREPARING A SCATTER DIAGRAM

When N is large, even when N is moderate in size, and when no calculating machine is available, the customary procedure is to group
data in both X and Y and to form a scatter diagram or correlation
diagram. The choice of size of class interval and limits of intervals
follows much the same rules as were given previously in Chap. 3.

However, for the sake of a clearer illustration of the procedure, a smaller number of classes will be employed in the problem now to be described. The data were scores earned by a class in educational measurements in two objectively scored examinations, one of which stressed statistical methods and the other of which stressed tests and measurements.

In setting up a double grouping of data, a table is prepared with columns and rows—columns for the dispersions of Y scores within each class interval for the X scale, and rows for the dispersions of X scores within each class interval for the Y scale. Along the top of the

Table 6.3   Correlation of ungrouped data
computed from the original measurements

X	Y	X^2	Y^2	XY
13	7	169	49	91
12	11	144	121	132
10	3	100	9	30
8	7	64	49	56
7	2	49	4	14
6	12	36	144	72
6	6	36	36	36
4	2	16	4	8
3	9	9	81	27
1	6	1	36	6
Sums 70	65	624	533	472
ΣX	ΣY	ΣX^2	ΣY^2	ΣXY

$$r^2{}_{xy} = \frac{[N\Sigma XY - (\Sigma Y)(\Sigma Y)]^2}{[N\Sigma X^2 - (\Sigma X)^2][N\Sigma Y^2 - (\Sigma Y)^2]}$$

$$= \frac{(4{,}720 - 4{,}550)^2}{(6{,}240 - 4{,}900)(5{,}330 - 4{,}225)}$$

$$= \frac{(170)^2}{(1{,}340)(1{,}105)}$$

$$= \frac{28{,}900}{1{,}480{,}700}$$

$$= .019518$$

$$r_{xy} = \sqrt{.019518}$$

$$= +.14$$

table (see Table 6.4) are listed the score limits for the class intervals in test X. Along the left-hand margin are listed the score limits for the class intervals in test Y. We make one tally mark for each individual's X and Y scores. For example, if one individual had a score of 83 in test X and a score of 121 in test Y, we place a tally mark for him in the *cell* of the diagram at the intersection of the column for interval 80–84 in X and the row for interval 120–124 in Y. All other individuals are similarly located in their proper cells.

When the tallying is completed, we write the number of cases, or the *cell frequency*, in each of the cells. Next we sum the cell frequencies in the rows separately, recording each frequency in the last column under the heading f_y. When this column is filled, we have the total frequency distribution for test Y. We also sum the cell frequencies in all the columns, writing them in the bottom row with its heading f_x. When completed, this row gives us the total frequency distribution for test X. We can check the summing of the cell frequencies by adding up the last row and last column. Their sums should, of course, both equal N; in this case, 87. The check does not, however, guarantee correct tallying. This can be checked partly when we correlate either test with another one and compare total frequency distributions or when we have knowledge of the correct frequency distribution of Y or of X from any other source. There are times when it is wise to do the entire tallying two times and to compare all cell frequencies in the two attempts. It is very easy to place a tally mark in the wrong cell.

Table 6.4   **A scatter diagram of the scores in two achievement tests**

X: Scores in first achievement test

	60–64	65–69	70–74	75–79	80–84	85–89	90–94	95–99	f_y
135–139								1	1
130–134				1	1		1		3
125–129				1		2	1		4
120–124			1	4	4	6	2		17
115–119			7	5	7	2	1		22
110–114	1	4	2	9	4	2			22
105–109	1	1	2	5	1				10
100–104	1	3		1	1				6
95–99		2							2
f_x	3	10	12	26	18	12	5	1	87 N

Y: Scores in second achievement test

COMPUTING THE PEARSON r FROM A SCATTER DIAGRAM

When the product-moment r is computed from a scatter diagram, the formula becomes

$$r_{xy} = \frac{\dfrac{\Sigma x'y'}{N} - (M_{x'}M_{y'})}{(\sigma_{x'})\,(\sigma_{y'})} \qquad \begin{array}{l}\text{(Pearson } r \text{ from grouped and}\\ \text{coded data)}\end{array} \qquad (6.5)$$

where x' and y' = deviations of the coded values for X and Y from their respective means

$M_{x'}$ and $M_{y'}$ = means of coded values x' and y', respectively

$\sigma_{x'}$ and $\sigma_{y'}$ = standard deviations of coded values x' and y', respectively

The correlation between X and Y is identical to that between the coded values x' and y'; hence formula (6.5) gives us the correlation r_{xy} without any need for decoding.[1] The details of application of this equation will now be explained and illustrated.

Computing the standard deviations. From Table 6.5 we have all the necessary information for applying formula (6.5):

$$M_{x'} = \frac{\Sigma fx'}{N} = \frac{20}{87} = .230$$

$$M_{y'} = \frac{\Sigma fy'}{N} = \frac{-30}{87} = -.345$$

$$\sigma_{x'} = \sqrt{\frac{\Sigma fx'^2}{N} - M^2{}_{x'}} = \sqrt{\frac{206}{87} - .0529} = \sqrt{2.3149} = 1.52$$

$$\sigma_{y'} = \sqrt{\frac{\Sigma fy'^2}{N} - M^2{}_{y'}} = \sqrt{\frac{224}{87} - .1190} = \sqrt{2.4557} = 1.57$$

Determining the sum of the cross products. The new process to be mastered here is the calculation of the cross products, or products of the moments, and their sum, in other words, $\Sigma x'y'$. It is best to begin with the idea that every cell has its own $x'y'$ product and to keep that idea in mind. In fact, it is well to determine the $x'y'$ product for every cell in which individuals fall and to write it in, as was done in Table 6.5.

The $x'y'$ product for any cell is simply the product of the x' value times the y' value of that cell, close watch being kept of algebraic

[1]One of the requirements originally set up by Galton for a correlation coefficient is that it should be independent of the size of unit or the location of the zero point for either X or Y. The basic equation is $r = \Sigma z_x z_y / N$, where z_x is a standard score for X [that is, $z_x = (X - M_x)/\sigma_x$], and z_y is a standard score for Y.

Table 6.5   **Scatter diagram for computing a Pearson *r***

X: Examination in statistics

Y: Examination in educational measurements	60–64	65–69	70–74	75–79	80–84	85–89	90–94	95–99	f_y	y'	fy'	fy'^2	Σx'y' +	Σx'y' −
135–139								$^{16}1_{16}$	1	+4	+4	16	16	
130–134			1 ·	$^{3}1_{3}$	^{6}		$^{9}1_{9}$		3	+3	+9	27	12	
125–129				1		$^{4}2_{8}$	$^{6}1_{6}$		4	+2	+8	16	14	
120–124			$^{-1}1_{-1}$	4	$^{1}4_{4}$	$^{2}6_{12}$	$^{3}2_{6}$		17	+1	+17	17	22	1
115–119				7	5	7	2	1	22	0	0	0	0	0
110–114	$^{3}1_{3}$	$^{2}4_{8}$	$^{1}2_{2}$	9	$^{-1}4_{-4}$	$^{-2}2_{-4}$			22	−1	−22	22	13	8
105–109	$^{6}1_{6}$	$^{4}1_{4}$	$^{2}2_{4}$	5	$^{-2}1_{-2}$				10	−2	−20	40	14	2
100–104	$^{9}1_{9}$	$^{6}3_{18}$		1	$^{-3}1_{-3}$				6	−3	−18	54	27	3
95–99		$^{8}2_{16}$							2	−4	−8	32	16	
f_x	3	10	12	26	18	12	5	1	87		−30	224	134	−14
x'	−3	−2	−1	0	+1	+2	+3	+4		Σfy'	Σfy'^2			
fx'	−9	−20	−12	0	+18	+24	+15	+4	+20	=Σfx'				
fx'^2	27	40	12	0	18	48	45	16	206	=Σfx'^2				
Σx'y' +	18	46	6	0	7	20	21	16	134	Σx'y' = + 120				
Σx'y' −			1	0	9	4			−14					

signs. This matter is easily checked, of course, by making sure that the sign of every $x'y'$ product is positive in the upper right quarter of the chart and also the lower left quarter, but that all signs are negative in the upper left and lower right quarters. This rule presupposes that the X measurements are increasing from left to right and that the Y measurements are increasing from below upward.

Having given every cell its $x'y'$ value and having recorded it in the upper left-hand corner of the cell, we next note how many individuals have that $x'y'$ value—in other words, the frequency in that cell. We multiply the cell product by the frequency, and in Table 6.5 these products are recorded with algebraic sign in the lower right-hand corners of the cells. All that remains now is to sum them. We do this both in the columns and in the rows for the sake of checking, for this is an unusually critical number in the correlation formula, and because the many steps involved in deriving it present many opportunities for errors. The last two columns in Table 6.5 are devoted to the sums of $fx'y'$ values in the rows. We keep the sums of the positive products in one of these columns and the sums of the negative products in the other. The last two rows of the table are reserved likewise for summing the positive and negative sums in the columns. Summing everything in the last two columns (also in the last two rows) of the table gives us $\Sigma x'y'$, and the two estimates should agree exactly.

For the illustrative problem, the positive sum is 134 and the negative is −14, leaving a net positive sum $\Sigma x'y'$ of 120. We now have everything we need for calculating r. Applying formula (6.5), we have

$$
\begin{aligned}
r_{xy} &= \frac{\dfrac{120}{87} - (.23)(-.345)}{(1.52)(1.57)} \\
&= \frac{1.3793 + .0794}{2.3864} \\
&= \frac{1.4587}{2.3864} \\
&= .61
\end{aligned}
$$

Interpretations of a coefficient of correlation

HOW HIGH IS ANY GIVEN COEFFICIENT OF CORRELATION?

Any coefficient of correlation that is not zero and that is also statistically significant denotes some degree of relationship between two variables.[1] But we need further discussion of the matter, for the strength of relationship can be regarded from a number of points of view, and it is not correct from any one of them to say that the degree of relationship is exactly proportional to r. The coefficient of correlation does *not* give directly anything like a percentage of relationship. We cannot say that an r of .50 indicates two times the relationship that is indicated by an r of .25. Nor can we say that an increase in correlation from $r = .40$ to $r = .60$ is equivalent to an increase in correlation from $r = .70$ to .90. The coefficient of correlation is an index number, not a measurement on a linear scale of equal units. It should be noted that an r of −.60 indicates just as close a relationship as an r of +.60.

PARTICULAR USES HAVE A BEARING ON INTERPRETATION OF r

The question regarding size of r cannot be fully answered without making reference to particular uses of r. One common use is to indicate the agreement of scores on an aptitude test with measures of academic or of vocational success. Such a correlation is known as a *validity coefficient*. It is an index of the predictive validity of a test. Chapter 18 will deal extensively with the subject of validity. Common experience shows that the validity coefficient for a single test may be expected within the range from .00 to .60, with most indices in the lower part of that range. Validity coefficients for composite scores

[1] For a treatment of the topic of statistical significance of a coefficient of correlation, see Chap. 8. "Statistical significance" of r, in this context, means that there is a very small probability that the coefficient obtained in the sample is a chance deviation from a population correlation of zero.

based upon combinations of several different kinds of tests are likely to be distinctly higher, ranging up to .80 in rare instances but hardly ever above the latter figure. Many who have employed tests for vocational guidance or vocational selection have followed a tradition, which was originated by C. L. Hull[1] some 35 years ago, that the minimum validity coefficient for a test of practical usefulness is about .45. Recent experiences have shown that this standard is too rigid and that there are many considerations other than validity which determine the usefulness of a test in any given situation, as will be shown in Chap. 15.

It is well recognized that a *reliability coefficient*, which could be found by correlating two forms of the same test, is usually a much higher figure than a validity coefficient. Following the leadership of T. L. Kelley,[2] there has been general agreement that, to be sufficiently reliable for discriminating between individuals, a test should have a reliability coefficient of at least .94. Some have been more liberal in this regard, allowing a minimum of .90, while others have settled for even lower values. The higher standards are rarely attainable, and it is safe to say that most tests in use fail to meet them. As a matter of fact, there are many very useful tests whose reliability coefficients are in the .80's and even below. It is coming to be recognized that validity is much more important than reliability, and, in fact, it is possible for a test to be sufficiently valid for practical purposes without being very reliable. Tests with reliability coefficients as low as .35 have been found useful when utilized in batteries with other tests.[3] Such tests have been known with validities as high as .35. They could theoretically have validities much higher than that. Reliability and validity depend upon many considerations that we cannot go into here. These problems will be treated in Chaps. 17 and 18. It is sufficient to say here that one must be a relativist when dealing with problems of test reliability and validity. The student's interpretation of a coefficient of correlation, like his interpretation of other statistics, is subject to considerable revision as he comes to know more about its uses. While these qualifications mentioned regarding reliability and validity need to be made, the fact remains that in practice we expect reliability coefficients to be in the upper brackets of r values, usually .70 to .98, and validity coefficients to be lower, usually .00 to .80.

When one is investigating a purely theoretical problem, even very

[1]Hull, C. L. *Aptitude Testing.* Tarrytown-on-Hudson, N.Y.: World, 1928. Chap. 8.
[2]Kelley, T. L. *Interpretation of Educational Measurements.* Tarrytown-on-Hudson, N.Y.: World, 1927. Pp. 210 *ff.*
[3]Guilford, J. P. New standards for test evaluation. *Educ. psychol. Measmt.,* 1946, **6,** 427–428.

small correlations, if statistically significant (most probably not zero), are often very indicative of a psychological law. Whenever a relationship between two variables is established beyond reasonable doubt, the fact that the correlation coefficient is small may merely mean that the measurement situation is contaminated by some factor(s) uncontrolled or not held constant. One can readily conceive of an experimental situation in which, if all irrelevant factors had been held constant, the r might have been 1.00 rather than .20. For example, the correlation between an ability score and academic achievement is .50, since both are measured in a population whose academic achievement is also allowed to be determined by effort, attitudes, marking peculiarities of the instructors, etc. Were all the other determinants of achievement held constant and were both aptitude and marks perfectly measured, the r would be 1.00 rather than .50. This line of reasoning indicates that where any correlation between two things is established at all, and particularly where there is a causal relationship involved, the fundamental law implies a perfect relationship. Thus, in nature, correlations of zero or 1.00 are expected to be the rule between variables when their effects are experimentally completely isolated. The fact that we obtain anything else is because of the inextricable interplay of variables that we cannot measure in isolation.

The practical conclusion from this is that *a correlation is always relative to the situation under which it is obtained, and its size does not represent any absolute natural fact.* To speak of *the* correlation between intelligence and achievement is absurd. One needs to say *which* intelligence, measured under *what* circumstances, in *what* population, and to say *what kind* of achievement, measured by *what* instruments, or judged by *what* standards. *Always, the coefficient of correlation is purely relative to the circumstances under which it was obtained and should be interpreted in the light of those circumstances, very rarely, certainly, in any absolute sense.*

How much faith one should place in any relationship shown by a coefficient of correlation also depends upon the urgency of the outcome. There are probably many medical treatments, such as some inoculations, vaccines, and the like, concerning which the knowledge is rather incomplete, which are administered even though the correlation between the treatment and survival (or between nontreatment and death) is of the order of .10 to .20. Although the probabilities of survival may be increased by only 1 per cent by the treatment, the saving of 1 life in 100 is regarded as worth the effort. If a procedure in education promised only 1 per cent improvement over guesswork, we should probably pay little attention to it, because the seriousness of the outcome would not justify the means.

Graphic representations of correlations

In presenting the facts of correlation to the layman, who is probably not accustomed to thinking in terms of numerical indices in any case and who has probably never heard of the coefficient of correlation, it is better to convey the idea of a relationship in other ways, preferably in the form of a diagram of some kind. Figures 6.5 and 6.6 are two examples of how this might be done. Figure 6.5 is a bar diagram showing for each level of aptitude score, on a nine-point scale (stanine scale), the percentage of pilot students who were graduated from flying schools. The actual percentages are given for those who are interested in simple numbers. In spite of the unusually large samples, the percentages are given to two significant digits only. The number of students in each stanine group is given for the benefit of those who have some appreciation of the stability offered by large samples.

The other diagram, Fig. 6.6, shows the average rating of flying proficiency made by cadets at each stanine level, and only the average. Some investigators connect successive pairs of points with lines, but in this particular instance the linear trend is so clear that a straight

Fig. 6.5. *Correlation between the pilot-aptitude score (pilot stanine) and the criterion of graduation-elimination from flying training in the AAF, illustrated by means of a bar diagram.* (Based upon Stanines: Selection and Classification for Air Crew Duty. Washington, D.C.: Headquarters, Army Air Force, 1946.)

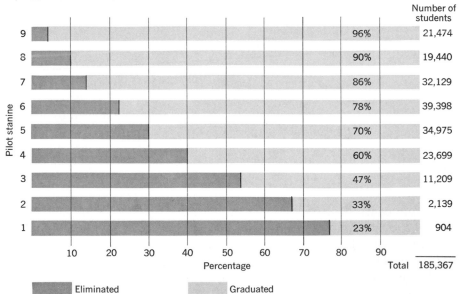

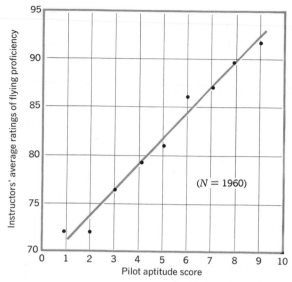

Fig. 6.6. *Correlation between pilot-aptitude scores and instructors' ratings of flying proficiency illustrated by means of a regression line that is based upon the averages of ratings for different aptitude-score levels.*

line has been drawn by inspection to fit the trend. It is assumed that minor deviations that occur are due to sampling errors. A warning should be given in connection with this type of figure. It can give an impression of degree of correlation far in excess of that justified. Not shown are the widths of dispersions of individuals, at different stanine levels, in this case. Although the averages of columns do not deviate much from a straight line, many individual cases may deviate considerably. There are ways of representing average discrepancies of individuals from such a regression line (see Chap. 15) which could be used to give the reader some idea of their importance.

Assumptions underlying the product-moment correlation

The student should be warned, before leaving this chapter, about the restrictions that should be observed in the use of the Pearson product-moment coefficient of correlation. The most important requirement for the legitimate use of the Pearson r is that the trend of relationship between Y and X be rectilinear—in other words, a straight-line regression. This can be determined, as a rule, by inspection of the scatter diagram. If the distribution of the cases within the correlation diagram appears to be elliptical, without any indications of a decided bending of the ellipse, the chances are that the relationship is rectilinear. Even if it is not, the deviation from a straight-line relationship may be so slight that we may assume rectilinearity as a first approximation, and the degree of correlation indicated by r will be fairly close to any index of correlation, such as the *correlation ratio* (see Chap. 14), that is applied when there is curvature in the trend. When there is an obvious bending of the distribution of cases, a correlation ratio, or some other special coefficient, is indicated as the best index of correlation.

There are in educational and psychological measurements certain factors that produce artificially curved scatters in the correlation diagram. This may happen when one or both distributions taken alone are badly skewed and the skewing is produced artificially by the faulty measuring scale, with its systematically shifting unit of measurement. If there is good reason to believe that this may be the case, one solution would be to normalize the skewed distribution by methods described in Chap. 19. When distributions are corrected for skewness, the curvature in the regression is frequently eliminated, and linearity is then obtained. If curvature still remains, then the Pearson r is not to be used to indicate the amount of correlation.

There is nothing in what has been said to demand that the Pearson r be computed only with normal distributions. The forms of distributions may vary, so long as they are fairly symmetrical and unimodal; even rectangular ones will do. To take care of cases of irregular and discontinuous distributions, other kinds of correlation methods are presented in Chap. 14.

Derivation of some correlation formulas

DERIVATION OF FORMULA (6.2)

Let us begin with the most common formula,

$$r_{xy} = \frac{\Sigma xy}{N\sigma_x\sigma_y}$$

Formula (6.2) differs from this only in its denominator term. What needs to be demonstrated is that its denominator $\sqrt{(\Sigma x^2)(\Sigma y^2)} = N\sigma_x\sigma_y$. Substituting the basic formulas for the two standard deviations,

$$N\sigma_x\sigma_y = N \sqrt{\frac{\Sigma x^2}{N}} \sqrt{\frac{\Sigma y^2}{N}}$$

Putting both expressions under the same radical, since $\sqrt{a}\sqrt{b} = \sqrt{ab}$,

$$N\sigma_x\sigma_y = N \sqrt{\left(\frac{\Sigma x^2}{N}\right)\left(\frac{\Sigma y^2}{N}\right)}$$

$$= N \sqrt{\frac{(\Sigma x^2)(\Sigma y^2)}{N^2}}$$

$$= \sqrt{(\Sigma x^2)(\Sigma y^2)}$$

PEARSON r COMPUTED FROM RAW SCORES, X AND Y

In terms of standard scores, the Pearson formula is

$$r = \frac{\Sigma z_x z_y}{N}$$

Substituting raw-score equivalents,

$$r = \frac{1}{N} \Sigma \left(\frac{X - M_x}{\sigma_x} \right) \left(\frac{Y - M_y}{\sigma_y} \right)$$

which can also be written

$$r = \frac{1}{N\sigma_x \sigma_y} \Sigma (X - M_x)(Y - M_y)$$

Expanding the expression at the right,

$$r = \frac{1}{N\sigma_x \sigma_y} \Sigma (XY - XM_y - YM_x + M_x M_y)$$

Distributing the summation,

$$r = \frac{1}{N\sigma_x \sigma_y} (\Sigma XY - \Sigma XM_y - \Sigma YM_x + \Sigma M_x M_y)$$

$$= \frac{1}{N\sigma_x \sigma_y} (\Sigma XY - NM_x M_y - NM_x M_y + NM_x M_y)$$

$$= \frac{1}{N\sigma_x \sigma_y} (\Sigma XY - NM_x M_y)$$

which can be used as one computing formula for r, if means and standard deviations are known. If not, we can replace M_x with $\Sigma X/N$, M_y with $\Sigma Y/N$, σ_x with $1/N \sqrt{N\Sigma X^2 - (\Sigma X)^2}$, and σ_y with $1/N \sqrt{N\Sigma Y^2 - (\Sigma Y)^2}$. We then have

$$r = \frac{\Sigma XY - N \left(\frac{\Sigma X}{N} \right) \left(\frac{\Sigma Y}{N} \right)}{N \frac{1}{N} \sqrt{N\Sigma X^2 - (\Sigma X)^2} \frac{1}{N} \sqrt{N\Sigma Y^2 - (\Sigma Y)^2}}$$

Multiplying both numerator and denominator by N,

$$r = \frac{N\Sigma XY - (\Sigma X)(\Sigma Y)}{\sqrt{N\Sigma X^2 - (\Sigma X)^2} \sqrt{N\Sigma Y^2 - (\Sigma Y)^2}}$$

The two terms in the denominator may be placed under the same radical, for $\sqrt{a}$ times $\sqrt{b}$ is equal to $\sqrt{ab}$.

EXERCISES

1. Using the first 10 pairs of scores in the list in Data 6*A*, compute a Pearson *r* between parts I and II. Use formulas (6.1) and (6.2). Find a similar coefficient, using the last 10 pairs of scores in the same two variables. State your conclusions.

2. Correlate the first 10 pairs of scores for parts II and III, using formulas (6.3) and (6.4). Correlate the same two parts, using the last 10 pairs and the same formulas. State your conclusions.

3. Prepare a scatter diagram for the correlation of parts III and IV, including all 40 cases. Compute a Pearson *r*, using formula (6.5). State your conclusions.

*Data 6A   Scores earned by 40 high-school students in seven parts of the Guilford-Zimmerman Aptitude Survey**

Part I Verbal Comprehension	Part II Reasoning	Part III Numerical Operations	Part IV Perceptual Speed	Part V Spatial Orientation	Part VI Spatial Visualization	Part VII Mechanical Knowledge
22	11	24	29	27	39	30
8	5	22	40	16	23	21
19	6	44	36	14	12	21
32	8	72	32	21	20	33
13	2	25	46	25	20	29
24	5	30	47	2	6	8
22	4	38	49	15	37	35
35	1	54	53	34	28	16
18	7	37	51	37	46	30
13	10	61	50	38	46	35
53	23	56	45	22	41	38
15	9	42	48	18	5	18
34	18	30	25	40	58	46
15	2	42	48	12	21	17
27	4	28	28	31	26	24

*Part I is a vocabulary test; part II is composed of arithmetic-reasoning problems; part III is composed of simple number operations; part IV is on matching visual objects differing very little; part V involves awareness of spatial relationships; part VI requires imagination of an object turned in space; and part VII is on common knowledge of tools and their use, automobile parts and functions, and common trade knowledge. The intercorrelations in this particular sample will be found to be generally low except between parts I and II and between V and VI.

Data 6A (continued)

Part I Verbal Comprehension	Part II Reasoning	Part III Numerical Operations	Part IV Perceptual Speed	Part V Spatial Orientation	Part VI Spatial Visualization	Part VII Mechanical Knowledge
19	9	32	40	11	13	19
29	4	24	37	26	0	27
24	9	42	58	21	21	23
27	9	54	54	23	20	30
16	5	42	44	29	24	34
56	12	67	48	20	40	26
22	5	58	48	28	41	20
32	4	57	33	20	4	16
18	8	49	47	19	36	42
24	15	87	52	36	34	26
22	12	14	48	25	16	27
22	10	38	46	21	0	20
21	21	32	33	11	43	37
13	10	52	40	29	35	11
23	3	60	49	43	13	37
2	10	29	49	10	21	27
20	4	50	55	22	8	27
25	11	76	43	26	20	26
14	6	40	38	35	8	46
11	2	32	56	37	4	26
2	9	61	45	20	10	20
38	17	56	67	25	20	35
16	6	61	42	29	23	21
14	4	17	44	26	7	21
23	25	61	48	23	29	16

4. Do the same as in Exercise 3 for parts V and VI, or any other pair of parts. How many pairs of coefficients of correlation are possible with Data 6A? State a general rule for the number of intercorrelations when there are n variables.

5. Compute the Pearson r for Data 6B. Interpret your findings.

6. Find five Pearson r coefficients reported in the literature. Tell what variables were being correlated in each case. Interpret the results. Are the coefficients about the sizes you would have expected for the things correlated? Were there any special conditions that may have biased the amount of correlation in one way or another?

Data 6B   **A scatter diagram of reaction-time measurements and grades earned in general psychology**

Reaction time to auditory stimulus	Grades in psychology								
	55–59	60–64	65–69	70–74	75–79	80–84	85–89	90–94	95–99
.180 –.189					1				
.170 –.179						1			
.160 –.169				2	1	1		1	
.150 –.159					1	1	1		
.140 –.149	1			1	2	1	1	1	
.130 –.139	1			6	2	6	1	3	
.120 –.129			1		2	3	3		1
.110 –.119				2	1	2			
.100 –.109								1	

ANSWERS

1. The seven parts of the *Aptitude Survey* were designed to measure different abilities that are relatively independent, and hence to correlate low with one another. The correlation r_{12} (between part I and II) is found to be −.16 and +.47 in the first and last 10 pairs of scores, respectively. (Incidentally, this somewhat large discrepancy shows how widely the correlation between the same two variables can fluctuate from sample to sample, when samples are very small.) The correlation for all 40 pairs is +.37. Typical correlations in larger samples have been .25, .57, and .40, for college men, high-school boys, and high-school girls, respectively.[1]
2. r_{23} (parts II and III): .18 and .49. In larger samples (the same as in answer to Exercise 1) r_{23} was .18, .37, and .33.
3. $r_{34} = .25$. In larger samples it was .20, .07, and .31.
4. $r_{56} = .27$. In larger samples it was .61, .34, and .46. The number of pairs of variables equals $n(n-1)/2$.
5. $r = -.075$ between reaction time and grades in psychology.

[1]For additional information on intercorrelations of these tests, see Michael, W. B., Zimmerman, W. S., and Guilford, J. P. An investigation of the nature of the spatial-relations and visualization factors in two high-school samples. *Educ. psychol. Measmt.*, 1951, **11**, 561–577.

7 Probability and mathematical distributions

THUS far, we have been dealing exclusively with descriptive statistics, statistics that enable us to summarize masses of data and to arrive at single descriptive numbers, either for single distributions or for degrees of relationships between variables. In the chapters immediately following we shall be concerned almost exclusively with the estimation of corresponding population values and with the question of how much confidence we should have in those estimates.[1] Most of the developments in the field of statistics during the past 30 years have been in the area of sampling statistics, statistical inference, and tests of significance. This has been a great boon to the experimental investigator, for it has enabled him to plan his experiments more wisely and to know whether or not his conclusions are sound.

The need for mathematical models

THE ROLE OF MATHEMATICS IN SCIENCE

Concerning the great value of mathematics in general in science there can be no argument, if we view the development of science as a whole, culminating in modern theoretical physics. Whether or not we believe that the universe, including man and his behavior, is constructed along mathematical lines, the application of mathematical ideas and forms in describing it is an undeniably profitable practice. Think, for example, of all the consequences of $e = mc^2$, Einstein's equation explaining the equivalence of mass and energy. This equation is a mathematical model, an expression in symbolic form of a structural idea that describes a whole range of physical phenomena.

Mathematics exists entirely in the realm of ideas. It is a logic-based system of elements and relationships, all of which are pre-

[1]For definitions of "population" and "sample" see p. 137.

cisely defined. It is a completely logical language that can be applied
to the description of nature because the events and objects of nature
have properties that provide a sufficient parallel to mathematical
ideas. There is *isomorphism* (similarity of form) between mathematical ideas and phenomena of nature. Even if the description of nature
in mathematical terms is never completely exact, there is enough
agreement between the forms of nature and the forms of mathematical expression to make the description acceptable. The approximation
is often so close that once we have applied the mathematical description we can follow where the mathematical logic leads and come out
with deductions that also apply to nature.

Take, for example, the normal distribution curve, which we shall
investigate further in this chapter. The normal, or Gaussian, curve
is entirely a mathematical idea. It is incorrect to refer to it as either
a biological or a psychological curve. It is a particular mathematical
model that happens to describe groups of natural objects so well that
we can often use its properties to make inferences and predictions
about those objects or groups. We have already done this in interpreting the standard deviation, in Chap. 5. We need now to become
better acquainted with the normal distribution curve in order to
capitalize further upon its properties. We shall also meet other statistical models which we can use.

A TYPICAL EXPERIMENT

As an illustration of the foregoing statements, let us consider a typical experiment in which a statistical model is needed. The experiment
is in the area of extrasensory perception (ESP): the general problem
of whether or not one who perceives objects (the sender) can transmit
directly to another person (the receiver) any information about the
objects without the use of the receiver's senses.

Suppose that an experiment with the Duke University ESP cards
is properly designed to prevent the receiver from being influenced by
any cues except possible telepathic stimulation. The materials are
five different symbols, each on a different card; each symbol is repeated five times in a set of 25 cards. The deck is thoroughly shuffled
so that the cards should come up at random. As each card comes up,
the sender reads it silently and the receiver records his judgment as
to which symbol is being perceived. The card is returned to the deck,
which is reshuffled, and the next card to be transmitted is selected.

Over a run of 25 trials, suppose the receiver gives 8 correct judgments. Does this result show evidence of ESP or does it not? Without
the aid of statistical inferences we should never be able to answer
this question. There are two alternative hypotheses to be tolerated
before the experiment and before a decision is made as to the mean-

ing of the outcome. One is the hypothesis that some genuine ESP has been at work; the other is that only the laws of chance have produced the result. We know that even by guessing, the receiver could be correct part of the time. Now we cannot find a mathematical model that would enable us to predict how many correct responses there should be if there has been some ESP operating. But we can find a model that will tell us how many correct responses to expect if the outcome is a purely random one, due to the "laws of chance," as we sometimes say.

Without very much mathematical sophistication, it is easy to see that with the receiver merely guessing which of five symbols is being "transmitted," there is one chance in five of being correct, if the receiver guesses at random. In this one-out-of-five situation, over many runs of 25 trials each, on the average he should be correct 5 times by chance. The statistical model that we apply should therefore include an expected score of 5.

But that is not all. We can also readily see that in a relatively short run of 25 trials, by what is popularly called "lucky guessing" the receiver might make a score of 6, 7, or more correct responses. If he is "unlucky," his score might just as well go below 5 to about the same extent. The model, therefore, also involves a family of chance outcomes, which has to be described. This can be done mathematically, as we shall see. To state the question of statistical inference more precisely, we ask whether the obtained score of 8 could be one of the chance-generated outcomes and, if it could be, how likely is it that it could so occur. If a score of 8 or some even higher score could happen by chance extremely rarely, we can reject the hypothesis that it is chance generated, which leaves us with some degree of confidence in the other hypothesis, that ESP is responsible.

Principles of probability

There have been several mentions thus far in this chapter of random events, chance, and probability. We therefore need to look into some basic mathematical ideas involving probability. They are basic to the models used in testing hypotheses and drawing statistical inferences. It is well known that the mathematics of probability arose out of interest in gambling and games of chance. Wagering on outcomes of events is a popular pastime. Usually, the wagerer bases his odds on his appreciation of subjective probability regarding outcomes of various kinds. Mathematical descriptions of the known chances in a situation permit much better-informed bases for making bets. Such information takes much of the guesswork out of gambling, just as it takes much of the guesswork out of a scientist's evaluation of his experimental results. With application of an appropriate probability model, he can state accurately the odds for his making right or wrong conclusions.

As is customary in introducing the mathematics of probability, let us begin with some common games of chance – tossed coins, tossed dice, and drawing of playing cards. In each case there is a specified event, which can turn out in two or more ways. A tossed coin can land with a head or a tail showing. A die can land with one of six numbers of dots on top. Drawing a card from a thoroughly shuffled deck of 52 ordinary playing cards will give a card from one of four suits (club, diamond, heart, or spade) and from one of the 13 denominations within one of those suits. The chance of the coin landing with a head is 1 in 2; the chance of a tail is also 1 in 2. The chance of a die coming with a two spot is 1 in 6; the same is true for any other particular number of spots. In each case, the probability of the event occurring in the way in which we are interested (sometimes called the favored way) is the *ratio of the number of ways in which that favored way can occur to the total number of ways the event can occur.* This is the logical definition of probability. There is one way in which a coin can give head and a total of two ways in which the coin can fall (excluding the extremely unlikely case of standing on edge). The probability of a head is $\frac{1}{2}$ (also expressible as .5). The probability of a tail is also $\frac{1}{2}$ or .5. The number of ways a single die can yield a six spot is 1 and the total number of ways the die can fall is 6, so the probability of a six spot is $\frac{1}{6}$ or .167.

Let us apply the definition to the drawing of playing cards. What is the probability that a card drawn at random will be a spade? The number of favorable ways is 13, the total number of ways is 52, so the probability of drawing a spade (any spade) is $\frac{13}{52}$, which equals $\frac{1}{4}$ or .25. What is the probability of drawing a queen? There are only 4 queens and a total of 52 cards, so the probability is $\frac{4}{52}$ or $\frac{1}{13}$. What is the probability of drawing the queen of hearts? There is only one way in which this could happen, so we have $\frac{1}{52}$ as the probability.

Mathematically, a probability is symbolized by p, which may range from zero, when there is no chance whatever of the favored event, to 1.0, when there is absolute certainty: nothing else could happen. The probabilities we have just been considering are purely theoretical ones, based upon the a priori knowledge of the frequencies of the favored event and of all events, including the favored one and all its alternatives in the situation. It is known that if we actually toss a coin a finite number of times, the ratio of the number of heads to the number of tosses would probably not come out exactly ½. For a definition of probability that is more fully in accord with the outcomes of events, therefore, we need the following modification, although it is not always explicitly stated:

$$p = \lim_{n \to \infty} \frac{n_f}{n}$$

This expression states that as the number of times (n) the event occurs becomes indefinitely large, the ratio of the number of favored outcomes (n_f) to n approaches the probability p as a limit. It is also necessary to stress two requirements: *that the ways of occurrence of the event must be equally likely and they must be mutually independent.* "Mutual independence" means that one event has no effect whatever on any other event. Granting unbiased coins, dice, and cards, the occurrences of heads and tails are equally likely, the occurrences of different sides of a die coming up are equally likely, and in drawing a card from a well-shuffled deck, any card has as much chance as any other of being drawn.

The addition theorem.   We can ask other kinds of questions regarding events in games of chance. In tossing a die, what is the probability of *either* a 1 *or* a 2 coming up? The probability of a 1 is ⅙, and the probability of a 2 is ⅙. There are *two* ways in which the favored event can occur, out of a total of 6 ways, and therefore, by definition, the probability is ²⁄₆. Note that this probability is the sum of the two separate probabilities. Thus, probabilities are additive.

What is the probability of obtaining four or more spots? The specification "four or more" includes the outcomes 4, 5, and 6. Adding the three probabilities, we have ³⁄₆ or ½ as the probability of the alternate outcomes. In tossing a coin, what is the probability of getting a head *or* a tail? The addition ½ + ½ gives us 1.00, which means that we are certain to obtain either a head or a tail.

Applying this principle to drawing cards, we may ask the probability of drawing either a spade or a club. The two separate probabilities are ¼ and ¼, which, summed, give ½. What is the probability of drawing a queen or a king? The answer is ¹⁄₁₃ + ¹⁄₁₃ or ²⁄₁₃. In general, *the probability of alternative outcomes is the sum of the probabilities of the outcomes taken separately.*

The multiplication theorem.   We have just treated the either-or kind of case. Here we are concerned with the "this *and* that" kind of case—the *probability of combined outcomes.* In two independent throws of a coin, what is the probability that the outcome will be two heads (a head *and* a head)?

It will help to go back to the basic definition of probability—the relative frequency of an outcome: the ratio of the number of favored ways to the total number of ways. In tossing two coins (either two different coins simultaneously or one coin in succession two times), what is the total number of ways in which to get the outcome? If we wrote them all out, we should have the following: HH HT TH and TT. That is, when the first is a head, the second can be either head or tail and when the first is a tail the second can be either head or tail. There are four total ways and only one favored way (HH), so the probability is ¼. Here the probability of the first event coming out H is ½ and the probability of the second event coming out H is also ½. The probability of the combination of the two outcomes is ½ × ½, or ¼. The probability of each of the other outcomes is also ¼, and the four add up to 1.0, as they should. We are certain to have one of the four.

We can state another kind of question. What is the probability of getting one (and only one) head? This specification describes the HT and TH cases, of which there are two. The addition theorem applies. The probability for this is ²⁄₄ or ½. What is the probability of obtaining at least one head? This statement includes also the case HH, so the probability is ¾.

Problems of the following sort are of special interest to those who deal with dice. What is the probability of throwing 12 spots (a pair of sixes)? Here we have two events, the throw of two dice, and a specified combination of two outcomes (six spots in each case). According to the principle of multiplication of probabilities, we have ⅙ × ⅙ = ¹⁄₃₆ as the probability of obtaining a pair of sixes. The same probability would apply to a pair of one spots. What is the probability of obtaining a total of 11 spots in throwing two dice? The total number of ways in which two dice can fall is 36 because for every way the one falls there are six independent ways in which the other one can fall. Eleven spots can come from a six on the first and a five on the second, or vice versa: two ways. Two over 36 is ¹⁄₁₈ as the probability for exactly 11 spots. There is special interest in a total of seven spots in two throws. A seven could occur by combinations of 1–6, 2–5, 3–4, 4–3, 5–2, or 6–1: altogether, six ways. The probability is ⁶⁄₃₆ or ⅙—the highest for any combination, as any experienced dice-thrower knows. A total of seven spots is therefore six times as likely to happen as any specified pair with equal numbers.

Binomial distributions

We should be ready, now, to consider mathematical models that rest upon the principles of probability, the first of which is the binomial type of distribution. It can be readily explained by reference to coin tossing.

THE BINOMIAL EXPANSION

We saw that the independent tossing of two coins yielded four possible outcomes, which could be classified in three categories: cases with 2 heads, 1 head, and 0 head, with frequencies of 1, 2, and 1, respectively. In this list of frequencies we have a frequency distribution, which could be plotted with numbers of heads on the abscissa and frequencies on the ordinate, respectively.

Now let us take the case with three coins tossed independently. We could write out all the possible combinations of outcomes for the three successive coins as follows:

	Score	f
HHH	3 heads	1
HHT		
HTH	2 heads	3
THH		
HTT		
THT	1 head	3
TTH		
TTT	0 head	1
	Total	8

From this distribution we can say that the probability of obtaining exactly 2 heads is $\frac{3}{8}$ and the probability of obtaining exactly 3 heads is $\frac{1}{8}$. The latter outcome agrees with out multiplicative theorem, in that $\frac{1}{2} \times \frac{1}{2} \times \frac{1}{2} = \frac{1}{8}$. What is the probability of obtaining *at least* two heads? Here we would apply the additive theorem: $\frac{1}{8} + \frac{3}{8} = \frac{4}{8} = \frac{1}{2}$. Half the outcomes are two or more heads and half are one or fewer heads. The distribution is symmetrical about the middle. Figure 7.1

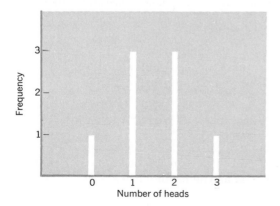

Fig. 7.1. *A simple binomial frequency distribution, showing the numbers of times out of eight trials one should expect 0, 1, 2, and 3 heads, from tossing three coins on each trial.*

shows how we may regard the results as forming a frequency distribution. Each frequency is represented by a vertical bar because of the lack of continuity on the base line.

The binomial equation. We could go on, considering problems with 4, 5, 6, and more coins, generating all the possible combinations and their frequencies. We should expect symmetrical distributions, with the number of categories equal to $n + 1$, where n is the number of coins. A mathematical way of deriving the probabilities for such problems makes use of a well-known kind of equation known as the *binomial expansion*. For the case of two coins, the equation is

$$\left(\frac{1}{2} + \frac{1}{2}\right)^2 = \left(\frac{1}{2}\right)^2 + 2\left(\frac{1}{2} \times \frac{1}{2}\right) + \left(\frac{1}{2}\right)^2$$
$$= \frac{1}{4} + \frac{1}{2} + \frac{1}{4}$$

This is just as in basic algebra, where the student learns that $(a + b)^2 = a^2 + 2ab + b^2$. It will be seen that the three terms in the expansion of $(\frac{1}{2} + \frac{1}{2})^2$ represent the probabilities of obtaining 2, 1, and 0 heads, respectively (or 0, 1, and 2 heads: the distribution is symmetrical). For the case of three coins,

$$\left(\frac{1}{2} + \frac{1}{2}\right)^3 = \left(\frac{1}{2}\right)^3 + 3\left(\frac{1}{2}\right)^2\left(\frac{1}{2}\right) + 3\left(\frac{1}{2}\right)\left(\frac{1}{2}\right)^2 + \left(\frac{1}{2}\right)^3$$
$$= \frac{1}{8} + \frac{3}{8} + \frac{3}{8} + \frac{1}{8}$$

Besides the four terms expressing the probabilities of occurrence of the four outcomes, 0 to 3 heads, the numerators express the frequencies with which each kind of outcome occurs. Since the denominator term expresses the total number of outcomes, each ratio expresses a probability.

We are now ready for the basic and general equation for the expansion of a binomial. The exponent n in each case represents the number of coins. The two terms within parentheses are probabilities, each for the single outcomes for one coin. The first $\frac{1}{2}$ is the probability of obtaining a head and the second is the probability of *not* obtaining a head. In this case, not obtaining a head is equivalent to obtaining a tail, because there are only two mutually exclusive outcomes. In other cases, as in throwing two dice, the not-favored cases are of different kinds. For the throwing of two dice, the equation would be stated: $(\frac{1}{6} + \frac{5}{6})^2$. Expansion of this binomial would yield the probabilities for three different outcomes: 2, 1, and 0 one spots, respectively, if a one spot is the favored outcome. The expansion of this binomial gives $\frac{1}{36}$, $\frac{10}{36}$, and $\frac{25}{36}$ as the probabilities for obtaining 2, 1, and 0 one spots in throwing two dice.

As stated before, the symbol for a probability is p. The symbol for the nonoccurrence of the same outcome is q. $p + q$ always equals 1.0. Either outcome A or outcome not-A is bound to occur. With the number of events signified by n, the general binomial expansion is

$$(p + q)^n = p^n + \frac{n}{1}p^{(n-1)}q + \frac{n(n-1)}{1 \times 2}p^{(n-2)}q^2$$

$$+ \frac{n(n-1)(n-2)}{1 \times 2 \times 3}p^{(n-3)}q^3$$

$$+ \frac{n(n-1)(n-2)(n-3)}{1 \times 2 \times 3 \times 4}p^{(n-4)}q^4 + \cdots + q^n \quad (7.1)$$

Since $p + q = 1$, $p + q$ raised to any power n also equals 1, and the entire expression to the right of the equality sign equals 1. Thus, the terms represent a partitioning of the total probability into components.

Applying equation (7.1) to the case of six coins ($n = 6$), the equation reads

$$\left(\frac{1}{2} + \frac{1}{2}\right)^6 = \left(\frac{1}{2}\right)^6 + 6\left(\frac{1}{2}\right)^5\left(\frac{1}{2}\right) + \frac{6 \times 5}{1 \times 2}\left(\frac{1}{2}\right)^4\left(\frac{1}{2}\right)^2$$

$$+ \frac{6 \times 5 \times 4}{1 \times 2 \times 3}\left(\frac{1}{2}\right)^3\left(\frac{1}{2}\right)^3 + \frac{6 \times 5 \times 4 \times 3}{1 \times 2 \times 3 \times 4}\left(\frac{1}{2}\right)^2\left(\frac{1}{2}\right)^4$$

$$+ \frac{6 \times 5 \times 4 \times 3 \times 2}{1 \times 2 \times 3 \times 4 \times 5}\left(\frac{1}{2}\right)\left(\frac{1}{2}\right)^5 + \left(\frac{1}{2}\right)^6$$

$$= \frac{1}{64} + \frac{6}{64} + \frac{15}{64} + \frac{20}{64} + \frac{15}{64} + \frac{6}{64} + \frac{1}{64} = 1$$

Thus, the frequencies for the cases of 0 to 6 heads are as seen in the numerators of the fractions in the various terms.

Finding numbers of combinations. The multiplications written out in the various terms of the binomial expansion just given can be expressed much more economically, for they represent the numbers of different combinations of heads of different numbers that can be found among six coins. There is only one way to obtain a combination of six heads with six coins: they must all be heads. In how many ways can we obtain five heads, using six coins? With five heads, the sixth is a tail. There are only six possible positions in which the tail can appear: as the first, second, third, etc., coin, up to the sixth. Hence, there are only six combinations of five heads each. In how many ways can four heads distribute themselves among six coins?

A symbol for a combination of r things among n things is nCr, and the standard formula is

$$nCr = \frac{n!}{r!(n-r)!}$$ (General formula for finding the number of combinations of r things among a total of n)   (7.2)

where $n!$ should be read "*n factorial*," which means the multiplication of n by every integer below it, i.e., $n(n-1)(n-2)(n-3) \cdots 1$; r = number of elements combined out of the total number, n; and $r!$ is r factorial with meaning similar to that of $n!$ To return to the question of how many ways we can combine 4 heads among 6 coins, $n = 6$ and $r = 4$. The number of combinations is

$$6\,C4 = \frac{6!}{4!\,2!}$$
$$= \frac{6 \times 5 \times 4 \times 3 \times 2 \times 1}{(4 \times 3 \times 2 \times 1) \times (2 \times 1)}$$

We see that the first four elements in the denominator also appear in the numerator, and hence they cancel, leaving[1]

$$6\,C4 = \frac{6 \times 5}{2 \times 1} = 15$$

It will be noted that this is the coefficient for the third term in the expansion of the equation $(\frac{1}{2} + \frac{1}{2})^6$. Each coefficient is such a solution for the number of combinations as r varies from 6 to 0. The use of equation (7.2) is quite general. The reader need not worry about a zero factorial; it can be taken as equal to unity.

The Pascal triangle.   For the special, but common, case of $p = q = \frac{1}{2}$, the easiest way of determining the frequencies for expansions of binomials when n is small is to utilize Pascal's triangle, illustrated in Table 7.1. Starting with the case $n = 2$, we have two frequencies, 1 and

[1]As an exercise, the student might write out all 15 of the combinations containing four heads and two tails, two of which would be H H H H T T and T H T H H H.

Table 7.1   **Pascal's triangle for cases up to** *n = 10*

n													Sum
1						1		1					2
2					1		2		1				4
3				1		3		3		1			8
4			1		4		6		4		1		16
5		1		5		10		10		5		1	32
6	1		6		15		20		15		6		1	64
7	1		7		21		35		35		21		7		1	128
8	1		8		28		56		70		56		28		8		1	256
9	1		9		36		84		126		126		84		36		9		1	512
10	1		10		45		120		210		252		210		120		45		10		1	1,024

1, with a total of 2. The frequencies for $n = 3$ can be written by putting 1 at either extreme and a 2 in the middle category. Note that the 2 is the sum of the two frequencies on either side of it in the row above. The third row is generated in the same fashion from the second, and so on down the triangle. Except for the 1's at the extremes, each frequency is the sum of the two just above it. The sums at the extreme right of the rows are 2 to the power n.

THE MEAN AND VARIANCE OF A BINOMIAL DISTRIBUTION

Just as we describe distributions of samples of measurements by giving their means and variances or standard deviations, we can also describe particular binomial distributions. The mean and variance of a binomial distribution are readily computed from knowledge of p and n. The mean is given by the equation

$$\overline{M}_b = np \qquad \text{(Mean of a binomial distribution)} \qquad (7.3)$$

The variance is given by

$$\overline{\sigma}_b^2 = npq \qquad \text{(Variance of a binomial distribution)} \qquad (7.4)$$

where p = probability of the favored outcome

$q = 1 - p$

n = the number of replications (occurrences) of the event

The bars in the symbols $\overline{M}$ and $\overline{\sigma}$ indicate that we are dealing with *parameters* rather than statistics. Parameters are mathematically exact constants, not estimates from samples. For the distribution describing the frequencies to be expected in tossing ten coins, with $p = \frac{1}{2}$ and $n = 10$, the mean equals 5.0 and the variance equals 2.5. The student might check this by actually computing the mean number of heads and the variance from the last distribution in Table 7.1.

SOME SIMPLE APPLICATIONS OF THE BINOMIAL MODEL

In research on behavior the binomial model is often found to apply quite well. Assume that we have a true-false test of 10 items or, a parallel case in animal research, a sequence of 10 two-choice trials for a rat. We suspect that the behavior in either case will not be entirely random, that in the long run there is a bias toward right responses, but to exclude the possibility that the behavior *is* random, we need to set up the random-behavior hypothesis in the form of a binomial expressed by $(\frac{1}{2} + \frac{1}{2})^{10}$. Let us say that the student taking the test does flip a coin every time he tries the next item and that the rat does something equivalent in his trials. The binomial model, expanded, would have the frequencies seen in the bottom row of the Pascal triangle in Table 7.1, representing the various numbers of right answers given by the subject. The expected, chance-generated number of right responses is 5. Does the student or the rat do enough better than 5 so that we may reject the chance hypothesis and tolerate in its place the hypothesis that he knows something about what he is doing? We shall encounter many such problems in later chapters, and we shall find that the question about "enough better" can be answered mathematically.

Let us return to the ESP problem with which we started this whole discussion. In that experiment, the subject has one chance in five of being correct by chance: the probability of a correct response is $\frac{1}{5}$. With 25 trials, the expected chance-generated score would be 5. The binomial would be $(\frac{1}{5} + \frac{4}{5})^{25}$. Expansion of this binomial in order to determine the probabilities for all the possible scores from 0 to 25 would be a formidable task, except on a high-speed computer. It would not be necessary to derive all those probabilities, for our interest would be in the scores as high as, or higher than, the one made by a particular person. The two examples are probably sufficient to show the kinds of problems to which the binomial distribution can be applied. The opportunities for its use are numerous, but we shall leave actual applications to later chapters, particularly Chap. 10.

The normal distribution

RELATION OF THE NORMAL DISTRIBUTION TO THE BINOMIAL DISTRIBUTION

It is easy to show the relation between the normal distribution and the binomial distribution. If we plot the frequencies given in the bottom row of Table 7.1, for the case of $n = 10$, we have a bar diagram as in Fig. 7.2, with 11 score categories, where the score is the number of heads expected. Imagine similar graphs where n equals 20, then 50, then larger and larger numbers, keeping the total width of the distribution the same. The stair steps of the bar diagram become smaller and smaller until they merge into a smooth contour. *The normal distribution is the limit of the binomial distribution where $p = .5$ and n becomes indefinitely large.* This has been proved mathematically, but the proof will not be given here.

Superimposed upon the bar diagram in Fig. 7.2 is a normal distribution whose mean and standard deviation are the same as those for the binomial distribution: 5.0 for the mean and 1.58 for the standard deviation, from the use of formulas (7.3) and (7.4). The agreement of the two distributions would be even more apparent if the binomial distribution were drawn in the form of a frequency polygon. The bar diagram is preferred for a binomial distribution because the scores are discrete numbers: there is a lack of continuity over the range of possible score values. The comparison of the two distributions can be

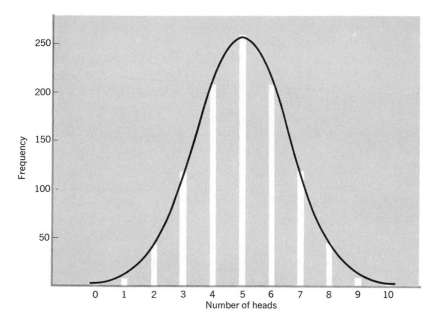

Fig. 7.2. *A binomial frequency distribution of expected numbers of heads from tossing 10 coins 1,024 times. Superimposed is a normal distribution that has the same mean and standard deviation as the binomial distribution.*

done analytically by comparing category frequencies, as in Table 7.2. The discrepancies are mostly small, but the largest is 6.5 for the model category. The normal-distribution frequencies add up to 1,023.5, or half a case short. This is partly because some of the cases in the normal distribution extend beyond the terminal values of 0 and 10 for the binomial distribution. If we find the cumulative distributions of proportions for the two sets of frequencies (see the last two columns of Table 7.2), we see that the majority of the discrepancies are .001 and the largest is only .005. The discrepancies are greatest near the center of the distributions. Since it is the frequencies near the tails that are crucial in hypothesis testing that we do with either kind of distribution, we see why the normal distribution may often be substituted for the binomial as a model for chance-generated results.

THE EQUATION FOR THE NORMAL-DISTRIBUTION CURVE

The general equation that describes mathematically the normal-distribution curve is often written

$$Y = \frac{N}{\sigma \sqrt{2\pi}} e^{\frac{-x^2}{2\sigma^2}} \qquad \text{(General equation for the normal-distribution curve)} \qquad (7.5)$$

where Y = frequency

N = number of observations

σ = standard deviation of the distribution

π = 3.1416 (approximately)

e = 2.718 (approximately), the base of the Napierian
system of logarithms

x = deviation of a measurement from the mean $(X - \overline{M})$

Examination of the equation suggests some features of the normal curve. With fixed N and σ, all elements are constants except x, the independent variable. Since x is squared, either negative or positive values of it have the same effect and yield the same Y; hence the curve is bilaterally symmetrical. As x increases, since x^2 has a negative sign, the exponent of e decreases and Y also decreases. Y is at a maximum when $x = 0$, for that is when the exponent of e is a maximum. The mean of the distribution is 0 and the mode and median are also at 0. These features have been mentioned before, but now we see the mathematical reasons.

THE CUMULATIVE NORMAL DISTRIBUTION

Much of the use of the normal distribution in statistical operations is concerned with proportions of the area or surface under the normal curve in relation to certain distances on the base line. As the first approach to this subject, we consider the cumulative normal distribu-

Table 7.2   *Comparison of similar binomial and normal distributions (with same means and standard deviations) with respect to frequencies and cumulative proportions*

Score (heads)	Frequencies		Cumulative proportions	
	Binomial	*Normal*	*Binomial*	*Normal*
10	1	1.8	1.000	1.000
9	10	10.5	.999	.998
8	45	42.5	.989	.988
7	120	116.1	.945	.946
6	210	211.6	.828	.833
5	252	258.5	.623	.626
4	210	211.6	.377	.374
3	120	116.1	.172	.167
2	45	42.5	.055	.054
1	10	10.5	.011	.012
0	1	1.8	.001	.002
Sum	1,024	1,023.5		

tion. We have already seen how ordinary obtained frequency distributions, normal or otherwise, can be cumulated, first in Chap. 3 and in another example in Table 7.2. We start with the frequency in the lowest category and successively add on the frequency in higher categories in order.

The last column in Table 7.2 is a cumulation of actual frequencies in a normal distribution, with the frequencies in 11 categories. In approaching this problem mathematically in a more general manner, an indefinitely large number of categories is assumed (with correspondingly smaller numbers of cases in the categories, where N is constant). The process is known as *integration*, in integral calculus. The equation for the cumulative normal distribution reads

$$Y = \int_{-\infty}^{x} \frac{N}{\sigma\sqrt{2\pi}} e^{-\frac{x^2}{2\sigma^2}} dx \qquad \begin{array}{l}\text{(Equation for the}\\ \text{cumulative normal}\\ \text{distribution)}\end{array} \qquad (7.6)$$

where the symbols are exactly the same as in equation (7.5), except for two additions. The symbol $\int$ is the integration sign, which can be interpreted as "the sum of" what follows it. The limits of integration are $-\infty$ (an infinitely large negative value) at the lower end and x at the upper end. The lower tail of the normal distribution extends to the left indefinitely. The category areas (frequencies) summed are all those below any particular chosen value of x. The expression dx at the right in the equation simply indicates that very small increments of x are involved in the summation and lets us know that the increments are on x.

THE UNIT NORMAL DISTRIBUTION

To help us in doing computations where either the noncumulative or the cumulative normal distribution is concerned, tables have been prepared. To save space, the tables do not provide for all possible cases of N and all cases of σ. Instead, they adopt a particular curve with $N = 1$ and $\sigma = 1$. The mean, of course, remains at zero. Under these conditions, the total area under the curve is equal to 1, and all frequencies are proportions. Such are Tables B and C in Appendix B.

With both N and σ equal to 1.0, equation (7.5) becomes

$$y = \frac{1}{\sqrt{2\pi}} e^{-\frac{z^2}{2}}$$

Areas under the normal-distribution curve

Since the normal-curve tables are limited to the standard case in which $N = 1$ and $\sigma = 1$, in applying the tables to situations in which N and σ have other values, it is necessary for us to convert measurements into standard form, which means finding *standard scores*. A standard score, z, is a deviation from the mean in terms of the standard deviation as the unit. The transformation into a standard score is performed by using the equation

$$z = \frac{x}{\sigma_x} = \frac{X - M_x}{\sigma_x} \qquad \text{(A standard score derived from a deviation score or an obtained score)} \qquad (7.7)$$

The normal distribution involved in Table 7.2 has a mean of 5 and a standard deviation of 1.58. The z corresponding to an X of 5 would, of course, be zero. The z corresponding to a score of 6 would be

$$z = \frac{6 - 5}{1.58} = \frac{1}{1.58} = +0.63$$

The standard score corresponding to an X of 2 would be

$$z = \frac{2 - 5}{1.58} = \frac{-3}{1.58} = -1.90$$

It is with such z values that we enter Table B in Appendix B. Next, we shall try a number of different kinds of problems pertaining to relations between areas under the curve and z values.

PROPORTION OF THE AREA BETWEEN THE MEAN AND SOME MEASUREMENT OR SCORE

In connection with interpreting a standard deviation, we have already had occasion to say that the interval extending one standard deviation on either side of the mean includes about two-thirds of the cases. To say the same thing in another way, from the mean to $+1\sigma$ are to be expected about one-third of the cases, and from the mean to -1σ, another one-third of the cases. We can verify this by referring to Table B and looking up the proportion of the area between the mean and 1σ (i.e., a z equal to 1.00). The area given to four decimal places is .3413, or 3,413 ten-thousandths of the area. If there were a normal distribution with 10,000 cases, 3,413 of them would be expected between the mean and 1σ. In terms of percentage, it would be 34.13 per cent, or 34.13 cases in 100. The total interval from $+1\sigma$ to -1σ contains twice this area, or .6826, or 68.26 per cent. Figure 7.3

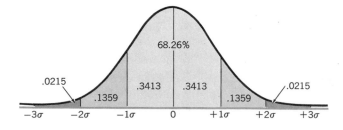

Fig. 7.3. *Different proportions of area under the normal curve within the limits of the various 1σ units on the base line.*

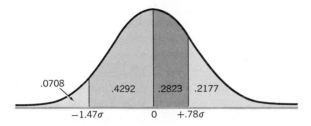

Fig. 7.4. *Proportions of the area under the normal curve within certain standard-score limits on the base line.*

illustrates these facts graphically. We now see that this is a little more than two-thirds (which would be 66.67 per cent), but with small deviations from normality occurring in empirical data, we can afford to be so rough with our expectation as to state it as two-thirds.

From Table B, we can also see that between the mean and a point 2σ distant (either above or below, i.e., either $+2\sigma$ or -2σ), we should expect .4772 of the total surface, or 47.72 per cent of the cases. Included in the range from -2σ to $+2\sigma$, we should find twice this proportion, or .9544 of the area, or 95.44 per cent of the cases. From the mean to 3σ is .4987 of the area, and in both directions from the mean to 3σ we find twice this, or .9974 of the area. Only 26 cases in 10,000 (10,000 − 9,974), therefore, should be expected *beyond* the range from -3σ to $+3\sigma$ in a large sample.

To take another example of a less special nature, how much of the area under the normal curve will be found between the mean and $+0.78\sigma$? From the table, we find this to be .2823. In still another problem, what proportion of the cases lies between the mean and -1.47σ? From the table, we find this to be .4292. Figure 7.4 illustrates these two cases. It will be seen that the positive or negative sign of z merely tells us whether the area extends above the mean or below. The numerical *size* of z, whether positive or negative, determines the *amount* of area between the mean and the point.

Thus far we have begun each problem of this type with some particular z or standard measurement. Let us now start the problem a step or two further back and begin with some raw score or measurement. In the more practical case, we begin with X, not z. In the memory-test data, we may inquire what proportion of the cases come between the mean (26.1) and a point of 35 on the scale of measurement. This point deviates 8.9 X units from the mean ($X - M = +8.9$). This is the deviation x. The standard score z is x/σ, which equals $8.9/6.45 = +1.38$. *Everything must be transformed into standard measure before the probability table may be utilized.* Entering the table with a z of 1.38, we find the corresponding area to be .4162 (see Fig. 7.5). In other words, 41.62 per cent of the cases in a normal distribution would be found between the mean and 35 points on the scale. In the memory-test data, 41.62 per cent of 86 is 35.8, or, in whole num-

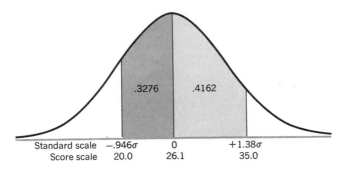

Fig. 7.5. *Proportions of the area under the normal curve between the mean and selected scores on the scale of scores for the memory test.*

bers, 36 cases. In a similar manner, which the student should verify, between the mean and a score of 20, .3276 of the cases are to be expected, or approximately 28. Between the mean and a score of 15 about 39 cases of the 86 are to be expected, and if we go on down to a score point of 5, we find 49.95 per cent of the cases.

THE AREA ABOVE OR BELOW A CERTAIN POINT ON THE SCALE

For a given deviate or standard score, Table B also gives us the proportion of the area above a certain point on the scale or below it. Above a point at $+1\sigma$ will be found .1587 of the area. When a vertical line is erected at $+1\sigma$ (see Fig. 7.6) it divides the total area under the curve into two portions, the one to the right of the line being the smaller of the two. Below the point $+1\sigma$ is the remainder of the area, or the larger portion (found in column B of the table), including .8413, or 84.13 per cent of the area. If we were interested in the point -1σ, the larger portion under the curve is now to the right of the point of division and is found in column B, whereas the portion to the left, being the smaller of the two, is found in column C. The situation is just reversed in the case where the division comes at $+1\sigma$. In this kind of problem it is necessary to keep in mind whether the area we wish to know is under the smaller end of the curve, all on one side of the mean, or whether it is under the larger side of the curve extending across the mean.

The proportion of the area above the point at $+0.78\sigma$ is in the smaller portion and, found in column C, it is .2177. The area below

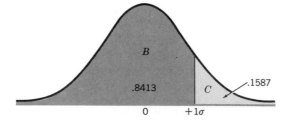

Fig. 7.6. *Proportions of the area under the normal curve above and below the standard score of $+1\sigma$.*

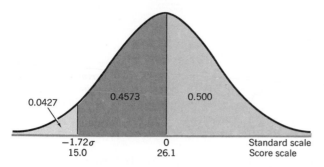

Fig. 7.7. *Proportions of the area under the normal curve above and below a selected score on the scale for the memory test.*

-1.47σ is also under the smaller portion of the curve and, from column C, we find that it is .0708 (see Fig. 7.4). The area *above* the point -1.47σ would be equal to $1.0 - .0708$, which is .9292. Or it can be found from column B, since it occupies the larger portion under the curve, and this also gives us .9292. Or, from Fig. 7.4, we can see that it is the sum of the area from the point to the mean (.4292) plus .500, which gives the same result.

In the memory-test data, where the mean is 26.1 and σ is 6.45, we may ask for the percentage of the cases to be expected below a score of 15. The deviation from the mean is 11.1. When this is divided by 6.45, we find that the z score is -1.72. Corresponding to a z of -1.72 is an area of .0427 in the tail of the normal curve (see Fig. 7.7). We may expect 4.27 per cent of the cases below a score of 15, or, out of 86, 3.7 cases. Above a score of 15, we should expect the remainder of the cases, naturally, i.e., a proportion of .9573, a percentage of 95.73, and in number of cases, 82.3.

POINTS ABOVE OR BELOW WHICH CERTAIN PROPORTIONS OF THE CASES FALL

The next problems reverse the processes that have just been described. Before, we had given points on the scale of measurement to determine areas; now we have given areas from which to determine points on the scale. For example, above what point in the normal curve does the highest 10 per cent of the cases come? Ten per cent is a proportion of .10. We could now use Table B in reverse, but it is much more convenient to utilize Table C, which gives the proportions in even steps. We are faced with a problem that gives the proportion in the tail of the curve, so we look in the last column for C, the smaller area. We find the z score corresponding to it to be 1.2816. This should be with a plus sign, since we are talking about the highest 10 per cent (see Fig. 7.8). Had we asked below what point does the *lowest* 10 per cent fall, the answer would have been -1.2816σ. If the question is, "Above what score do the highest 80 per cent of the cases lie?" we are then dealing with the larger proportion under the curve; accordingly we look for the proportion of .80 in the first column of Table C. The

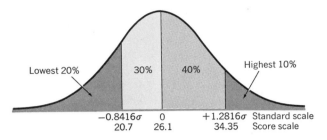

Fig. 7.8. *Score points above or below which certain percentages of the cases are expected in the memory-test distribution, assuming normality of distribution.*

corresponding z score is -0.8416σ (see Fig. 7.8). Had we asked for the point below which is the *lowest* 80 per cent, the answer would have been $+0.8416$.

To apply these same questions to the memory-test data, we need go a step further and transform the z scores into terms of the raw-score scale. The highest 10 per cent come above a z of $+1.2816$. Multiplying this by σ (which is 6.45), we obtain the deviation (x) of $+8.27$. The mean (or 26.1) plus 8.27 gives us a score of 34.37 points. The highest 10 per cent in a near-normal curve with mean of 26.1 and σ of 6.45 would therefore be expected above the point 34.37. It happens that this point comes close to the division point between two class intervals, or 34.5. In the actual distribution (see Table 3.6), 10 cases, or close to 12 per cent, were scores of 35 or above, which is good agreement. Ten per cent would have called for 8.6 cases, or 9 in whole numbers.

Above what raw score may the highest 80 per cent of the cases, which we found to come above a z score of -0.841σ, be expected? The deviation of this point from the mean is -5.43 points, or a score of 20.67. This comes close to another division point between class intervals, namely, 20.5. In the actual distribution, 71, or 82.5 per cent, of the cases are above a score of 20.5. Again the agreement between obtained proportion and expected proportion is quite close. To take one more case, which yields a point exactly between class intervals, we ask above what point are 93.2 per cent of the cases? The point turns out to be a score of 16.5 points (the student should verify this). The actual percentage of cases above this score point is 92 – again a very close agreement.

Other tests and other mathematical models

In this chapter we have dealt with some fundamental matters which are basic to the concepts of the several chapters to follow. We shall see how the principles of probability and the binomial and normal distributions are used in drawing conclusions about "true" means, standard deviations, correlation coefficients, and the like, and how much confidence we should have in those conclusions. We shall see how we can decide whether obtained differences between such statistics indicate any "real" differences in the phenomena under investigation. We shall find that additional models are needed to make certain tests of hypotheses, including Student's t distribution, the F distribution, and the chi-square distribution, which open up a whole new set of possibilities of procedures for the use of the scientific investigator and the technical worker.

EXERCISES

1. In drawing one card from a shuffled deck, what is the probability of drawing:
a. A jack?
b. A club?
c. A red card?
d. A black heart?
e. A spade that is not a face card (jack, queen, or king)?

2. In tossing four coins, what is the probability of obtaining:
a. The sequence H T H T?
b. Four heads?
c. Three tails?
d. Four heads *or* three tails?
e. No heads in two successive throws?

3. In tossing two dice, what is the probability of obtaining:
a. A 2 and a 3?
b. A 2 and then a 3?
c. A total of 5 spots?
d. On repeating a throw of two dice (i.e., throwing two dice twice in succession), what is the probability of repeating exactly 7 spots?

4. A clinical psychologist is told that two of the five patients whose Rorschach (ink-blot-test) protocols he has been given are schizophrenics and three are neurotics.
a. In how many different ways could the psychologist assign the two schizophrenics to the five protocols by random selection?
b. What is the probability of his being completely correct by guessing?

5. For the ESP experiment, with 25 trials and a probability of 1/5 of being correct in each trial, write the appropriate binomial (without expanding it).

6. What is the mean and the standard deviation of the binomial distribution for the preceding problem?

7. Expand the binomial $(1/3 + 2/3)^4$.

8. Toss a set of six pennies 64 times. After each throw, note and record the number of heads. Compare your obtained frequencies with the expected frequencies (seen in Table 7.1). Plot a bar diagram for the obtained binomial distribution and a frequency polygon for the expected distribution. Compute the mean and standard deviation of your obtained distribution and of the expected distribution.

9. Determine the standard scores (z) for the following scores in the distribution for Data 7A: 40, 55, 72, 85.

10. Find the proportions of the areas under the unit normal distribution curve between the mean and the following z scores: $-2.15, -1.85, -0.19, +0.375, +1.10$.

11. Assuming a normal-distribution model, find the proportions and numbers of cases to be expected between the mean and the following scores in Data 7A: 45, 65, 75, 58.35.

12. Find the proportions of the area in the unit normal distribution *above* the following scores: $+2.15, +1.62, +0.175, -0.36, -1.90$; also *below:* $-1.225, -0.6745, +0.05, +1.75, +2.30$.

13. Find the proportions and numbers of cases to be expected in distribution 7A *above* the following score points: 55, 65, 69.5, 41.5; also *below* the following score points: 45, 56, 77.5, 61.5. Where possible, compare these frequencies with the obtained frequencies.

14. Give in terms of standard measurements, z, the points *above* which the following percentages of the cases fall in the unit normal distribution: 85, 55, 35, 42.3, 9.4.

15. Give the z score *below* which the following proportions of the cases fall: .14, .62, .375, .418, .729.

16. *Below* what score points in distribution 7A should we expect the following numbers of cases: 11, 63, 123, 162? Compare with actual cumulative frequencies.

Scores	f
82 – 85	1
78 – 81	8
74 – 77	8
70 – 73	5
66 – 69	34
62 – 65	21
58 – 61	39
54 – 57	32
50 – 53	20
46 – 49	7
42 – 45	3
38 – 41	0
34 – 37	1
Sum	179
Mean	61.1
σ	8.4

*Data 7A **Distribution of spelling-test scores in a superior group of freshmen***

*The test was one of the Cooperative series, and the scores are T scores (see Chap. 19).

ANSWERS

1. *a.* $1/13$; *b.* $1/4$; *c.* $1/2$; *d.* 0; *e.* $5/26$.
2. *a.* $1/16$; *b.* $1/16$; *c.* $1/4$; *d.* $5/16$; *e.* $1/256$.
3. *a.* $1/18$; *b.* $1/36$; *c.* $1/9$; *d.* $1/36$.
4. *a.* $5C2 = 10$; *b.* $1/10$.
5. $(1/5 + 4/5)^{25}$.
6. Mean: 5.0; SD: 2.0.
7. $1/81 + 8/81 + 24/81 + 32/81 + 16/81 = 1.00$.
9. -2.51; -0.73; $+1.30$; $+2.84$.
10. p: .4842; .4678; .0753; .1461; .3643.
11. p: .4726; .1786; .4510; .1282.
    f: 84.4; 32.0; 80.7; 22.9.
12. p above: .0158; .0526; .4306; .6405; .9713.
    p below: .1104; .2500; .5199; .9599; .9893.
13. p above: .7660; .3214; .1587; .9902.
    f above: 137.1; 57.5; 28.4; 177.2.
    p below: .0276; .2720; .9745; .5191.
    f below: 4.9; 48.7; 174.4; 92.9.
14. z: -1.0364; -0.1257; $+0.3853$; $+0.1942$; $+1.3165$.
15. z: -1.0803; $+0.3055$; -0.3186; -0.2070; $+0.6098$.
16. X_e: 48.1; 57.9; 65.2; 72.0.
    f_e: 11; 63; 123; 163.
    f_o: 9; 67; 121; 160.

8 *Statistical estimations and inferences*

IN this chapter we raise the very important question as to how near the "truth" are statistical answers such as means, standard deviations, proportions, and the like. As was said in Chap. 1, measured samples are usually employed to represent larger populations. From the statistical point of view, a population is any arbitrarily defined group. The term will be more fully explained in later paragraphs.

Sampling has to be limited for practical reasons; ordinarily we cannot measure total populations, or at least it is generally inefficient and unnecessary to do so. Yet we usually wish to generalize beyond our sample, arriving at scientific decisions that transcend the observations made at a particular time and in a particular place, or reaching administrative decisions that apply to larger groups of individuals. In earlier chapters we have been concerned primarily with *descriptive statistics*. The computed values were used to describe the properties of particular samples. If we want to apply those same statistics beyond the limits of samples, we must know how much risk we take of being wrong. In general terms, the statistics stressed in this chapter are designed to do that very thing. They are known as *sampling statistics*.

To be more specific, when we obtain the mean of a sample that is measured in some respect, before we say that this obtained mean also describes the mean of the population sampled, we need to find some basis for believing that it does not deviate very far from the population mean. Fortunately, there is a statistical procedure that will inform us about how far our obtained mean probably deviates from the population mean, provided certain conditions, to be explained later, have been satisfied. The statistic that will do this is known as the *standard error of the mean*. In a similar manner, there are standard errors of other sample statistics—medians, standard deviations, proportions, correlation coefficients, and the like—which inform us of the accuracy of our obtained figures as estimates of the corresponding population values.

Some principles of sampling

Before going into the treatment of sampling statistics, it is necessary to understand clearly the essential facts about the process of
sampling. The application of sampling statistics depends upon certain *conditions* of sampling. If these are not satisfied, standard errors, no matter how accurately computed, may give wrong impres-
sions. At best, they give us only estimates from which we can make
decisions and draw conclusions, never with complete conviction but
with various degrees of assurance. After making this frank confes-
sion as to the limitations of sampling statistics, it should also be as-
serted that without them we can hardly draw any generalized conclusions at all that would be of scientific or practical value.

POPULATIONS AND SAMPLES

It is time that we had a better definition of *population*. Some statisticians call it *universe*. In any case, the statistician's idea of population is quite different from the popular idea. Rarely would any statistical study regard the entire population of a nation, a city, or of
some geographical region as its *universe*.

The population in a statistical investigation is always arbitrarily
defined by naming its unique properties. It might be the entering
freshman class in a certain university, or the part of the freshman
class entering a certain college or even a certain course. It might be
the male sixteen-year-olds in a given school district; the children of
Mexican parentage in a certain city; or the registered Democratic
voters in the New England states. All these examples are of groups
of human individuals. Populations could, of course, be defined as
species, or phyla, or orders of animals or of plants.

There are also populations of observations or of reactions of a certain kind – simple reactions to sound stimuli, word-association reactions, judgments of pleasantness of colors, and the like – from the
psychological laboratory. It is probably the nonhuman groups that
have seemed to require the more general term *universe* as an alternative to the more restricted term *population*. In this volume we shall
use the term *population* in the broad sense to include all sets of individuals, objects, or reactions that can be described as having a
unique pattern of qualities.

Parameters and statistics. If we were to measure all the individuals of a population and actually compute the indices of central
value, dispersion, and correlation, as we ordinarily do for samples,
we should obtain what the statistician calls *parameters*. The population parameters exist whether we compute them or not.

Figure 8.1 illustrates the distinction between population param-

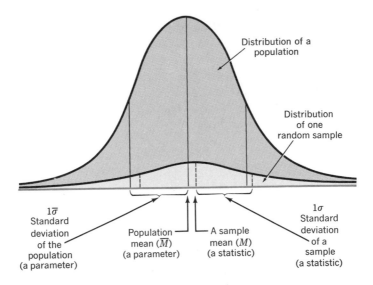

Distribution of a
population

Distribution
of one
random sample

$1\overline{\sigma}$
Standard
deviation
of the
population
(a parameter)

Population
mean ($\overline{M}$)
(a parameter)

A sample
mean (M)
(a statistic)

1σ
Standard
deviation
of a
sample
(a statistic)

Fig. 8.1. *A comparison of a population distribution and a
sample distribution, also of population parameters and
sample statistics.*

eters and sample statistics. The larger distribution is that of the entire population. The smaller distribution is of a sample drawn at
random from that population. The population parameters, mean and
standard deviation, are symbolized by $\overline{M}$ and $\overline{\sigma}$, each with a bar over
it.[1] It will be noted that in this particular sample the mean (M) and
the standard deviation (σ) do not coincide exactly in size with their
corresponding parameters ($\overline{M}$ and $\overline{\sigma}$). This is characteristic. A second
sample would be expected to have still different M and σ, but also
similar to $\overline{M}$ and $\overline{\sigma}$ in size.

The same sort of parallel could be illustrated with respect to propor-
tions ($\overline{p}$ and p), semi-interquartile ranges ($\overline{Q}$ and Q), and coefficients of
correlation ($\overline{r}$ and r). By careful and adequate sampling we hope to
arrive at statistics that will approximate the corresponding parameters very closely. From the observed statistics we wish to make
sound inferences concerning the population parameters. By the use
of standard errors and other sampling statistics, to be discussed

[1] The bar over a quantity often indicates "the mean of." For example, $\overline{X}$ is
sometimes used to indicate the "mean of X." Some writers on statistics use
the Greek letter μ and σ to stand for the population parameters, mean and
SD, respectively, and Roman letters M and s to stand for sample statistics.
The use of $\overline{M}$ and $\overline{\sigma}$ for the parameters here is consistent with one operational
conception, to the effect that these parameters are the means of a very large
number of sample M's and σ's.

later, we estimate how far our obtained statistics may have deviated from their corresponding parameters.

Random sampling.   It should be kept in mind that the use of sampling statistics (standard errors and the like) rests on the assumption that the sampling has been random. The best definition of random sampling is that it is selection of cases from the population in such a manner that *every individual in the population has an equal chance of being chosen. In addition, the selection of any one individual is in no way tied to the selection of any other.* This calls to mind a well-conducted lottery, selective-service numbers, coin tossing, throwing dice, and other operations that allow the "laws of chance" to operate freely.

There are several ways of favoring random sampling from populations. For a population of individuals, if all members are arranged in alphabetical order and one wishes to draw one person in every hundred, the first case might be taken by blind pointing within the first hundred names and every hundredth one following in the list automatically chosen. Tables of random numbers have been published as an aid in random sampling.[1] The numbers themselves have been placed in sequence by some kind of lottery procedure. If individuals in a population are numbered in sequence and thus identified by number, selections can be made by following the random numbers in any systematic way. A random sample should be fairly representative of the population, though in any particular sample, if it is a small one in particular, by chance it may not be so representative as we would like.

Biased sampling.   In a biased sample there is a systematic error. Certain types of cases have an advantage over others in being selected. The likelihood of individuals being chosen differs from one to another. A common example of this in educational research is the voluntary return of questionnaires. The names of those who are to receive the questionnaires may, to be sure, be randomly chosen from a much larger group. But suppose that only 60 per cent of those circularized return the questionnaires, which is not an atypical event. The 60 per cent who do return the data might possibly be representative, but there is a strong presumption that in the decision to return or not to return the instrument there is room for biasing forces to work. Those forces may or may not be relevant to the content of the questionnaire itself. But if the information requested implies favorable or unfavorable facts about the respondent, his associates, or his work, it is quite natural to expect that those with a

[1]Examples are Tippett, L. H. C. *Random Sampling Numbers*. New York: Cambridge, 1927; and Lindquist, E. F. *Design and Analysis of Experiments*. Boston: Houghton Mifflin, 1953. Appendix.

"good" showing will be more inclined to reply than those with a "bad" showing. If the trait of cooperativness or of responsibility or of dependability of the respondent is involved in the data or even correlated with something wanted in the data, there is also a strong likelihood of bias.

A colossal example of biased sampling is that of the *Literary Digest* public-opinion poll during the 1936 presidential campaign. Several million postcard ballots were said to have been circulated, certainly anticipating a sample of most generous size. But the mailing lists were made up from telephone directories and automobile registration lists. It so happened that in the poll a majority of the telephone subscribers and car owners voted for the candidate who lost, while the non-telephone subscribers and non-car owners voted at the polls in a more decisive way for the successful candidate. Among those who received postcard ballots there was also probably a selection as to which ones would be most likely to take the trouble to return the card. Those who were most discontented with things as they were and wanted a change would take the trouble to register a protest straw vote. Those who were contented or who felt somewhat secure as to the outcome would be less likely to return the card. This would also tend to make the vote appear to favor the losing candidate, who was running against an incumbent.

The scientific investigator must be eternally vigilant to the possibility of biased sampling. A good, systematic control of experimental conditions is designed to prevent biased samples or to make known their effects. Where there is less than customary experimental control of the observations, every possible effort should be made to know the conditions under which the data are obtained. Thorough knowledge of the conditions should be a basis for deciding whether selection of cases has been biased. Knowledge of conditions is also essential for the sake of accurate definition of the population sampled.

Stratification in sampling.   One common procedure that is introduced in sampling to help to prevent biases and also to ensure a more representative sample is known as stratification. Stratification is a step in the direction of experimental control. It operates with subgroups of more homogeneous composition within the larger population.

A very common example is to be found in public-opinion-polling practices. Suppose the issue to be investigated is public attitude toward a certain piece of labor legislation. It is quite likely that people in the two major political parties would tend to lean in opposite directions on such an issue. It is probable that people of different socio-economic categories—professional, business, office worker, semi-skilled laborer, and unskilled laborer—would react with some systematic differences on the issue. It is possible, though not so likely, that individuals of the two sexes would tend to respond somewhat differently. Other divisions of the population, such as rural versus urban, regional, and educational groups, might also show systematic differences on the issue. In other words, subgroups of the population are considered with respect to any variable that is suspected of correlating appreciably with the variable being studied. It does not matter that some of the variables are themselves intercorrelated unless such an intercorrelation is very high, in which case it would be superfluous to control selection of samples on both of two variables so closely related.

Having decided which variables are important in sampling, the entire population is studied to see what proportions fall into each category, e.g., what proportions are Democrat or Republican, male or female, urban or rural, in each socioeconomic group, and so on. Any sample to be obtained, then, should have proportional representations from all subgroups. Within each defined subpopulation – for example, a male, professional, Republican, New England group – random sampling may then be carried out. Random selection of cases would also be made within each of the other defined subpopulations in appropriate numbers. The total sampling procedure here described has been called *stratified-random sampling.*

The importance of the proportional-representation principle and its advantage over a purely random sampling can be readily demonstrated. Suppose that 55 per cent of the Republicans and 45 per cent of the Democrats are in favor of a certain labor bill. In the general population let us assume that 60 per cent are registered Democrats and 40 per cent are registered Republicans. In a random sample of 100 voters one would expect in the long run to draw the two party representatives in about the same ratio, $60/40$. This would vary from sample to sample, however, even to the extent that the majority could be reversed; for example, it could even be $45/55$. In the typical polling sample we should expect a majority of voters against the bill. If the sample should by chance contain a majority of Republicans, however, the majority might favor the bill. If stratification were applied, we should make sure that the ratio is $60/40$, and with this restriction imposed upon the random sampling we should expect the general population sentiment to be more accurately reflected. Thus it can be seen that a stratified-random sample is likely to be more representative of a total population than is a purely random sample.

Purposive samples.   A *purposive sample* is one arbitrarily selected because there is good evidence that it is very representative of the total population. Experience has shown in public-opinion polling that there are certain states or regions that come close to national opinion time after time. If one is willing to depend upon this experience, one may use the limited population as the source of the sample to use as a "barometer" for the total population. This is a convenient procedure, but it has the disadvantage that much prior information must have been obtained. There is also a risk that conditions may change to the extent that the particular segment of population no longer represents the total or does not represent it on some new issue.

Incidental samples. The term *incidental sample* is applied to those samples that are taken because they are the most available. Many a study has been made in psychology with students in classes of beginning psychology as the samples merely because they are most convenient. Results thus obtained can be generalized beyond such groups with considerable risk.

Generalizations beyond any sample can be made safely only when we have defined the population that the sample represents in every significant respect. If we know the significant properties of the incidental sample well enough and can show that those properties apply to new individuals, those new individuals may be said to belong to the same population as the members of the sample. By "significant properties" is meant those variables that correlate with the experimental variables involved. They are the kind of properties considered above in connection with stratification of samples. It is unlikely that membership in a political party would have much bearing upon the results of certain experiments performed upon sophomores in a beginning psychology course, but such variables as age, education, social background, and the like may definitely be pertinent.

Inferences regarding averages

THE DISTRIBUTION OF MEANS OF SAMPLES

Suppose that we are dealing with a population whose mean ($\overline{M}$) is 50.0 and whose standard deviation ($\overline{\sigma}$) is 10.0 on the measuring scale we are using. Such a distribution is illustrated by the top diagram in Fig. 8.2. We do not know these population parameters ordinarily, but for the sake of illustration we shall assume that we do know them here.

Sampling distributions. Suppose, next, that we proceed to draw random samples, all of equal size, one at a time, from this population. To satisfy the conditions of random sampling in a strictly mathematical sense, we should replace each member drawn, after noting its value, before drawing the next member. Each individual should have an equal opportunity of being selected in *every* drawing. Having lost one member, the population is different from what it was orginally. When the population is very large, as compared with the size of sample, however, we can forget about this *replacement* requirement

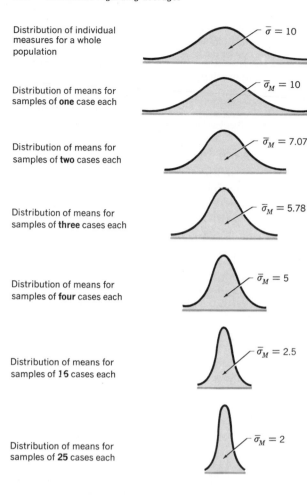

Distribution of individual measures for a whole population — $\bar{\sigma} = 10$

Distribution of means for samples of **one** case each — $\bar{\sigma}_M = 10$

Distribution of means for samples of **two** cases each — $\bar{\sigma}_M = 7.07$

Distribution of means for samples of **three** cases each — $\bar{\sigma}_M = 5.78$

Distribution of means for samples of **four** cases each — $\bar{\sigma}_M = 5$

Distribution of means for samples of **16** cases each — $\bar{\sigma}_M = 2.5$

Distribution of means for samples of **25** cases each — $\bar{\sigma}_M = 2$

Fig. 8.2. *Showing the hypothetical decrease in variability or fluctuation of the means of samples as we increase the size of the sample drawn from a large population.* (Modified from Lindquist, E. F. A First Course in Statistics. Boston: Houghton Mifflin, by permission.)

for practical purposes. In this case, one sample would "hardly be missed"; that is, its loss would change the chance conditions only to an inconsequential degree. When the size of sample is not decidedly smaller than the size of population, it is possible to make allowance for this fact.

To take a specific example of random sampling, with the same population described above in mind, let the size of each sample be 25. The sample mean will not only differ from sample to sample but will also usually deviate from the population parameter (in this example, the mean of 50.0). If we have a number of such sample means, we may treat them just as if each were a single observation and set up a frequency distribution of them. This is known as a *sampling distribution.* Such a frequency distribution will be close to the normal form when the population distribution is not seriously skewed and when N is not small (i.e., not less than about 30).

Normality of distribution of single cases in the total population favors normal distribution of means and of other statistics computed from samples drawn from that population. Even when the population distribution departs from normality, however, the distribution of means of samples drawn from it tends to be normal, unless the samples are too small. The smaller the sample, the more the form of distribution of the population affects the form of distribution of the means.

A knowledge of the form of sampling distribution of a statistic is very important. Our ability to draw conclusions known technically as *statistical inferences* depends upon knowing the form of distribution of sample statistics. Without knowledge of the form of sampling distribution, many a scientific result would remain inconclusive. This is where the use of models comes in. The reasons for this will be clearer as we go into the subject of interpretation of standard errors.

THE STANDARD ERROR OF A MEAN

At this stage of getting acquainted with sampling distributions, we are most interested in the dispersion of statistics, in this case, the dispersion of sample means. The reason is that the amount of this dispersion gives us the clue as to how far such sample means may be expected to depart from the population mean. If we are to use a sample mean as an estimate of the population mean, any deviation of such a sample mean from the population mean may be regarded as an error of estimation. The standard error of a mean tells us how large these errors of estimation are in any particular sampling situation. *The standard error of a mean is a standard deviation of the distribution of sample means.* To distinguish such a standard deviation from the more familiar one that applies to dispersions of individual observations, we call it a *standard error*. In later discussions it will often be referred to by the abbreviation SE.

In order actually to *compute* the standard error of a mean, we need two items of information: the population parameter $\bar{\sigma}$ and the size of sample N. Since we do not ordinarily know $\bar{\sigma}$, it would seem that we could but rarely, indeed very rarely, compute this standard error. There are satisfactory ways of *estimating* it, however, as we shall see later. The formula for *computing* the standard error of a mean is

$$\bar{\sigma}_M = \frac{\bar{\sigma}}{\sqrt{N}} \qquad \text{(Standard error of an arithmetic mean computed from a known population parameter)} \qquad (8.1)$$

where $\bar{\sigma}$ = standard deviation of the population and N = number of cases in the sample (not the number of means in the distribution of means).

Sample size and the standard error of a mean. The standard error of the mean is therefore *directly* proportional to the standard deviation of the population and *inversely* proportional to the size of the sample. More precisely stated, σ_M is inversely proportional to the square root of the size of sample. As the individuals of a population scatter more widely, so will the means of samples drawn from that population also scatter more widely. But as we include more individuals in each sample drawn, the *less* widely can the means scatter from their central value. In the limiting case, if the sample includes the entire population, the deviation of the sample mean from the population mean can then be only zero, and σ_M is zero.

In Fig. 8.2 are shown graphically several instances of samples when N varies. The smallest possible sample occurs when $N = 1$. The mean of each sample is then identical with the individual's measurement in that sample. The dispersion of such means is as great as the dispersion of the total population; σ_M then equals σ, which we have assumed to be 10. When each sample contains two cases, $\sigma_M = 10/\sqrt{2} = 7.07$; when each sample contains four cases, $\sigma_M = 10/\sqrt{4} = 5$; and so on. The remaining cases in Fig. 8.2 should now speak for themselves.

ESTIMATING THE STANDARD ERROR OF A MEAN FROM KNOWN STATISTICS

Formula (8.1) requires our knowing the parameter σ in order to *compute* the standard error of a mean. In ordinary practice we must be satisfied with an *estimate* of this standard error. Two ways for making this estimate will be described.

Estimation of σ_M from σ. In describing a sample, we usually compute σ as well as the mean. When σ is known, we may estimate the statistic σ_M by the formula

$$\sigma_M = \frac{\sigma}{\sqrt{N-1}} \qquad \text{(Standard error of a mean estimated from σ)} \qquad (8.2)$$

The reason for the expression $N - 1$ in this formula can be better understood after we consider the next estimation method. Some writers recommend that for large samples (N of 30 or above) we simply substitute σ for σ in formula (8.1), in which case we should have the ratio $\sigma/\sqrt{N}$ instead of the ratio $\sigma/\sqrt{N-1}$. This overlooks the fact that σ is actually a biased estimate of σ for samples of any size; the smaller the sample, the greater the bias. There is no sudden change in this condition at an N of 30. The result of using formula (8.2) is identical with that from the next procedure, which is favored by many statisticians.

Estimation of σ from a sample. The standard deviation computed for a sample is likely to be smaller than that for the population from which the sample came. Recall from the discussion in Chap. 5 that as samples become smaller the total range of measures is more and more curtailed. This comes about from the fact that extreme deviations in the population are rare and in small samples are likely to be missed.

This fact also has an effect upon the standard deviation, though to a smaller extent. In the smaller samples particularly, σ gives an estimate of the population $\bar{\sigma}$ that is biased downward.

A less biased estimate of σ is given by the formula

$$s = \sqrt{\frac{\Sigma x^2}{N-1}} \quad \text{(Best estimate of population standard deviation)} \tag{8.3}$$

where $\Sigma x^2 =$ sum of squares of deviations in the sample and $N =$ number of cases in the sample. Statisticians say that s^2 is an unbiased estimate of the population variance $\bar{\sigma}^2$ but that s involves a little bias as an estimate of the population standard deviation $\bar{\sigma}$. The reasons for this are rather involved and need not concern us here. In any case, the bias in s is smaller than that in σ, when they are used as estimates of $\bar{\sigma}$.

Degrees of freedom.   Formula (8.3) involves an important concept that will be liberally utilized hereafter when sampling errors (deviations of statistics from parameters) are mentioned, particularly in connection with small samples.

Compare formula (8.3) with the basic one for the standard deviation of a sample [formula (5.4)] and it will be found that they are identical except for the denominators, which are $(N-1)$ and N, respectively. The difference between the two may seem very slight (and it *is* slight numerically when N is reasonably large), but there is a very important difference in meaning. In this particular formula, $(N-1)$ is known as the number of *degrees of freedom*, which is symbolized by df. This is a key concept developed during the last 30 years in what has been known as *small-sample statistics*. The number of degrees of freedom will not always be $(N-1)$ but will vary from one statistic to another, as will be pointed out in various places later. Let us see why the df is $(N-1)$ here.

The "freedom" part of the concept means *freedom to vary*. The standard deviation is computed from the variance, and the variance is computed from deviations from the mean. Statisticians often express the matter by saying that 1 degree of freedom is "used up" when we use the sample mean as an estimate of a parameter mean. This leaves $(N-1)$ degrees of freedom for estimating the population variance and standard deviation.

A numerical example will make this clearer. Let us assume five measurements: 5, 7, 10, 12, and 16, the mean of which is 10.0. We now use this value as an estimate of the population mean. A mathematical requirement or property of the arithmetic mean is that the sum of the deviations from it equals zero. The five deviations in this sample are -5, -3, 0, $+2$, and $+6$, the sum of which is zero. With this condition satisfied, i.e., the sum equal to zero, how many of these deviations could be simultaneously altered (as if by taking new samplings) and still leave the sum equal to zero? With a little thought or trial and error it will be seen that if any four are arbitrarily changed, the fifth is thereby fixed. We could make the first four −8, −4, +1, and −2, which would mean that for the sum to equal zero the fifth has to be +13. Try any other changes and if the sum is to remain zero one of the five deviations is automatically determined. Thus only four $(N − 1)$'s are "free to vary" within the restriction imposed.

There were N degrees of freedom in computing the mean because the cases were presumably sampled entirely independently. If they were not independently sampled, there were less than N degrees of freedom in computing the mean. Freedom means independence, and only when there is independence of observations can the "laws of chance" operate freely and the mathematics based upon the "laws of chance" be applied.[1]

The SE of a mean estimated directly from a sum of squares. Whether we precede the estimation of the standard error of a mean by computing σ or s from the sample, we find ourselves performing the same steps, but in a different order. These steps are dividing by $(N − 1)$ and by N. If we should happen to have no interest in knowing the value of either σ or s, we can combine these two operations in a single equation, and we have the formula

$$\sigma_M = \sqrt{\frac{\Sigma x^2}{N(N − 1)}} \qquad \text{(Standard error of a mean estimated directly from a sum of squares)} \qquad (8.4)$$

A recapitulation. To emphasize the distinctions that have just been made, let us recapitulate, with definitions of the various symbols.

$\bar{\sigma}$ = a standard deviation of a population, a parameter.

σ = a standard deviation of a sample from the population, computed by the expression $\sqrt{\Sigma x^2/N}$, a statistic.

s = estimated standard deviation of the population derived from a sample by the expression $\sqrt{\Sigma x^2/(N − 1)}$, a statistic.

σ_M = standard error of the mean (also symbolized as SE_M), estimated by the expression $\sqrt{\Sigma x^2/N(N − 1)}$ or, equivalently, by $\sigma/\sqrt{N − 1}$.

$\bar{\sigma}_M$ = a standard error of a mean, for samples of a certain size, which we could compute if we actually knew the value of $\bar{\sigma}$, which we do not; hence this quantity has only theoretical meaning; it will not be encountered again.

[1]For an excellent discussion of the general subject of degrees of freedom, see Walker, H. M. Degrees of freedom. *J. educ. Psychol.*, 1940, **31**, 253–260. See also Johnson, P. O. *Statistical Methods in Research.* Englewood Cliffs, N.J.: Prentice-Hall, 1949.

Three kinds of distributions are involved in connection with these values. The quantity $\bar{\sigma}$ describes the dispersion of the distribution of the entire population of measurements (of persons or of observations). The quantity σ describes the amount of dispersion of the distribution of a particular sample drawn from the population. The quantity s pertains to the same sample distribution and is computed from it, but it is used to estimate $\bar{\sigma}$, the dispersion in the population distribution. The quantity σ_M pertains to an entirely different distribution; a *sampling* distribution of all the means of the samples of a certain size that would be drawn randomly from the population. Reference again to Fig. 8.1 will show a population distribution and a sample distribution, each composed of single observed measurements. Reference again to Fig. 8.2 will show a number of *sampling* distributions (all except the first one), composed of means of samples.

INTERPRETATION OF A STANDARD ERROR OF A MEAN

We are now ready to apply the standard-error formula to a concrete instance and to consider the interpretation of the obtained SE. To revive an illustration already employed, the ink-blot data, we find that σ is 10.45 and N is 50. Applying formula (8.2), $\sigma_m = 10.45/\sqrt{49} = 1.49$. For simplicity in discussion, let us round this to 1.5.

When we estimate this standard error, we are essentially asking, "How far from the population mean are the sample means, like this one we obtained, likely to vary in random sampling?" We do not know what the population mean is, but from the value 1.5 we conclude that means of samples of 50 cases each would not deviate from it in either direction more than 1.5 units about two-thirds of the time. We may conclude this because in a sample as large as 50 we may assume that the sample means are normally distributed. This assumption makes possible a number of inferences that we could not make without it. Remember that even when the population distribution is not normal, the means derived from sampling from the population are likely to be almost normally distributed.

Since, as we have already seen, in these ink-blot data we may conclude that two-thirds of the sample means (when N is 50) will lie within 1.5 units, plus or minus, of the population mean, we can also say that there is only 1 chance in 3 for a sample mean to be further than 1.5 units from the population mean in either direction. Or we can say that the odds are 2 to 1 that sample means will be within a range of 3 units, the middle of which is the population mean. The standard error thus brackets a range within which to expect sample means. We shall expand this idea in the discussion to follow.

Hypotheses concerning the population mean. The kind of conclusion that we should most like to make is slightly different from the one just given. We are attempting to estimate the population mean, knowing the sample mean. We should therefore like to know how far away from the sample mean the population mean is likely to be.

It might seem that, if we can say that two-thirds of the sample means are within one SE of the population mean, we could also say that the odds are 2 to 1 that the population mean is within one SE of the sample mean. But note that the last statement implies a normal distribution about the *sample* mean, whereas, actually, the sampling distribution is about the *population* mean. Logically, we cannot reverse the roles of $\overline{M}$ and M in this manner. But through some mathematical reasoning, which we can explain only briefly here, we can do something equivalent. The process results in setting up *confidence limits* and *confidence intervals* for the population mean.

Since we do not know the population mean, we are free to make some guesses, or hypotheses, about its value. No matter what reasonable hypothesis we choose, the estimated standard error still applies to the distribution of expected sample means about this hypothetical value.

In the ink-blot problem, the sample mean was 29.6. Let us select in turn a number of hypothetical population means. They should, of course, be somewhere in the neighborhood of the sample mean. Figure 8.3 shows five normal sampling distributions, each about a different hypothesized $\overline{M}$ and each with a standard error (SE) of 1.5. The hypothesized means are all above 29.6; they could just as well have been chosen below that value. They are at the values 30.0, 31.0, 32.0, 33.0, and 34.0.

Consider, first, the hypothesis that is farthest from the sample mean, namely, a hypothetical $\overline{M}$ of 34.0. A sample mean of 29.6 deviates 4.4 score units from this hypothetical $\overline{M}$. This deviation gives a

Fig. 8.3. *Hypothetical sampling distributions of means, corresponding to various hypotheses concerning the value of the population mean, when the obtained sample mean is 29.6 and the standard error of the mean is 1.5.*

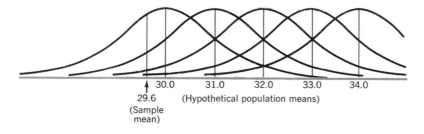

30.0   31.0   32.0   33.0   34.0

29.6   (Hypothetical population means)

(Sample mean)

z (standard-score value) of $4.4/1.5 = 2.95$. Since we are dealing here with a sampling distribution whose elements are means, not single observations, and whose constants are estimated parameters, let us use the symbol $\bar{z}$ to indicate such a standard-score value. We may enter the normal-curve tables with such a value, as we would for an ordinary z.

We next ask what is the probability of a deviation as large as this occurring by random sampling. This probability is twice the proportion of the area under the tail of the normal curve beyond the point at $\bar{z} = 2.95$. When we say "a deviation as large as this," we actually mean a deviation as large *or larger*. For a deviation of 4.4, we could just as well have chosen a hypothetical $\bar{M}$ that far *below* the obtained mean, in other words at $29.6 - 4.4$, or a score of 25.2. The obtained mean is $2.96\ \bar{z}$ above this hypothetical mean, just as it is $2.96\ \bar{z}$ below the hypothetical mean of 34.0. Thus, we have two hypothetical normal distributions to consider. The area under one tail of the normal distribution beyond a $\bar{z}$ of 2.96 is .0016, as found from Table B (Appendix B). In the two tails the combined area is twice .0016, or .0032. We can conclude that, if the population mean were as far removed from the obtained mean as 34.0, there is only the slim chance of 32 in 10,000 for a mean of 29.6 to occur by random sampling. Since the odds of this occurring are so small, we can reject with confidence the hypothesis that the population mean is 34.0, or that it is 25.2.

The next hypothesis is for $\bar{M}$ equal to 33.0, which gives a deviation of 3.4 and a $\bar{z}$ of 2.28. The area under the normal curve beyond this point is .0113. Twice this area is .0226. If the population mean were actually as far removed as 33.0, there are only about 2 chances in 100 for a departure such as a sample mean of 29.6 to occur. If we reject this hypothesis, there are only 2 chances in 100 that we would be wrong. Although we cannot reject this hypothesis with as much confidence as we could the previous hypothesis, we can still do so with a high level of assurance.

If we hypothesize an $\bar{M}$ of 32.0, the deviation is 2.4, $\bar{z}$ is 1.61, and the tail area (doubled) is .1074. The chances for a random deviation this large are more than 10 in 100. If we hypothesize that $\bar{M} = 31.0$, the deviation is 1.4, $\bar{z}$ is 0.94, and the probability for so large a deviation is .348. We cannot very well reject the hypothesis that the population mean is 31.0. There would be considerable risk in doing so. In fact we can say that this hypothesis is rather plausible.

But other hypotheses are even more plausible. If we choose the hypothesis that $\bar{M} = 30.0$, the deviation is 0.4, $\bar{z}$ is 0.267, and the area beyond this deviation is .788 of the total. Thus, as we approach the sample mean with our hypothetical population mean, the odds in favor of greater deviations than the obtained one keep increasing, and the hypothesis becomes more and more plausible. The maximum plausibility would be reached when the hypothesis is 29.6, in other words, when it coincides with the sample mean. From this point of view, we can say that the sample mean (when other information is lacking) is the most probable and most defensible estimate of the population mean. It is an unbiased estimate, since the deviations are as likely to be positive as negative.

Confidence limits and confidence intervals. From this discussion it is clear that we are confronted with a sliding scale of confidence with respect to the location of the population mean. Values remote from the sample mean can be rejected with much confidence; as we approach the sample mean, hypothetical values can be rejected with less and less confidence. It is not customary to do all the calculation we have just done in order to interpret a mean and its standard error. By common consent an arbitrary choice has been made to adopt two particular *levels of confidence*. One is known as the 5 per cent level, or .05 level, and the other as the 1 per cent level, or .01 level.

At the .05 level there is a deviation that leaves 5 per cent of the area in the two tails of the normal distribution: 2.5 per cent in each tail. In large samples (N as large as 30), this area at either end is marked off at a $\bar{z}$ value of plus or minus 1.96. See Fig. 8.4, where the intervals and tail probabilities (p) are marked off, as well as the confidence intervals, $CI_{.95}$ and $CI_{.99}$. The .01 level leaves 1 per cent of the area in the two tails, .5 of 1 per cent in either tail. The $\bar{z}$ that marks

Fig. 8.4. *A normal distribution showing the ranges of the confidence intervals at the .95 level and the .99 level, with limiting points in terms of standard-error distances from the obtained mean.*

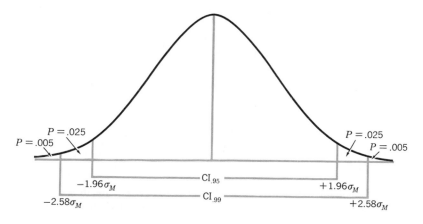

off this much area at either end is 2.58. These percentages and these $\bar{z}$ values are applied regardless of the size of the mean or of its standard error. It must be remembered, however, that they apply only to large samples.[1]

For the ink-blot problem, a $\bar{z}$ of 1.96 corresponds to a score deviation of 2.9 (which is 1.96 times σ_M). All hypotheses of population means differing more than 2.9 from the sample mean can be rejected at the .05 level. Only once in 20 times would we be in error by making this decision. (This once would be when the deviation is *really* due to chance). Since these *confidence limits* are 2.9 units from the sample mean, they come at score values of 29.6 − 2.9 and 29.6 + 2.9, or at 26.7 and 32.5, respectively. The score limits of 26.7 and 32.5 mark off a *confidence interval* within which the population mean probably lies. The probability to be associated with this interval is .95 (i.e., 1.00 − .05). See Fig. 8.3.

We can make a similar interpretation in connection with the .01 level. All hypothetical means differing more than 3.9 (3.9 is 2.58 times σ_M) from the sample mean can be rejected, with only 1 chance in 100 of being wrong in doing so. The confidence interval is from 25.7 to 33.5, and the probability to be associated with it is .99. We have a high degree of assurance that the population mean is between 25 and 34. The odds are 99 to 1 in favor of this conclusion. Whether we wish to stake our case on the .05 limits or the .01 limits depends upon our inclinations. In the next chapter we shall find a more extended discussion of the choice of standards of confidence.[2]

From the arithmetic that has been done in recent paragraphs, it can be seen that the confidence intervals for a mean can be set up by applying the following formulas:

$$\text{CI}_{.95} = M - 1.96\sigma_M \text{ to } M + 1.96\sigma_M \qquad \text{(Confidence intervals} \qquad (8.5a)$$
$$\text{CI}_{.99} = M - 2.58\sigma_M \text{ to } M + 2.58\sigma_M \qquad \text{for a mean)} \qquad (8.5b)$$

where $\text{CI}_{.95}$ stands for the confidence interval at the .95 level and $\text{CI}_{.99}$ the corresponding interval at the .99 level.

Comparisons of some obtained means and standard errors. Let us apply the interpretation of σ_M to some other data. The practical usefulness of an obtained statistic is often more apparent when we compare it with its counterpart derived from different data. Table 8.1 gives means of Army General Classification Test scores for samples

---

[1]For testing such hypotheses and for determining confidence intervals with small samples, Student's t and the t distribution should be used in place of $\bar{z}$ and the normal distribution (see Chap. 9 for a discussion of t).

[2]Other confidence levels sometimes used are the 10 per cent, or .10, level (when $\bar{z}$ is 1.65); the .02 level (when $\bar{z}$ is 2.33); and the .005 level (when $\bar{z}$ is 2.81).

*Table 8.1   Comparisons of means and their confidence intervals on the Army General Classification Test as applied to men from different civilian occupational categories**

Occupation	N	M	σ	σ_M	$CI_{.95}$	$CI_{.99}$
Accountant	172	128.1	11.7	0.88	126.4 – 129.8	125.8 – 130.4
Lawyer	94	127.6	10.9	1.13	125.4 – 129.8	124.7 – 130.5
Reporter	45	124.5	11.7	1.76	121.1 – 127.9	120.0 – 129.0
Sales clerk	492	109.2	16.3	0.74	107.7 – 110.7	107.3 – 111.1
Plumber	128	102.7	16.0	1.42	99.9 – 105.5	99.0 – 106.4
Truck driver	817	96.2	19.7	0.69	94.8 – 97.6	94.4 – 98.0
Farm hand	817	91.4	20.7	0.72	90.0 – 92.8	89.5 – 93.3
Teamster	77	87.7	19.6	2.23	83.3 – 92.1	81.9 – 93.5

*From Harrell, T. W., and Harrell, M. E. Army General Classification Test scores for civilian occupations. *Educ. psychol. Measmt.*, 1945, 5, 229 – 240. By permission.

derived from different civilian occupational groups. For the sake of illustration, we will assume that each occupational group represents a different population, as designated, and that sampling of scores was random within each population. What do the standard errors and confidence intervals in this table tell us?

The mean in which we would have the greatest confidence, as representing the status of the general occupational population, is that for the truck driver. The odds are about 2 to 1 that this sample mean of 96.2 does not deviate more than .7 from the mean of all truck drivers that this sample represents. There is confidence at the .95 level that the interval 94.8 to 97.6 contains that mean and there is confidence at the .99 level that the interval 94.4 to 98.0 contains it: a total range of about 4 units. The mean in which we have least confidence is that for teamsters because of its σ_M of 2.23. For teamsters, our confidence at the .99 level should tolerate the hypothesis of the population mean in the interval of 81.9 to 93.5, a range of nearly 12 units.

Incidentally, the relation of σ_M to both σ and N can be seen roughly by comparison of the data for the occupational groups. On the whole, the largest standard errors come for samples where N is smallest — for lawyer, reporter, plumber, and teamster — though the rank orders are not perfect within this list of four. Where sample sizes are comparable, as for lawyer and teamster, and for accountant and plumber, the value for σ_M is more apparently in proportion to the standard deviation of the sample. It can be seen that, if the sample is sufficiently large, the standard error can be brought below one scale unit.

SOME SPECIAL PROBLEMS CONCERNING THE SE OF A MEAN

We shall now consider several conditions that have a bearing upon the standard error and the steps that may be taken to deal with them.

When sampling is not random. It has been repeatedly stressed that sampling statistics, including standard errors, apply only when sampling has been random. The reason is that the mathematics of the situation are exact only when sampling has been random. It is then that we may apply a chance-generated mathematical model, such as the normal distribution. Any condition that tends to interfere with randomness of selection of observations, therefore, will make the estimation of standard errors and their application in drawing conclusions inaccurate, if not misleading.

There are several noteworthy situations that depart from the random requirement. Some would lead to standard errors that are too small to describe the actual distributions of means, and others would lead to standard errors that are too large. In the former case, we should have too much confidence in the accuracy of the mean, and in the latter we should have too little. Certain variations in the standard-error formulas have been developed to take care of some of these special situations.

Samples with bias. The effect of biased sampling upon the distribution of means can be strikingly illustrated by reference to some data on the training of pilots in the AAF during World War II. All pilot students were given a battery of classification tests from which was derived for each man a "pilot stanine," or composite pilot-aptitude score. Every month at the completion of preflight training, students were formed into class groups, each sent to a different primary flying school. In one study which covered a six-month period, 269 such classes had been sent to 58 training schools divided among three AAF Flying Training Commands. The mean stanine for approximately 52,000 students was 5.56. This value may be taken as the population mean in this situation. The standard deviation of the population was assumed to be 1.96, which should have been ensured by the use of the stanine scale. The average size of sample (each class group in a single school) was 195.[1] From this information, using formula (8.1), we compute a standard error of 0.14. From this we should expect two-thirds of the 269 mean stanines to deviate not more than 0.14 from 5.56, if the sampling had been random. What are the facts?

When the 269 means were actually conpiled in a frequency distribution and their standard deviation computed, the dispersion of means was actually found to be very much larger than expected (see Table 8.2). Where one should expect a range of means within the limits 5.2

[1] Actually, some classes deviated from 195 in number. For the sake of illustration, however, we may treat the samples as if they were of constant size.

Table 8.2   **Sampling statistics concerning 269 class groups of pilots in primary training during a period of six months in three training commands of the AAF during World War II***

Variable	Expected results		Obtained results		
	σ_M	Range	M	σ	Range
Pilot stanine	0.14	5.2–6.0	5.56	0.37	4.6–6.9
Graduation rate	3.4	56–75	65.3	9.5	40–90
Validity coefficient	.073	0.32–0.74	0.53	.088	0.21–0.71

*Including the pilot stanine, or composite pilot-aptitude score; the graduation rate, or percentage of a class graduating; and validity coefficient, a biserial coefficient of correlation between stanine and graduation versus elimination.

to 6.0, the actual range was from 4.6 to 6.9. Where the expected standard deviation of the distribution of means was 0.14, the actual standard deviation was 0.37. A comparison of the expected and obtained distribution of means is shown in Fig. 8.5.

The obvious conclusion is that the sampling of aviation students in pilot classes was most probably not random. One can surmise some of the causes after looking into the procedures by which class groups were formed. In each preflight class (i.e., each month) a small percentage of students would fail to pass the course and would be held over, probably to qualify for flight training in the next class. There was a tendency for the "holdovers" to be sent together to the same flight schools. They tended to be of low pilot aptitude. There may also have been some geographical differences in pilot aptitude which would tend to make the averages of stanines differ systematically somewhat from one Command to another. This hypothesis could be subjected to experimental check by comparing Command averages. There were probably other reasons for students of similar aptitudes to gravitate together, with a consequent biasing of samples.

Another study was made of the graduation rates (percentage of a class group graduating) in different samples. The pertinent data are given in Table 8.2. From the overall graduation rate of 65.3 and the size of sample, we should expect [by formula (8.11)] a standard deviation of the distribution of the 269 rates to be 3.4. Actually it was 9.5. Since the probability of graduation for any cadet was strongly correlated with his aptitude score, we should expect the bias in sampling on aptitude to be reflected in biased samples as to graduation rate. This is probably not the whole story, however. There were many other conditions which could contribute to marked variations in graduation rate besides variation in aptitude. Weather conditions

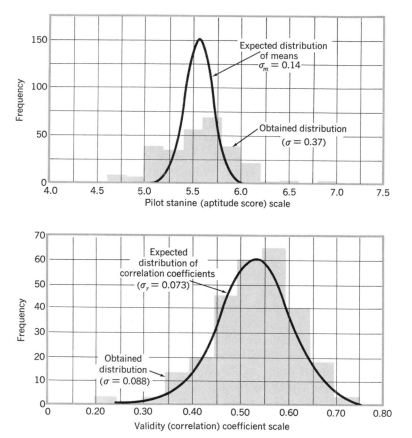

Fig. 8.5. *Distribution of expected and obtained sample means, also of expected and obtained validity coefficients, in connection with 269 samples (class groups) of AAF pilots in primary training during a five-month period in about 60 different schools. Especially to be noted is that the obtained distribution of means was much wider than expected, indicating nonrandom sampling, while the distribution of validity coefficients was about as expected, indicating random sampling. This difference is possible because two different kinds of sampling are involved for the two statistics.*

varied from school to school and from month to month. Training practices and policies may have varied, in spite of close regulation. Instructor and test-pilot judgments were not standardized and may have varied from school to school.

A third study is mentioned now for comparison, although it involves the sampling errors of coefficients of correlation, which are treated later. This study is concerned with the variation in validity coefficients in the same 269 class groups. The validity of the pilot stanine for predicting the training success of pilots was indicated by what is known as the biserial coefficient of correlation (see Chap. 14). This has approximately the same value as a Pearson product-moment r but is computed when one of the variables, assumed to be normally distributed, is forced into two categories. The two categories for the training criterion were those who graduated and those eliminated. The standard error for a biserial correlation equal to .53, when the size of sample is 195, amounts to .073 [computed by formula (14.8)]. The expected and obtained statistics are given in Table 8.2 and illustrated in Fig. 8.5. In drawing the distribution curve, a normal distribution of the coefficients was assumed, whereas the expected distribution should be slightly negatively skewed. The obtained distribution of the 269 coefficients was actually so skewed. At any rate, since the obtained standard deviation (.088) was not so very different from the expected one (.073), we may conclude that if there was biased sampling with respect to the validity of pilot stanines it was of minor importance.

Although there were seemingly enormous variations in validity from school to school and from time to time, amounting to a total range of .21 to .71, such variations may be regarded as due mostly to sampling errors. Incidentally, this example shows by just how much obtained correlation coefficients may deviate from the population parameter even with samples as large as 195. Any single obtained coefficient may be anywhere in the range of such a distribution, but the saving feature is that extreme deviations are highly improbable and small ones most probable. These illustrations should demonstrate more clearly some of the practical uses of standard errors, as well as the importance of random sampling, if we are to make accurate and useful interpretations.

When observations are not independent. Random sampling also implies independence of observations. In the preceding examples, observations were not independent because certain restricting conditions tied cases together: if one student was chosen to go to a certain school at a certain time, one or more others like him were also chosen with him. There are other situations where this occurs, often without the investigator's being aware of it. It is most likely to occur when sampling is obtained from subgoups of the population.

Suppose that we have an experiment in which there are 10 subjects and each has 10 trials in each experimental session. For each session we do not have 100 independent observations. Nor do we have merely 10 observations. Because there are individual differences, the 10 observations in each set (from each person) will be somewhat homogeneous, having been derived from a single source. In the larger setting of the 100 observations, they are not independent. In computing σ_M for these 100 observations, the number of degrees of freedom is not 99. It is difficult to say just what the number of df should be. The most conservative approach would be to assume 10 observations, each being the mean derived from one individual, and 9 df. But this would lead to an overestimate of the standard error. In the situation described, we have what is called *cluster sampling*. For special treatments of this subject that include formulas for estimating σ_M, the reader is referred to discussions by Marks and by Jarrett and Henry.[1]

Estimates regarding other statistics

THE STANDARD ERROR OF A MEDIAN AND OTHER CENTILES

The variability of sample medians is about 25 per cent greater than the variability of means when the population is normally distributed. Under this condition the standard error of a median can be estimated by the formula

$$\sigma_{Mdn} = \frac{1.253\sigma}{\sqrt{N}} \qquad \text{(Standard error of a median estimated from } \sigma\text{)} \quad (8.6)$$

As applied to the ink-blot-test data,

$$\sigma_{Mdn} = \frac{(1.253)(10.45)}{\sqrt{50}} = 1.85$$

In samples drawn at random from the population, two-thirds of the sample medians of ink-blot scores, when N equals 50, will be expected within 1.85 units of the population median. Since the population is assumed to be normally distributed, we may also say that the sample medians would not deviate from the population *mean* more than 1.85 units, two-thirds of the time. The median may thus be used as an estimate of the population mean, but with less confidence than we have in the use of the sample mean for the same purpose.

We have seen before that the median is a centile point. It can be symbolized as $C_{.50}$, to indicate that it is the X value below which 50 per cent of the cases occur, or a proportion of .50. There are standard errors for other centile points, each different, depending upon which centile value we are talking about: $C_{.25}$, $C_{.75}$, the two quartile points, or some other, perhaps $X_{.90}$, for example. The general equation is

[1]Marks, E. S. Sampling in the revision of the Stanford Binet Scale. *Psychol. Bull.*, 1947, **44**, 413–434; Jarrett, R. F., and Henry, F. M. The relative influence on error of replicating measurements or individuals. *J. Psychol.*, 1951, **31**, 175–180.

$$\sigma_c = \frac{1}{y_p} \sqrt{\frac{pq}{N}} \qquad \text{(Standard error of a centile-point value)} \qquad (8.7)$$

where the subscript c stands for centile, p is the proportion of cases below the centile point, $q = (1 - p)$, and y_p is the ordinate in the unit normal distribution corresponding to p.

From this general formula we can see that the standard error of a median is just a special case and also see whence the constant 1.253 came. In a normally distributed population, the ordinate at the median is equal to $1/\sigma \sqrt{2\pi}$. Substituting this term for y_p in formula (8.7), and with $\sqrt{pq}$ equal to .5, we have

$$\frac{.5\sigma \sqrt{2\pi}}{\sqrt{N}} = \frac{.5\sigma \sqrt{6.283}}{\sqrt{N}} = \frac{1.253\sigma}{\sqrt{N}}$$

THE STANDARD ERROR OF A STANDARD DEVIATION

The standard deviation also fluctuates from sample to sample. For a sample of a given size, the sampling distribution is somewhat skewed for small samples (N less than 100) but approaches the normal form so closely with large samples drawn from a normally distributed population that we can draw inferences about a population $\bar{\sigma}$, knowing a sample σ and its standard error. The SE of σ is estimated by the formula

$$\sigma_\sigma = \frac{\sigma}{\sqrt{2N}} \qquad \text{(Standard error of a standard deviation)} \qquad (8.8)$$

Applying this formula to the standard deviation for the sample of accountants mentioned in Table 8.1, where σ is 11.7,

$$\sigma_\sigma = \frac{11.7}{\sqrt{2(172)}} = 0.63$$

Comparing formula (8.8) with formula (8.2) for the SE of a mean, we see that a population standard deviation is more accurately estimated than is a population mean, when we compare them as to their respective sampling errors. The denominators of these two formulas contain the values $2N$ and $(N - 1)$, respectively, which means that the σ_M is more than 40 per cent greater than σ_σ. In one sense, it is fortunate that the standard deviation is more stable than the mean, because both σ_M and σ_σ are estimated from it. What is said here in connection with σ also applies to s, since in large samples the two are very similar in value. Knowing σ_σ, we could set up confidence limits and confidence intervals in a manner similar to that described for the mean.

THE STANDARD ERRORS OF FREQUENCIES, PROPORTIONS, AND PERCENTAGES

Data in terms of frequencies, percentages, and proportions are so common in the social sciences that the problem of their stability in sampling is very important. Out of 30 students who attempted a certain test item, 18 succeeded and 12 failed. How much confidence can we have that the 18 successes represent the actual success rate for the larger population these 30 students represent?

This particular problem should be recognized as calling for a binomial sampling distribution, with mean Np, which is 18, and variance Npq, which is $30 \times .6 \times .4$, or 7.20. The square root of this value gives the standard deviation of this particular binomial distribution, which is 2.7. Since we are dealing with a sampling distribution, the 2.7 is the standard error of the mean or the frequency 18. The general formula is

$$\sigma_f = \sqrt{Npq} \qquad \text{(Standard error of a frequency)} \tag{8.9}$$

where N = number of cases in the sample

p = proportion in the category of interest

$q = 1 - q$

First, we need to offer an important qualification. Comparison of the binomial data given here and in Chap. 7 will show that in the latter place we were dealing with purely hypothetical frequencies and proportions, whereas here we are dealing with observed or empirical data. The value of p that should actually be utilized in formula (8.9) is the population parameter. That value is unknown here. We use in its place our best estimate of the population parameter $\bar{p}$, the observed statistic p. The latter is a fairly good estimate of $\bar{p}$ when samples are reasonably large. It can be pointed out that the outcome of formula (8.9) depends relatively more upon the size of N than upon that of p or q, because the product pq remains fairly uniform between .20 and .25 for a considerable range of values for p (namely, for p between .27 and .73). If we have better information concerning the population $\bar{p}$, from some previously obtained data or from some a priori reasoning, we should use the better estimates of $\bar{p}$.

To return to the test-item problem, finding the SE of 2.7, we interpret it as we have other SE's we have encountered. For the most exact interpretation, we should utilize a binomial distribution, the expansion of the binomial $(.6 + .4)^{30}$, but the calculation would be prohibitive without the use of an electronic computer. As pointed out in Chap. 7, we may often use the normal distribution as a good approximation when the minimum frequency (Np or Nq) is 10 or more. Here the smaller frequency is 12, so the normal approximation may be applied. On this basis, finding 1.96σ to be 5.4, we may conclude with confidence at the .95 level that the obtained frequency of 18 does not deviate more than 5.4 units from the population value.[1]

The standard error of a proportion. Since a proportion p is equal to a frequency divided by N, the standard error of a proportion is equal to

$$\sigma p = \frac{1}{N}\sqrt{Npq} = \sqrt{\frac{pq}{N}} \quad \text{(SE of a proportion)} \quad (8.10)$$

Out of 100 students who were quizzed, 65 of them said that they regularly read a morning newspaper. Does this proportion of .65 represent the larger population of students very closely? By formula (8.10), the standard error of this proportion is .048, or roughly .05. The .95 confidence interval has limits of approximately .55 and .75; the .99 confidence interval has limits of .52 and .78. The whole of the latter range is above .50, and hence we may make the further inference that the majority of students represented by this sample (randomly drawn) reads morning newspapers, and in this inference we should have a high degree of confidence.

The standard error of a percentage. If we wish to work in terms of percentages, we should remember that a percentage, P, is 100 times a proportion and that $Q = 100 - P$; the formula then is

$$\sigma_P = 100\sqrt{\frac{pq}{N}} = \sqrt{\frac{PQ}{N}} \quad \text{(SE of a percentage)} \quad (8.11)$$

HYPOTHESES CONCERNING A POPULATION CORRELATION, r[†]

The mathematical basis for the standard error of a Pearson coefficient of correlation is rather complicated, and the same is true with respect to its confidence intervals. The difficulty is in the form of sampling distribution for r. Only when the population $\bar{r}$ is near zero and when N is rather large (30 or greater) will the sampling distribution approach the normal form. Reference to the first part of Fig. 8.6 will show that the limit of $r = 1.0$ puts a real restriction upon the varia-

[1] In all these instances in which the actual distribution is binomial, it should be noted that we are dealing with discrete data: frequencies can change only a full unit at a time. On the other hand, we are interpreting the SE's on continuous scales. Where samples are large, such approximations are good; with small samples, as we shall see in Chaps. 9 and 10, a "correction for continuity" should often be applied.

[†] The population correlation is ordinarily symbolized by the Greek letter rho (ρ). The use of $\bar{r}$ here is consistent with symbols used for other population parameters, such as $\bar{M}$ and $\bar{\sigma}$. There is a special rank-order coefficient of correlation that lays prior claim to the symbol ρ, with some possible source of confusion when the parameter coefficient is also symbolized with ρ.

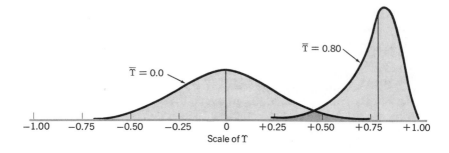

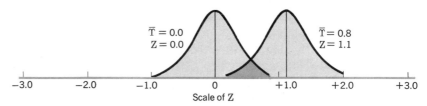

Fig. 8.6. *Distributions of sample coefficients of correlation when N is very small and when the population correlations are .00 and .80. Corresponding to them are distributions of Fisher's* **z** *coefficients. Conversion of r to* **z** *brings about symmetrical sampling distributions, regardless of the size of r.*

tion around a population $\bar{r}$ of .8, with a marked negative skew. A similar situation would occur for an $\bar{r}$ of $-.8$, except there would be a positive skew. Another difficulty is that the form of distribution also differs with the size of sample, particularly among small samples.

With small obtained r's, our chief interest is whether or not they represent significant departures from population $\bar{r}$'s of zero. With an N as large as 50 and an obtained r not greater than .50, we may test the hypothesis that the correlation in the population is zero, by using the standard error

$$\sigma_{r=0} = \frac{1}{\sqrt{N}} \qquad \begin{array}{l}\text{(Approximate standard error of } r \\ \text{for testing the hypothesis of} \\ \text{zero correlation)}\end{array} \qquad (8.12)$$

With an obtained correlation of .30 and with a sample of 52 pairs of observations, $\sigma_{r=0} = 1/\sqrt{52} = .14$. A deviation of .30 from the hypothesized zero is $.30/.14$ standard-deviation units from zero, or equivalent to a $\bar{z}$ of 2.1. This $\bar{z}$ is slightly above that required for rejection of the hypothesis at the .05 level of confidence. There are fewer than five chances in a hundred that an r could deviate as much as .30 in either direction from a population correlation of zero (when $N = 52$).

R. A. Fisher has developed a method of testing the hypothesis of $\bar{r} = 0$, for an obtained r under much more general circumstances, including samples as small as 3. In a normal bivariate population (distributions normal in both X and Y), when the population $\bar{r}$ is zero, a parameter t can be estimated by the formula

$$t = \frac{r\sqrt{N-2}}{\sqrt{1-r^2}} \quad \begin{array}{l}\text{(t ratio for testing the significance}\\ \text{of a coefficient of correlation)}\end{array} \qquad (8.13)$$

We shall see much more of Student's t in the next chapter and thereafter. It was developed by W. S. Gossett, who published modestly under the name of "Student." Like the standard score z, t is computed by dividing a deviation such as x (or $X - M$) by the standard deviation of the distribution. In applying the previous formula for $\sigma_{r=0}$, .30 was divided by .14 and the result interpreted as $\bar{z}$. In this particular application of t, things are not that simple. The $N - 2$ in the numerator is the number of degrees of freedom. In computing a Pearson r, two sample means are used from which to compute the deviations that are used: hence, the loss of $2df$.

Fisher demonstrated that the t given by formula (8.13) is distributed as in Student's distribution. The interpretation of an obtained t by formula (8.13) is to be made with the use of Table D in Appendix B. For any given number of degrees of freedom (here 50), we see in Table D that an r of .273 is significant at the .05 level and an r of .354 is significant at the .01 level. If our decision had been to reject the hypothesis (that $\bar{r} = 0$) at the .05 level, we should have concluded that the population correlation is not zero.

Fisher's z coefficient. In order to set up confidence limits and intervals and to gain in general any inferences concerning the accuracy of sample r's not near zero, it is necessary to resort to another innovation of Fisher's—his z transformation procedure. His z coefficient, into which any r can be transformed mathematically, does have a normal sampling distribution regardless of the size of N and the size of population $\bar{r}$. Nor is an estimate of the population $\bar{r}$ needed in order to determine the standard error of z. Fisher's z should not be confused with the standard score z; it will be printed in boldface to distinguish it.

The range of z is from $-\infty$ to $+\infty$, but when r reaches .995, z is still short of 3.0. Up to an r of .25, z and r are approximately equal. Even when r is .50, z is only a little larger, being .56. The transformation formula is

$$\mathbf{z} = \frac{1}{2}[\log_e(1+r) - \log_e(1-r)] \quad \begin{array}{l}\text{(Transformation of}\\ r \text{ into Fisher's z)}\end{array} \qquad (8.14a)$$

or

$$\mathbf{z} = 1.1513\log_{10}\frac{1+r}{1-r} \qquad (8.14b)$$

where $\log_e$ stands for a logarithm to the base e, the Napierian system of logarithms.[1] For general practice, Table H (Appendix B) may be used for the transformation of r to z and z to r. One would not report final results in terms of z but convert back to the more familiar r value.

The standard error of z is simply

$$\sigma_z = \frac{1}{\sqrt{N-3}} \quad \text{(Standard error of Fisher's} \quad \text{z coefficient)} \tag{8.15}$$

Thus, σ_z is independent of the size of the correlation coefficient and depends only on N. Consider the case of a correlation of $+.61$ with $N = 84$. From this information, $\sigma_z = 1/\sqrt{84-3} = \frac{1}{9} = .111$. For an r of .61 Table H gives a corresponding z of .71. We imagine a normal distribution with a mean of .71 and a standard deviation of .111. To obtain the confidence interval at the .95 level, we subtract and add .111 $\times$ 1.96, which is .22. This gives limits of .49 and .93, still on the z scale. The corresponding r's, from Table H, are .455 and .73. Note that these values are not symmetrically placed about the r value of .61, but they give a well-estimated interval within which to expect the population $\bar{r}$ with .95 confidence.

Some special problems of estimation

In this section we shall consider some modifications and applications of the sampling statistics already explained. These have to do with unusual sampling situations, including stratified sampling, sampling with matched samples, and sampling from a finite population.

SAMPLING IN A STRATIFIED POPULATION

Stratifying, in sampling, tends to restrict the dispersion of sample means and of other statistics, preventing their scattering as much as would occur in a completely random sample. Consequently, the σ_M derived in the usual manner would be an overestimate. Such a standard error gives an exaggerated picture of statistic fluctuations.

Certain modifying procedures have been developed for the case of stratified-random sampling. The most general and serviceable formula for the SE of a mean is

$$\sigma_M = \sqrt{\frac{\sigma^2 - \sigma^2_m}{N-1}} \quad \text{(SE of a mean taking into account} \quad \text{stratification in sampling)} \tag{8.16}$$

where σ^2 = variance in the total sample and σ^2_m = variance among means of subgroups. Each subgroup is a sample representing a

[1]For the benefit of the mathematically sophisticated student, z is the hyperbolic arc tangent of r, or $z = \tanh^{-1} r$.

stratum within which there has been random sampling. In the following formula for σ^2_m, note that the variance σ^2_m is weighted, i.e., the contribution of each subset of data to the variance is in proportion to its size. The formula

$$\sigma^2_m = \frac{1}{N} [N_1(M_1 - M)^2 + N_2(M_2 - M)^2 + \cdots + N_k(M_k - M)^2] \quad (8.17)$$

(Weighted variance of means of sample sets)

where $N_1, N_2, \ldots, N_k$ = numbers of cases in sets 1 to k, respectively

$$N = N_1 + N_2 + \cdots + N_k$$

M = weighted mean of composite sample

Similar formulas apply to the SE of a proportion:

$$\sigma_p = \sqrt{\frac{pq - \sigma^2_m}{N}} \qquad \text{(SE of a proportion corrected for stratification)} \qquad (8.18)$$

where p = proportion observed in the entire sample, all strata combined

$q = 1 - p$

N = number in total sample

σ^2_m = variance of strata proportions about p

The solution for σ^2_m needed in formula (8.18) is given by the formula

$$\sigma^2_m = \frac{1}{N} [N_1(p_1 - p)^2 + N_2(p_2 - p)^2 + \cdots + N_k(p_k - p)^2] \qquad (8.19)$$

(Weighted variance of sets of sample proportions)

where $p_1, p_2, \ldots, p_k$ = proportions observed in different sets

$N_1, N_2, \ldots, N_k$ = corresponding numbers of cases in sets

N = total number of cases

p = proportion in composite of sets[1]

SAMPLING STATISTICS IN MATCHED SAMPLES

In some investigations, sampling is restricted by matching. Experimental and control groups are often equated in some respects while studying the effect of some varying condition upon a measured outcome. Groups are frequently "equated" for such matching variables as chronological age, mental age, IQ, socioeconomic level, or for initial score on some particular task or test.

As in the case of stratified sampling, it is worthwhile matching samples only on variables that are correlated with the measured variable—the variable on which we note the experimental outcome.

[1]It should be said that unless differences between means (or proportions) are not large in relation to the standard deviations of the sets, there is little reduction in the SE of the mean from the use of formulas (8.16) and (8.18).

The matching may be by pairs (for example, for every individual in the experimental group there is a similar one in the control group) or by total group (ensuring that the means, standard deviations, and skewings are practically the same for the matching variable in the two groups).

SE of a mean in a matched sample. It follows logically that if we try to keep successive samples constant with respect to the mean on some variable positively correlated with the experimental variable, the means on the latter will also be kept more constant, depending upon the extent of the correlation. The standard error of a mean should then be smaller under this restriction. The general formula is

$$\sigma_M = \frac{\sigma}{\sqrt{N-1}}\sqrt{1 - r^2_{mx}}$$

$$= \sigma\frac{1 - r^2_{mx}}{\sqrt{N-1}}$$

(SE of a mean corrected for effects of matching)   (8.20)

where r_{mx} is the correlation between the matching variable and the experimental variable.

Inspection of formula (8.20) will show that the first factor, $\sigma/\sqrt{N-1}$, is the customary standard error. What the second factor, $\sqrt{1 - r^2_{mx}}$, does is to modify downward the size of the standard error. The larger r becomes, the greater the correction effect. The correlation has to be as high as .866 in order to make the correction as much as .50, in which case the SE is half as large as it would be without matching. The same change in σ_M could be accomplished by quadrupling the size of the sample without matching. When r_{mx} is .707, the reduction is equivalent to that obtainable by doubling the size of the sample in random sampling. These two examples give some idea of the economy of measurement to be achieved by matching samples.

If the matching has been done on the basis of more than one variable, the correlation called for in formula (8.20) is the multiple correlation (see Chap. 16) between a combination of the matching variables and the experimental variable. In the combination the components should be weighted according to a multiple-regression equation. If the weights depart from the optimal ones indicated by this procedure, the correlation-of-sums formula may be applied (see Chap. 16). Matching on the basis of many variables is ordinarily not worth while unless the matching variables are themselves relatively independent, i.e., uncorrelated with each other.

Sometimes a sample group is matched on the *same* variable, as when we give a pretest (from which the groups are matched) and a posttest (on which experimental outcomes are compared), with intervening experience or practice. In this case, the paired cases are identical individuals. The variability of means to be expected from successive sampling of this kind is indicated by the following estimate of the SE:

$$\sigma_M = \frac{\sigma}{\sqrt{N-1}} \sqrt{1 - r_{xx}} \qquad \text{(SE of a mean for matching on the experimental variable)} \qquad (8.21)$$

where r_{xx} is the test-retest reliability (see Chap. 17) of the measurements on the experimental variable. The reader who may be familiar with the reliability statistics described in Chap. 17 will recognize the product $\sigma \sqrt{1 - r_{xx}}$ as the *standard error of measurement* of individuals. Dividing this by the square root of the number of degrees of freedom will indicate the dispersion of means of measurement.[1]

The SE of a proportion in a matched sample. The same principles just discussed in connection with means also apply to proportions. When samples have been matched on the basis of some outside variable correlated with the categorical variable on which the proportion is based, by analogy to formula (8.20) we have

$$\sigma_p = \sqrt{\frac{pq}{N}} \, (1 - r^2_{mx}) \qquad \text{(SE of a proportion in matched samples)} \qquad (8.22)$$

where r_{mx} is the correlation between the matching variable and the experimental variable. The coefficient should be a point-biserial r (see Chap. 14). The matching variable could be a composite, as in the case of means. If the matching variable is the experimental variable, the correlation term should be the reliability coefficient, r_{xx}, by analogy to formula (8.21). SE's of percentages and of frequencies would be estimated by simple modifications of formula (8.22), when samples are matched.

SAMPLING STATISTICS FROM FINITE POPULATIONS

The discussions of sampling statistics thus far have pertained to the general case of infinite populations, or smaller populations sampled with replacement of every case after it has been drawn. The populations have always been assumed to be very large relative to the size of the samples.

In some situations the population may be finite and not many times larger than the sample. For example, the population might be students taking Psychology 1 in the year 1965 in a certain college. This restriction means that successive samples would have a much better chance of containing identical individuals, which would lead to greater similarity of means. If the size of the population is known, we can take it into account in estimating the SE and hence obtain a more realistic figure for it. A serviceable formula is

[1]For further information on SE's in matched and other restricted samples, see Peters and Van Voorhis, *op. cit.* Pp. 132–135.

$$\sigma_M = \frac{\sigma}{\sqrt{N-1}} \sqrt{1 - \frac{N}{N_p}} \qquad \text{(SE of a mean corrected for size of population)} \qquad (8.23)$$

where N_p is the number in the total population.

It can be seen that, as N_p becomes very large compared with N, the correction term under the radical at the right approaches 1.0, and the SE is then estimated by the customary formula. When the sample contains one one-hundredth of the population, the value of the factor at the right reduces to .995. The SE is then only ½ of 1 per cent lower than it would be without the correction.

A similar formula for the SE of a proportion obtained from a finite population is

$$\sigma_p = \sqrt{\frac{pq}{N}\left(1 - \frac{N}{N_p}\right)} \qquad \text{(SE of a proportion in a finite population)} \qquad (8.24)$$

Although these special formulas are not so basic or so commonly used as those presented earlier in this chapter, it is well to take advantage of them where they apply. Stratifying and matching samples are good experimental procedures, not only because experimental controls increase our knowledge of conditions affecting the outcomes of an experiment but also because they make estimations of population parameters more accurate, as indicated by smaller standard errors. Inferences can then be made with more accuracy and more confidence. Nor is a smaller standard error the only advantage, for, as we shall see, further kinds of inferences are based upon knowledge of standard errors, in determining significance of differences and in testing statistical hypotheses in general.

EXERCISES

1. Compute the standard errors of the means for Data 8*A* and interpret your results.

2. Determine the confidence limits and confidence intervals at both the .95 and .99 levels.

3. Compute the standard errors of the two medians and the two 90th centile points for Data 8*A*. Interpret your results.

4. Compute the standard errors of the two standard deviations in Data 8*A* and interpret your results.

5. Compute the standard errors of the frequencies, proportions, and percentages for passing students in Data 8*B* and interpret your results.

6. The correlation between an interest-inventory score and the estimated degree of satisfaction in a certain vocational assignment was .43 in a sample of 101.
   a. Find the SE of r on the assumption of a population correlation of zero.

Data 8A　**Results from a test of the ability to name facial expressions in the Ruchmick Photographs**

Statistic	Men	Women
N	95	164
M	21.1	22.0
SD	3.62	3.15
Mdn	21.5	22.2

Data 8B　**Numbers of students in two groups who passed each of three items in a psychological examination**

Item	Group I	Group II
A	24	26
B	33	32
C	30	40
N	37	65

b. Find the standard score $\bar{z}$ for the obtained coefficient of correlation and draw a conclusion regarding its significance.

c. Use Table D in Appendix B and interpret the obtained r with reference to relevant information you find in the table.

d. Compute Fisher's t by using his formula. Compare inferences from this source with those from the other solutions.

7. Compute Fisher's t for the following combinations of r and N:

r	.25	.25	.50	.50
N	25	50	25	50

8. Transform the r of .43 (mentioned in Exercise 6) into Fisher's z, determine the SE of this z, and find the confidence limits for r.

9. Data 8*C*, boys and girls taken together, represent a stratified-random sample of scores earned by two groups differing in sex. The mean of special interest is that for the two groups combined. The problem is to obtain an estimate of the standard error of the mean of the total distribution, taking into account the fact of stratification.

a. Estimate the SE of the mean with and without making allowance for stratification.

b. As a check on the given SD of the total distribution, estimate that same SD from the information given in Data 8*C*, applying equation A10*b* (Appendix A), remembering that, in general, $\Sigma x^2 = N\sigma^2_x$.

10. For use in another problem, assume that the boys represented in Data 8*C* were selected randomly from a population numbering only 200.

a. Estimate the SE of the boys' mean on the basis of this information.

b. Compute the SE of the mean for the same data, assuming sampling from a very large population, and compare the two results.

Data 8C

	Boys	Girls	Both
N	60	80	140
M	7.30	9.70	8.67
σ	3.30	3.60	3.67
σ^2	10.89	12.96	13.4834

ANSWERS

1. σ_M: .373, .247.
2. .95 limits: 20.4 and 21.8; 21.5 and 22.5.
   .99 limits: 20.1 and 22.1; 21.4 and 22.6.
3. σ_{Mdn}: .47, .31; $\sigma_{C.90}$: .175, .133.
4. σ_σ: .26, .17.
5. σ_f, group I: 2.90, 1.89, 2.38; σ_f, group II: 3.95, 4.03, 3.92; σ_p, group I: .077, .051, .064; σ_p, group II: .060, .062, .060 ($\sigma_p = 100\sigma_p$).
6. $\sigma_{r=0} = .10$; $\bar{z} = 4.30$. From Table D, an r of .254 is needed for significance at the .01 level, with 100 df.
7. t: 1.24, 1.79, 2.77, 4.00.
8. $z = .46$; $\sigma_z = .102$; .95 limits: .25 and .58; .99 limits: .20 and .62.
9. *a.* σ_M (for the stratified sample) = .295; σ_M (for the same sample assuming completely random sampling) = .311.
10. *a.* σ_M (corrected for finite population) = .361.
    b. σ_M (for a very large population) = .430.

9 *Significance of differences*

IN the preceding chapter our attention was centered on the estimation of population parameters from experimentally observed sample values and on making inferences regarding the accuracy of those estimates. We were thus concerned with one statistic at a time. In this chapter the emphasis is to be on deviations of one population parameter from another, or, more accurately stated, on whether two observed statistics, such as two means, two proportions, or two correlation coefficients, indicate differences in a corresponding pair of parameters. We observed something of the process of hypothesis testing in the discussion of the logic underlying confidence limits and confidence intervals for means and in inferring whether a coefficient of correlation differs significantly from zero. A tested hypothesis is often called a "null hypothesis." In this chapter we shall continue to investigate null hypotheses, and learn more about the use of Student's t distribution.

SOME FEATURES OF A NULL HYPOTHESIS

The expression is "*a* null hypothesis" rather than "*the* null hypothesis," because such a hypothesis takes different forms, depending upon which statistic is involved in the process of hypothesis testing. The application of a null hypothesis to the correlation coefficient in Chap. 8 is a good example. In this connection, the null hypothesis is that the population correlation is zero. A correlation of .30 was obtained in a sample of 52 pairs of observations. Under these conditions (N greater than 30 and r not greater than .50) we could adopt as the chance model a population correlation of .00, and to go with it a sampling distribution with a mean of .00 and a standard deviation of approximately $1/\sqrt{52}$, or .14. With a normal distribution of this description, a correlation deviating 1.96σ or more from the mean could occur with a probability of less than .05. The obtained correlation of .30 is more than the deviation required for rejection of the null hypothesis at the .05 level of confidence. The obtained r is not sufficiently large, however, for rejection of the null hypothesis at the .01 level of confidence;

for then r would have to be 2.58σ or larger (.36 or larger) in order to meet the .01-level criterion. Remember that .01 of the area under the normal distribution lies beyond 2.58σ from the mean at the two extremes.

Some investigators would say that the correlation that has been obtained is significant but not *very* significant. Other investigators would adopt the level for rejection—the .05 level or the .01 level, or some other (.10, .02, and .001 are other commonly adopted probabilities)—in advance of making the test, and then the decision "to reject or not to reject" is automatic. The probability level adopted, .05, .01, or some other, is technically called α (the Greek letter alpha).

In the correlation problem that we have just used as an example, if we reject the null hypothesis we infer that there is some degree of correlation; the population parameter is probably not zero. We could then legitimately proceed to set up a confidence interval for it. If we do not reject the null hypothesis, we are saying that for all we know the real correlation in the population could be zero (we cannot decide that it *is* zero) and there is nothing more to do, except perhaps to plan another experiment. Our inferences could go even further, taking into account the particular variables that were being correlated. Suppose one variable, X, were the score on a personality-trait scale, perhaps for the trait of activeness, and variable Y is the order in which the examinees completed the inventory (fastest worker ranked N, slowest ranked 1). The null hypothesis in this case is that there is no correlation between activeness and rate of work on the test. Rejection of the null hypothesis could lead to the statement that those who score high for activeness are likely to complete the test more rapidly. Failure to reject the hypothesis leaves us with no positive conclusion; the correlation could be zero between activeness score and speed of work on the test, or some correlation near zero.

The null hypothesis for a difference between means. As another example, let us suppose that we have done an experiment to see whether a certain condition or treatment will make a difference in how much food rats will consume after all the rats have been deprived of food for the same number of hours. One serving of food contains some alcohol, the other none. In two samples of 20 rats each, two means are obtained: 24.8 pellets with alcohol, 21.3 without. Are the two sample means far enough apart to give us confidence that there is a genuine difference in food consumption? The modifier "genuine" pertains to population values. With sample means fluctuating as they do in sampling, it is possible that the obtained difference of 3.5 pellets could have arisen by random sampling from the "same" population— same, that is, with respect to food consumption. Or, it could be a matter of two different populations that are in fact the same with regard to food consumption. In either case, the difference of 3.5 is one that could reasonably occur by random sampling, with samples of 20. In this application, the null hypothesis is that the "true" difference is zero, the population difference is zero, or there is a difference of zero between population parameters, to state the same idea in several ways.

Now it is only common sense to have more confidence in the belief that an observed difference means a genuine population difference when the observed difference is large. But without a statistical test, we are unable to draw any conclusion as to how improbable the null hypothesis is—i.e., how much confidence should be placed in the belief that the obtained difference reflects a real difference.

Now the investigator who thought of testing whether the presence of alcohol in food will have an effect upon food consumption probably thought in terms of the positive hypothesis first—that there will be an effect. It may seem rather indirect to test a positive hypothesis by testing its alternative, a null hypothesis. But that is precisely what we have to do, for, as stated in Chap. 7, we can set up a statistical model to represent a true null hypothesis, which we *can* test; we do not know how to represent the alternative—a positive hypothesis— even if it were true. If the null hypothesis is true, we can predict what would happen statistically; there is no way of predicting accurately what would happen if the alternative hypothesis were true. When the null hypothesis is not true, there is a host of other possibilities, each of which has to be tested in turn. The null hypothesis can be stated mathematically as a particular, well-defined, testable case.

Differences between means

In considering the significance of differences between means, it is necessary to examine two variations. There are different procedures commonly used when samples are large (30 or more) and when samples are small. When the means are independent, different procedures are used than when they are correlated. We shall begin with the case of large samples and independently sampled means.

THE STANDARD ERROR OF A DIFFERENCE BETWEEN UNCORRELATED MEANS

Means are independently sampled when derived from samples drawn at random from totally different and unrelated groups. In order to make a test of significance of a difference between two means, as usual, we need a special mathematical model describing what would happen in the case of purely random sampling of such pairs of means. With large samples, the model used is a normal distribution of differences $M_1 - M_2$, with a mean of zero and a standard deviation that is called the SE of a difference between means. Such a standard error can be estimated from the standard errors of the two means, σ_{M_1} and σ_{M_2}. The formula is

$$\sigma_{d_M} = \sqrt{\sigma^2_{M_1} + \sigma^2_{M_2}} \qquad \text{(SE of a difference between uncorrelated means)} \qquad (9.1)$$

Variances of sums and differences. The mathematical basis for this formula can be found in Proof 12 in Appendix A. When two variables X_1 and X_2 are summed, if each is normally distributed, the distribution of the set of sums $X_1 + X_2$ is normal, as well as the distribution of their differences $X_1 - X_2$. The variance of the sum σ^2_s is equal to $\sigma^2_1 + \sigma^2_2 + 2r_{12}\sigma_1\sigma_2$, where r_{12} is the correlation between X_1 and X_2. Similarly, the distribution of $X_1 - X_2$ is normal, with a variance σ^2_d equal to $\sigma^2_1 + \sigma^2_2 - 2r_{12}\sigma_1\sigma_2$. When r_{12} equals zero, the variance of the difference is reduced to the first two terms, the square root of which is the standard deviation. The same mathematics applies to distributions of means in sampling distributions, and hence is the basis for formula (9.1). This is why means must be independent or uncorrelated when formula (9.1) is used.

A test of a sex difference. Let us apply formula (9.1) to a typical problem. Two groups, one of 114 men and the other of 175 women, were given the same word-building test. In this test the score is the number of words one can build out of six letters in 5 min. The results are summarized in Table 9.1. The women's mean of 21.0 is 1.3 points higher than that of the men. This mean difference is very small numerically, but in view of the relatively large samples, we should expect the obtained means to be very close to the population means; perhaps, therefore, it indicates a real sex difference. The stability of each mean is indicated by its SE, which is .572 for the men and .371 for the women.

Table 9.1 **Means and other statistics in the comparison of men and women in a word-building test**

Statistic	Men	Women
N	114	175
M	19.7	21.0
σ	6.08	4.89
σ_M	.572	.371
σ_{d_M}	.682	
D_M	1.3	
$\bar{z}$	1.91	

Just as sample means are distributed normally about the population mean when N is large, the sample differences between means are also distributed normally. The central value about which the differences between means fluctuate is also a population value. We do not know what that population value is. We are most concerned, first, in determining whether there is any difference at all, and second, if it is significant, in determining its approximate size.

A distribution of $\bar{z}$ ratios. In accordance with the usual null hypothesis, we assume a sampling distribution of differences, with the mean at zero, or at $\bar{M}_1 - \bar{M}_2 = 0.0$.[1] The deviation of each sample difference, $M_1 - M_2$, from this central reference point is equal to $(M_1 - M_2) - (\bar{M}_1 - \bar{M}_2)$, or $M_1 - M_2 - 0$. The deviation of each sampled difference given in terms of standard measure would be the deviation divided by the standard error, which gives us a $\bar{z}$ value. In terms of a formula,

$$\bar{z} = \frac{M_1 - M_2}{\sigma_{d_M}} \quad \text{(A } \bar{z} \text{ ratio for a difference between means)} \qquad (9.2)$$

The numerator, to be quite complete, should read $M_1 - M_2 - 0$, as was stated above. But since the zero has no contribution to make to the computation, it is dropped in ordinary practice. It will help the investigator using this formula to think more clearly if he remembers that, logically, zero belongs there.

Figure 9.1 shows a sampling distribution of $\bar{z}$ ratios. This distribution is real, though rarely or never derived by using actual data, since every difference we obtain by random sampling, with N's constant, provides its own $\bar{z}$ value. We could actually take a series of 100 or more paired samples, compute $M_1 - M_2$ and σ_{d_M} for each pair, and consequently obtain a $\bar{z}$. The frequency distribution of the 100 or more $\bar{z}$'s we could set up from those data would approach the distribution in Fig. 9.1.

Testing the null hypothesis. For the word-building test we have the information (see Table 9.1) that the difference in the obtained sample is -1.3. The algebraic sign of the difference does not concern us at this time; we are interested in its amount. The standard error $\sigma_{d_M} = .682$. From this,

$$\bar{z} = \frac{1.3}{.682} = 1.91$$

The value 1.91 tells us how many σ_{d_M}'s the obtained difference extends from the mean of the distribution. The mean, under the null hypothe-

---

[1] Actually, we could arbitrarily adopt any other difference we preferred, to be the hypothesis tested. It is customarily a zero difference that is tested because it is of special interest, usually with the expectation that it will be rejected, thus favoring the experimental hypothesis.

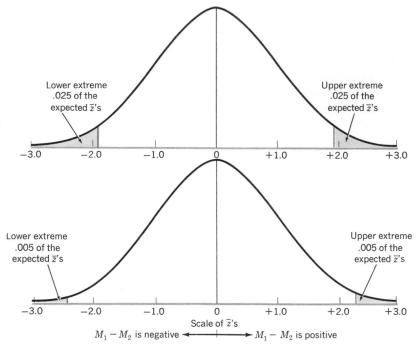

Fig. 9.1. *Two sampling distributions of $\bar{z}$, each with a mean of 0, which corresponds to a hypothetical difference between means equal to zero. The shaded areas in the tails represent the critical regions of extreme $\bar{z}$'s, which lead to rejection of the null hypothesis at the .05 and .01 levels in the first and second distributions, respectively.*

sis that is being tested, is a difference of zero. Since the sample is large, we may assume a normal distribution of the $\bar{z}$'s. The obtained $\bar{z}$ fails to reach the .05 level of significance (which for large samples is 1.96); consequently we would not reject the null hypothesis and we would say that the obtained difference is not significant. There may actually be some difference, but we have not enough assurance of it. There are more than 5 chances in 100 that a difference as large as this one, or larger, could have happened by random sampling from the same population — same with respect to word-building ability. A more practical conclusion would be that we have insufficient evidence of any sex difference in word-building ability, at least in the kind of population sampled. Note that the conclusion was *not* stated to the effect that we have demonstrated that there is *no* sex difference in word-building ability. *We cannot prove the truth of the null hypothesis; we can only demonstrate its improbability.*

Had the $\bar{z}$ test turned out very significant, i.e., with less than 1 chance in 100 that by chance a $\bar{z}$ could be so large, we should then have been interested in the *size* of the difference.[1] Our interest would then have reverted to the standard error of the difference and the probable limits it suggested for the size of the difference. This procedure is so similar to that for determining the probable size of any population parameter that we need not go through the steps here. A confidence interval and confidence limits could be set up by the usual procedures.

THE STANDARD ERROR OF A MEAN DIFFERENCE IN CORRELATED DATA

When the data are so sampled that there is a correlation between the means in the two variables measured, i.e., so that the means in pairs of samples tend to rise or fall together (positive correlation) or tend to be contrasting so that when one rises the other falls (a negative correlation), the SE of a difference is estimated by the formula

$$\sigma_{d_M} = \sqrt{\sigma^2_{M_1} + \sigma^2_{M_2} - 2r_{12}\sigma_{M_1}\sigma_{M_2}} \qquad \text{(SE of a difference between correlated means)} \qquad (9.3)$$

which is like formula (9.1), except for the last term, in which r_{12} is the correlation *between the two sets of means.*

Correlation between means. Fortunately, under the usual circumstances of random sampling, the correlation between the two sets of means is approximately equal to the correlation between two sets of single measurements in a sample. Since we ordinarily have only two samples with two means, from which we could not compute r_{12} between the means, this fact is a great convenience.

But in order to compute the correlation between single measurements, we must have the individual measurements in the two samples paired off in some manner. For example, if the same group of students takes the same word-building test twice instead of two different groups taking it, we have the same individual's score in the first trial to pair off with his score in the second trial. Or if, in comparing males and females in the test, we want to standardize our two groups better by taking a brother and a sister from each family or if we pair boy with girl with respect to age, IQ, or social status, or all such factors, then if these factors of common family, age, IQ, or social status have any relation to word-building score, they will automatically introduce correlation between the two samples. We compute a coefficient of correlation in the manner described in Chap. 6 and introduce it into formula (9.3).

[1] Some investigators refer to a difference or a deviation that is significant at or beyond the .01 level as being "very significant"; one significant between the .05 and .01 levels as being "significant"; and one significant below the .05 level as being "insignificant." The usual practice, however, is to state the probabilities.

In Table 9.2, we find two sets of knee-jerk measurements, both from the same 26 men but under two conditions. In the first case (T), the subjects were squeezing a hand dynamometer just before the stimulus struck the knee, and in the second case (R) the "relaxed" knee jerk was obtained in a relaxed, sitting posture. Will the average man show a real difference in height of knee jerk between the tensed condition and the relaxed condition? The two means, with a difference of 3.39 deg, suggest that a hypothesis that there is a genuine difference is vindicated. But we want to be sure that this large a difference could not have happened by random sampling from a population of measurements in which the actual difference is zero.

Significance of difference with and without considering correlation. If we were to assume no correlation between the tensed and normal measurements of knee jerk, we should apply formula (9.1), or we should apply formula (9.3) with an r_{12} equal to zero, which is actually the same thing. Such a σ_{d_M} turns out to be 2.37 deg of arc. The $\bar{z}$ ratio is 3.39/2.37, or 1.43. This $\bar{z}$ falls decidedly short of the .05 level of significance. We should conclude, erroneously, that although there is some difference, it is not significant. So far as these indications go, we should not be called upon to reject the null hypothesis; the difference of 3.39 could represent merely a result of random sampling.

When we compute a coefficient of correlation between the two sets of measurements, we find it to be +.82. This means that the men appeared rather closely in the same rank order in both the tensed and the relaxed conditions. If a man has a high kick under normal conditions, he will be likely to have a correspondingly high kick under tensed conditions. If a man is low in the one case, he is likely to be low in the other. If the sampling is random, there would be a similar correlation between *means* under the two conditions. If another group of 26 men had a higher normal average response than this one, it would be likely also to have a higher tensed average response.

When means rise and fall together in successive sampling, they tend to maintain the same difference between them. In the special case of a perfect positive correlation ($r = +1.0$), the difference between means would remain constant. If all the sample differences between means were identical, their dispersion would be zero and σ_{d_M} would be zero. We should then be almost certain of a difference in the obtained direction. A correlation of +.82 is less than 1.00, however; thus there is still some room for variability among the differences. But from the above line of reasoning, we can see that the σ_{d_M} is going to be smaller than it was when we assumed an r equal to zero.

By the use of formula (9.3) we find the σ_{d_M} to be 1.10, which is less than half the previous estimate of 2.37. The $\bar{z}$ ratio is now 3.39/1.10 =

Table 9.2 **Strength of the patellar reflex under two conditions, tensed and relaxed, for 26 men, and differences between them (measurements are in terms of degrees of arc)**

T Tensed	R Relaxed	T − R Difference
31	35	− 4
19	14	+ 5
22	19	+ 3
26	29	− 3
36	34	+ 2
30	26	+ 4
29	19	+10
36	37	− 1
33	27	+ 6
34	24	+10
19	14	+ 5
19	19	0
26	30	− 4
15	7	+ 8
18	13	+ 5
30	20	+10
18	1	+17
30	29	+ 1
26	18	+ 8
28	21	+ 7
22	29	− 7
8	4	+ 4
16	11	+ 5
21	23	− 2
35	31	+ 4
26	31	− 5
Σ 653	565	+88
M 25.12	21.73	3.39
σ 7.17	9.45	5.50
σ_M 1.43	1.89	1.10

3.06. A $\bar{z}$ above 3 is obviously in the "very significant" category.[1] We therefore feel very confident that the difference is genuine. This is not to say that we feel confident that the actual difference is exactly 3.39: it might be more or less than that.

Since we might have expected the results to be in this direction, a *one-tail test* could have been made. The tests made thus far have been two-tail tests. If the investigator were to predict a difference in one direction in advance, he would make a one-tail test instead of a two-tail test. He would test the hypothesis that the mean difference is *zero or negative*, as opposed to the hypothesis that the difference is positive. The significance level he would adopt would be either .025 or .005 for a positive deviation of 1.96σ or 2.58σ, respectively. The subject of one-tail tests will be discussed more fully in Chap. 10.

Testing differences by pairing observations.   In setting up an experiment with two matched groups of subjects or two corresponding groups of measurements for statistical comparison, it is well to pair off cases if possible so that a correlation can be computed.

Often when such pairing is not carried out, there is a correlation between the means of the samples anyway; the full formula for the SE of a difference could not then be applied, and the σ_{d_M} by formula (9.1) is overestimated. It is true that under these circumstances, if the correlation is positive, we can say that the correct σ_{d_M} is smaller and that the correct $\bar{z}$ ratio is larger than the one we estimated. When we have a significant $\bar{z}$ under these circumstances. we can be sure that the $\bar{z}$ we would obtain by taking into account the positive correlation would be even larger.

One difficulty is that when the $\bar{z}$ obtained under these circumstances is too small to be significant we cannot come to any definite conclusions, and least of all can we conclude that the actual difference is probably zero. For, had we considered the correlation, we might have found a significantly large $\bar{z}$. The process of matching and the inclusion of the correlation factor in the σ_{d_M} formula are said to increase the *power of the test*. By this is meant that the test is more sensitive to a difference when it is genuine. As a result, we are more likely to avoid the error of accepting the null hypothesis when it is incorrect.

It is important that pairing individuals or observations be done on some meaningful basis. Pairing is not worth doing except on the basis of some variable that correlates with the measurements on which the two groups are to be compared. For example, if we were to compare two groups of boys as to ability to do a high jump, one group

---

[1]A sample of 26 pairs of observations would be regarded as a small sample by most investigators. A small-sample *t* test would lead to the same conclusion in this instance, however.

after training of a certain kind and the control group without such training, it would be important that the two groups be equated as to age, among other factors. Ability in the high jump, regardless of training, is dependent upon age, and hence correlated with it, but the ability is probably not correlated significantly with a grade earned in arithmetic, therefore there would be no point in matching the groups on this variable.[1]

An SE of a difference obtained directly from differences.   When individuals have been paired off, we can find the desired statistics directly from differences between pairs. In Table 9.2 we find the difference in knee-jerk measurements $(T - R)$, given with algebraic signs, for every individual. If we sum the differences and divide by N, we obtain the mean of the differences, which is equal to the difference between the means. If we calculate the SE of the mean of these differences, we have σ_{d_M}. The σ_{d_M} is thus obtained in the most direct manner. We need not even know the SE's of the two means or the amount of correlation present; yet our direct procedure has taken these things into account.

The σ_{d_M} for the knee-jerk data obtained in this manner is identical to the value we found previously, taking r_{tr} into account, as it should be. The interpretations and conclusions concerning the mean difference are as usual. This more direct method is strongly recommended whenever it can conveniently be applied.

DIFFERENCE IN MEANS FROM SMALL SAMPLES

The distinction between large-sample and small-sample statistics is not an absolute one, the one realm merging into and overlapping the other. If one asks, "How small is N before we have a small sample?" the answers from different sources vary. There is general agreement that the division is in the range of 25 to 30. The truth of the matter is that the needs for small-sample treatment of data increase as N decreases and they may become critical very quickly below an N of 30. Small-sample methods apply regardless of the size of N, but they become imperative for N much below 30.

The sampling distribution of t.   We have already seen that for small samples, some statistics exhibit sampling distributions that depart from normality in various ways; for example, distributions of correlation coefficients, proportions, and standard deviations are often skewed. Another kind of change in sampling distributions is in *kurtosis*, the degree of steepness of the middle part of the distribution. A normal distribution is *mesokurtic*, which means neither very peaked nor very flat across the top. Curves tending toward rectangu-

[1]Matched sampling is also treated in Chap. 8.

lar form are called *platykurtic*. Those more peaked than normal are called *leptokurtic* (see Fig. 9.2).

Many of the small-sample statistical tests are based upon the statistic known as Student's *t*. Actually, *t* is defined as we have defined $\bar{z}$. It is the ratio of a deviation from the mean or other parameter, in a distribution of sample statistics, to the standard error of that distribution. In the case of either $\bar{z}$ or *t* we have a sampling distribution. Imagine that we computed the ratio for every single sample drawn from the same population with *N* constant. A frequency distribution of these ratios would be a *t* (or $\bar{z}$) distribution.

The difference between $\bar{z}$ and *t* is one of degree of generality. Statistic $\bar{z}$ is normally distributed and is so interpreted. It applies when samples are large and sometimes under other restrictions, as when derived from samples of *p* or *r*. Statistic *t*, on the other hand, applies regardless of the size of sample. Where the sampling distribution of $\bar{z}$ is restricted to one degree of kurtosis (that applying to the normal distribution, a kurtosis of 3.0), the sampling distribution of *t* may vary in kurtosis. Student's *t* distribution becomes increasingly leptokurtic as the number of degrees of freedom decreases (see Fig. 9.3). As the df becomes very large, the distribution of *t* approaches the normal distribution.

Figure 9.3 shows *t* distributions with differing df involved. The most important feature of a leptokurtic distribution, as compared with the normal distribution, for the purposes of hypothesis testing, is the difference at the tails. The tails are higher for the leptokurtic distribution. The effect of this is that we have to go out to greater deviations in order to find the points that set off the regions significant at the .05, .01, and other standard levels. From Fig. 9.3 it can be seen that the *t* distribution for 25 df comes very close to the normal distribution, but the one for 9 df definitely does not. Before we decide to accept a normal-curve approximation to the *t* distribution when there are 25 df, however, let us consider what difference it would make in the significance limits.

Significance limits in t distributions. In distributions of *t*, significant values have been determined at the .05 and .01 levels. These are

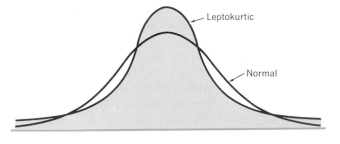

Fig. 9.2. *Showing a comparison of a normal distribution with a leptokurtic distribution when their means and standard deviations are approximately equal.*

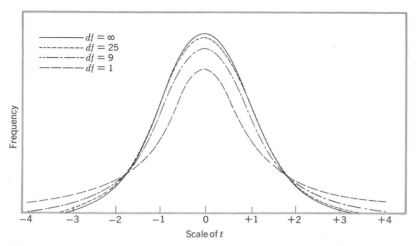

Fig. 9.3. *Sampling distributions of Student's t for various numbers of degrees of freedom. As the df becomes very large, the distribution of t approaches the normal distribution as its limit.*

listed in the last column of Table D (Appendix B). Reference to that table will show that when the number of df is infinite the two *t* values are 1.960 and 2.576, the same as for the normal distribution. With 1,000 df the critical values are different from those figures only in the third decimal place. For 100 df there is a small change in the second decimal place. The limits with 100 df are 1.984 and 2.626. Rough limits, by rounding, of 2.0 and 2.7 would do very well even down to about 30 df. With only 10 df, however, *t*'s of 2.23 and 3.17 would be required for the .05 and .01 significance levels. With small samples, then, it becomes imperative to consider the changing *t* values needed for significance. Even when the number of df is greater than 30, if *t* turns out to be near the critical limits for rejection of hypotheses, it would be well to refer to Table D to find the exact values.

FISHER'S *t* FORMULAS

Fisher has provided several formulas designed for the computation of *t*. We have already noted his formula for use in connection with a coefficient of correlation in the preceding chapter.

   The t test of a difference between means.   When means are uncorrelated, the *t* formula for testing their difference is

$$t = \frac{M_1 - M_2}{\sqrt{\left(\dfrac{\Sigma x^2_1 + \Sigma x^2_2}{N_1 + N_2 - 2}\right)\left(\dfrac{N_1 + N_2}{N_1 N_2}\right)}}$$
   (Fisher's *t* for testing a difference between uncorrelated means)   (9.4)

where M_1 and M_2 = means of the two samples

Σx^2_1 and Σx^2_2 = sums of squares in the two samples

N_1 and N_2 = numbers of cases in the two samples

The complete numerator should read $M_1 - M_2 - 0$, to indicate that it represents a deviation of a difference from the mean of the differences. The denominator as a whole is the SE of the difference between means, as the t ratio requires.

In writing the σ_{d_M} in this form, we take the null hypothesis quite seriously. That is, if there is but *one* population, there should be but one estimate of the population variance. In the first term under the radical we have combined the sums of squares from the two samples (in the numerator) and the degrees of freedom (in the denominator) that come from the two samples. The expression $N_1 + N_2 - 2 = (N_1 - 1) + (N_2 - 1)$. The effect of the second expression under the radical is to give the SE of the mean difference.

When two samples are of equal size, i.e., $N_1 = N_2$, formula (9.4) simplifies to

$$t = \frac{M_1 - M_2}{\sqrt{\dfrac{\Sigma x^2_1 + \Sigma x^2_2}{N_i(N_i - 1)}}} \qquad \begin{array}{l}(t \text{ for difference between uncorrelated} \\ \text{means in two samples of equal size)}\end{array} \qquad (9.5)$$

where N_i = size of either sample.

When means of paired samples are not independent but correlated, the best formula to use for deriving t directly from sums of squares is

$$t = \frac{M_d}{\sqrt{\dfrac{\Sigma x^2_d}{N(N - 1)}}} \qquad \begin{array}{l}(t \text{ for differences between correlated} \\ \text{pairs of means)}\end{array} \qquad (9.6)$$

where M_d = mean of the N differences of paired observations and x_d = deviation of a difference from the mean of the differences.

The procedure implied by this formula was actually applied in connection with the knee-jerk data under two experimental conditions (see Table 9.2). The number of df to use with t in this case is $N - 1$, where N is the number of *pairs* of observations. For the knee-jerk problem $N = 26$ and there are 25 df, which indicates (from Table D) that t's of 2.06 and 2.79 are significant at the customary levels. The obtained t is 3.06.

When t tests do not apply. If there is a good reason to believe that the population distribution is not normal but is seriously skewed, and especially if the samples are small, t tests do not apply. For skewed distributions, Festinger and others have suggested substitute tests.[1] There are also available, as substitutes for the t test, a number of distribution-free tests, some of which are described in Chap. 12.

The reader should also be warned that if the two samples have markedly differing variances the t test is questionable. Whether or not two sample variances are significantly different can be determined by making an F test, which is described later in this chapter. Cochran and Cox[2] have provided a method for meeting the case of unequal variances. One should also have some hesitation in using t formulas if the N's in the two samples differ markedly. Differing N's do not seem to affect the use of formulas (9.1) and (9.3) in the same way. Boneau[3] has investigated by means of sampling from non-normal distributions, with unequal variances of samples, and with differing N's, the effects of conditions such as these, which violate the assumptions of the t test, upon rejections of hypotheses at the .05 and .01 levels. On the whole, t is not markedly affected except by rather strong violations, unless N is very small.

Differences between proportions and frequencies

DIFFERENCES BETWEEN UNCORRELATED PROPORTIONS

When a null hypothesis is assumed with regard to two observed proportions, Fisher recommends that we use just one estimate of the population variance and not two estimates, one from each sample p. This suggestion calls for finding a weighted mean of the two sample proportions, after the manner of formula (4.10). Repeating that formula here, with minor variation, the estimated population proportion is

$$\bar{p}_e = \frac{N_1 p_1 + N_2 p_2}{N_1 + N_2} \qquad \text{(Weighted mean of two sample proportions to estimate a population proportion)} \qquad (9.7)$$

The test of significance of a difference between proportions is not suited to small-sample techniques. The sampling distribution of $p_1 - p_2$ approaches the normal form when both of the Np's or Nq's, whichever is smaller in either sample, are as large as 10. The test of significance is therefore made through use of a $\bar{z}$ ratio. The formula for such a $\bar{z}$ is

[1]Festinger, L. The significance of difference between means without reference to the frequency distribution function. *Psychometrika*, 1946, **11**, 97–105.
[2]Cochran, W. G., and Cox, G. M. *Experimental Designs*. New York: Wiley, 1950.
[3]Boneau, C. A. The effects of violations of assumptions underlying the t test. *Psychol. Bull.*, 1960, **57**, 49–64.

$$\bar{z} = \frac{p_1 - p_2}{\sqrt{\bar{p}_e \bar{q}_e \left(\dfrac{N_1 + N_2}{N_1 N_2} \right)}}$$ (A $\bar{z}$ for a difference between uncorrelated proportions)   (9.8)

where $\bar{q}_e = 1 - \bar{p}_e$.

To apply the last two formulas, let us take the case in which two groups of students were sampled. In the first group (of 100), 60 members said they approved the manner in which the President was doing his job, and in the second group (of 50), 35 said that they approved. Thus, p_1 is .60 and p_2 is .70; N_1 is 100 and N_2 is 50. The estimated population proportion, given by a weighted mean, is

$$\bar{p}_e = \frac{60 + 35}{100 + 50} = \frac{95}{150} = .6333$$

The variance of the estimated population proportion is .6333 times .3667, which equals .2322. Applying formula (9.8),

$$\bar{z} = \frac{.70 - .60}{\sqrt{.2322 \left[\dfrac{100 + 50}{(100)(50)} \right]}} = \frac{.10}{\sqrt{(.2322)(.0300)}} = \frac{.10}{.0835} = 1.20$$

A $\bar{z}$ of 1.20 falls short of significance at the .05 level. Therefore, we do not reject the hypothesis that the two sample proportions arose from the same population. The sentiment with regard to approval of the President could have been equally strong in the two samples.

When the two samples are of equal size, with $N_1 = N_2 = N_i$, formula (9.8) simplifies to

$$\bar{z} = \frac{p_1 - p_2}{\sqrt{\dfrac{2 p_e q_e}{N_i}}}$$ (9.9)

in which p_e is a simple mean of p_1 and p_2, and N_i is the number of cases in each sample.

This formula applies in a study in which 400 college men and 400 college women were asked whether or not they found the word "symphony" pleasant. The proportions responding affirmatively were .6850 for men and .8875 for women. Thus we have

$$\bar{z} = \frac{.8875 - .6850}{\sqrt{\dfrac{2(.1681)}{400}}} = \frac{.2025}{\sqrt{\dfrac{.3362}{400}}} = \frac{.2025}{.0029} = 6.99$$

where $\bar{p}_e$ is .78625 and $p_e q_e$ is .1681. The hypothesis of no sex difference should be rejected beyond the .01 level of confidence.

It may have been noted that in both problems p_1 and p_2 were assigned so as to yield a positive difference and a positive $\bar{z}$. In making a two-tail test, the sign of $\bar{z}$ is immaterial, since the region for rejection of the null hypothesis is in both positive and negative extremes of the sampling distribution. In the first of the two problems, let us suppose that the first group, in which p_1 was .60, was composed of Republicans and the second group, in which p_2 was .70, was composed of Democrats, and the President was a Democrat. Then we should properly apply a one-tail test. The hypothesis tested is that there is a zero difference *or a negative one*, where the difference tested is $p_2 - p_1$. By the alternative hypothesis, $p_2 - p_1$ is expected to be a positive difference. If alpha, the probability of extreme $\bar{z}$ deviations remains at .05, the region for rejection is above a $\bar{z}$ of 1.64 rather than 1.96. It is much easier to find a significant $\bar{z}$ in a one-tail test than in a two-tail test, with the same alpha. Since alpha gives the probability of wrongly rejecting a null hypothesis, there is no more danger of committing this kind of error in making the one-tail test than in making the two-tail test.

We can make a one-tail test, also, in the case of reactions to the word "symphony." Since the word pertains to art, and in our culture it is more accepted for females than males to show pleasure in response to things artistic, we should have expected an outcome in the obtained direction. In neither problem, as it turned out, would a one-tail test have changed the decisions: to accept the tested hypothesis in the first case and to reject it in the second. In the second case the tested hypothesis was, as usual, that there would be a zero or negative $\bar{z}$ when the difference was $p_2 - p_1$ (women's proportion minus the men's). In other instances the one-tail test may lead to rejection of the tested hypothesis where the two-tail test would not.

Correction for continuity.   Even when the N_p or N_q product (whichever is smaller) is between 5 and 10, it is possible to make a $\bar{z}$ test if we make a correction for continuity. This will be more fully explained in the next chapter. Here we shall only remind the reader that frequencies, from which p's are derived, change by discrete jumps, whereas the $\bar{z}$ parameter is a continuous variable. When we use the normal curve as an approximation to the binomial, the smaller the samples the more important it is to take this discrepancy into account. An allowance for continuity can be made by introducing an adjustment in the numerators of formulas (9.8) and (9.9). The numerator, $p_1 - p_2$, should be reduced in absolute size (whether it is positive or negative) to the extent of the value

$$\frac{1}{2}\left(\frac{1}{N_1} + \frac{1}{N_2}\right) \quad \text{or} \quad \frac{1}{2}\left(\frac{N_1 + N_2}{N_1 N_2}\right)$$

If the smallest N_p or N_q is less than 5, we can still possibly resort to the use of a chi-square test, which is described in Chap. 11.

DIFFERENCES BETWEEN CORRELATED PROPORTIONS

For the case in which the sampled proportions are correlated, an economical procedure has been proposed by McNemar.[1] The formula avoids the necessity for computing the standard error of the estimated population proportion as well as the correlation coefficient. As with correlated means, we expect to find correlated proportions in two samples when the same individuals are involved in both, or when we are dealing with matched pairs, such as twins, siblings, litter mates, and the like.

Suppose that we have administered two test items to a sample of 100 students. Item I is answered correctly by 60 of the group and item II by 70. Is item II actually easier than item I? In making the $\bar{z}$ test to answer this question, we must definitely face the possibility of correlation between the two items and consequently between the two proportions. To handle this problem properly, we need to arrange the data in the form of a four-cell contingency table, as in Table 9.3. At the left are the four frequencies of those who pass item I and either pass or fail item II, and the frequencies of those who fail item I and either pass or fail item II. At the right in Table 9.3 are letter symbols which stand for the four categories. Using these symbols, the formula reads

$$\bar{z} = \frac{b - c}{\sqrt{b + c}} \qquad \text{(A } \bar{z} \text{ ratio for difference between correlated proportions)} \qquad (9.10)$$

(See Table 9.3 for definition of symbols.)

It will help to ensure the proper application of this formula if we note that the symbols b and c stand for the discordant cases in the four-cell table. In this problem, b and c stand for individuals who pass one item and fail the other. It will help to know that the difference $b - c$ divided by N equals the difference between p_1 and p_2. It is there-

[1]McNemar, Q. Note on the sampling error of the difference between correlated proportions or percentages. *Psychometrika*, 1947, **12**, 153–157.

Table 9.3 **A four-cell contingency table of frequencies of students who passed or failed each of two test items**

Frequency table
Item II

Item I		Fail	Pass	Both
	Pass	5	55	60
	Fail	25	15	40
	Both	30	70	100

Symbolic table
Item II

Item I		Fail	Pass	Both
	Pass	b	a	$a + b$
	Fail	d	c	$c + d$
	Both	$b + d$	$a + c$	N

fore the difference between two *frequencies*, i.e., $b - c = Np_1 - Np_2$. To find the difference that is being tested in the numerator of the $\bar{z}$ ratio is not new. The denominator must therefore somehow represent the SE of a difference between frequencies *with the correlation between them taken into account*. In this formula, too, there is implied but one estimate of the population variance, and it is derived from an average of the sample proportions. What we are actually testing with formula (9.10) is whether the *change* in frequencies is significant.

Solving formula (9.10) as applied to the test-item data, we have

$$\bar{z} = \frac{5 - 15}{\sqrt{5 + 15}} = \frac{-10}{\sqrt{20}} = -2.24$$

We infer that the difference is significant between the .05 and .01 levels – item II is probably easier than item I.

It is informative to see what the outcome would have been had we applied formula (9.9) without taking into account the amount of intercorrelation. With $\bar{p}$ estimated to be .65,

$$\bar{z} = \frac{.10}{\sqrt{\dfrac{2(.65)(.35)}{100}}} = 1.48$$

From the latter result we would have concluded that the difference was insignificant. This demonstrates how a decision may be altered drastically when the correlation term in the standard-error formula is taken into account. Without it, we run the risk of making the error of not rejecting the null hypothesis when it is false. The correlation (ϕ coefficient)[1] between the two items amounts to +.58. One restriction in the application of formula (9.10) is that $b + c$ should be 10 or greater.

Differences between coefficients of correlation

In the preceding chapter it was noted that the sampling distribution of the Pearson r is so variable, depending as it does upon the sizes of both N and r, that only under highly restricted conditions could a $\bar{z}$ distribution be used. No test of differences between population $\bar{r}$'s based upon standard errors of r is very satisfactory. The best recourse is using Fisher's transformation to z, whose standard error is related only to N and not to r.

WHEN COEFFICIENTS OF CORRELATION ARE UNCORRELATED

With uncorrelated r's, as when we have two correlations between the same two variables, X_1 and X_2, derived from two totally different and unmatched samples, the standard error of a difference between Fisher's $\bar{z}$'s can be computed by the formula

[1]See Chap. 14 for explanation of the ϕ coefficient.

$$\sigma_{d_z} = \sqrt{\frac{1}{N_1 - 3} + \frac{1}{N_2 - 3}} \qquad \text{(SE of a difference between two independent z coefficients)} \qquad (9.11)$$

Consider two r's, r_{12}, from two different samples, .82 and .92. The corresponding z coefficients (from Table H) are 1.16 and 1.59, respectively; corresponding N's are $N_1 = 50$ and $N_2 = 60$. From these data,

$$\sigma_{d_z} = \sqrt{1/47 + 1/57} = .197$$

and

$$\bar{z} = \frac{1.59 - 1.16}{.197} = 2.18$$

The sampling distribution of Fisher's z is normal; therefore the sampling distribution of $z_1 - z_2$ is also normal, and $\bar{z}$ may be interpreted as a standard score. The difference in z's deviates from a difference of 0.0 to the extent of 2.18σ, which means that it is significant at the .05 level. We reject the null hypothesis of no difference in the z's, a decision that can also be made with respect to the difference between the two r's.

WHEN COEFFICIENTS OF CORRELATION ARE CORRELATED

There is one kind of comparison of r's that comes up sufficiently often to call for treatment when the r's are correlated. It is the case in which the correlations are r_{12} and r_{13}, in other words, the correlations of two variables X_2 and X_3 with the same third variable X_1. An example of this is the comparison of two validity coefficients; we have correlated two predictor-test variables with the same criterion of successful behavior of some kind. Perhaps one of the two predictors is a new one that someone claims to be superior to an older one. Let us say that the older one, X_2, correlates .45 with the criterion of academic achievement, a score on an algebra-achievement test, X_1. The new test correlates .55 with the same criterion. The sample is composed of the same 200 students for the two validity coefficients. Is the second test genuinely superior to the old one in validity?

For this particular kind of problem, Hotelling[1] has developed a t test which takes into account the correlation between r_{12} and r_{13}. The Hotelling formula is

$$t_{d_r} = (r_{12} - r_{13}) \sqrt{\frac{(N-3)(1 + r_{23})}{2(1 - r^2_{23} - r^2_{12} - r^2_{13} + 2r_{23}r_{12}r_{13})}} \qquad (9.12)$$

The number of df may be taken as $N - 3$.

[1]Hotelling, H. The selection of variates for use in prediction, with some comments on the general problem of nuisance parameters. *Ann. math. Stat.*, 1940, **11**, 271–283.

In order to apply formula (9.12) to the two validity coefficients, X_{12} and X_{13}, we need to know the intercorrelation r_{23}, which is .60. Then, with $N = 200$,

$$t_{d_r} = (.55 - .45) \sqrt{\frac{197(1 + .60)}{2[1 - .3600 - .3025 - .2025 + 2(.60)(.45)(.55)]}}$$

$$= .10 \sqrt{\frac{315.20}{.864}}$$

$$= 1.91$$

The alternative hypothesis is that the r of .55 represents a genuinely higher correlation than the r of .45; hence a one-tail test is called for. If we adopt the .05 level and a one-tail test, the t needed is 1.64. This can be determined from the normal-curve table, for with large N's, $\bar{z}$ is interchangeable with t for hypothesis-testing purposes. We would accordingly reject the hypothesis being tested: that the true difference in correlation is either zero or negative.

Differences between variances

We saw in Chap. 8 that the process of finding usable standard errors for standard deviations is precluded except for very large samples. The same limitation applies to testing the significance of differences between standard deviations by the method used in the case of other statistics. Fortunately, procedures have been developed that apply to measures of variations in large and small samples alike. One of them involves a variance ratio, signified by the symbol F, which has known sampling distributions. By this approach, we can test whether or not two variances could probably have arisen by random sampling from the same population of observations, or from two populations with the same variance.

WHEN TWO VARIANCES ARE INDEPENDENT

When estimates of population variance are obtained from two independent samples (with no matching of samples in any way involved) their difference is tested, not by the usual operation of subtraction, or $s^2_1 - s^2_2$, but by forming their ratio, s^2_1/s^2_2. The ratio that satisfies the null hypothesis completely is equal to 1.00. As the ratio departs from 1.00 the differences are greater. In comparing two sample variance estimates (there are other uses of the F ratio, some of which will be seen in Chap. 13), it is customary to put the larger s^2 in the numerator, giving a ratio greater than 1.00. The equation for an F ratio is[1]

---

[1]It is of interest that the F ratio was proposed by G. W. Snedecor, who based it upon earlier work by R. A. Fisher, in honor of whom the ratio was symbolized by F.

$$F = \frac{s^2_1}{s^2_2} \qquad s^2_1 \text{ being greater than } s^2_2 \qquad\qquad (9.13)$$

It should be noted that the variances being compared are the estimates of population variance, s^2, not the sample variance, σ^2.

A small set of data will illustrate the operation of this procedure. Assume that two sets of scores, in one of which $N_1 = 8$ and in the other $N_2 = 5$, have sums of squares $\Sigma x^2_1 = 132$ and $\Sigma x^2_2 = 26$. The numbers of degrees of freedom are 7 and 4, respectively, so the estimated population variances, independently derived, are $132/(N_1 - 1) = 18.86$ and $26/(N_2 - 1) = 6.5$. The variance ratio, F, is $18.86/6.5$, which equals 2.90.

The sampling distribution of F. In random sampling, the distribution of F can be predicted from mathematical relationships. The shape of the distribution depends upon the two degrees of freedom involved, but the general shape is that of marked positive skew, with a mean of 1.0, as we might expect. Figure 9.4 shows three distribution curves of F for three different pairs of numbers of degrees of freedom, df_1 and df_2. These curves are probability distributions, the total surface having a value of 1.00 (the sum of all probabilities for different values of F).

In Appendix B, Table F gives the F limits that are significant at the .05 and .01 levels for different combinations of df's. For the illustrative problem above, the df's are 7 and 4, for the numerator and denominator of the ratio, respectively. We look for the numerator df at the heading of the appropriate column and for the denominator df at the heading of the appropriate row of the table. We find the F values significant at the .05 and .01 levels at the intersection of the appropriate column and row. For the combination of df's 7 and 4, we find the two significance levels to be F's of 6.09 and 14.98, respectively. The obtained F of 2.90 does not come close to the smaller of these two values. We therefore do not reject the null hypothesis and decide that so far as variances are concerned, the two samples could well

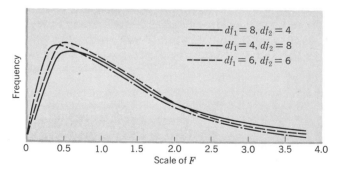

Fig. 9.4. *Sampling distributions of Snedecor's F ratio for various combinations of degrees of freedom.*

have come from the same population or from two populations that have equal variances. The same decision applies to variabilities.

In this particular use of the variance ratio F, we have to consider an important modification in interpreting an obtained F by the use of Table F. This is because Table F is set up in terms of two-tail tests. The arbitrary placing of the larger variance in the numerator doubles the probability of obtaining deviations above the mean, in other words, on the right side of the distribution. Consequently, we have to double the probabilities of the .05 and .01 regions, making them .10 and .02, respectively. In other uses of the F ratio, where the larger variance is not arbitrarily placed in the numerator, the .05 and .01 probabilities still hold. Such cases will be seen in Chap. 13.

WHEN VARIANCES ARE CORRELATED

When the two variances to be compared arise from samples that are matched in some way, there is likely to be some positive correlation between the variances, and the F test does not apply. A t test has been developed, however, to take care of such cases.

Suppose we are interested in determining whether a group of subjects changes in variability in performance of the same task due to intervening practice between an initial and a final test. There will naturally be some positive correlation between initial and final test scores. To take a specific case, suppose the initial variance estimate is 3.75 and the final one is 12.28. Other needed information is an N of 54 and a correlation of .65. The formula for t is

$$t = \frac{(s^2_2 - s^2_1)\sqrt{N-2}}{2s_1 s_2 \sqrt{1 - r^2_{12}}}$$ (t ratio for testing difference between correlated variances)   (9.14)

where s_1 and s_2 are the two estimates of population variance derived from two matched samples, N is the number of cases in the sample, and r_{12} is the correlation between observations in samples one and two. Inserting the illustrative values,

$$t = \frac{(12.28^2 - 3.75^2)\sqrt{54 - 2}}{2(3.75)(12.28)\sqrt{1 - .65^2}}$$
$$= \frac{136.7359\sqrt{52}}{92.1000\sqrt{.5775}}$$
$$= 1.41$$

Table D (Appendix B) shows that it takes a t of 2.00 to be significant at the .05 level when there are 50 df. The resulting t fails to reach that level of significance, so we do not reject the hypothesis of no difference in variances, in a two-tail test.

A more convenient formula for computing purposes, one which does not require the computation of the variances or the coefficient of correlation, is given by Walker and Lev.[1] It is

$$t = \frac{(\Sigma x^2_2 - \Sigma x^2_1)\sqrt{N-2}}{2\sqrt{\Sigma x^2_1 \Sigma x^2_2 - (\Sigma x_1 x_2)^2}} \tag{9.15}$$

Differences between changes

EXPERIMENTS WITH EXPERIMENTAL AND CONTROL GROUPS

In experimental work we very frequently have a design involving the comparison between an experimental and a control group. The two groups are probably selected to begin with by matching them, either person to person or group to group, with respect to some quality or qualities. The experimental group is given treatment A; the control group is not. There is a final test, by which the members of both groups are measured.

Let us suppose that the final test is identical in kind with the initial test on which matching was effected. The experimenter's chief interest is therefore probably centered on the amount of change in the experimental group as compared with that in the control group. How can he best reach a decision about this comparison of changes?

In the experimental results there are essentially four means, and among these four means there are, altogether, six differences, four of which are of special interest (see Fig. 9.5). The two means from the initial tests (which we may call M_{E1} and M_{C1} for experimental and control groups, respectively) may be compared to determine whether matching has been successful. A test of statistical significance of a difference between these means (D_1) would be justified only if no matching operations had been applied i.e., only if the two groups were chosen at random from a pool. Formula (9.1) then would apply.

We also have two means from the final tests, M_{E2} and M_{C2}, for the experimental and control groups, respectively. The comparison of

[1]Walker, H. M., and Lev, J., *Statistical Inference*. New York: Holt, 1953.

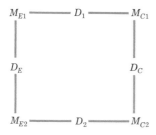

Fig. 9.5. *Diagram to illustrate four meaningful differences between pairs of means in an experiment having an experimental and a control group and pre- and posttests.*

these two means, if that is the crucial test adopted by the experimenter, would be made using formulas (9.1) and (9.2), if sampling was not matched. If matching has been done person to person, the test of the significance of this difference should, of course, take into account the correlation term in the use of formula (9.6).

If the matching has been done in terms of means and other statistics, not person to person, the following formula will apply:

$$\sigma_{d_M} = \sqrt{(\sigma^2_{M_1} + \sigma^2_{M_2})(1 - r^2_{mx})} \qquad \begin{array}{l}\text{(SE of a difference} \\ \text{for matched groups)}\end{array} \qquad (9.16)$$

where r_{mx} is the correlation between the matching variable and the experimental variable. If the two variables are one and the same, as in the illustration above, substitute the reliability (test-retest) coefficient r_{xx} (but do not square it) for r^2_{mx}. Note that the SE of the two means used here should not have been computed by formula (8.21), since the latter involves the correction for matching. To use such SE's in formula (9.16) would effect a double correction.

Comparison of the means M_{E2} and M_{C2}, or the difference D_2, is not the best way to reach a conclusion. It will give us a statistical inference regarding those two outcomes but not necessarily an answer to the question for which the experiment was designed. Suppose that the experimenter could reject the null hypothesis regarding D_2. Perhaps there was also a corresponding real difference latent in the original test. Perhaps sampling errors did not permit this difference to show up in the difference between means M_{E1} and M_{C1}, or D_1. Remember that we cannot prove the truth of a null hypothesis.

Another approach that the experimenter might think of taking is to compare first and second means in each group. He might test the significance of the differences $M_{E2} - M_{E1}$ and $M_{C2} - M_{C1}$, or D_E and D_C. If the former is significant but the latter is not, he might conclude that there is a genuine difference in behavior changes in experimental and control groups—that the experimental group changed but the control group did not. Such a conclusion would not be safe. Again, we do not know whether the two groups actually started on a par, since we cannot prove the null hypothesis.

If the two groups changed in the same direction, which is a common result where learning is concerned, the fact that one change is significant and the other not may rest on a very small difference in the $\bar{z}$ ratio. It is the *net* difference in change in which we should be interested. It is the sampling errors in this difference that should determine our conclusion. None of the comparisons mentioned thus far takes into account all possible sampling effects.

What we need, then, is a statistical test of the difference between *changes*. The simplest approach is to treat the *changes* as the quantities to be compared, whether they are means of changes or sets of individual changes. There are several ways of estimating the standard error of the mean change, depending upon how the two groups were formed.

With D_E standing for the mean change of the experimental group ($D_E = M_{E2} - M_{E1}$) and D_C standing for the mean change of the control group ($D_C = M_{C2} - M_{C1}$), we are testing the significance of the difference $D_E - D_C$. If the two groups were chosen at random, we apply formula (9.1), having determined in the usual manner the SE's of D_E and D_C. If the two groups have been matched person to person, it is best to determine pairs of change values and apply formula (9.6). In other words, every change value is treated just as if it were any measured datum.

Application to a learning experiment. To illustrate, let us consider the data in Table 9.4. Assume that a combination of group E and a control group C is composed of 50 pairs of identical twins, one member of each pair assigned to each of the two groups. The experiment is on transfer effects in learning. Group E receives five practice trials, the first and last of which are on a criterion task, to provide initial and final scores, respectively. The three intervening trials were on a somewhat similar task, practice on which was expected to yield some net positive transfer effect. Group C had only initial and final trials on the criterion task, filling the equivalent amount of intervening time with a different kind of supposedly irrelevant activity that required about the same degree of effort and alertness as did the relevant intervening task for the E group. From the four means shown in Table 9.4, their standard errors, and certain intercorrelations, several tests of significance are possible, as discussed above.

First, the E and C groups have a slight mean difference on the initial test, but the $\bar{z}$ of 1.46 for this difference is so small as to fail to

Table 9.4 **Illustration of tests of significance of gains**

	Group E		Group C		r_{ec}	Difference $(M_E - M_C)$	σ_{D_M}	$\bar{z}$
	M_E	σ_M	M_C	σ_M				
Initial status	42.5	1.40	41.8	1.38	.92	0.7	0.48	1.46
Final status	48.2	1.48	43.4	1.41	.72	4.8	1.08	4.44
Gain $(M_2 - M_1)$	5.7	1.26	1.6	0.76	.15	4.1	1.47	2.99
$\bar{z}$		4.53		2.10			2.99	

reach significance at the .05 level in a two-tail test, which requires a $\bar{z}$ of 1.96.[1] A two-tail test is appropriate here because there is no a priori reason to expect any difference to be in favor of either group. We may conclude that the two groups can be regarded as probably not being initially different, but we cannot say they are equal.

There is little or no question that the two populations, from which the E and C samples came, differ with respect to average performance at the final trial of the experiment. The $\bar{z}$ is 4.44, which is significant well beyond the .01 level, in a one-tail test (a $\bar{z}$ of 2.33 is required). A one-tail test is made with the final-score means because we have reason to expect that the relevant practice should yield a higher mean for group E.

Although the final-score difference, $M_{E2} - M_{C2}$, and the conclusion derived from it seem rather decisive, the fact is that group E did slightly better on the criterion test at the start of the experiment. A statistical test that takes the initial difference into account is based upon the gain scores.[2] The mean gain for group E is 5.7 and that for group C is 1.6. Is the difference between these two *gains* statistically significant? Taking into account the small correlation of .15, and applying formula (9.3) to the standard errors of the means of gains (1.26 and 0.76), we find a $\bar{z}$ of 2.99, which provides a more satisfactory test of differences in learning for the two populations than does the $\bar{z}$ of 4.44.[3] The difference is still significant beyond the .01 level.

As a matter of interest, the differences between initial and final mean scores are shown for each group, with tests of significance. There were correlations between initial and final scores (not given in Table 9.1), and they were taken into account in computing the SE's of the means and of their difference. From the two $\bar{z}$ ratios we learn that even the control group made a significant gain (at the .05 level in a one-tail test) from its limited practice in the two trials. This finding is all the more reason for testing the significance of the difference in *gains* in the two groups rather than the difference between final scores.

[1]The correlation .92, used in computing the σ_{d_M}, is found by pairing off initial scores for pairs of twins, an E twin with a C twin, in each case, and applying formula (6.1), or one of its derivatives.

[2]A gain score is $X_2 - X_1$ for each subject: $X_{E2} - X_{E1}$ in the E group and $X_{C2} - X_{C1}$ in the C group. The mean of the gains is equal to the difference between means: $M_{E2} - M_{E1}$ and $M_{C2} - M_{C1}$ in the two groups.

[3]In general, by a principle too involved to explain here, a correlation between gains can be very low even though the correlations between initial and between final scores are high (.92 and .72, in the two groups here). The reason is that although the correlations between initial and final scores within each group, E and C, are substantial or high, and although initial and final scores are strongly correlated, differences between them have considerable freedom to vary somewhat independently, hence to correlate little.

EXERCISES

1. Estimate the standard error of the difference between means for Data 8*A* and make a $\bar{z}$ test. Interpret your results.

2. Estimate the SE of the difference between means for Data 9*A* and make a $\bar{z}$ test. Interpret your results.

3. Compute a t for the difference between means in the following data: $N_1 = 11$; $N_2 = 26$; $M_1 = 17.5$; $M_2 = 14.8$; $\Sigma x^2{}_1 = 44$; $\Sigma x^2{}_2 = 65$. The means and variances are uncorrelated.

4. Apply a t test to the difference between means for the first ten pairs of observations of knee-jerk data in Table 9.2. Interpret your results.

5. Make $\bar{z}$ tests for differences between groups for the proportions derived from Data 8*B*, for each of the three items. Interpret your results.

6. In a certain precinct, 200 voters cast votes in both the 1956 and 1960 elections. Of these, 20 switched from the Democratic candidate for President to the Republican candidate, whereas 10 switched in the reverse direction. Was there a significant trend?

7. In a group of 145 boys the correlation between tests *A* and *B* was .65 and in a group of 135 girls the correlation between the same two tests was .75. Was there a genuine difference in the size of correlation in the two groups?

8. The predictive validity of a composite score with a pass-fail criterion in flying training was indicated by a correlation of .55 for 150 trainees whereas the validity coefficient for another composite score made up of different tests was .45. The correlation between the two composites was .60. Was one composite more valid than the other?

9. Apply an *F* test to the two variances represented in Exercise 3. Interpret your results. Is the application of the t test for differences between means in Exercise 3 justifiable? Explain.

10. Is there a significant difference between the two standard deviations given in Data 9*A*? Answer the question by making a t test.

11. Assume that the same 55 girls of Data 9*A* repeated very similar tests with the following means, 27.1 and 23.5, for nouns and verbs,

Data 9A   **Quantity written in sentence**
construction from 10 sets of three
nouns each and 10 sets of three verbs
each, the subjects being 55 girls

Statistic	Nouns	Verbs
M	24.7	22.8
SD	6.31	5.42

$$r_{NV} = .67$$

respectively. The two SD's on the second occasion were 5.12 and 5.04, respectively. The corresponding retest reliabilities were .87 and .75, respectively. The intercorrelation between the two tests on the second occasion was .60. Compute the following statistics and interpret your results:

a. The SE's of the means on the second occasion.
b. The SE's of changes in scores in the nouns and verbs, with $\bar{z}$ ratios.
c. The SE of the difference between means on the second occasion, with a $\bar{z}$ ratio.
d. The SE and the $\bar{z}$ ratio for the difference in mean *changes* in the two tests (assuming the correlation between changes to be zero).

ANSWERS

1. σ_{d_M} = .448; $\bar{z}$ = 2.01. Null hypothesis rejected at the .05 level.
2. σ_{d_M} = .658; $\bar{z}$ = 2.89. Null hypothesis rejected at the .01 level.
3. t = 4.25 (σ_{d_M} = .635). With 35 df, null hypothesis is rejected at the .01 level.
4. t = 2.07. With 18 df, t is not significant.
5. σ_{d_p} = .103, .099, .092; $\bar{z}$ = 2.42, 4.04, 2.04. Difference for item A significant at .05 level, for item B at .01 level, and for item C, not significant.
6. $\bar{z}$ – 1.83. No significant trend indicated.
7. $\bar{z}$ = 1.65. Probably no real difference.
8. t = 2.17. Significant at the .05 level.
9. F – 1.69. Difference either in variances or in SD's not significant.
10. t = 1.50. Not significant.
11. *a.* σ_M: .697. .686.
  b. σ_{d_M} (nouns) = .426; σ_{d_M} (verbs) = .506.
  c. σ_{d_M} = .619; $\bar{z}$ = 5.82.
  d. σ_{d_c} = .662; $\bar{z}$ = 2.57.

10   Hypothesis testing

ALTHOUGH we have examined the process of testing hypotheses in the preceding chapters, we did so without going very deeply into the logic of statistical decision making. We shall now look further into the matter, for a deeper understanding of the problems and principles involved is especially necessary before considering a greater variety of applications. There are qualifications and elaborations to be made in connection with what has already been presented in Chaps. 8 and 9. In addition to the general considerations of statistical decision making and the errors involved in that process, we shall also direct our attention to the sizes of samples needed to achieve certain levels of confidence that our decisions are correct and to some statistical tests utilizing binomial distributions.

Some rules for statistical decisions

Let us begin with a simple psychophysical test situation. A student asserts that he can distinguish between two tones whose stimuli differ by only 2 cycles per second. That is his hypothesis – that he possesses genuine power to discriminate so small a difference in pitch. We doubt him, which means that we adopt a null hypothesis. Out of six presentations of stimuli, how many should we require him to judge correctly before we give up our hypothesis and yield to his? Our hypothesis implies that when he judges the pair of stimuli he might just as well flip a coin and report "second higher" for "heads" and "second lower" for "tails." By such guessing, we should expect him to be correct half the time, or 3 times out of 6. But how many more than 3 correct judgments will it take to convince us that he is not merely guessing, for it would be unusual indeed if he could guess all 6 correctly?

In a set of six trials, there are seven possible outcomes – all the way from 6 correct to 0 correct judgments. Table 10.1 lists the seven possibilities and the probability of each event occurring by random sam-

Table 10.1 **Expected occurrences and probabilities of specified numbers of correct judgments in making six judgments at random**

Number of correct judgments	Times expected in 64 sets of judgments	Probability of this number occurring in random sampling	Probability of as many or more occurring	Probability of as few or less occurring
6	1	$1/64$	$1/64$	$64/64$
5	6	$6/64$	$7/64$	$63/64$
4	15	$15/64$	$22/64$	$57/64$
3	20	$20/64$	$42/64$	$42/64$
2	15	$15/64$	$57/64$	$22/64$
1	6	$6/64$	$63/64$	$7/64$
0	1	$1/64$	$64/64$	$1/64$

pling. According to the probabilities, we should expect only *one* "score" of 6 in 64 samples of 6 judgments each; we should expect 6 scores of 5, 15 scores of 4, and so on. These expectations are according to the expansion of the binomial $(1/2 + 1/2)^6$, as we saw in Chap. 7. The model we apply here to describe the null hypothesis is this binomial distribution.

TESTING DEVIATIONS FROM EXPECTED VALUES

In determining whether the student's hypothesis about his acuity for pitch discrimination should be accepted, we are interested in how far the score he obtains deviates from the one most to be expected by chance. The most probable chance-generated score in this situation is 3 correct judgments: the mean of the binomial distribution, given by $np = 6 \times .5 = 3.0$. How much deviation from a score of 3 does the student need in order to lead us to reject the null hypothesis and to tolerate, if not to accept, his alternative hypothesis?

A score of 6 would be expected $1/64$ of the time. One chance in 64 lies between the familiar .05 and .01 levels commonly applied as standards of rejection of the null hypothesis. But before we conclude that we should reject the null hypothesis, we have to consider whether we are making a one-tail or a two-tail test.

One-tail versus two-tail tests. If we begin the experiment with the belief that the student's judgments are developed either by chance or they are not, we must use a two-tail test. For the alternative hypothesis—that his judgments are not directed by chance—there are *two* possible outcomes: an extreme positive deviation or an extreme negative deviation. Either outcome falls into a single *logical* region,

called a *critical region,* in spite of the fact that the two extremes occur at opposite tails in a frequency distribution. If this is our line of
thought as we start the experiment, we must remember that a deviation provided by a score of 0 is just as probable and just as significant
as a score of 6. The confidence level attached to the occurrence of a
score of 0 is $1/64$, so that the probability of *either* a 0 or a 6 (by the addition theorem of probability) is $2/64$ or $1/32$. The two-tail test thus also
leads to a rejection of the null hypothesis beyond the .05 level (with a
probability less than .05 but not less than .01). The statistical decision
would be the same in this particular example, whether we make a
one-tail or a two-tail test.

In this psychophysical problem, a score of 0 would be interesting
to interpret. Of course, if we had adopted in advance a critical region
for rejection at the .01 level of confidence, no further conjectures
would be called for. But if we had adopted the .05 level, and the obtained score were 0, we might naturally ask what this could mean,
psychologically. It could indicate a bias of some kind, one that operates toward making a discrimination in the wrong direction. The
source of the bias might be inferred, perhaps from additional information from another source. Any such hypothesis might furnish the
starting point for a new experiment, with new conditions.

If we were to adopt the one-tail test in the illustrative experiment,
scores below 3 would be regarded differently. First, we have less interest in them. Since the difference of opinion which brought the experiment about involved two alternatives—either the student *can*
or *cannot* sense a difference between a pair of stimuli differing by 2
cycles per second—a one-tail test seems more logical than a two-tail
test. If he *surpasses* our adopted standard, statistically defined, we
will give credence to his belief. *Any* other score, then, whether it is
on the positive or the negative side of the mean, is in the noncritical
region and has the same meaning: no significant positive deviation,
no ability. All outcomes not in the critical region are regarded as
generated by chance. The student's hypothesis is supported (some
would even say "accepted") if the result comes out in the critical
region, which contains only the score of 6. The null hypothesis is supported or "accepted" if any score in the noncritical region, including
scores 0 through 5, is obtained. The region of rejection of the null
hypothesis in the two-tail test includes scores 6 and 0; the noncritical
region, scores 1 through 5.

Figure 10.1 illustrates the difference between one- and two-tail
tests applied with the normal-curve sampling-distribution model,
and with the same confidence level of .05; the critical regions have
been shaded. For the two-tail test, the critical region is evenly divided
in the two tails of the normal distribution at distances of 1.96σ from

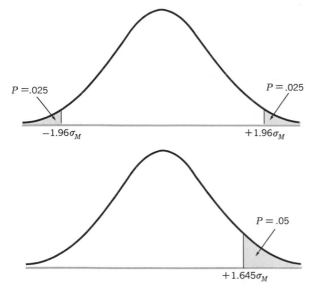

Fig. 10.1. *Two sampling distributions of means, showing the extreme (shaded) portions of area lying in the critical zone when the level of significance, alpha, is .05, for the two-tail test (where the critical zone is in two equal parts in the two tails) and for the one-tail test (where the critical zone is all at one end of the distribution).*

the mean. It is all at one end of the distribution, beginning at a distance of 1.645σ from the mean, for the one-tail test.

Combining probabilities in critical regions. In the psychophysical problem we concluded that a score of 6 is significant between the .05 and .01 levels, whether we apply a one- or a two-tail test. Let us ask whether a score of 5 would be significantly different from the mean in either case.

This question does not ask whether a score of precisely 5 is significant, even though it makes sense to state the probability of obtaining a score of exactly 5, and we see such a probability given in Table 10.1. What we are asking really is whether a score of 5 *or higher* deviates far enough from the mean to be sufficiently rare to lead to rejection of the hypothesis of a chance-generated mean of 3. This question makes sense, because if a score of 5 is far enough removed to be significant, all scores further removed must also be significant. In the one-tail binomial-model test in this psychophysical experiment, the critical region under discussion combines scores of 5 and 6. The probabilities of these two scores individually are $^{6}/_{64}$ and $^{1}/_{64}$, respectively. The probability of obtaining a 5 *or* a 6 is the sum of the two probabilities, by application of the additive theorem regarding probabilities (see Chap. 7). The probability of obtaining a score of 5 or higher is $^{7}/_{64}$, which is decidedly in the noncritical region, and therefore we do not reject the null hypothesis. Just for comparison, if we were applying a two-tail test, we should include scores of 1 and 0 in the critical region also, giving a total probability of $^{14}/_{64}$, or almost $^{1}/_{4}$.

SOME MORE GENERAL CONCEPTIONS OF HYPOTHESIS TESTING

From the preceding discussion it can be seen that a sampling distribution provides not only a model for what should happen in a particular chance situation but also a basis for a clear-cut division of the total outcome space[1] into two mutually exclusive regions for rejection and acceptance of alternate hypotheses, once we have adopted either a one-tail test or a two-tail test along with a confidence level. We shall now put these ideas in more general form.

Let us say that the hypotheses with which we are concerned have to do with a sex difference in verbal-comprehension ability. Logically, there are *three* alternatives: (1) males have more ability than females; (2) females have more ability than males; or (3) there is no sex difference connected with this ability. Expressed in terms of symbols, these three alternatives may be expressed as follows: $\overline{M}_m > \overline{M}_f$, $\overline{M}_m < \overline{M}_f$, and $\overline{M}_m = \overline{M}_f$, where the $\overline{M}$'s stand for population means and the subscripts for male and female.

An investigator who approaches this problem with an open mind simply asks "Is there a genuine sex difference here?" He would make a two-tail test. He would combine the first two alternatives into one, stated: $\overline{M}_m \neq \overline{M}_f$ (the mean for males is not equal to that for females). His alternatives in his statistical test would be this hypothesis against the third, $\overline{M}_m = \overline{M}_f$. He is prepared to find a significant deviation from a zero difference in either direction, and if a significant difference is found, to accept it. If he rejects the null hypothesis, in accepting the alternative, $\overline{M}_m \neq \overline{M}_f$, he also accepts the algebraic sign as being meaningful. For if he were to mark off confidence limits for the mean difference, the confidence interval would be entirely or predominantly on one side of the point of zero difference. Using the information provided by the algebraic sign, he could not only reject the null hypothesis but also make a decision between the two possibilities included in the hypothesis $\overline{M}_m \neq \overline{M}_f$.

An investigator who thinks he has reason to favor the hypothesis $\overline{M}_m > \overline{M}_f$ or the hypothesis $\overline{M}_m < \overline{M}_f$, either on logical grounds or from previous experience, or both, would make a one-tail test. If he believes that females are superior to males in verbal-comprehension ability, he will reduce the situation to two alternatives by making another kind of combination. That is, his hypothesis to be tested will be $\overline{M}_m \geqq \overline{M}_f$, with the alternate hypothesis (which he expects to be true), $M_m < M_f$. He would expect a significant deviation in the negative direction in the distribution of the quantities $\overline{M}_m - \overline{M}_f$ about the hypothetical mean (of the distribution of differences between pairs of sample means) of zero.

[1]Such as the area under the unit normal distribution or the total of the frequencies of cases in a binomial distribution.

In either of the tests, one- or two-tailed, the reduction of three alternative hypotheses to two is an important simplifying step that facilitates decision making. The two alternatives are often symbolized by H_0 and H_1. H_0 represents the hypothesis that is tested and H_1 its alternative.

Errors in statistical decisions

THE CHOICE OF SIGNIFICANCE LEVEL

Thus far, we have not considered very seriously the question of what significance level or levels to adopt. This topic might well have been discussed under "rules for statistical decisions," but it is so intimately connected with errors of decision that it is better discussed here.

Since the investigator controls the adoption of the significance level that is to set a boundary between the critical and noncritical regions, some guidance is required on this subject. Most statisticians insist that the investigator adopt a single standard of significance before the study or experiment starts. When the time for making a decision comes, it is easy to make, because one follows the rule adopted in advance. The reasons for statisticians' insistence on this procedure will soon become apparent. Despite this urging, many investigators prefer not to adopt in advance any rigid standard of rejection or acceptance of hypotheses. They appear to be content to observe the level of significance achieved (in accordance with conventional limits such as the .05 and .01 levels) and to report their findings. We cannot discuss this matter adequately without considering errors in decision and their consequences.

Two kinds of errors of statistical decision. The choice of a standard of significance depends very much upon the amount of risk we are willing to take of being wrong in making the statistical decision to accept or reject the tested hypothesis. Two distinct types of error are possible:

   Type I: rejecting hypothesis H_0 when in fact it is true.
   Type II: accepting hypothesis H_0 when in fact it is false.
Figure 10.2 clearly displays these two kinds of errors in relation to two decisions and two alternatives for H_0 (true or false). With two categories of decision and two of veracity, four combinations are possible, two being correct decisions and two incorrect decisions.

Probabilities of errors of types I and II. The probability of making a type I error is very simply and directly indicated by α, the probability level the investigator chooses for rejecting H_0. Whether he makes a one- or two-tail test, an alpha of .05 means that there are five chances in a hundred of his being wrong in rejecting H_0 when it is true, i.e., of making a type I error. If he adopts the .01 level of sig-

DECISION

	Reject H_0	Accept H_0
H_0 true	Type I error $p = \alpha$	Correct
H_0 false	Correct	Type II error $p = \beta^*$

*β varies, depending upon the actual value
of the parameter whose value is being studied.

Fig. 10.2. *The four cases generated by combinations of two decisions (reject or accept the tested hypothesis) with two actual situations (tested hypothesis true or false). Errors of types I and II are identified in two cells of the table.*

nificance, there is only one chance in a hundred of being wrong. With alpha equal to .001 there is only one chance in a thousand of being wrong. Thus, alpha not only indicates the probability of making an error of type I, but its relationship to that probability tells us that the smaller we make alpha, the less likely we are to make a type I error. Why, then, not adopt an extremely small alpha and practically never make such a mistake?

The trouble is that as we decrease α, we automatically increase the chances of making an error of the second type—of accepting the tested hypothesis when it is false. The probability of making an error of type II is symbolized by β (beta). Alpha and beta are inversely related: as the one decreases the other increases. Alpha is under our direct control; beta is only indirectly under our control through its inverse relation to alpha. But it should be said immediately that the relation between α and β, although inverse, is by no means simple. (The ways of estimating β will soon be explained.) For a concrete view of the inverse relationship, see Fig. 10.1. The shaded portions are in the critical regions: the regions for rejection of H_0. The clear areas under the normal curves represent noncritical regions: regions of acceptance of hypothesis H_0. It is easy to see that as the shaded areas are made smaller, the noncritical regions grow larger, and if the true parameter is not exactly at the mean, the decision to accept H_0 is in error. Thus, increasing the amount of clear space increases the chances of errors of type II. Remember, however, that the amount of clear space is by no means a simple indicator of the size of beta. Beta plus alpha does not equal 1 except under a very special condition, which will be brought out later.

Relative importance of errors of types I and II. The crux of the dilemma is how much weight we want to give to errors of the two kinds. The overly cautious scientist abhors the error of type I more than that of type II. He wants to be very sure that his finding is not due to chance. The conventional choice of alpha as small as .05 and .01 is evidence of the caution exercised by most investigators against making a type I error. Such decisions on choice of alpha are almost always made without consideration for beta. The result of too much caution, and very small alphas, is that relatively few nonchance conclusions are drawn and few differences and relationships are accepted as "established."

Some kind of balance is called for. Considerations external to the data themselves should be noted and given weight. There may be serious theoretical or practical reasons why it would be costly to make one kind of error or the other. Thus, this question ultimately cannot be decided on purely statistical grounds. If certain common-sense decisions can be reached regarding the relative seriousness of the consequences of making each type of error, statistical statements can then often be introduced which will further guide the choice of alpha.

In research on important theoretical issues, such as whether or not telepathy and clairvoyance exist, or whether there is inheritance of acquired traits, a higher-than-usual level of confidence (lower α) may well be demanded. The potential social impact of conclusions about these questions justifies such practice. If the investigation is on the selection of the best of several insecticides when one is sorely needed and none does any harm to noninsects, a larger α might well be tolerated. If it is a matter of the use of a new anesthetic, in a concentration needed for effectiveness, but with a danger of death if given in overdose, a much smaller α might well be demanded.

In general scientific practice, where externally determined risks are of little or no consequence, there is another possibility. Instead of confining ourselves to a two-choice decision—rejection or acceptance—we might allow a third possibility, that of suspended judgment, which usually calls for a replication of the experiment. For example, if the deviation is significant at the .01 level or better we might reject H_0; if the deviation is smaller than the boundary of the critical region at the .10 level, we might accept H_0. Between the two levels, .10 and .01, we might suspend judgment.

THE PROBABILITY OF AN ERROR OF TYPE II

When we wrongly reject hypothesis H_0, we are rejecting a specific value—for example, a difference of zero or a correlation of zero—and we have an available estimate of the probability of being wrong, namely, α. When we wrongly *accept* hypothesis H_0, however, there are many other values that may be correct. In this fact lies an important difficulty of estimating the probability of being wrong in making a type II error. We can make such estimates only for *specific* alternative hypotheses. Lacking a good reason for choosing any other hypothetical value, as a specific alternative hypothesis, H_s, the best we

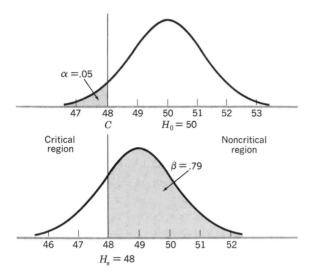

$\alpha = .05$

47   48   49   50   51   52   53
       C $H_0 = 50$

Critical   Noncritical
region   region

$\beta = .79$

46   47   48   49   50   51   52
      $H_s = 48$

Fig. 10.3. *Illustration of the probability of an error of type II as the area under the normal curve lying in the noncritical zone, when the tested hypothesis is a mean of 50, the test is one-tailed with alpha of .05, and the special, alternative hypothesis is a mean of 48.*

can do is to select arbitrariiy a number of reasonable alternatives, each in the vicinity of the value for H_0. We shall next apply this approach, computing a probability β for a number of specific alternative hypotheses.

Determining beta probabilities for a one-tail test. The simpler case is that with a one-tail test. Consider the hypothetical problem in which an aptitude test has been given to a certain group of 50 students in the ninth grade randomly chosen from a school system. The national norm for the test is a mean of 50 with a standard deviation of 8.63. The teacher's impression is that his group averages a little below the national norm. A statistical one-tail test is made to determine whether the mean score for the group is significantly below the norm. The mean score obtained for the group was 48.2. With an SE of the mean of 1.22, the obtained mean failed to reach a deviation significant at the .05 level.

This experimental situation is shown graphically in the first distribution in Fig. 10.3. With alpha equal to .05, it takes a deviation of 1.64σ to be significant, or a deviation of 2.0 score points. The critical region marked off by an alpha of .05 has its upper boundary at a score of exactly 48. This boundary is denoted as C, for critical limit. The noncritical region is above C. It figures very importantly in determining the beta probabilities, because it is the region representing all acceptances of hypothesis H_0.

Although hypothesis H_0 can be accepted, the truth may be that the population mean is located somewhere other than at exactly H_0. As a first choice for a specific alternative H_s, let us consider the value 49. Now we have to think in terms of a new hypothetical sampling distri-

bution, normal in form, with an SE of 1.22 but with a mean of 49. The
second distribution in Fig. 10.3 shows this new hypothetical picture.
The critical limit is still at 48, with critical and noncritical regions
below and above it, respectively, as before. All the score values above
48 still represent those which, if obtained as sample means, would
lead to acceptance of H_0, but now not so much of the sampling distribution is above the critical point. Therefore an error of type II would
not be made so often.

The probability of a type II error is given by the shaded area under
the normal-distribution curve in Fig. 10.3. This proportion of the area
is evaluated in the usual way, from knowledge of the z value of a score
at the cutoff point, 48. The z for a score of 48 is given by the ratio
$(48 - M)/\sigma$, which is $(48 - 49)/1.22$, or -0.82. From the normal-curve
table we find the shaded area to be .79, which is the beta probability
for the H_s of 49. We go through similar procedures for other H_s values
in the region of 48, with results as shown in Table 10.2. It will be noted
that the beta proportions vary from a high of .993 when the H_s is 51,
down to .007 when the H_s is 45. The higher the special hypothetical
mean, the more the area of the sampling distribution is above the
critical point, *which remains at 48 throughout these operations.* We
include $H_s = 50$, in spite of the fact that it was also H_0. When H_s
equals H_0, we find that β is the complement of α: that is, α plus β
equals 1.0. This is the only instance in which that simple relationship
holds. The noncritical part of the first distribution in Fig. 10.3 is
obviously .95 of its total area.

*Table 10.2   Determination of
probabilities of errors of type II and
power values of a one-tail test of the
hypothesis that $\overline{M} = 50.0$, with
$\sigma_M = 1.22$ and $\alpha = .05$*

H_s*	$\overline{z}$	β	$1 - \beta$
51	-2.46	.993	.007
50	-1.64	.95	.05
49	-0.82	.79	.21
48	0.00	.50	.50
47	$+0.82$	.21	.79
46	$+1.64$	.05	.95
45	$+2.46$	.007	.993

*H_s = an alternative hypothesis; $\overline{z}$ = the
ratio $(48 - H_s)/1.22$; β = probability of an
error of type II; $1 - \beta$ = the power value.

The power of a statistical test; power functions. Where beta gives us the probability of making a type II error, its complement, $1 - \beta$, generally indicates the probability of *not* making a type II error. The way not to make a type II error is to reject hypothesis H_0. The probability of rejecting hypothesis H_0 when it is not true is known as *the power of a statistical test*. The last column of Table 10.2 gives the power indices under the conditions of various (hypothesized) true population values in the illustrative problem. As the true mean decreases, the power increases, since the lower the actual mean of the population, the less likely will its sample means go into the non-critical region.

The relationship of the power index, $1 - \beta$, to hypothetical parameters ($\overline{M}$) is a continuous function. In Table 10.2 only selected parameter values are represented for H_s. A plot of the relation of the power index to H_s is shown in Fig. 10.4. Such a function can be similarly constructed to fit any particular case of hypothesis testing. The curve will vary under different conditions. Had we chosen a smaller alpha, the betas would have been larger, as one can see from considering what would happen in Fig. 10.3 if the critical limit were at 47.5 instead of 48, for example. If the betas are larger, the power indices become smaller. In the illustrative problem, the one-tail test was at the lower end of the distribution. When it is at the upper end, the power function is found to be a rising curve on the upper side of H_0. With a two-tail test the power function is composed of two branches, as we shall see next.

Determining the beta probabilities in a two-tail test. Finding the beta probabilities of type II errors in the instance of a two-tail test is a bit more complicated, but follows the same principles as for a one-

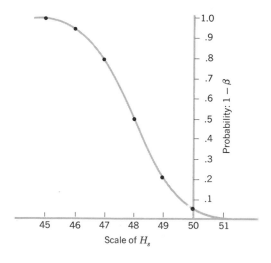

Fig. 10.4. *A power function for a one-tail test, with the probability $1 - \beta$ shown as a function of various special alternative hypothetical means H_s.*

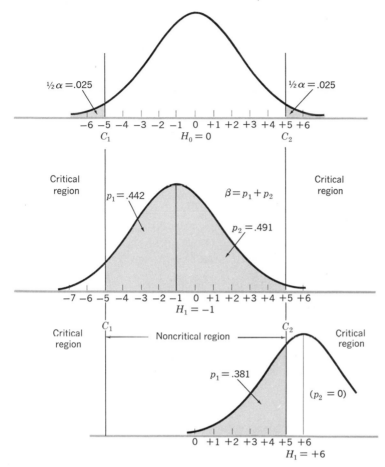

Fig. 10.5. *Illustration of the determination of the probability of committing an error of type II with a two-tail test, with alpha equal to .05 and a special alternative hypothesis of a mean difference of +6.*

tail test. This procedure will be illustrated by another hypothetical problem. This time, the hypothesis to be tested, H_0, is that there is no difference between two population means, $\overline{M}_1$ and $\overline{M}_2$. The size of sample was 50, with an SE of 2.55 and an alpha of .05, divided in two tails of a normal distribution. The first distribution in Fig. 10.5 illustrates the sampling of differences $\overline{M}_1 - \overline{M}_2$, with two critical limits of C_1 and C_2, dividing the total range of differences into a central, noncritical region and two critical regions on either side.

Again, we must successively adopt different H_s values and determine a beta for each. The second distribution in Fig. 10.5 illustrates the case of H_s equal to −1 (the supposition that $\overline{M}_1 - \overline{M}_2 = -1$). The sampling distribution of mean differences is about a mean of -1, with an SE of 2.55. As before, the beta probability is represented by the total area under the sampling distribution falling within the noncritical region. It is most feasible to determine this area in two portions: that below the mean of the sampling distribution for H_s and that above, indicated by p_1 and p_2, respectively. We note the z deviation on the base of this distribution at the point C_1, which is at a value of -5 on the scale of differences. The z is therefore found by the usual ratio, $(X - M)/\sigma$, which, in this case, is $(-5 - M_d)/\sigma_{d_M}$, or $(-5 - -1)/2.55$, or -1.57. From the normal-curve table, the area between -1.57 and the mean is .442. This is the p_1 component contributing toward beta. In a similar manner, we find that C_2 cuts the sampling distribution at a z of $+2.35$, which marks off .491 of the area from the mean. The sum of the two components, p_1 and p_2, is .933. This is beta, the probability of making the type II error under the conditions of the chosen critical limits and the chosen H_s of a difference of -1.

Table 10.3 presents other betas found in a similar manner for H_s values from $+4$ to -4. Within this range, both critical limits are involved. Beyond this range, only one critical limit is appreciably

Table 10.3 **Determination of the probabilities, β, that errors of type II will be made, assuming various hypothetical differences between means, also the probabilities by which a power function is determined (see Fig. 10.5)**

H_s*	$\bar{z}_1$	$\bar{z}_2$	p_1	p_2	β	$1 - \beta$
+12		−2.75	.003	.000	.003	.997
+10		−1.96	.025	.000	.025	.975
+ 8		−1.18	.152	.000	.152	.848
+ 6		−0.39	.381	.000	.381	.619
+ 4	−3.53	+0.39	.500	.152	.652	.348
+ 2	−2.75	+1.18	.497	.381	.878	.122
0	−1.96	+1.96	.475	.475	.950	.050
− 2	−1.18	+2.75	.381	.497	.878	.122
− 4	−0.39	+3.53	.152	.500	.652	.348
− 6	+0.39		.000	.381	.381	.619
− 8	+1.18		.000	.152	.152	.848
−10	+1.96		.000	.025	.025	.975
−12	+2.75		.000	.003	.003	.997

*H_s = the hypothetical difference being tested; $\bar{z}_1$ = the ratio $(-5 - H_s)/2.55$; $\bar{z}_2$ = the ratio $(5 - H_s)/2.55$; $\beta = p_1 + p_2$.

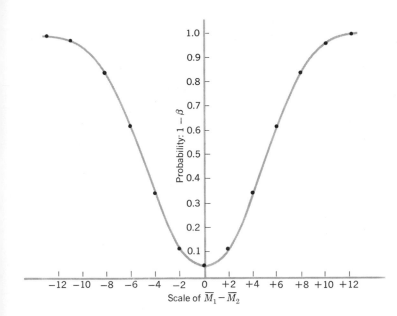

Fig. 10.6. *A power function for a two-tail test of differences between means.*

concerned, and the procedure must be somewhat different. Note the third distribution in Fig. 10.5, which illustrates this kind of case. Here the H_s is +6, which is *above* the limit C_2. The p_1 region is now still in the lower part of the sampling distribution, but it is the *tail* area rather than the area between z and the mean. With this difference, the rest of the operations are just the same. The value of p_2 is zero for all H_s hypotheses at and above C_2, and p_1 is zero for all H_s below C_1.

The power function in a two-tail test. The procedure for obtaining a power function is just the same as in a one-tail test. It is composed of relations of the power values $1 - \beta$ to H_s. Table 10.3 shows that the power value is at a minimum equal to alpha when $H_s = H_0$, as before. Figure 10.6 presents the graphic picture of the power function.

If a one-tail test had been applied to the differences between means in this illustrative problem, with the same critical point at the end of the distribution (alpha equal to .025), the betas would have been much smaller and the power of the test correspondingly greater. For the same size of deviation from the null hypothesis and the same obtained deviation found in the sample, then, a one-tail test is more powerful than a two-tail test.

Ways of increasing power of statistical tests. There are other ways of increasing the power of a statistical test. Some kinds of tests are more powerful than others, and in the succeeding chapters references to power will occasionally be made. But the most important factor in increasing the power of a statistical test is reducing the size of the SE. The most obvious way in which to reduce the size of the SE is to use a larger N, since $SE = s/\sqrt{N}$. Other devices for reducing the SE include using matched samples and stratified samples, as pointed out in Chap. 8. We shall next consider the question of what size of samples would be needed to bring the probability of errors of decision down to desired levels.

Needed sample sizes

In starting an investigation, the question inevitably arises, "How large a sample do I need?" Statistical thinking enables us to develop satisfactory answers to that question, provided we have enough information of certain kinds. Heretofore, we have been concerned with a quite different question, namely, how much deviation from a null hypothesis we need for rejection of that hypothesis, given a sample of a certain size. Now, given a deviation of a certain size, we ask how large a sample is needed to reject the tested hypothesis.

The question is often of practical significance. In a survey like the Gallup poll, for example, one is constantly faced with the question of how large a number of individuals must be interviewed. In this connection, and in others, we should remember that it is not numbers alone that guarantee predictive utility of information. That mere numbers, as such, are not sufficient to guarantee predictive success was brought home decisively by a notorious *Literary Digest* poll during the presidential election of 1936. Although the number of voters sampled ran into the millions, the voters who really determined the election were not adequately represented in the sample. A good poll sees to it that every kind of group of voters, where group differences count at all, is proportionately represented in the poll. When this is accomplished, it is surprising to the uninformed person how small a total sample can yield a valid predictive index. In other words, it is not only a matter of numbers; it is also a matter of how the cases are selected, as was discussed in Chap. 8.

ESTIMATION OF SAMPLE SIZE NEEDED ON THE BASIS OF ALPHA ONLY

The question of sample size should ordinarily be answered with due consideration to errors of decision of both types, I and II, and this can be done. But sometimes not enough information is available to take into consideration errors of type II; nevertheless, a great deal can be done simply in terms of ensuring rejection of a null hypothesis at a specified level of significance. We shall consider this kind of case first.

Let us assume a public issue where majority vote is decisive. Let us also assume that a sample of opinion is properly obtained, with good representation of the voting population.[1] The null hypothesis implies a mean of .50. We ask first how large a sample will be needed to give us confidence that an obtained poll result of 55 per cent in favor of the proposition means a majority sentiment in that direction and is not merely a chance-generated result from a population that is split exactly 50-50.

If a discrepancy of as much as 5 per cent is to be significant at the .05 level, the deviation of .05 (for the 5 per cent excess demanded) must deviate as much as $1.64\sigma_p$ from the mean of a normal distribution in a one-tail test. We need to know how small the SE must be in order that the deviation of .05 shall equal $1.64\sigma_p$.

The general solution of this problem can be reached through a modified equation for a $\bar{z}$ ratio, solving that equation for N. A general equation for $\bar{z}$ is

$$\bar{z} = \frac{d}{\sigma_m} = \frac{d}{\dfrac{\sigma}{\sqrt{N}}} = \frac{d\sqrt{N}}{\sigma}$$

where d = a hypothetical deviation from the mean that we wish to be significant at a given level of alpha, and $\bar{\sigma}$ is the population SD (an estimate of it, s_x, or σ_{p_e}, may be substituted). Multiplying through by $\bar{\sigma}$ and transposing,

$$d\sqrt{N} = \bar{z}\bar{\sigma}$$

and

$$\sqrt{N} = \frac{\bar{z}\bar{\sigma}}{d}$$

Squaring both sides,

$$N = \frac{\bar{z}^2\bar{\sigma}^2}{d^2} \qquad \begin{array}{l}\text{(Size of } N \text{ needed in order to achieve} \\ \text{a significant deviation of a specified} \\ \text{amount, } \alpha \text{ being known)}\end{array} \qquad (10.1)$$

In each particular case, $\bar{z}$ is determined by the alpha that is selected, in a one-tail test, and by ½ alpha in a two-tail test. Applying formula (10.1) to the polling problem, where $\bar{z} = 1.64$, $d_p = .05$, and the population variance is $\overline{pq}$,[1]

[1]For the case of stratified sampling that is usually applied in public-opinion polling, SE's appropriate to such data should be used (see Chap. 8). The formula given here assumes purely random sampling.
[2]The expression $\overline{pq}$ is the variance for a point distribution (where observed values are 1 and 0 only).

$$N = \frac{1.64^2(.5 \times .5)}{.05^2}$$
$$= \frac{2.6896(.25)}{.0025}$$
$$= 268.96, \text{ or } 269 \text{ as an integer}$$

A similar application of the same formula to the two-tail case, where, with an alpha of .05 $\bar{z}$ is 1.96, gives a needed N of 384. It requires an N of 384 to lead to the rejection of the hypothesis that the population is evenly divided on the issue when the obtained deviation is .05 in either direction.

But where much is at stake, we should not be satisfied with these odds against the null hypothesis. We might reduce the probability of an error of type I to .01 by lowering alpha to that quantity. In this case, the obtained p must be at $2.58\sigma_p$, and formula (10.1) estimates a required N of 666. On very critical issues, we might demand a much smaller d_p than .05; it might be .01. With d_p equal to .01 and an alpha of .05, N should be 9,604. With the same d_p and an alpha of .01, N would need to be about 16,640. Thus, for the detection of very small differences with high assurance against errors of type I, samples must be of considerable size.

SIZE OF SAMPLE WHEN ERRORS OF TYPE II ARE SPECIFIED

The procedure just described is satisfactory when the results are sufficiently decisive to reject H_0. Then we need be concerned with a type I error, and the alpha level tells the probability of having made that kind of error. But if the outcome is in the noncritical region and we do not reject the tested hypothesis, what is the possibility that we have overlooked some genuine departure from H_0, that we have made an error of type II? The following procedures allow for the likelihood of such an error.

The case of a one-tail test. The procedures for estimating the N needed to fit a specified test situation do not differ between a one- and a two-tail problem. But there are different logical problems, and therefore the two cases will be discussed separately.

In order to solve any specific problem, there is certain information we must have and certain choices must be made. We must choose not only alpha but beta as well, which means we must weigh carefully the alternatives of risking each kind of error. We must know the value of H_0 for the hypothesis we want to test, and we must adopt a specific alternative hypothesis, H_a, a requirement that we encountered before in consideration of beta probabilities. Another piece of needed information is a good estimate of the population standard deviation.

As an illustration, let us return to the problem of aptitude testing, in which a one-tail test was applied. The H_0 value was an assumed national-norm value of 50.0. The sample size was 50 and the best estimate of the population $\bar{\sigma}$ was 8.63, giving an SE of 1.22. Let us say that the specific alternative hypothesis (H_a) adopted is a mean score of 48. Keeping the alpha level at .05, let us say that we will take the risk of .10 of an error of type II; that is, beta equals .10. The alpha of .05 and the beta of .10 indicate that we are more willing to risk an error of type II than of type I: we are more concerned about wrongly rejecting hypothesis H_0 than we are about wrongly accepting it when the obtained mean deviates −2 from H_0.

Figure 10.7 presents the situation graphically. The sampling distribution about the mean H_0 is given at the right, with the critical limit C_α being determined at $-1.64\sigma_M$ by the choice of .05 for alpha. The critical region for rejection is left of C_α. The sampling distribution on the assumption that 48 is the true mean is at the left. The region for errors of the second kind is to the right of the critical limit C_β, which now also becomes a critical limit for deciding to accept H_0 when H_a is actually true. The curves overlap in such a way that *the minus deviation of $\bar{z} = -1.64$ from mean H_0 coincides with a plus deviation of +1.28 from mean H_a*. The fact that C_α and C_β are at identical values on the scale of means is the key to the solution of the problem of sample size.

The reason is that we can express both C_α and C_β in terms of known or assumed information, including the constant N, which we are trying to find. Let us begin with the very familiar expression for a standard score or deviate:

Fig. 10.7. *Two sampling distributions illustrating the arrangement whereby a certain deviation from the mean H_0 (the tested hypothesis) with an alpha probability of .05 is identical with the deviation from the mean H_a (the alternative hypothesis) with a beta probability of .10. The illustration applies to the problem of estimating the size of sample needed to reject hypothesis H_a under the conditions illustrated, for a one-tail test.*

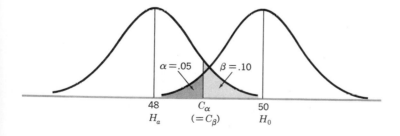

$$\bar{z}_\alpha = \frac{C_\alpha - H_0}{\sigma_M}$$

where $\bar{z}_\alpha$ is the deviate of C_α in the distribution about H_0. Multiplying through by σ_M,

$$\bar{z}_\alpha \sigma_M = C_\alpha - H_0$$

and transposing terms, and changing signs throughout,

$$C_\alpha = H_0 + \bar{z}_\alpha \sigma_M$$

In order to introduce N, let us substitute $\bar{\sigma}/\sqrt{N}$ for σ_M, which gives

$$C_\alpha = H_0 + \bar{z}_\alpha \frac{\bar{\sigma}}{\sqrt{N}}$$

By analogous development, we can derive a parallel equation with an expression for C_β in connection with the distribution about H_a:

$$C_\beta = H_a + \bar{z}_\beta \frac{\bar{\sigma}}{\sqrt{N}}$$

Since C_α and C_β are identical in value, we can equate their equivalents:

$$H_0 + \bar{z}_\alpha \frac{\bar{\sigma}}{\sqrt{N}} = H_a + \bar{z}_\beta \frac{\bar{\sigma}}{\sqrt{N}} \tag{10.2}$$

Substituting in this equation the known and estimated values, we have

$$50 + (-1.64) \frac{8.63}{\sqrt{N}} = 48 + 1.28 \frac{8.63}{\sqrt{N}}$$

$$50 - \frac{14.1532}{\sqrt{N}} = 48 + \frac{11.0464}{\sqrt{N}}$$

which reduces to

$$2 = \frac{25.1996}{\sqrt{N}}$$

$$2\sqrt{N} = 25.1996$$

$$\sqrt{N} = 12.5998$$

and $N = 158.75$ or, rounding to the next higher whole number, 159. It would thus require a sample of 159 to reject the hypothesis that the population mean for the students in question is 50, with only a 5-per-cent chance of doing so wrongly, and at the same time with only a 10-per-cent chance of wrongly accepting the hypothesis when the population mean is in fact 48. To put the matter more simply, with some loss of precision, we might say that with a sample as large as 159 we could discriminate between population means of 50 and 48 with relatively small risks of being wrong.

A general formula for estimating N. It is not necessary to do all this in ordinary practice. Starting with equation (10.2), we may solve for N by the following steps. First, transpose H_a and the expression $(\bar{z}_a \sigma)/\sqrt{N}$; then

$$H_0 - H_a = \bar{z}_\beta \frac{\sigma}{\sqrt{N}} - \bar{z}_a \frac{\sigma}{\sqrt{N}}$$

Collect terms on the right and let $H_0 - H_a = D_{0a}$, the distance between the two hypothetical means; then

$$D_{0a} = (\bar{z}_\beta - \bar{z}_a) \frac{\sigma}{\sqrt{N}}$$

Multiplying both sides by $\sqrt{N}/D_{0a}$, we have

$$\sqrt{N} = \frac{\sigma(\bar{z}_\beta - \bar{z}_a)}{D_{0a}}$$

Squaring both sides,

$$N = \frac{\sigma^2(\bar{z}_\beta - \bar{z}_a)^2}{D^2_{0a}} \tag{10.3}$$

Applying this formula to the data we have just employed,

$$N = \frac{8.63^2 [1.28 - (-1.28)]^2}{2^2}$$

$$= 158.75$$

The validity of this solution can be checked by computing a new SE of the mean, using the new N, and then determining whether the two hypothetical means, 50 and 48, with a new critical limit, would yield a beta probability of .10.

The case of a two-tail test. For an illustration with a two-tail test, let us use the same data from which beta probabilities were derived in testing the difference between two means. H_0 was for a mean difference of zero. Alpha for the two-tail test was .05; in the two critical regions, $\alpha/2$ is .025. Retaining the same alpha, let us tolerate an error of type II with a probability of .10. The two distributions in Fig. 10.8 represent the situation, including the fact that the choice of hypothetical value to be discriminated from H_0 is at -4, which is the adopted H_a.

It will be noted that with the H_a of -4, only the lower critical region

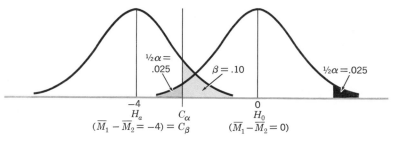

Fig. 10.8. *An illustration parallel with that in Fig. 10.7, for the case of a two-tail test.*

is involved. It would be impossible to have acceptances of H_0 with only .10 probability of H_a being true in such a way as to involve the upper critical region. Thus, the problem is essentially like that for the one-tail situation, with the careful use of $\alpha/2$ and its corresponding $\bar{z}_\alpha$ value. Here $\alpha/2$ is .025 and $\bar{z}_\alpha$ is therefore −1.96. C_β, which is made identical in value with C_α, marking off .10 of the area in the upper tail of the distribution for hypothesis H_a, is at a $\bar{z}_\beta$ distance of 1.28.

The only information lacking for the use of formula (10.3) is the population standard deviation. The standard error of the mean used previously was 2.55. With an N of 50 that was used, the estimated population standard deviation, σ_x, is 2.55 times $\sqrt{50}$, or 18.0. The critical limit. C_α or C_β is at a $\bar{z}_\alpha$ of −1.96 and a $\bar{z}_\beta$ of +1.28. The D_{0a} distance is 4 units. Thus we have

$$N = \frac{18^2 (-1.96 - 1.28)^2}{4^2}$$

= 211.6 or, in whole numbers, 212

It is interesting to note that if we specify a beta probability of .50, $\bar{z}_\beta$ becomes zero. In this case formula (10.3) reduces essentially to formula (10.1), in connection with which the probability of an error of type II is presumably ignored. From this fact we see that in not specifying the beta probability in solving for N to achieve a desired alpha, we are actually adopting a beta of .50, with the result that we are as likely to make a type II error as not to make it.

Testing hypotheses with the binomial model

Something more must be said regarding the use of the binomial model in hypothesis testing. We saw a simple example of this kind of application early in this chapter, in the case of the student with the psychophysical-judgment problem. The particular model used was the distribution of probabilities given by expansion of the binomial $(\frac{1}{2} + \frac{1}{2})^6$. Exact probabilities could be stated for departures from the mean of the distribution. Wherever the probabilities of two alternative, mutually exclusive events add up to 1.0, use of such an approach is possible. So many experimental situations can be brought under such a pattern that the binomial test has very wide application.

As we saw in Chap. 7, when the mean Np is sufficiently large, a binomial distribution approaches a normal distribution with the same mean and variance so closely that a z test can be applied. This was the approach taken in Chap. 8, where large samples were supposed. The polling problem used earlier in this chapter to illustrate the estimation of the size of sample required to reject a null hypothesis is another example employing the normal-curve approximation. The normal-curve substitution is a much more efficient way of testing a hypothesis where the binomial model applies, but with the smaller samples in which this approach can be taken, there is a need for a minor *correction for continuity*. This kind of correction will be explained, and some varied problems in which the binomial model can be applied will be mentioned.

CORRECTION FOR CONTINUITY

In a certain elementary-psychology laboratory experiment, there is the problem of determining whether students can perceive from photographs whether or not a man has been convicted of a crime. Pictures of 20 pairs of men matched for certain qualities are exhibited, with the student to judge which one of a pair is probably the criminal. The null hypothesis calls for 10 correct responses, provided only random guessing has accounted for the score. How much higher must the score be before it may be taken to indicate the operation of something other than chance?

Now we could expand the binomial $(\frac{1}{2} + \frac{1}{2})^{20}$, but that would be quite a task without the aid of a high-speed computer. For help in such problems, where N does not exceed 25, Table O in Appendix B is provided. It gives exact probabilities to three decimal places of outcomes in one tail of a binomial distribution, when $p = q = \frac{1}{2}$. For example, with $N = 20$, as in the criminal-judgment problem, we find the first entry of .001 under the heading of either category 3 or category $N - 3$ (i.e., 17: either is the same distance from the mean). This means that a score as high as 17 (which includes 18, 19, and 20, also) would occur by chance only once in 1,000 times. The same statement can be made about a score as low as 3 or lower. The next entry at the right in the row for N of 20 is .006, which means that a score of 16 or higher would be expected 6 times in 1,000. This is beyond the .01 level. A score of 14 would not achieve significance at the .05 level (one-tail), for the probability given for the category of 14 $(N - 6)$ or higher is .058.

But for the experimental problem at hand, Np equals 10, which is large enough to justify a normal-curve approximation. Yet N is small enough to require a correction for continuity. The appropriate normal-curve model is given in Fig. 10.9. The SE of this distribution is $\sqrt{Npq} = 2.236$. We can put to this distribution the same questions just put to the binomial distribution: what are the probabilities of scores as high as 16, 15, and 14?

At this point, the correction for continuity must be considered. The binomial distribution is on a scale of integral values, where 16 means exactly 16.0 and 15 means exactly 15.0. The probabilities found in Table O pertain to observations at exact, integral scores. The normal curve, however, is on a base line with continuity, where fractional values have real meaning. A score of 16 extends from 15.5 to 16.5. When we ask the probability for a score of 16 or higher in connection with the normal-curve model, the critical point is not at 16.0 but at exactly 15.5.

A score point of 15.5 deviates 5.5 units from the mean of 10. A deviation of 5.5 divided by the SE, 2.236, gives $\bar{z} = 2.47$. Reference to the normal-curve table shows that there are about 7 chances in 1,000 of reaching that deviation. Table O gives .006, which shows that, with correction for continuity, we have an excellent approximation. A score of 15 begins at 14.5, a deviation of 4.5 units from the mean. The corresponding $\bar{z}$ is 2.01. The corresponding probability is .022, which is

Fig. 10.9. *Illustration of the need for correction for continuity when a normal-curve model is substituted for a binomial-distribution model having the same mean and standard deviation. Integral values are points on a binomial scale, but are represented by ranges of values on a normal-curve scale.*

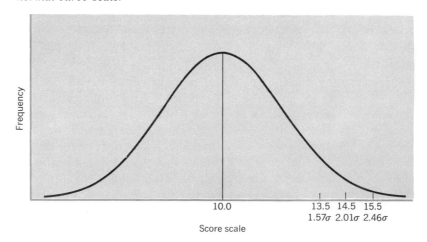

Frequency

10.0   13.5 14.5 15.5
                     1.57σ 2.01σ 2.46σ

Score scale

very close to the .021 given for a score of 15 in Table O. Now if we had used a deviation of 5.0 for a score of 15, the $\bar{z}$ would have been 2.24 and the tail probability .013, appreciably too small.[1]

The need for a correction for continuity is thus clearly demonstrated by this example. The correction is made simply by deducting .5 from the deviation of the integral-score value from the mean. If one chooses particular score *points* on the normal-curve base line, of course, no such correction is needed. It is needed only when talking about integral score *categories*. We shall see a similar need for correction in certain applications of chi square in the next chapter.

Some other applications of binomial tests.   It would be unfortunate if we left the impression that the binomial model is useful only when $p = q = \frac{1}{2}$, although no doubt this is one of the more common cases. Let us return to the ESP problem mentioned in Chap. 7, where there is a probability of $\frac{1}{5}$ of making a correct chance response in guessing the ESP cards. Let us suppose a sample run of 50 guesses, for which the model is the binomial $(\frac{1}{5} + \frac{4}{5})^{50}$. The mean, Np, is 10 and the SE is $\sqrt{50 \times .2 \times .8} = 2.83$. We may use a normal distribution with a mean of 10 and an SE of 2.83. This time, let us ask a different kind of question. What scores higher than 10 will indicate significance at the .05 and .01 levels?

The $\bar{z}$ deviations in a one-tail test must be 1.64 and 2.33, at the .05 and .01 levels, respectively. The product of each of these times the SE gives the deviation x in each case, with $1.64 \times 2.83 = 4.6$ and $2.33 \times 2.83 = 6.6$. Added to 10, these deviations give score points of 14.6 and 16.6. Remembering the need for a correction for continuity, we conclude that an integral score of 15 is needed for significance at the .05 level and a score of 17 for significance at the .01 level.[2]

Departures from random conditions.   Other common applications occur in connection with multiple-choice tests (with two to five possible responses) and similar situations of various kinds. A word of caution should be offered concerning such applications, however. Experience tends to show that in the absence of knowledge human beings do *not* always guess at random. They sometimes exhibit patterns of responses or pattern habits. With such biases present, hypotheses based upon chance distributions must be advanced with caution and sometimes are precluded.

The presence of bias cannot easily be detected, but one kind of evidence of it would be a "significant" deviation in an "unreasonable"

[1]The student might check the probabilities for a score of 14 or greater, with and without correction for continuity, in comparison with the result from Table O.
[2]By overlooking the slight discrepancies between the limits 14.6 and 16.6 and the actual score limits of 14.5 and 16.5.

direction, as when in a guessing situation a significantly large number of *wrong* responses or judgments occurs. Goodfellow has shown in connection with "experiments" on telepathy over the radio, for example, when an audience made five successive guesses of "black" versus "white," there were a number of common sequence patterns.[1] Alternations occur less frequently than one would expect by chance, runs are avoided, and certain initial responses may be favored, sometimes in response to an incidental cue that the experimenter overlooks. The presence of such nonrandom effects is bothersome, but there are experimental controls that may help to reduce their occurrence. There is probably enough randomness in a wide range of behavior to permit profitable use of statistical tests that depend upon that condition.

EXERCISES

1. Suppose that we ask an observer to arrange a series of weights in rank order from heaviest to lightest, the differences between them being very small. What is the probability that he could place them in perfect rank order by random guessing? For each set of weights, regardless of the number of weights in the set, there is only one way of achieving the correct order. The total number of ways for a set is $k!$ (k factorial), where k is the number of weights in the set.

a. For the cases in which k is 3, 4, 5, 6, and 7, in turn, determine the total number of ways in which the weights could be ordered.

b. State the probability for the case of perfect ordering for each set.

c. Which of these probabilities lead to rejection of the random-guessing hypothesis at the .05, .01, and .001 levels?

2. In a discrimination-learning experiment, a rat has two alternative responses, one of which is correct in each trial. The correct response is on the right in random sequence. During a particular set of 12 trials, the rat is correct in 9.

a. Set up a binomial model that should be used in testing the null hypothesis.

b. State the hypothesis.

c. Determine the probability of a score as high as 9 (in a one-tail test), using the appropriate binomial model (see Table O).

d. Do the same, using the best-approximating normal distribution.

3. An observer is told that he will hear one of three speech sounds in a series of stimulations. He is given sets of three sounds each for identification of the "right" sound, with a total of 30 such trials. How many correct responses must he give in the 30 trials if we are to regard his success as significant at the .05 and the .01 levels in a one-tail test?

a. State the binomial model that applies (without expanding it).

b. Make a test by using the most appropriate normal-curve model. What are the mean and SD for that model?

[1]Goodfellow, L. D. The human element in probability. *J. gen. Psychol.*, 1940, 24, 201–205.

4. A certain four-choice test contains 40 items.
a. How large a score must a student make before you feel that he probably knows something about the subject matter of the examination? Define "probably" statistically.
b. How large a score before you feel that he definitely knows something about the subject? Define "definitely" statistically.

5. In the kind of polling problem mentioned in this chapter, with a hypothetical mean of 50.0 per cent, in a sample of 144 interviewees, determine what percentage points mark off the critical regions with alphas of .05 and .01, in turn,
a. in a one-tail test, and
b. in a two-tail test.
c. Why is the correction for continuity not applied in solving these problems?

6. On the polling problem, again, with $\overline{M}_p = .50$ and $N = 144$:
a. Determine the beta probabilities for the one-tail test in the upper tail, with alpha of .05, at H_s values of .45, .50, .55, .60, .65, and .70.
b. Derive the power function and plot it on graph paper.

7. In an examination composed of five-choice items, how many items would you need to include in order to have confidence at the .05 and the .01 levels (in a one-tail test):
a. That a score of 30 per cent right indicates knowledge of the subject matter of the examination?
b. Answer the same question with respect to 25 per cent correct responses.

8. Also in connection with the polling problem, assuming a one-tail test (with $\overline{\sigma} = .5$ and with $\overline{z} = 1.645$ at the .05 level):
a. Determine the size of sample needed with $\alpha = .05$ and $\beta = .05$ and with the alternative hypothesis, H_a, at .55.
b. Do the same, with $H_a = .51$.
c. Repeat parts a and b, disregarding errors of type II.
d. What beta probabilities are associated with the solutions in c?

ANSWERS
1. a. k: 6, 24, 120, 720, 5,040.
   b. p: 1/6, 1/24, 1/120, 1/720, 1/5,040.
   c. The p for 4 weights indicates significance beyond the .05 level; that for 5 weights, beyond the .01 level; only that for 7 weights indicates significance beyond the .001 level.
2. a. Binomial model: $(1/2 + 1/2)^{12}$.
   b. The rat's choices of responses are in purely random sequence.
   c. Binomial solution: $p = .073$ (in a one-tail test).
   d. Normal-curve solution: $\overline{M} = 6$; $\sigma_f = 1.73$; $\overline{z} = 1.45$; $p = .074$.
3. a. Binomial: $(1/3 + 2/3)^{30}$; $\overline{M} = 10$; $\sigma_f = 2.58$.
   b. Mean = 10.0; SD = 2.58; approximate integral scores required, 15 and 17, respectively.
4. $\overline{M} = 10$; $\sigma_f = 2.74$; score points: 15.4 and 16.4; integral scores: 15 and 17, respectively.
5. a. Critical percentage points: 56.8 and 59.6, at .05 and .01 levels, respectively.

    b. Critical percentage points at .05 level: 41.9 and 58.1; at the .01 level: 39.4 and 60.6.

    c. The critical points pertain to the hypothetical normal-curve model only, not to obtained integral scores.

6. *a.* The beta probabilities: .998, .950, .672, .225, .025, and .001, for hypothesized values .45 to .70, respectively.

    b. The plotted values should be the complements of the betas just listed, i.e., $1 - \beta$ in each case.

7. *a.* *N*: 44 and 87, at the .05 and .01 levels, respectively.

    b. *N*: 174 and 347, at the .05 and .01 levels, respectively.

8. *a.* With H_a at .55, $N = 1{,}082.41$, or 1,083.

    b. With H_a at .51, $N = 27{,}060$.

    c. With H_a at .55, $N = 271$; H_a at .51, $N = 6{,}765$.

    d. Associated with the latter *N*'s are beta probabilities of .50 and .50.

11   Chi square

ALTHOUGH the statistical tests covered thus far are quite varied and their applications are numerous, they do not provide for all our needs. One reason is that they are limited to the evaluation of one statistic or one difference at a time. In this chapter and the next two, we shall examine a considerably expanded repertoire of statistical tests. The first of these to be considered is the versatile statistic called chi square.

General features of chi square

Chi square is used with data in the form of frequencies, or data that can be reduced to frequencies. This includes proportions and probabilities. One important feature of chi square is its additive property, which makes possible the combination of several statistics or other values in the same test. Thus, a hypothesis involving more than one set of data can be tested for significance.

THE BASIC NATURE OF CHI SQUARE

The fundamental nature of chi square can be very simply, if not completely, explained on the basis of what is already known about z, the standard score or measure. When there is one degree of freedom, chi square is identical with z^2, or

$$\chi^2 = z^2 = \frac{(X - \bar{M})^2}{\bar{\sigma}^2} \qquad \text{(Mathematical relation of} \atop \chi^2 \text{ to } z^2\text{, with 1 df)} \qquad (11.1)$$

where X is any measurement in a normally distributed population, $\bar{M}$ is its mean, and $\bar{\sigma}$ is its standard deviation. Now suppose that we have a sampling situation in which there are k mutually independent measures of X. There are also k mutually independent z values and k mutually independent χ^2 values. It is a most useful property of χ^2 that a sum of k mutually independent chi-square values is also a χ^2, with k degrees of freedom.[1] In terms of an equation,

[1]For a rather detailed mathematical development of chi square, see Lewis, D. *Quantitative Methods in Psychology*. New York: McGraw-Hill, 1960.

$$\chi^2 = \Sigma z^2 = \sum \frac{(X - \overline{M})^2}{\sigma^2}$$

where it is understood that k values are summed.

Chi square as a sampling statistic. Like $\overline{z}$, chi square can also be used as a sampling statistic. Just as $\overline{z}$ has a sampling distribution, so has chi square. The sampling distribution of $\overline{z}$ is normal, but since χ^2 is related more directly to $\overline{z}^2$ its sampling distribution is definitely not normal. Something will be said about its sampling distribution below. Here we shall pursue further the relation of χ^2 to $\overline{z}$.

Suppose we have taken a very limited opinion poll in a small sample of married, male, graduating seniors in a certain university. Of the 40 men who were questioned, 28 of them felt that it is a good idea for undergraduates to be married and 12 disagreed. Could these frequencies have arisen from a population in which the opinion is evenly divided on the experimental question? The null hypothesis for this instance of hypothesis testing is a 50-50 division.

With the 50-50 hypothesis, the expected frequency in a sample of 40 is Np, which equals $40 \times .5 = 20$. We therefore assume a population distribution of frequencies with a mean of 20 and a variance of Npq, where $p = q = .5$. In using chi square, the mean is known as an *expected frequency, f_e.* With it is to be compared an *obtained frequency, f_o.* Does the obtained frequency of 28 differ significantly from the frequency of 20, to be expected on the basis of the null hypothesis?

The $\overline{z}$ test and the chi-square test. If we make the ordinary $\overline{z}$ test, we have the usual operations to perform. Using the new symbols for the numerator,

$$\overline{z} = \frac{f_o - f_e}{\sqrt{Npq}} = \frac{28 - 20}{\sqrt{40 \times .5 \times .5}} = 2.53$$

This $\overline{z}$ is a little short of significance at the .01 level.

From the relationship indicated in formula (11.1),

$$\chi^2 = \overline{z}^2 = \frac{(f_o - f_e)^2}{Npq}$$

For this kind of problem, where $p = q = .5$, the expression Npq can be written as $f_e/2$, since $f_e = Np$ and $q = \frac{1}{2}$. This change gives us a formula for chi square

$$\chi^2 = \frac{2(f_o - f_e)^2}{f_e} \qquad \begin{array}{l} \text{(Chi square in testing a null} \\ \text{hypothesis for two frequencies} \\ \text{in alternate categories)} \end{array} \qquad (11.2)$$

by shifting the 2 to the numerator. It should be noted that the ratio of the square of the difference (between f_o and f_e) to f_e is the basic mathematical definition of chi square. More accurately stated, χ^2 is the *sum* of such ratios. Implied in formula (11.2) is actually a sum of two ratios of identical value, because of the 2 in the numerator. Relating this to the illustrative data, it should be pointed out that there are actually two observed frequencies, an f_o of 28 men and an f_o of 12. The double use of the same difference here illustrates another peculiarity of chi square — the attention to negative as well as to positive deviations. Here they have identical values, except for algebraic sign, but we shall find that elsewhere they may differ in value. The use of deviations in both directions also calls our attention to the fact that basically we have made a two-tail test, just as we often do in making a $\bar{z}$ test.

Let us see what the chi square is for the polling data. Applying formula (11.2),

$$\chi^2 = \frac{2\,(28-20)^2}{20} = \frac{128}{20} = 6.4$$

This value is interpreted by reference to the sampling distribution of chi square with 1 df.[1] Like the distribution of t, the frequency distribution of chi square differs in shape, depending upon the number of df. Table E in Appendix B gives the chi squares corresponding to extreme proportions under the χ^2 distribution curves. The first row in Table E gives the distribution with 1 df, which applies to our illustrative problem. Looking across the row we find that the obtained chi square of 6.4 is a little below 6.635, which is the value of chi square above which are .01 of the chance-generated chi squares. The inference that we may not reject the null hypothesis at the .01 level is the same as for the $\bar{z}$ test. This is not surprising, of course, since with 1 df $\chi^2 = \bar{z}^2$. Taking the square root of the chi square of 6.4, we find a $\bar{z}$ of 2.53, which checks with the value obtained earlier.

If the chi-square and $\bar{z}$ tests give identical answers regarding significance, it might be asked why we need anything but $\bar{z}$. The quickest answer is that the relation to $\bar{z}$ holds only for 1 df; there are numerous hypotheses to be tested where there is more than 1 df. The $\bar{z}$ test is limited to the case of 1 df; chi square is not.

The more versatile nature of chi square arises from its additive property, the secret of which lies in the squaring of the deviations. This virtue is analogous to the additivity of the squared coefficient of correlation, r^2, where r itself lacks that property. We shall soon

[1] Although we have summed two chi squares, they are not *mutually independent;* one is free to vary but the other is then determined in each case.

see that many *sets* of observations provide a number of frequency values, for each of which a null hypothesis can be stated and a test of the departures of the obtained frequencies from those expected from the null hypothesis is needed. Chi square enables us to make such combined tests, or tests of combined data.

Computation of $\bar{z}$ and χ^2 from observed frequencies. In a set of two observed frequencies such as we have in the illustrative polling problem, it is possible to compute $\bar{z}$ or χ^2 without finding the expected frequency f_e, where $Np = N/2$. First, let us express all values in formula (11.2) in terms of the two observed frequencies, f_1 and f_2, where f_1 is arbitrarily the larger of the two. The difference $f_o - f_e$ is half the difference between f_1 and f_2. That is, $f_o - f_e$, without algebraic sign, equals $(f_1 - f_2)/2$. The expected frequency f_e is equal to $N/2$, which also equals $(f_1 + f_2)/2$. Substituting these values in formula (11.2),

$$\chi^2 = \frac{2(f_o - f_e)^2}{f_e} = \frac{2(f_1 - f_2)^2/4}{(f_1 + f_2)/2}$$

$$= \frac{(f_1 - f_2)^2}{f_1 + f_2} \qquad \begin{array}{l}\text{(Chi square computed from two} \\ \text{observed frequencies in} \\ \text{alternate categories)}\end{array} \qquad (11.3)$$

Since with 1 df, $\bar{z} = \chi$, taking square roots of both sides of (11.3) gives

$$\bar{z} = \frac{f_1 - f_2}{\sqrt{f_1 + f_2}} \qquad \begin{array}{l}\text{(Standard deviate } \bar{z} \text{ computed from} \\ \text{observed frequencies in two} \\ \text{alternate, mutually exclusive} \\ \text{categories)}\end{array} \qquad (11.4)$$

And since $f_1 + f_2 = N$, we have the interesting conclusion that under these circumstances $\bar{z} = (f_1 - f_2)/\sqrt{N}$. The student should check on the applicability of these formulas by computing χ^2 and $\bar{z}$ for the polling data.

A CHI SQUARE FOR THREE SIMULTANEOUS COMPARISONS

Let us carry our exploration of the nature of chi square a bit further by bringing in more clearly the additive principle. Let us use another polling problem, in which two groups of individuals respond to a question by giving one of three responses. The data are fictitious but perhaps realistic. Thirty men and 30 women in selected samples of students were asked the question: Should the average woman graduate work for a postgraduate degree? Each student answered by saying "Yes," "No," or "Undecided." The frequencies of these three responses for men and women are listed in Table 11.1.

The major interest in data such as these would be in whether there is a genuine sex difference in reactions. There are three ways in

Table 11.1 **Numbers of men and women students who responded "Yes," "No," and "Undecided" to the question: Should the average woman graduate work for a postgraduate degree?**

Response	f_o			f_e		$f_o - f_e$		$(f_o - f_e)^2$		$(f_o - f_e)^2/f_e$		
	M	W	Both	M	W	M	W	M	W	M	W	Both
Yes	9	15	24	12	12	−3	+3	9	9	0.75	0.75	1.50
No	12	2	14	7	7	+5	−5	25	25	3.57	3.57	7.14
Undecided	9	13	22	11	11	−2	+2	4	4	0.36	0.36	0.72
Sums	30	30	60	30	30	0	0			4.68	4.68	$9.36 = \chi^2$

which the two sexes could be compared, each in terms of one of the three response categories. We could find three chi squares, one for each pair of frequencies for the three responses, and we could sum the three chi squares to determine whether the *set* of frequencies for the men is significantly different from the *set* of frequencies for the women. Let us make the test of the null hypothesis (no sex difference) for all the frequencies taken together. For the computation of a chi square from a table with any number of cells there is a more general, standard formula, which reads

$$\chi^2 = \sum \frac{(f_o - f_e)^2}{f_e} \qquad \text{(General computing formula} \atop \text{for chi square)} \qquad (11.5)$$

The first step is to find the expected frequencies that correspond to the obtained frequencies. Since the total numbers of men and women are identical, the null hypothesis should lead us to expect the same number of "Yes" responses for the two sexes, the same number of "No" responses, and the same number of "Undecided" responses. We have to consider the number of each kind of response that was given by the two sexes combined. There were 24 "Yes" responses, which, evenly divided, gives f_e's of 12 for each of the sexes (see Table 11.1). The 14 "No" responses divide evenly to give 7 and 7. The 22 "Undecided" responses give 11 and 11. The f_e's in each column should sum to 30, and they do.

Next we find the deviations $f_o - f_e$, which are numerically 3, 5, and 2, with opposite signs for men and women, for the three response categories, respectively. They should sum to zero in each column, and they do. Squared, they give 9, 25, and 4, respectively, for both men and women. Dividing each of the squared discrepancies by its corresponding f_e, and summing the pair of ratios in each row, we find a chi square for each row. These chi-square values appear in the last column of Table 11.1. The sum of the three is 9.36, which is the chi square for the whole table of six frequencies. This value indicates how far the six obtained frequencies depart from the frequencies we should have expected if there were no sex difference.

Interpretation of an obtained chi square. In order to draw any inference concerning whether or not a chi square of 9.36 indicates a significant departure from the null hypothesis, we have to relate that value to the appropriate sampling distribution of chi square. Reference to Table E in Appendix B will give us the basis for a decision, but we have to consider first the number of degrees of freedom in order to know which line in Table E is appropriate to this problem.

In deciding on the number of df for this problem, we can be guided somewhat, but not entirely, by the previous illustrative problem. There we had two frequencies and one degree of freedom. There only one of the two frequencies was free to vary, once the other was determined, for $f_1 + f_2$ must add up to N. Applying this reasoning to the data in Table 11.1, we might expect to find three degrees of freedom, because there are three pairs of frequencies, each pair adding up to a fixed total. There is another kind of restriction to be considered, however, that is provided by the sums of the columns. Once two *pairs* of frequencies are established, the third pair is determined as well. The conclusion is that the obtained chi square has 2 df. In Table E, we find that for 2 df, in the second row of chi squares, a value as large as 9.36 could occur by random sampling alone a little less than once in a hundred times ($p < .01$). We can reject the null hypothesis of no sex difference with a high degree of confidence.

Looking now at the three chi squares for the three rows, we see that it was the sex difference in "No" responses that was almost entirely the source of the overall significant chi square. In fact, taking only the "No" responses, with one degree of freedom, we find a difference significant beyond the .01 level, the chi square of 7.14 exceeding the required 6.635 (from Table E). If these were genuine data, a natural psychological inference (to be distinguished from a statistical inference) would be that men are decidedly more in favor of denying women the privilege of working for postgraduate degrees, but when it comes to favoring the privilege, or being undecided about it, we cannot say that they are less inclined than women.

THE SAMPLING DISTRIBUTIONS OF CHI SQUARE

Table E is based upon the sampling distributions of chi square, with different numbers of df from 1 to as high as 30. The shapes of sampling distributions of χ^2 may be seen in Fig. 11.1, where the curves for 1, 2, 4, 6, and 10 df are shown. A distribution of z is normal. Squaring z to obtain chi square (with 1 df) does two things. It makes all

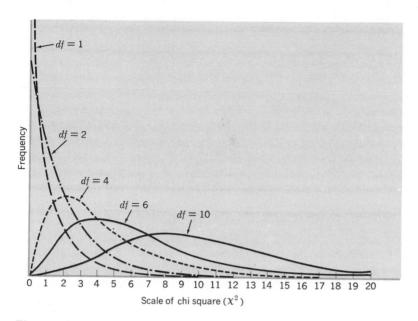

Fig. 11.1. *Sampling distributions of chi square for various degrees of freedom.* (After Lewis, D. Quantitative Methods in Psychology. New York: McGraw-Hill, 1960.)

values positive, so that instead of having a distribution symmetrical about zero, we have a distribution all on the positive side of zero. Squaring z's of 0, 1, 2, 3, 4, and 5 gives z^2 values of 0, 1, 4, 9, 16, and 25. Obviously, the second effect is to change the shape of the distribution by piling up the frequencies near 0 and 1 and spreading the larger values.

Remember that for higher degrees of freedom, each chi square comes from a summing of chi squares, each with 1 df. Where the summed chi squares are mutually independent, they come in chance combinations. As the number summed in each set increases, the chances of zero sums decrease, and the mode of the distribution moves away from zero. It cannot easily be proved here, but with 2 or more df the principle is that the mode is at a chi-square value of df − 2. The mode for 2 df is at zero; the mode for 10 df is at 8 (see Fig. 11.1). By 30 df the χ^2 distribution is virtually symmetrical, and it approximates the normal form. Even with fewer than 30 df it would be possible to find where χ^2 falls in one tail of the normal curve and to interpret it as one would interpret z. But the tabled values of χ^2 are very convenient up to 30 df.

So much for the general features of chi-square distributions; of more critical importance are the regions for rejections of null hypotheses. As with statistics $\bar{z}$ and t, each chi-square distribution curve can be described by an equation; it is also possible to state the proportion of the total area that lies under the curve above a given χ^2 value. As indicated earlier, a chi-square test is a two-tailed test. Although the tail area under the curve is only at the higher end of the range, remember that the squaring of z that is implied combines extreme negative cases of z with the extreme positive ones. If a one-tail test *should* be wanted for a particular case, it can be made by cutting the probabilities given in Table E in half. A one-tail test is hardly logical, however, unless one is dealing with a clear case of a simple outcome that can go in either of two opposite directions. Many sets of data to which chi square is applied are too complex for application of a one-tail test.

Chi square in a contingency table

Consider the data in Table 11.2, which is an example of a contingency table because it sets forth two possibly related variables — intelligence level and marital status. Whether or not an individual in the data is married may be contingent upon his intelligence. In the table we have two samples: one is composed of 206 young, American males who, when they were in school, had been regarded as feeble-minded in terms of IQ. Their IQ's were in the range 60 to 69. The other group was composed of 206 men of similar age (in their twenties) whose IQ's were near 100.[1] At the time the study was made, the proportions of married men were .408 and .539, for the feeble-minded and normal groups, respectively. One question we could ask is, "Is this difference in marital status statistically significant?"

Another way of asking the same question is whether the married and unmarried groups differ significantly with respect to intelligence. Another, more comprehensive question is, "Is there any cor-

[1]Baller, W. R. A study of the present status of adults who were mentally deficient. *Genet. Psychol. Monogr.*, 1936, 18, 165–244.

Table 11.2 **Solution of chi square in a contingency table for data relating marital status to normal versus feeble-minded status with respect to intelligence**

Marital status	f_o		
	Feeble-minded	Normal	Both
Married	84	111	195
Unmarried	122	95	217
Sum	206	206	412

relation between being married and level of intelligence in this combined population?" Being married or unmarried and being normal or feeble-minded are two genuine dichotomies (discrete groups), calling for the special correlation coefficient known as ϕ (see Chap. 14). The phi coefficient for these data is .13. Is this small coefficient significantly different from zero? Such a question normally suggests a t test such as we saw in Chap. 9. But the usual t test pertaining to an ordinary Pearson r does not apply to ϕ. We can, however, apply a chi-square test, which will be demonstrated next.

CHI SQUARE AS A TEST OF INDEPENDENCE

The null hypothesis for a contingency table such as Table 11.2 is that there is no correlation: the two variables (marital status and intelligence) are independent in the population in question. The application of a chi-square test to the data in Table 11.2 is the same as for the data in Table 11.1. Using the fact that there are equal numbers of feeble-minded and normal subjects, we should expect to find both the married and the unmar ed to be equally divided with respect to intelligence category, with f_e s of 97.5 for the married group and f_e's of 108.5 for the unmarried group. The differences $f_o - f_e$ are all 13.5, with two negative and two positive values. The difference squared is the same for all four cells. The chi square for the table as a whole is 7.10.

The number of degrees of freedom of the appropriate chi-square distribution is 1. The reason for this is similar to that in the preceding polling problem. It can also be seen from the fact that, with the four marginal totals established, after finding one cell frequency the other three are completely determined. With 1 df, a chi square of 7.10 is significant beyond the .01 level, at which level we find a χ^2 of 6.635 in Table E.

DEGREES OF FREEDOM IN A CONTINGENCY TABLE

The general rule about the number of degrees of freedom in a contingency table of any size is that

f_e		$f_o - f_e$		$(f_o - f_e)^2$		$(f_o - f_e)^2/f_e$		
Feeble-minded	Normal	Feeble-minded	Normal	Feeble-minded	Normal	Feeble-minded	Normal	Both
97.5	97.5	13.5	−13.5	182.25		1.87	1.87	3.74
108.5	108.5	−13.5	13.5	182.25		1.68	1.68	3.36
206	206	0.0	0.0			3.55	3.55	7.10

$$\text{df} = (r-1)(k-1)\quad\begin{array}{l}\text{(Number of degrees of freedom in a}\\\text{contingency table of } r \text{ rows and}\\k \text{ columns)}\end{array}\qquad(11.6)$$

where r is the number of rows and k is the number of columns. For the four-cell table, with an r of 2 and a k of 2, df = 1, as we have seen.

COMPUTING EXPECTED CELL FREQUENCIES

Thus far, the computing of the expected frequencies f_e has been simple because of an even division of marginal frequencies in one of the variables. Very often the marginal frequencies are not evenly distributed and a more general procedure is needed. A method for computing the expected cell frequencies in a contingency table of any number of rows and columns is illustrated by the limited 3×3 table shown in Table 11.3. Let the f's with double subscripts stand for the obtained cell frequencies. The sums of the rows are symbolized by $f_a, f_b,$ and $f_c,$ and the sums of columns by $f_1, f_2,$ and $f_3.$ The expected frequency for any cell in row r and column k can be found by the formula

$$f_{e(rk)} = \frac{f_r f_k}{N}\quad\begin{array}{l}\text{(Expected frequency for a cell}\\\text{in row } r \text{ and column } k)\end{array}\qquad(11.7)$$

Thus, the expected frequency corresponding to f_{b3} would be derived from the product $(f_b)(f_3)$ divided by N. The expected frequency for the married-normal subgroup in Table 11.2, in row A and column 2 is equal to

$$\frac{(195)(206)}{412} = 97.5$$

Table 11.3 **Schema and symbols for computation of expected cell frequencies in a contingency table**

Rows	Columns			Sums of rows
	1	2	3	
A	f_{a1}	f_{a2}	f_{a3}	f_a
B	f_{b1}	f_{b2}	f_{b3}	f_b
C	f_{c1}	f_{c2}	f_{c3}	f_c
Sums of columns	f_1	f_2	f_3	N

Let f_r stand for a sum of any row, for example, f_a, $f_b, \ldots$, etc.

Let f_k stand for a sum of any column, for example, f_1, $f_2, \ldots$.

CHI SQUARE WHEN FREQUENCIES ARE SMALL

When we apply chi square to a problem with 1 df and when any cell frequency is less than 10, we should apply a modification known as *Yates's correction for continuity.* This correction consists in reducing by .5 each obtained frequency that is greater than expected and in increasing by the same amount each frequency that is less than expected. This has the effect of reducing the amount of each difference between obtained and expected frequency to the extent of .5. The result is reduction of the size of chi square.

The correction is needed because of the fact that a computed chi square, being based on frequencies, which are whole numbers, varies in discrete jumps whereas the chi-square table, representing the distributions of chi square, gives values from a continuous scale. When frequencies are large this correction is relatively unimportant, but when they are small a change of .5 is of some consequence. The correction is particularly important when chi square turns out to be near a point of division between critical regions.

An example of Yates's correction. In a public-opinion poll conducted some years ago, sentiment was sampled concerning attitudes toward radio newscasts.[1] Some 43 interviewees in one sample were asked the question, "Do you find it easier to listen to news than to read it?" The sample had been stratified into higher and lower socioeconomic status, 19 being in the former and 24 in the latter. The numbers responding "Yes" to the question in the two groups were 10 and 20, respectively. The problem to be investigated is whether there was a real difference between the two groups in their opinions on the question.

The data have been arranged in the usual manner in Table 11.4. Two of the expected frequencies are less than 10. Let us carry through the computations first *without* Yates's correction and then with it to see what difference it will make in the conclusion.

Without the correction, the cell deviations would all equal 3.26. This value squared is 10.63. Applying formula (11.5) and solving, we find that chi square equals 4.76, which is significant between the .05 and .01 levels. *With* the correction, the cell deviation in all cells is 2.76 (rather than 3.26), which squared is 6.72. Here chi square becomes 3.43, and thus fails to reach the .05 level of significance. One would have much more confidence in the interpretation of the second result than the first. The correction will not always make a difference of this kind in the conclusion, but the correction should be used in a problem like this.

[1] From Cantril, H. The role of the radio commentator. *Publ. Opin. Quart.*, 1939, **3**, 654–662.

Table 11.4   Computation of chi square for responses of two socioeconomic groups to preference for radio news to reading a newspaper

Response	Obtained frequencies			Expected frequencies		
	Lower	Higher	Both	Lower	Higher	Both
Yes	20	10	30	16.74	13.26	30
No	4	9	13	7.26	5.74	13
Both	24	19	43	24	19	43

It should be noted that the correction of .5 is applied to *all* cells in the table even though only one or two frequencies are small. Note also that it is low *expected* frequencies that determine whether the correction shall be applied, not low observed frequencies. It is also applied only to instances of 1 df, including 2 × 2 and 1 × 2 tables. In larger tables the need for the correction is not so great and it would be complicated to apply. It is also possible to combine categories in such a way as to get rid of small expected frequencies. Examples of this will be seen later.

Testing significance by direct computation of probability.   There are lower limits to utilizable frequencies, beyond which even Yates's correction is inadequate. If any expected frequency is less than 2, we should not apply the computing formulas for chi square, even with the correction. If there is 1 df and there is a frequency less than 2, it is still possible to answer the question, "Given the marginal frequencies, what is the probability that distributions among the four cells could be as extreme as this one, or one more extreme?" The probability, and hence the level of significance, can be determined without computing chi square.

For the special case of a fourfold table in which two equal groups of observations are being compared, Table N in Appendix B will serve to answer the question of statistical significance. It was designed for the following very common type of problem. Let us say that an experimental group of 30 individuals is administered a dose of dramamine sulfate and a control group of 30 individuals is administered a placebo before a rough flight in an airplane. Of the experimental group 5 become airsick and 25 do not; of the control group 18 become airsick and 12 do not.

In Table N, each row pertains to two groups each of a certain size, N_i. In the illustrative problem, $N_i = 30$. To use Table N, locate the row that applies, in this case the row for $N_i = 30$. Next, find the column headed with the number that corresponds to the smallest frequency in the fourfold table. In this problem that frequency is 5, the number in the experimental group who became airsick. Given these two values, 30 and 5, we ask the question, "How many cases are needed in the other group corresponding to the smallest cell frequency to achieve chi squares significant at the .05 and .01 levels?" Corresponding to the frequency of 5 is the frequency of 18 airsick cases in the control group. Table N tells us that it would take 13 cases of airsickness in this group to be significant at the .05 level and 16 cases of airsickness to be significant at the .01 level. The obtained frequency of 18 exceeds both those values and is therefore a basis for concluding that we have significance beyond the .01 level.

Table N has solutions based upon exact probabilities up to an N_i of 20 and solutions by formula with Yates's correction for N_i's greater than 20.[1]

OTHER WAYS OF COMPUTING CHI SQUARE IN A 2 × 2 TABLE

In a fourfold-table problem, since the difference is the same for all cells, the formula for chi square can be written

$$\chi^2 = (f_o - f_e)^2 \sum \left(\frac{1}{f_e}\right) \qquad \text{(Chi square in a 2 × 2 contingency table)} \qquad (11.8)$$

That is, chi square equals the common difference squared times the sum of the reciprocals of the four f_e's. As applied to the marital-status problem,

$$\chi^2 = 13.5^2 \left(\frac{1}{97.5} + \frac{1}{97.5} + \frac{1}{108.5} + \frac{1}{108.5}\right)$$
$$= 182.25\,(.01026 + .01026 + .00922 + .00922\,)$$
$$= 7.10$$

If the data are arranged in a 2 × 2 table as shown in Table 11.5, another convenient formula for the computation of chi square is

$$\chi^2 = \frac{N(ad - bc)^2}{(a + b)(a + c)(b + d)(c + d)} \qquad \text{(Alternative formula for chi square in a four-cell, 2 × 2 table)} \qquad (11.9)$$

Applied to the opinion-poll data,

$$\chi^2 = \frac{43[(10)(4) - (20)(9)]^2}{(30)(19)(24)(13)} = 4.74$$

[1]For dealing with contingency tables where the sums of columns N_i are not equal, exact probabilities can be computed by methods described by Walker, H. M., and Lev, J. *Statistical Inference.* New York: Holt, 1953. Pp. 104–108. A useful table is also provided in Siegel, S. *Nonparametric Statistics for the Behaviorial Sciences.* New York: McGraw-Hill, 1956.

*Table 11.5 **Symbolic arrangement of data in a 2 × 2 contingency table illustrated by the public-opinion data***

Variable I

	Lower	Higher	Both
Higher	b	a	$a + b$
Lower	d	c	$c + d$
Both	$b + d$	$a + c$	N

Variable II

Socioeconomic group

	Lower	Higher	Both
Yes	20	10	30
No	4	9	13
Both	24	19	43

Response

The answer is within rounding error of that computed earlier by formula (11.2).

The last solution was done without Yates's correction. The same formula with Yates's correction incorporated reads

$$\chi^2 = \frac{\left(N|ad - bc| - \dfrac{N}{2}\right)^2}{(a + b)(a + c)(b + d)(c + d)} \qquad \text{[Same as (11.9), with Yates's correction]} \qquad (11.10)$$

Note that the difference $ad - bc$ is taken as positive, as indicated by the vertical lines enclosing it.

OTHER GENERAL COMPUTING FORMULAS FOR CHI SQUARE

It is possible to compute chi square by using formulas that require less information than is involved in the use of formula (11.5). By expanding the expression $(f_o - f_e)^2$ and simplifying, we arrive at the equation

$$\chi^2 = \sum \left(\frac{f^2_o}{f_e}\right) - N \qquad \text{(Formula for chi square without finding } f_o - f_e) \qquad (11.11)$$

Making use of the fact that, from formula (11.7), $f_e = f_r f_k / N$, and substituting this expression in (11.8), we have

$$\chi^2 = N\left[\sum \left(\frac{f^2_{rk}}{f_r f_k}\right) - 1\right] \qquad \text{(Formula for chi square without finding } f_e\text{'s)} \qquad (11.12)$$

where $f_{rk}, f_r,$ and f_k are defined as in (11.7).[1]

CHI SQUARE IN OTHER THAN 2 × 2 TABLES

In the very first example, we examined the case of chi square computed from a two-cell table. We shall now consider cases in which either r or k, or both, exceed two. For such a case, let us consider the

[1]These two formulas were suggested by Stephen Brown. For complete accuracy, the ratios in formula (11.12) should be carried to four or five decimal places.

data in Table 11.6, which has three categories each way. The object of the study which developed this particular set of data was to determine whether the ability to distinguish among the taste qualities of three popular brands of cola beverages is related to the amount of experience with cola drinking. Each of 79 individuals had been tested with pairs of sample cola brands; each achieved a score, which was the number of correct identifications he made. On the basis of the scores, the subjects were divided into three categories. The same subjects were also grouped in categories as "heavy," "medium," or "light" cola drinkers, according to the number of times per week they said they drank any colas. It is a reasonable psychological hypothesis that ability to discriminate should be related positively to the amount of experience.

Let us test the alternative, null hypothesis, that the two variables are independent, by computing a chi square, applying formula (11.12). The work is laid out by steps in Table 11.6: first we find the f_r and f_k marginal sums, we square the cell frequencies to find f^2_{rk}, we find the $f_r f_k$ product for each of the nine cells of the table, and then we compute the ratios $f^2_{rk}/f_r f_k$ and their sums, which is 1.0694. It should be noted that four decimal places are retained in the ratios through this point. Deducting 1.0 from this figure leaves only .0694, which, multiplied by N, gives chi square. The final product is 5.48. With four degrees of freedom [according to formula (11.6)], Table E tells us that this χ^2 fails to reach significance at the .05 level. There are at least 5 chances in 100 that so large a χ^2 could have arisen by chance with a genuinely zero correlation between cola experience and ability to discriminate brands.

Combining columns or rows. It was pointed out earlier that in a 2×2 contingency table, when expected frequencies are small, we may apply the correction for continuity. This leaves open the question of what to do in larger contingency tables with small expected frequencies. In larger tables, f_e's as small as 5 may be tolerated. When a frequency is less than 5, the best remedy is to note the row or column (whichever has generally smaller frequencies) in which the small frequency occurs, and combine that array (row or column) with one of its neighbors. Choosing the neighbor that also has smaller frequencies would be a good policy, but other common-sense considerations should also be given some weight.

In the contingency table in Table 11.6, the smallest f_e appears (actually twice) in the last column, where the $f_r f_k$ product is 494. Dividing this by N (which is 79) gives an f_e of approximately 6. This value is not small enough to require combining arrays. If it were, the best combination to make would be the last two columns. After combining two arrays the computed chi square is generally smaller, but there is

*Table 11.6 A chi-square test of independence between amount of experience in drinking colas and ability to discriminate among three common brands**

	f_{rk}			
	0–3	4–6	7+	f_r
Heavy	10	14	3	27
Medium	7	9	10	26
Light	8	12	6	26
f_k	25	35	19	79

*From Thumin, F. J. Identification of cola beverages. *J. appl. Psychol.*, 1962, **46**, 359. Used by permission of the author and publisher. The three experience categories are defined as follows: Heavy = seven or more colas con-

compensation in the fact that the number of df is also smaller. It is possible that making such combinations will change one's decision as to the statistical significance of data.

Some special applications of chi square

CHI SQUARE WHEN PROPORTIONS ARE CORRELATED

Many of the applications of chi square involve the comparison of two proportions or percentages, as we have seen. In the examples thus far the two proportions were uncorrelated, for they were derived from different observations or individuals. We shall now consider some applications of chi square when proportions are correlated.

Test for two correlated proportions. For a difference between two correlated proportions we used in Chap. 9 a $\bar{z}$ test. Since with 1 degree of freedom χ^2 is equal to $\bar{z}^2$, we might expect a very direct estimate of chi square by squaring both sides of formula (9.10). This expectation is correct, and the formula is

$$\chi^2 = \frac{(b - c)^2}{b + c} \qquad \text{(Chi square for a difference between two correlated proportions)} \qquad (11.13)$$

where the symbols are as defined in Table 9.3.

It should be noted here, as in Table 9.3, that b and c indicate the numbers of cases that change categories between a first and second application of the experiment. Either the same individuals or matched individuals must be involved so that the numbers of changes may be counted. The illustrative problem in Chap. 9 involved 100 students who had attempted to answer two items. If there is correlation between the items there is also correlation between the proportions. The number of changing individuals denoted by b (answering the first correctly but not the second) was 5. The number of changing

f^2_{rk}			$f_r f_k$			$f^2_{rk}/f_r f_k$			Row sums
0 – 3	*4 – 6*	*7+*	*0 – 3*	*4 – 6*	*7+*	*0 – 3*	*4 – 6*	*7+*	
100	196	9	675	945	513	.1481	.2074	.0175	.3730
49	81	100	650	910	494	.0754	.0890	.2024	.3668
64	144	36	650	910	494	.0985	.1582	.0729	.3296
						.3220	.4546	.2928	1.0694

sumed per week; Medium = three to six; and Light = fewer than three. The subjects were asked to identify by taste a sample which was one of three well-known brands. The score is the number of correct identifications.

individuals denoted by c (answering the second correctly but not the first) was 15. Applying formula (11.13),

$$\chi^2 = \frac{(5 - 15)^2}{5 + 15} = 5.00$$

which is significant between the .05 and .01 points.

In small samples, Yates's correction should be incorporated in formula (11.10). This involves deducting 1 from the difference, where the difference is regarded as positive, before squaring.

Test for more than two correlated proportions. A chi-square test for differences among more than two correlated proportions is described by McNemar.[1]

CHI-SQUARE TEST OF THE HYPOTHESIS OF NORMAL DISTRIBUTION

One of the useful applications of chi square is in testing whether an obtained distribution of frequencies departs significantly from some standard, mathematically defined frequency distribution. The hypothetical distribution could be of various kinds—binomial, normal, Poisson, etc. The application of chi square for testing goodness of fit of data to a hypothetical curve will be demonstrated here in connection with a normal distribution. The data are 86 scores obtained from a memory test. The hypothesis to be tested is that the obtained frequencies merely represent chance deviations from corresponding frequencies in a normal distribution having the same mean and standard deviation as the obtained distribution. The size of N will also naturally have to be taken into account.

Finding the expected frequencies. The process of computing the expected frequencies in connection with a normal-curve hypothesis is quite different from computing them in a contingency table. The

[1]McNemar, Q. *Psychological Statistics.* 3d ed. New York: Wiley, 1962.

best-fitting normal distribution for any obtained frequency distribution is the one having the same mean and standard deviation as those computed from that distribution. The fit of the data to that best-fitting normal distribution may be close or not; in any event, no other normal curve would fit the data better. The mean of the distribution of memory-test scores, which is shown in column 8 of Table 11.7, is 26.1. The standard deviation is 6.45. These two items are sufficient information from which to start. The operating steps are shown in Table 11.7.

Before examining these steps, the reader may gain a greater understanding of the process by examining Fig. 11.2. There the best-fitting normal distribution has been drawn on the basis of the expected frequencies obtained in Table 11.7. The obtained frequencies are also shown by means of dots. By inspection, the fit seems much better on the right half of the curve than on the left half, but only two points depart notably from the curve. The chi square to be

Table 11.7 **Determination of expected frequencies in the score intervals for a memory test, on the assumption that the true distribution is normal**

(1) Scores	(2) X_u, Upper limit	(3) x_u, Deviation	(4) z_u, Standard score	(5) cp, Cumulative proportion	(6) cf, Cumulative frequency	(7) f_e, Expected frequency	(8) f_o, Observed frequency
47+				1.000	86.0	0.1	0
44–46	46.5	+20.4	+3.16	.999	85.9	0.2	0
41–43	43.5	+17.4	+2.70	.997	85.7	0.8	1
38–40	40.5	+14.4	+2.23	.987	84.9	2.2	4
35–37	37.5	+11.4	+1.77	.962	82.7	5.0	5
32–34	34.5	+ 8.4	+1.30	.903	77.7	8.9	8
29–31	31.5	+ 5.4	+0.84	.800	68.8	13.4	14
26–28	28.5	+ 2.4	+0.37	.644	55.4	15.5	17
23–25	25.5	− 0.6	−0.09	.464	39.9	15.1	9
20–22	22.5	− 3.6	−0.56	.288	24.8	11.6	13
17–19	19.5	− 6.6	−1.02	.154	13.2	7.4	8
14–16	16.5	− 9.6	−1.49	.068	5.8	3.6	3
11–13	13.5	−12.6	−1.95	.016	2.2	1.5	4
8–10	10.5	−15.6	−2.42	.008	0.7	0.5	0
5–7	7.5	−18.6	−2.88	.002	0.2	0.2	0
					Sums 86.0		86

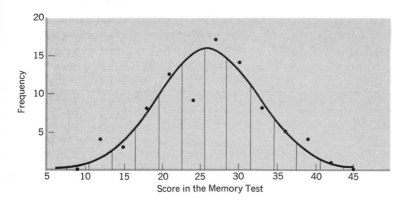

Fig. 11.2. *The best-fitting normal distribution curve with plotted frequencies obtained from administration of the memory test.*

computed summarizes the squared, vertical deviations of the points from the curve, in ratio to the expected frequencies, which, of course, lie exactly on the curve. The comparison of two frequencies, f_o and f_e, within each score interval is exactly like the comparisons we have made before. Each interval yields a chi square, which may be summed with others to give the overall chi square, as usual.

Let us return to the steps involved in Table 11.7. The main point is to work in terms of a unit normal distribution so that we may make use of the normal-curve tables. The first major step, therefore, is to go from the score scale of the memory test to the standard-score scale, on which the mean is zero and the standard deviation is 1.0. Another point is to work first toward cumulative frequencies since it is easier to find them directly from the normal-curve tables, and then to find the uncumulated frequencies.

In finding standard-score equivalents for the raw-score intervals, we select the exact upper limits of the score intervals because the aim is toward cumulative frequencies. The upper-limit values appear in column 2. It may be noted that two score intervals beyond those in which observed frequencies occur are included at both ends of the list. This step anticipates the fact that the best-fitting normal curve will have fractions of frequencies at the tails of the curve. It is important that we allow enough range, including those fractions, so that the expected frequencies will sum to N, which is 86 in this case.

A standard score z equals $(X - M_x)/\sigma_x = x/\sigma_x$. The next step in Table 11.7 is to deduct the mean, 26.1, from each X_u, giving x_u in column 3. Then we divide by σ_x, which is 6.45, to obtain the standard score z_u, column 4. Using the normal-curve table, Table B, for each z_u we find the corresponding proportion of the area under the unit normal curve *below* that z value.[1] These are the cumulative proportions, cp, which appear in column 5. Without a cp of 1.00 at the top interval, we would not reach the total of 86.0, and therefore that cp value has been added for the range of raw score 47 and above. This needed 0.1 could have been added at the lower end instead, or it could have been divided between the two ends, whichever seems more reasonable.

The cumulative frequencies that apply to the 86 scores in the actual distribution are found by the usual Np products: in this case, $N \times cp$. The cumulative score distribution appears in column 6. By making successive subtractions in column 6, we find the expected frequencies *within* the intervals in column 7. They may be compared directly with the corresponding observed frequencies that appear in column 8.

Computation of the chi square. Computation of the chi square for the goodness-of-fit problem is demonstrated in Table 11.8. The observed and expected frequencies are listed again in column 2, just as they were in columns 7 and 8 of Table 11.7, interchanging columns. The first consideration is that many of the expected tail frequencies are very small, many of them being less than 5.0. The first thing to do, therefore, is to combine tail categories until all f_e's exceed 5.0. This means combining five intervals at the upper end of the distribution and four at the lower end. The two frequency distributions are repeated in column 3, after making the combinations.[2] From here on, the steps are familiar, as shown in columns (4), (5), and (6). The sum of the ratios in column (6) is the chi square.

The number of degrees of freedom to be associated with this chi square is the number of categories minus 3. Three df are lost by the use of three parameters in finding the best-fitting curve and its frequencies: N, the mean, and the standard deviation. Although the observed frequencies were distributed in 11 categories, the process of combining intervals reduced to 8 the number used in computing the chi square. The number of df is therefore 5. Reference to Table E shows that the obtained χ^2 of 3.541 is greater than the value with .70 of the χ^2's above it (3.000), but not sufficiently large to equal the value with .50 of the χ^2's above it (4.352). We may, indeed, tolerate the hypothesis that the frequency distribution of memory scores arose by random sampling from a normally distributed population.

[1]In Fig. 11.2, a vertical line is drawn at the upper score limit of every interval. Each cp is represented graphically by the area under the curve below one of those limits, where the total area under the curve is equal to 1.0.

[2]Some writers demand a minimum, f_e of 10, but this hardly seems necessary. In this particular problem, for example, the decision regarding the normal-curve hypothesis would have been the same.

Table 11.8   **A chi-square test of the normal-distribution hypothesis applied to the distribution of memory-test scores**

(1)	(2)		(3)		(4)	(5)	(6)
	Original grouping		*Regrouped frequencies*		*Cell discrepancies*	*Squared cell discrepancies*	*Cell ratios*
Scores	f_o	f_e	f_o	f_e	$(f_o - f_e)$	$(f_o - f_e)^2$	$\dfrac{(f_o - f_e)^2}{f_e}$
47+	0	0.1					
44–46	0	0.2					
41–43	1	0.8					
38–40	4	2.2	10	8.3	+1.7	2.89	.348
35–37	5	5.0					
32–34	8	8.9	8	8.9	−0.9	0.81	.091
29–31	14	13.4	14	13.4	+0.6	0.36	.027
26–28	17	15.5	17	15.5	+1.5	2.25	.145
23–25	9	15.1	9	15.1	−6.1	37.21	2.464
20–22	13	11.6	13	11.6	+1.4	1.96	.169
17–19	8	7.4	8	7.4	+0.6	0.36	.049
14–16	3	3.6					
11–13	4	1.5	7	5.8	+1.2	1.44	.248
8–10	0	0.5					
−7	0	0.2					
Sums	86	86.0	86	86.0	0.0		$\chi^2 = 3.541$

In interpreting chi squares in connection with curve fitting, there is some opinion that considerations other than those pertaining to contingency tables and the like should be introduced. The standards for rejection of a hypothesis are much the same. But experience shows that when fits are even little better looking than the one we have just seen, probabilities of chi squares larger than those obtained become very great—even larger than .90. Some investigators consequently regard such chi squares with suspicion; they are said to indicate fits that are "just too good." For one thing, they might suggest that the computations should be checked for possible errors. Except for such errors, however, the writer believes that there is little cause for concern when one obtains such low chi squares. If a fit no better than the one shown in Fig. 11.2 is associated with a probability of .50 or greater, better-looking fits might well achieve probabilities as high as .90.

SIGNIFICANCE OF A COMBINATION OF TESTS

Sometimes we have made a $\bar{z}$, t, or F test in several similar, independent samples. Perhaps the sampling statistic was not significant beyond the adopted probability level in any sample, and yet the deviations from the value indicated by the null hypothesis were all in the same direction. In other instances, perhaps some of the samples gave significant results and some did not. Were the significant ones merely high *chance* deviations? Some method is obviously needed to make a single test of all the data.

If we happened to know that certain sets of the data came by random sampling from the same population, and the means and variances within those sets prove to be homogeneous, we should be justified in pooling the sets and making new tests of significance, with enlarged df and more power. But this is probably not the most efficient way, even if we already have the necessary information regarding homogeneity. There are ways of considering in combination the results of several significance tests already applied to the samples individually, one of which will be described.

A chi-square test of combined probabilities. It has been demonstrated that there is a mathematical way of transforming a probability into a chi square. In general, $\chi^2 = -2 \log_e p$, with 2 df. In this method, then, we need to know the value of the probability attached to each obtained sampling statistic. This can be found, of course, from tables of distributions of $\bar{z}$, t, or F, whichever test we are applying.

Where there are several probabilities involved, we can transform each into a chi square, then sum those chi squares and also sum their corresponding degrees of freedom. Because of the additive property of chi square, the sum is also a chi square with combined df. The computing formula is

$$\chi^2 = -4.605 \; \Sigma \log p_i \qquad \text{(11.14a)}$$

(Chi square for a combination of probabilities)

$$\chi^2 = -4.605 \log (p_1 p_2 p_3 \cdots p_k) \qquad \text{(11.14b)}$$

where p_i = probability that a deviation of the obtained size could occur by chance. The constant -4.605 represents the product of -2 times the constant 2.3026, which is needed because we are using common logarithms rather than Napierian logarithms. The sum has $2k$ degrees of freedom, where k is the number of tests made. It will be noted from the two forms of the equation that we may obtain the logarithm of each probability first, then sum them (11.14a), or we may find the product of all the probabilities and then find the one logarithm of the product. The latter solution is simpler when k is small.

Suppose that we have derived three estimates of correlation between the same pair of variables in three samples. In each sample we have tested the hypothesis of no correlation and obtained a $\bar{z}$ or a t ratio. The probability for such a $\bar{z}$ or t value would be found by reference to the normal or the Student distribution, respectively.[1] *The probability associated with a one-tail test is the one to use in formula* (11.14).[2]

In Table 11.9 we have, first, three coefficients of correlation from three independent samples. Each was based upon a sample in which $N = 50$. The N's need not be equal in order to apply this chi-square test. The SE of an r of zero when $N = 50$ is .143. Each r deviates from zero by the number of z units shown in the second column. One-tail tests give the probabilities in column 3. The logarithms of these probabilities are given in column 4.

As the student who remembers his algebra will recall, the four digits to the right of the decimal point are found in the table of logarithms (see Table K). The negative number at the left of each decimal point comes from the fact that each probability is a value less than 1.0. The rule is to make this number one more (in the negative direction) than the number of zeros to the right of the decimal point in p_i. The summing of these logarithms is done for the two components separately, after which an algebraic sum of the two component sums is found. The sum of the logarithms is a numerical value of −3.8416. Multiplying this by −4.605 from formula (11.14a), we find a chi square of 17.69. Reference to the chi-square table with 6 df shows this to be significant beyond the .01 level. Thus, a correlation that failed to be significant beyond the .01 level in any of the three samples is found to be in that region when the tests are combined.

Several restrictions and qualifications with regard to the use of this composite test should be noted. The combined tests must be based

[1]For probabilities from Student's distribution, see Walker and Lev, *op. cit.*, Table IX. For all but small samples, the normal distribution will serve.
[2]See Gordon, M. H., Loveland, E. H., and Cureton, E. E. An extended table of chi-square. *Psychometrika*, 1952, **17**, 311–316.

Table 11.9   Chi square for a combination of three probabilities

r_i	z_i	p_i	$\log p_i$
.294	2.056	.02	−2.3010
.222	1.552	.06	−2.7782
.168	1.175	.12	−1.0792

$\Sigma \log p_i = -3.8416 = -5 + 1.1584$

upon independent samples. The probabilities to be used should be from one-tail tests. If in the end a two-tail test is wanted, we must double the probability attached to the obtained chi square.

If several parallel tests of samples have been made, the combination that is tested should not be a selected one, for example, those with highest p_i values only. All legitimate single-sample tests that are clearly parallel should be included. If the deviation from the null hypothesis happens to be in the opposite direction for any of the samples, for those samples use q_i ($q_i = 1 - p_i$, where p_i is the smaller tail area) instead of p_i, but include such a sample.

EXERCISES

In each of the following exercises, state what hypothesis is being tested, the number of df involved, your statistical inference, and your experimental conclusion.

1. In polling at random 45 interviewees, we find that 32 favor a certain routing of a freeway, and the rest do not. Is it likely that the population concerned is evenly divided on the proposition?

2. Compute a chi square for the contingency table in Data 11*A*.

3. Compute a chi square for the contingency table in Data 11*B*.

Data 11A   Numbers of two groups differing in ability who passed a certain test item

Outcome	Low group	High group	Both groups
Passed	48	62	110
Failed	52	38	90
Both	100	100	200

Data 11B   Numbers of persons in two groups, depressed and not depressed in temperament, who responded in each of three categories to the question, "Would you rate yourself as an impulsive individual?"

Group	Response			
	Yes	?	No	Total
Depressed	72	45	133	250
Not depressed	106	35	109	250
Both	178	80	242	500

Data 11C   *Frequency distribution derived from tossing six coins 128 times and expected frequencies based on the hypothesis of a normal distribution with a mean of 3.0 and a standard deviation of 1.275, which were computed from the obtained frequencies*

Heads	<0	0	1	2	3	4	5	6	>6
f_o		4	14	23	38	36	12	1	
f_e	0.4	2.8	12.2	29.1	39.0	29.1	12.2	2.8	0.4

4. In an experimental group of 15 who were inoculated, two developed colds within a specified time period whereas in a control group of the same size, nine developed colds.
a. Determine chi square, with and without Yates's correction.
b. Make a test using Table N.

5. In 13 identical-twin pairs, 10 pairs had two criminals, and the remaining pairs had one criminal each. In 17 fraternal-twin pairs, three pairs had two criminals, and the remaining pairs had one criminal each. Set up a contingency table and compute a chi square.

6. On the application of a certain test before therapy, 25 of an experimental group were above the general median score and 15 were below. After therapy, 16 were above the median on the same test and 24 below. Eleven were above the median both before and after. Set up a contingency table and compute chi square.

7. A set of 6 pennies was tossed 128 times, with a resulting frequency distribution of 0 to 6 heads as shown in Data 11C. Although this is a binomial distribution, how well does a normal distribution having the same mean and standard deviation approximate it? The expected frequencies for a normal distribution of that kind are also given. Compute a chi square to test the goodness of fit.

8. In three pairs of independent samples, differences between means, $\bar{M}_1 - \bar{M}_2$, equaled 2.4, 1.7, and 5.2. The probabilities (one-tail tests) associated with these differences were .12, .35, and .015, respectively. What is the probability that a combination of differences as large as these could have occurred by chance?

ANSWERS
1. $\chi^2 = 8.02$; df $= 1$.
2. $\chi^2 = 3.96$; df $= 1$.
3. $\chi^2 = 10.12$; df $= 2$.
4. a. $\chi^2 = 7.03$ (without Yates's correction); df $= 1$.
      $\chi^2 = 5.17$ (with correction).
   b. From table N, $p \lessgtr .05$.
5. $\chi^2 = 8.27$ (with correction); df $= 1$.
6. $\chi^2 = 4.26$ (without correction); df $= 1$.
    $\chi^2 = 3.37$ (with correction).
7. $\chi^2 = 3.75$; df $= 2$. (Three categories combined at each end of the distribution)
8. $\chi^2 = 14.74$; df $= 6$.

12 Nonparametric or distribution-free statistics

IN the last 20 years, many new statistical procedures have been developed especially to take care of the experimental situation in which samples are small and the form of the population distribution is not normal. Some of these statistics will now be described.

Before an investigator resorts to them, however, he should consider whether any of the more powerful tests can be used. Some of the distribution-free, or nonparametric, methods have lower power to detect a real difference as significant. When there is any choice, therefore, we should prefer a parametric test, except where a quick, rough test will do. Even where there seems to be no choice we can sometimes create one, as will be seen in the following discussion.

TRANSFORMATION OF MEASUREMENT SCALES

Sometimes the nonnormal distribution in a population is caused by an inappropriate measuring scale or by restrictions that result in distorted scales. For example, distributions of simple reaction times are generally skewed positively. This comes about because of the restriction that no reaction time can be less than zero, because there is some minimal time below which the reacting subject cannot go, and because there is no restriction at the other side of the distribution. The effects of these restrictions are felt to some extent throughout the range, for the distribution is not simply truncated.

The question posed by such a situation is whether, by some transformation, we can convert the measurements into values on a new scale in which the distribution *is* normal. One justification for such a transformation would be an assumption that the underlying psychological variable or trait *is* normally distributed, if only we had an appropriate scale on which to measure it. Such reasoning is not necessary, however. Tests made of statistics on transformed scales lead to conclusions that hold for the natural phenomena under investigation. We saw this in connection with the transformation of r to Fisher's **z**.

One way to transform the reaction-time measurements is to find the logarithm of each value. This would condense the larger measurements into smaller scale ranges relative to the smaller measurements and thus reduce, if not eliminate, skewing. With the measurements thus transformed to log form, we could proceed to apply parametric tests, even in small samples.

Other nonlinear transformation procedures exist. One is the conversion of proportions or percentages into corresponding angle values in degrees of arc. In sampling, these are normally distributed where extreme proportions are not. For an excellent discussion of the subject of transformation, see Mueller.[1]

Tests of differences with correlated data

THE SIGN TEST

One of the simplest tests of significance in the nonparametric category is the sign test. Let us say that we have two parallel sets of measurements that are paired off in some way. The data in Table 12.1

[1]Mueller, C. G. Numerical transformations in the analysis of experimental data. *Psychol. Bull.*, 1949, **46**, 198–223.

Table 12.1 **Application of the sign test to 10 pairs of the knee-jerk data from Table 9.2**

$T*$	R	Sign of $T - R$
19	14	+
19	19	(0)
26	30	−
15	7	+
18	13	+
30	20	+
18	17	+
30	29	+
26	18	+
28	21	+

*T = knee-jerk measurement under tension; R = measurement under relaxation.

are 10 of the successive pairs of knee-jerk measurements presented originally in Table 9.2. The hypothesis to be tested is that they arose from random sampling from the same population. If this hypothesis were true, half the changes from T to R should be positive and half should be negative. Another way of stating the null hypothesis is to say that the median *change* is zero.

There are 10 pairs of observations; therefore, 10 changes are involved. But note that one change is zero. Since we cannot include this as either positive or negative, it is discarded, leaving nine changes for the test. The hypothesis now calls for 4.5 positive differences, whereas we obtained eight. Is this a significant deviation?

The obvious test to make is based upon the binomial distribution for $p = .5$ and $n = 9$. On this basis, eight or more plus signs could occur by chance 10 times in 512 trials (1 chance in 512 for exactly nine, plus 9 chances for exactly eight). For a one-tail test, this deviation is significant with P equal to approximately .02. For a two-tail test we double the probability, as usual, which gives a departure significant at the .04 level. We would make a two-tail test if our alternative hypothesis were that these results did not come from the same population, i.e., with respect to central value. We would make a one-tail test if the alternative hypothesis at the start were that the T values tend to be higher than the R values.

Table O in Appendix B will be useful in applying this sign test, since cumulative tail proportions for the binomial distribution (where $p = .5$) are given for each value of n up to $n = 25$. For cases in which the number of pairs is greater than 25, the normal-curve approximation may be used, as described in Chap. 10.

The assumptions involved in making the sign test include mutual independence of the *differences*. The two parallel sets of values may or may not be correlated. Nothing is assumed concerning the shape of the distribution or the equality of variances. The differences need not even be measured accurately, but the *direction* of each difference should be experimentally established.

One weakness of the sign test is that it does not use all the available information. If the measurements are on a scale of equal units, on which differences may be compared for size as well as for direction, the sign test ignores the information provided by size. It is said that, except for very small samples, the sign test is only about 60 per cent as powerful as a t test would be for the same data, where both apply. This difference in a power could be compensated for by increasing the size of sample. If we had applied the sign test to the entire data in Table 9.2, we should have found that 18 out of 25 signs were positive. By the use of the binomial distribution, this would indicate a deviation significant near the .02 level (one-tail test), which agrees with the result from the smaller sample of 10 pairs. In Chap. 9, however, the $\bar{z}$ test for the same complete data was significant almost to the .001 point in a one-tail test. The difference in sensitivity of the two tests in this particular illustration is appreciable.

THE SIGN-RANK TEST OF DIFFERENCES

Let us use as an illustration of the sign-rank test of differences the same data to which the sign test was just applied in Table 12.1.[1] The 10 pairs of knee-jerk measurements under tensed and relaxed conditions are repeated for convenience in Table 12.2. Here the numerical differences, with algebraic signs, are also listed. Unlike the sign test, however, this test utilizes the additional information of *sizes* of differences. As in the sign test, however, we cannot use zero differences, since the differences must be classified according to algebraic sign.

Having the differences with their algebraic signs, we first forget the signs and rank the differences according to size only, giving the smallest difference a rank of 1. There are two differences of 1. We do not know which one to call rank 1 and which rank 2, and so we give each of them an average rank of 1.5. The next smallest difference is 4, which is given a rank of 3, and so on until all nonzero differences are ranked.

[1]The sign-rank test and the composite-rank test, to be described later, have been attributed to Wilcoxon. See Wilcoxon, F. *Some Rapid Approximate Statistical Procedures.* Stamford, Conn.: American Cyanamid Co., 1949.

Table 12.2   **Application of the sign-rank test of differences, using the knee-jerk data**

$T*$	R	$T - R$	Rank of absolute difference	Ranks with minority sign
19	14	+5	4.5	
19	19	0		
26	30	−4	3	−3
15	7	+8	7.5	
18	13	+5	4.5	
30	20	+10	9	
18	17	+1	1.5	
30	29	+1	1.5	
26	18	+8	7.5	
28	21	+7	6	

$$T = -3$$

*T = knee-jerk score under tension; R = score under relaxation.

Next, we consider the algebraic signs of the differences. We single out all differences whose sign is in the minority. If there are fewer negative than positive signs, as here, we select all ranks corresponding to the differences having that sign. There is only one negative difference in Table 12.2. We put this rank with negative sign in the last column. We sum this column to give a statistic T.

The hypothesis tested is that the differences are symmetrically distributed about a mean difference of zero. If this were true, T would coincide with the mean of such sums of randomly selected ranks, $\overline{T}$, which is also half the sum of N successive ranks, and which would be given by the formula

$$\overline{T} = \frac{N(N + 1)}{4} \qquad \text{(Mean of sums of ranks)} \qquad (12.1)$$

The deviation obtained is $T - \overline{T}$. Wilcoxon has supplied a table giving the deviations significant at the .05, .02, and .01 levels (see Table P, Appendix B). Reference to Table P indicates that the obtained T of -3 (the algebraic sign does not matter in the use of the table) is significant at the .02 level (a two-tail test), when we have nine differences involved.

For an N greater than 25, the T values significant at various probabilities can be found by using the equations

$$T_{.05} = \overline{T} - 1.960 \sqrt{\frac{(2N + 1)\overline{T}}{6}}$$

$$T_{.02} = \overline{T} - 2.326 \sqrt{\frac{(2N + 1)\overline{T}}{6}} \qquad \begin{array}{c} (T \text{ statistics significant at} \\ \text{various levels)} \end{array} \qquad (12.2)$$

$$T_{.01} = \overline{T} - 2.576 \sqrt{\frac{(2N + 1)\overline{T}}{6}}$$

where $\overline{T}$ = mean of the sums of ranks and the radical expression is the standard deviation of the sampling distribution of T.

It will be seen that the outcome of this test agrees with that from the sign test for the same data. There will not always be this much agreement, and when there is not, the result of the sign-rank-difference test should be regarded as more dependable, since it rests upon more information.

For samples larger than 25, a standard deviation and a z ratio can be computed, and z can be interpreted in terms of the normal distribution. For a sample of size N,

$$\sigma_t = \sqrt{\frac{N(N + 1)(2N + 1)}{24}} \qquad (12.3)$$

and z is equal to $(T - \overline{T})/\sigma_t$.

Tests of differences with uncorrelated data

THE MEDIAN TEST

The median test involves finding a common median for the combination of the two samples being compared, as a first step. Next, the numbers of cases above and below the common median are counted in each sample, resulting in a fourfold contingency table, as in Table 12.3. The observations are not paired or correlated, and the N may differ in the two samples. Equal N's would make the test easier to apply, as will be seen. Finally, we find the chi square for the contingency table. With equal numbers of observations in each sample, we can conveniently use Table N in Appendix B for a test of significance without computing chi square.

The median of the 14 observations in Table 12.3 is 9.5. Values of 10 and above are easily segregated from those of 9 and below, as shown in the fourfold table. With such small frequencies, we should not compute chi square for this table. Reference to Table N indicates that chi square is not significant with a p greater than .05 (two-tail test).

The hypothesis tested is that the median is the same for both populations. Since the samples are likely to be small in making this test, exact probabilities should be obtained or Table N should be used. If a one-tail test is wanted, then a more exact p should be estimated and this p divided by 2.

Median test with more than two samples. Suppose that we have three samples, each from its own treatment or set of conditions. We want to test the homogeneity of their central values. For example, consider the three samples in Table 12.4.

The median of all 18 observations is 9.0. Since we have some 9's in the lists, we cannot make the point of dichotomy at exactly 9. In such

Table 12.3 **Application of the median test to two samples under conditions A and B**

Samples		Contingency table samples			
A	B				
14	5				
13	7		A	B	Both
10	6				
12	5	10+	5	2	7
15	11				
9	8	9−	2	5	7
9	10		7	7	

$Mdn = 9.5$

Table 12.4 **Application of the median test to more than two samples**

Samples		
D	*E*	*F*
2	10	12
7	7	15
5	12	9
6	14	16
8	9	14
3	8	
	10	
N_i 6	7	5

Mdn = **9.0**

Contingency table

	D	*E*	*F*	*All*
10+	0	4	4	8
9–	6	3	1	10
All	6	7	5	18

a situation we make it as near the median as we can. Let it be the point 9.5. We then set up a contingency table, as in Table 12.4. From these data, chi square is 7.82. With 2 df this chi square is significant near the .02 point. We reject the null hypothesis and say that the three medians are homogeneous.

THE COMPOSITE-RANK METHOD

When the observations are not paired, another method is to produce a single rank order for all values in the two samples. If the two samples came from the same population, in a single ranking the sums of the ranks belonging to the two samples should be equal, except for sampling errors. The composite-rank test is concerned with the departure of the two sums from equality.

Consider the two samples of seven cases each, in Table 12.5, obtained under conditions *A* and *B*. We assign the numerically lowest ranks to the lowest values. There are two lowest scores of 5, each of which receives a rank of 1.5. The score of 6 then receives a rank of 3, and so on, until the highest score of 15 receives a rank of 14 (which equals *N* unless there are ties for top place).

The sums of the ranks for conditions *A* and *B*, which we shall call R_a and R_b, are 71.5 and 33.5, respectively. The check for these sums is that they should add up to $N(N + 1)/2$, where there are *N* ranks. In this case, $71.5 + 33.5 = N(N + 1)/2$.

We select the smaller of the two sums, which happens to be R_b in this problem, as our sampling statistic. It is distributed about the mean of the sums, which is given by formula (12.1) but which will be called $\overline{R}$. For values of N_i (number in each sample) not greater than 20 and for samples of equal size ($N_a = N_b = N_i$), Wilcoxon has provided tables of the values of significant R's which are to be found in Table Q in Appendix B. With seven replications ($N_i = 7$), an R of 33.5 is significant between the .02 and .01 levels, a bit closer to the .02 level (two-tail test).

For the application when N_i exceeds 20, the R's significant at the three levels may be computed by the formulas

$$R_{.05} = \overline{R} - 1.960 \sqrt{\frac{N\overline{R}}{12}}$$

$$R_{.02} = \overline{R} - 2.326 \sqrt{\frac{N\overline{R}}{12}} \qquad \text{(Values of statistic } R \text{ significant} \qquad (12.4)$$
at three levels)

$$R_{.01} = \overline{R} - 2.576 \sqrt{\frac{N\overline{R}}{12}}$$

where $\overline{R}$ = mean of the sums of ranks and the radical expression is the standard deviation of the sampling distribution of R.

The Mann-Whitney U test. There is a generalization of the R test just described that takes care of samples of unequal size. For this more general case we have the Mann-Whitney U test. The hypothesis being tested is the same as for the R test, and the operations through to the finding of the sums of the ranks are the same as well. Either sum can be treated as statistic U. When N_a and N_b are both as large as 8, a $\bar{z}$ test can be used and $\bar{z}$ can be computed by the formula

Table 12.5 **Application of the
R test of a difference, based
upon the sum of ranks**

Measurements		Ranks	
A	B	A	B
14	5	13	1.5
13	7	12	4
10	6	8.5	3
12	5	11	1.5
15	11	14	10
9	8	6.5	5
9	10	6.5	8.5
		Σ 71.5	33.5
		R_a	R_b

$$\bar{z} = \frac{2U_i - N_i(N+1)}{\sqrt{\dfrac{N_a N_b (N+1)}{3}}} \qquad \text{(\bar{z} value for an obtained sum of}$$

(12.5)

ranks for a U test)

where U_i = one of the sums of ranks

N_a, N_b = replications in samples A and B

N = total number of cases = $N_a + N_b$

N_i = number of cases corresponding to U_i

As usual, $\bar{z}$ is interpreted in terms of the unit normal distribution curve. For very small samples, one or both of which is smaller than 8, Mann and Whitney provide tables of probabilities.[1] The U test is said to be more powerful than the median test. It should not be used if there are many tied ranks.

Tests of similarity of frequency distributions

THE KOLMOGOROV-SMIRNOV TEST OF GOODNESS OF FIT

The preceding chapter described a way of applying a chi-square test to infer whether or not a sample distribution could have arisen by random sampling from a population distributed normally with the same mean and standard deviation as the sample. An alternative method for testing goodness of fit of an obtained frequency distribution to a hypothetical distribution is the Kolmogorov-Smirnov (K-S) test.

One important difference between the K-S test and the χ^2 test is that the K-S test compares *cumulative* distributions. Another difference is that the comparison is made in terms of proportions rather than frequencies. The latter step arrives at a standard kind of numerical value that is unaffected by the size of sample. The method is simple to apply, requiring less computation than for chi square. The statistic used is the maximum difference found between corresponding pairs of cumulative proportions. A simple formula for it is

$$D = (cp_o - cp_e)_{\max} \qquad \text{(The Kolmogorov-Smirnov}$$

(12.6)

maximum-deviation statistic)

where cp_o and cp_e are the observed and expected cumulative proportions in the score interval on a measurement scale where the difference is greatest.

Table 12.6 shows the operations involved in using the K-S test. The observed frequencies are cumulated and then translated into proportions by dividing them by N (or multiplying by $1/N$). The expected frequencies would have to be obtained as in Table 11.7; here we can

[1] For extensive tables for the Mann-Whitney U test, see Siegel, S. *Nonparametric Statistics for the Behavioral Sciences.* New York: McGraw-Hill, 1956.

Table 12.6　**Testing goodness of fit by the Kolmogorov-Smirnov method**

Scores	f_o	cf_o	cp_o	cp_e	$cp_o - cp_e$
47+	0	86	1.000	1.000	.000
44 – 46	0	86	1.000	.999	+.001
41 – 43	1	86	1.000	.997	+.003
38 – 40	4	85	.988	.987	+.001
35 – 37	5	81	.942	.962	−.020
32 – 34	8	76	.884	.903	−.019
29 – 31	14	68	.791	.800	+.009
26 – 28	17	54	.628	.644	−.016
23 – 25	9	37	.430	.464	−.034
20 – 22	13	28	.326	.288	+.038
17 – 19	8	15	.174	.155	+.019
14 – 16	3	7	.081	.067	+.014
11 – 13	4	4	.047	.026	+.021
8 – 10	0	0	.000	.008	.008
5 – 7	0	0	.000	.002	−.002

$$D = .038$$

take them from Table 11.7. The last column lists the differences between pairs of proportions, the largest of which is .038. If D is statistically significant, the hypothesis of normal distribution is rejected.

Statistic D has a known, mathematically defined sampling distribution that is used in the interpretation of an obtained D. For some of the customary levels of significance, in a two-tailed test, D is significant if it equals or exceeds

$1.22/\sqrt{N}$, at the level of $p = .10$

$1.36/\sqrt{N}$, at the level of $p = .05$

$1.63/\sqrt{N}$, at the level of $p = .01$

for cases in which N is as large as 35. This limitation probably does not eliminate the possibility of using the K-S test for the curve-fitting test (there are other uses) in most cases in which one would want to test such a hypothesis. Actually, the limits given above would apply with little risk when N is as small as 25, unless D happens to be very close to one of those points.

From the result in Table 12.6, where $D = .038$ and N is 86, the quantity 1.22 divided by $\sqrt{86}$ is .132. The obtained D is well short of the D required for significance at the .10 level and we do not reject the hypothesis of normal distribution for the population from which the sample came. We cannot say whether the proportion of chance-generated D's exceeding .038 is the same as for the chance-generated χ^2's that exceed the obtained χ^2, but the general opinion is that the K-S test of goodness of fit is more powerful than the chi-square test used for the same purpose, which means that it would more often lead to rejection of the hypothesis being tested, at the same α level. This fact, when taken together with the relative ease of computing D and the applicability to samples with smaller N, makes the K-S test more attractive in this curve-fitting application.

THE KOLMOGOROV-SMIRNOV TWO-SAMPLE TEST

The Kolmogorov-Smirnov test has just been presented as a method of testing the hypothesis that an obtained frequency distribution arose from a normally distributed population. That particular application is often called a one-sample test, because only one sample distribution is involved. The sampled distribution is compared statistically with an assumed distribution, which derives its properties from a mathematical model.

The Kolmogorov-Smirnov (K-S) test is more generally useful in applications in which the two distributions compared are both samples. The hypothesis H_0 is that the two distributions arose by random sampling from the same population. The feature primarily compared is the numerical level on some scale; differences in variance or in kurtosis (sharpness or flatness) of the distributions have little effect on the test. Skewness has some effect because it is reflected in the general level of central tendency. The measurement scale need not have equal units: ordered categories are sufficient refinement for the purposes of the K-S test. Certain distinctions must be remembered when using this test. The test is not quite the same with large samples as with small ones, and two-tailed tests are different from one-tailed tests. These differences will now be explained.

The K-S test with small samples. The K-S test is applied as a small-sample test when N is 40 or less in each of the two distributions being compared. It is more readily and more satisfactorily applied if the samples are of equal size, with $N_1 = N_2$, for which case tables of values exist to facilitate its use.

For an illustration of an application of the K-S test, we have some data in Table 12.7. There are two distributions of scores from a Driver Attitude Survey, a personality inventory. From a much larger sample of men in military service during peacetime, with an average age of about 20, 15 men who had been cited for driving at excessive

Table 12.7   Application of the Kolmogorov-Smirnov test to the difference between 15 drivers who were cited for driving at excessive speeds and 15 drivers who were not cited, in terms of scores on a driver attitude scale

Score	f		cf		K_c
	Violator	Nonviolator	Violator	Nonviolator	
15	2		15	15	0
14	1		13	15	2
13	3	3	12	15	3
12	2	1	9	12	3
11	1	1	7	11	4
10	2	3	6	10	4
9	2	0	4	7	3
8	1	4	2	7	5
7	1	2	1	3	2
6	0	1	0	1	1

$$K = 5$$

speed on the street or highway were selected at random. A set of 15 nonviolators was also selected, each man following one of the violators in a large alphabetical roster. All men said they owned motor cars, but no information was available on the amount or kind of driving that was done. The violations occurred during about a year of military service.

According to previous information incident to the development of the inventory, which was designed to apply to all kinds of traffic violators, and from subsequent cross-validation information, men who receive higher scores on the Violator scale of the Driver Attitude Survey should be expected to earn more traffic-violator citations. This hypothesis calls for a one-tail test of the difference between these two groups. H_0 is that there is either no genuine difference or a negative one, and H_1 is that the speeders tend to have higher scores than the nonspeeders.

An essential step is to find cumulative distributions for the two samples, which has been done in Table 12.7. Ordinarily, the K-S test calls for the comparisons of cumulative proportions in parallel categories on the score scale, but with equal N's we may compare cumulative frequencies, thereby eliminating the need to find proportions. It should be understood that the values in the cf columns in Table 12.7 are actually $15/15$, $13/15$, $12/15$, and so on. As the denominator remains the same throughout the two columns, we can forget about it. The tables are set up in terms of the numerator (K) values only (see Table S).

The last operation in Table 12.7 is to find the category differences, K_c, which range from 0 to 5. The largest K_c is statistic K, in this case 5. Table S tells us that with 15 cases in each distribution, it takes a K as large as 7 or larger to be significant at the .05 level, in a one-tail test. Although the difference is in the predicted direction, it could have arisen by random sampling.

The K-S test with large samples. For a case with samples greater than 40, consider the data in Table 12.8. An instance in which the N's are unequal is chosen so as to illustrate the generality of the procedure. Both a one-tail and a two-tail test will be applied.

The basic data are scores on a very short inventory designed to show how much a person uses alcohol and what his attitude is toward using it in a way that might reflect detrimentally on his behavior. We might expect the score to reflect a more general disposition that would show up in the form of antisocial conduct. The test that is made is whether or not servicemen who have been court-martialed will tend to score higher on the inventory than servicemen who have not. The samples were selected from a much larger group totaling more than 800. With the roster in alphabetical order, each court-martialed case was taken as it came up and a similar, though somewhat larger, number of other names immediately following was chosen, with 40 in the first group and 60 in the second.

Table 12.8 **Application of the Kolmogorov-Smirnov test to two groups of servicemen, one group of which had been court-martialed and the other not, with respect to scores on an inventory designed to indicate attitude toward use of alcoholic beverages**

Score	f		cf		cp		d_c
	CM	Not CM	CM	Not CM	CM	Not CM	
9	2		40	60	1.000	1.000	.000
8	2		38	60	.950	1.000	.050
7	2	3	36	60	.900	1.000	.100
6	7	10	34	57	.850	.950	.100
5	5	6	27	47	.675	.783	.108
4	9	13	22	41	.440	.683	.243
3	6	12	13	28	.325	.467	.142
2	5	9	7	16	.175	.267	.092
1	2	6	2	7	.050	.117	.067
0		1	0	1	.000	.017	.017

$D = .243$

The major step in Table 12.8 is to arrive at cumulative distributions of proportions in the two samples, from which differences, d_c, are found. The signs of the differences are unimportant; we are concerned only with their sizes. The largest difference, which is .243, is the needed statistic D. We need to determine whether it is sufficiently large to lead to rejection of the null hypothesis.

Since the alternative to hypothesis H_0 is that the court-martialed group will tend to make higher scores, a one-tailed test is appropriate. For the purpose of making a one-tailed test, a chi square can be derived from D by means of the formula

$$\chi^2 = 4D^2 \left(\frac{N_1 N_2}{N_1 + N_2} \right)$$

(Chi square estimated from the Kolmogorov-Smirnov statistic D)   (12.7)

with 2 degrees of freedom, and where N_1 and N_2 are the numbers of observations in the two samples and D is the largest difference between any pair of cumulative proportions.

Applying the formula to the obtained D,

$$\chi^2 = 4(.243)^2 \left[\frac{(40)(60)}{40 + 60} \right]$$

$$= 4(.059049)(24)$$

$$= 5.669$$

The chi-square table tells us that to be significant at the .05 level a χ^2 with 2 df must be 5.991 or greater. The obtained D, as evaluated through the chi-square test, fails to achieve significance at the .05 level. We do not reject the hypothesis of no relationship between the two variables, as investigated.

Although the idea of making a two-tailed test for these data was rejected above, we can make such a test using the same data, for the sake of illustration. In the two-tailed test of D, the sampling distribution of D is utilized. To decide whether or not to reject the null hypothesis, it is sufficient to be able to determine quickly what size of D is needed to be significant at the customary levels, taking into account the N's involved in the samples, N_1 and N_2. Four of the critical values are

Significance level	Critical D value
.10	$1.22 \sqrt{\dfrac{N_1 + N_2}{N_1 N_2}}$
.05	$1.36 \sqrt{\dfrac{N_1 + N_2}{N_1 N_2}}$

.01 $1.63 \sqrt{\dfrac{N_1 + N_2}{N_1 N_2}}$

.001 $1.95 \sqrt{\dfrac{N_1 + N_2}{N_1 N_2}}$

In the alcoholic problem, N_1 is 40, N_2 is 60, and the radical term comes out equal to .204. If we choose the .05 level for α, .204 × 1.36 equals .277. The obtained D is not equal to or greater than .277; therefore we do not reject the null hypothesis.

The K-S procedure described takes care of all but small samples with unequal numbers of cases. According to Siegel, the chi-square approximation may also be applied, with little risk, to small samples when N's are unequal.[1] If we apply that procedure to the traffic-violator problem, where the largest difference was ⁵/₁₅, or ¹/₃, by formula (12.7),

$$\chi^2 = 4\left(\frac{1}{3}\right)^2 \left(\frac{15 \times 15}{15 + 15}\right)$$

$$= 4\left(\frac{1}{9}\right)(7.5)$$

$$= 3.333$$

A chi square of 3.333, with 2 df, is barely beyond the .20 level. This is also a one-tailed test, since it uses the transformation to chi square. There is a conservative error in applying this approximation test to small samples, i.e., the error is on the side of not rejecting the null hypothesis.

EXERCISES

In each of the following exercises, state the hypothesis being tested, your statistical inference, and the experimental conclusion.

1. Apply the sign test to the first 15 differences in Table 9.2.

2. Apply the sign-rank-difference test to the same data as in Exercise 1.

3. In three samples the observations were:
A. 9, 7, 2, 10, 8, 5
B. 10, 15, 12, 11, 16, 6
C. 18, 15, 14, 20, 10, 13
a. Apply the median test to all three samples.
b. Apply the median test to each pair of samples, using the same median value as in part a.

4. Apply the composite-rank test to the pairs of distributions given in Exercise 3.

[1]Siegel, *op. cit.* P. 135.

Data 12A **Hypothetical distributions of ratings assigned to 20 employees by raters** A **and** B

Rater	Rating				
	1	2	3	4	5
A	3	4	7	5	1
B	0	4	4	6	6

Data 12B **Hypothetical distributions of letter grades assigned to the same examination paper by two teachers**

Teacher	Grade				
	F	D	C	B	A
1	1	5	22	12	5
2	4	20	15	5	1

5. Apply the Kolmogorov-Smirnov test of goodness of fit to Data 11C.

6. Apply the Kolmogorov-Smirnov test to Data 12A.

7. Apply the Kolmogorov-Smirnov test to Data 12B.

ANSWERS

1. For a one-tail test, from Table O, $p = .090$.
2. $T = 16.5$; $.02 < p < .05$.
3. χ^2 (A versus B versus C) = 9.34, df = 2.
 χ^2 (A versus B) = 3.38; df = 1 (with Yates's correction).
 χ^2 (A versus C) = 5.49; df = 1.
 χ^2 (B versus C) = 0.00; df = 1.
4. R_a (A versus B) = 25.5; $.02 < p < .05$; $\overline{R} = 39.0$.
 R_a (A versus C) = 21.5; $p < .01$.
 R_a (B versus C) = 31.0; $p > .05$.
5. $D = .035$; $p > .10$.
6. $K = 6$; K of 9 required for $p < .05$ in a two-tail test.
7. $D = .40$; $p < .01$.

13 Introduction to analysis of variance

IT frequently happens in research that we obtain more than two sets of measurements on the same experimental variable, each under its own set of conditions, and we want to know whether there are any significant differences among the sets. We could, of course, pair off two sets at a time, pairing each one with every other one, and test the significance of the difference between means, or other statistics, in each pair.

Perhaps the variation of condition has been a qualitative one; for example, we have test scores for children from each of five neighboring states, or we have simple-reaction-time measurements under four different verbal instructions. Every other variable thought to be significantly related in a causal way to the experimental variable has been held constant. Perhaps the variation is a quantitative one: for example, retention scores obtained after different proportions of time spent in memorizing by the anticipation method versus the reading method, or arithmetic scores of children who have devoted different proportions of class time to drill in number operations versus concrete applications of numbers.

One practical problem involved in testing for significance of differences is the amount of labor involved. Five samples involve 10 pairs; six samples involve 15 pairs; 10 samples involve 45 pairs; and so on. There is a possibility that none of the differences between pairs would prove to be significant. In meeting this situation, it would be desirable to have some overall test of the several samples simultaneously to tell us whether *any* of the differences were significant. If the answer is "Yes," we can then examine pairs to see just where the significant differences are. If the answer is "No," our search is over without further ado.

There are more important logical and statistical reasons for wanting a single composite test. If we happened to have as many as a hundred differences to be tested, and if we found one of them significant at the .01 level and approximately five of them significant at the .05 level, we should actually conclude that *none* of the differences is significant. We could even have a few more than these meeting the significance standards due to chance. We should suspect even the large differences of being due to chance unless we have an excess number of them. A simultaneous test should be of such a nature that we can conclude whether the whole distribution of obtained sampling statistics could have happened by chance.

There is still another statistical reason for wanting to treat the data together. If we tested each pair separately, we would use as an estimate of the population variance only the data from the two samples involved. If we make the null hypothesis apply to *all* the samples—that they all arose by random sampling from the same population—we could use *all* the data from which to make a much more stable estimate of the population variance. We should have to assume, of course, that the variances from the different samples are homogeneous.

Although we saw some attention given to problems of composite tests of significance in Chap. 12, the methods described there have limited application. The reason is that when we can make the appropriate assumptions, there are more powerful parametric tests available. These come under the general heading of *analysis of variance*.

Analysis in a one-way classification problem

Consider again the case in which we have several samples of the same general character and we want to determine whether there are any significant differences among the means. The basic principle of such a test is to determine whether the sample means vary further from the population mean than we should expect, in view of the variations of single cases from the same mean.

TWO ESTIMATES OF POPULATION VARIANCE

In a single subsample, the amount of expected variation of single cases from the population mean is indicated by the statistic s^2, which is an estimate of the population variance, or parameter $\bar{\sigma}^2$. The variation of randomly sampled means about the population mean is indicated by the SE of the mean, squared, which is denoted by $\bar{\sigma}^2_M$ and is computed by the ratio $\bar{\sigma}^2/n$, where n is the size of each sample.[1] If we multiply this ratio by n, we obtain $\bar{\sigma}^2$, the population variance.

In other words, we have a way of estimating the population var-

---

[1] In connection with analysis of variance, we shall use n to stand for the number of cases in a subsample and N to stand for the number of cases in all subsamples in the problem combined. We shall deal first with the case in which all the subsample n's are equal.

iance from the variance among means. If there is no significant variation among the means, if they arose by random sampling from the same population (or from populations with equal means), the population variance estimated from them should be essentially the same as that estimated from the single observations. The test for determining the significance of the differences between two variances is the F test, which was described in Chap. 9. F is a ratio of two variances, as shown in Chap. 9. It is necessary to have two estimates of the population variance in order to form an F ratio. With appropriate df applied to the two variances being compared, we can interpret F as significant or not.

BETWEEN-SETS SUM OF SQUARES AND BETWEEN-SETS VARIANCE

Our attention will be directed next to the operations by which the two estimates of population variances are achieved, one from the means and one from the single observations. We have already seen that there is a basis for estimating the population variance from the means. The computational steps will now be described.

Suppose that we have k samples, or sets, of n cases each, where n is a constant. For each of the k means we should have the deviation

$$d_s = M_s - M_t \qquad \text{(Deviation of a set mean from the grand mean)} \qquad (13.1)$$

where M_s = mean of a set, where sets vary from 1 to k, and M_t = the grand mean, mean of means, or mean of all observations in all sets combined.

If we square all the deviations d_s and sum them, we should be on the way to finding the variance of the means about the estimated population mean, where M_t is our best estimate of that population mean. This variance is actually the *variance error* of the mean, which is the square of the SE of the mean. This variance is not exactly what we want. We want an estimate of the variance of *individual observations* about the population mean, not the variance of the means.

We ordinarily compute an estimated variance from a sum of squares of deviations of single observations. The sum of squares that we want, derived from the means, is given by the expression $n\Sigma d^2_s$. This statement can be made more reasonable by saying that each d_s value is shared by all n cases in the set in which it appears. It is as if we gave all the cases in that set the same deviation value. In estimating the variance of individual observations from the mean, we need as many deviations as there are observations. Thus the expression $n\Sigma d^2_s$ is an estimate of the sum of squares of deviations of all the individual observations from the population mean. Since it is derived from the means, it is called the *between-sets sum of squares*.

Looking at the matter a little more mathematically, it is as if we regard every observed measurement that we obtain in the experiment as a summation of three independent components: $M_t + d_s + e_r$. M_t makes no contribution to variance, since it is a constant. The term d_s is the set deviation from the mean $(M_s - M_t)$ and is the same for every case within a set but probably differs from set to set. The term e_r is a random error that differs from one observation to another. In the present context, e_r is a deviation of an observation from a set mean. The combination of d_s and e_r gives to each observation its unique value. Combined, they are the total deviation of an observation from M_t.

As will be explained in Chap. 16 and proved in Appendix A (see Proof 12), the variance of a sum of two independent variables is the sum of the variances of those two variables. Since both d_s and e_r are deviations from means, the means of their squares are estimates of variances: the former of between-sets variance and the latter of within-sets variance.

A *mean* of squares implies division of the sum of squares by the number of things squared. In estimating population variances, however, to overcome bias we divide instead by degrees of freedom. There are k deviations d_s involved, so that we have $k - 1$ degrees of freedom. One degree of freedom is lost in using the computed grand mean M_t. The *between-sets mean square*, $(MS)_b$, is therefore computed by the equation

$$(MS)_b = \frac{(SS)_b}{k - 1} = \frac{n \Sigma d^2_s}{k - 1} \qquad \text{(Between-sets mean square)} \qquad (13.2)$$

where $(SS)_b$ = sum of squares for between sets.

WITHIN-SETS SUM OF SQUARES AND WITHIN-SETS VARIANCE

If we may assume that the variances within the different samples are equal, except for random fluctuations, we may combine the sum of squares from all sets in order to obtain from this source an estimate of the population variance. As we combine sums of squares, we also combine degrees of freedom by which to divide the sum of squares. In each set sample the number of df is $n - 1$. In k samples combined we have $k(n - 1)$ df. This can also be expressed as $(N - k)$ df, since $N = kn$. One df is lost for each set mean used to find within-sets deviations.

In terms of a formula, the *within-sets mean square*, $(MS)_w$, is computed from the *within-sets sum of squares* by the equation

$$(MS)_w = \frac{(SS)_w}{k(n - 1)} = \frac{\Sigma x^2_s}{k(n - 1)} = \frac{\Sigma x^2_s}{N - k} \qquad \begin{array}{l}\text{(Within-sets}\\ \text{mean square)}\end{array} \qquad (13.3)$$

where $(SS)_w$ = within-sets sum of squares and x_s = a deviation of an observation from its set mean.

THE SOLUTION OF A ONE-WAY ANALYSIS-OF-VARIANCE PROBLEM

In Table 13.1 we have four sets of values, each value being the mean of a series of settings made by a different individual on the Galton bar (an instrument for matching lines for length).[1] Each subject was

[1]The reason for selecting different individuals randomly from the same population for each observation is that we wish to generalize the conclusions to the population in general; we could not do this if one observer were used for all observations. If the same set of observers had been used under each of the four treatments, this procedure would have complicated the experimental design, requiring some other kind of statistical treatment of the results.

Table 13.1   **Work sheet for the analysis of variance in four sets of measurements on the Galton bar**

The measurements (X)

	Set I	*Set II*	*Set III*	*Set IV*		
	114	119	112	117		
	115	120	116	117		
	111	119	116	114		
	110	116	115	112		
	112	116	112	117		
ΣX_s 562	590	571	577	2,300	ΣX
M_s 112.4	118.0	114.2	115.4	115.0	M_t

Deviations within sets (x_s)

+1.6	+1.0	−2.2	+1.6
+2.6	+2.0	+1.8	+1.6
−1.4	+1.0	+1.8	−1.4
−2.4	−2.0	+0.8	−3.4
−0.4	−2.0	−2.2	+1.6

Squares of deviations within sets (x^2_s)

2.56	1.00	4.84	2.56	
6.76	4.00	3.24	2.56	
1.96	1.00	3.24	1.96	
5.76	4.00	0.64	11.56	
0.16	4.00	4.84	2.56	
17.20	14.00	16.80	21.20	69.20 Σx^2_s

Deviations of set means from grand mean (d)

d	−2.6	+3.0	−0.8	+0.4	
d^2	6.76	9.00	0.64	0.16	16.56 Σd^2
nd^2	33.80	45.00	3.20	0.80	82.80 $n\Sigma d^2$

shown a constant horizontal line of 115 mm and asked to adjust another line until the two seemed equal. Four sets were obtained under four different conditions. A particular condition is often called a "treatment," in the context of analysis of variance. Is it likely that the observations all came by random sampling from the same general "population" of adjustments, or were there systematic differences sufficient to say that the data are really not homogeneous among the sets?

The following steps are carried out in the solution of the type demonstrated in Table 13.1:

Step 1. Compute the sums and means of the sets, the grand total ΣX, and the grand mean M_t.

Step 2. For every set, compute the deviations from the set means M_s. These are equal to $(X - M_s)$ and are called x_s.

Step 3. Square the deviations within sets to find each x^2_s. Sum these to obtain Σx^2_s, the sum of squares of deviations within sets.

Step 4. For each set, compute d_s, which equals $(M_s - M_t)$.

Step 5. Square each d_s and find $n\Sigma d^2_s$.

With all these calculations completed (see Table 13.1), we have the values for use in formulas (13.2) and (13.3). The Σx^2_s is 69.20, and the $n\Sigma d^2_s$ is 82.80. Dividing these by the appropriate numbers of degrees of freedom, we obtain the mean squares.

For this purpose we set up Table 13.2. Listing first the sum of squares for between sets and degrees of freedom that go with it, we obtain the ratio 27.60 as the variance estimated from the d's. For the corresponding values for within sets, we find the value 4.325 as an estimate of variance from the x's. The ratio of the between-sets mean square to the within-sets mean square gives an F ratio 27.6/4.325 = 6.38. The between-sets estimate of variance is more than six times the within-sets estimate.

Table 13.2   The total variance in the Galton-bar data subdivided into two components

Components	Sum of squares	Degrees of freedom	Mean square
Between sets	82.80	3	27.60
Within sets	69.20	16	4.325
Total	152.00	19	

$$F = \frac{27.6}{4.325} = 6.38$$

Interpretation of the F ratio. The significance of an F is determined by reference to Snedecor's table (Table F, Appendix B). In using this table, we have to consider the two different df values. For the numerator of F (almost always the larger variance) we look for the df_1 at the head of a column. For the denominator of F we look for df_2 at the left of a row. In our illustrative problem, there is a df_1 of 3, which can be found at the head of a column, and a df_2 of 16, which can be found at the left of a row. At the cell where the appropriate column and row intersect we find that it takes an F of 3.24 to be significant at the .05 point and an F of 5.29 to be significant at the .01 point, when the df are 3 and 16. The obtained F is greater than that required for significance at the .01 point, which is sufficient reason for rejecting the null hypothesis.

ASSUMPTIONS ON WHICH AN F TEST RESTS

As usual, a statistical decision is sound to the extent that certain assumptions have been satisfied in the data that are used. In analysis of variance there are usually four stated requirements:

1. The sampling within sets should be random, which, as usual, means observations that are mutually independent and with equal opportunity to occur.

2. The variances from within the various sets must be approximately equal. The within-sets mean square is commonly the denominator of F ratios, and consequently much depends upon its accuracy. Much variation among set variances leads to suspicion of an inaccurate estimate of the population variance from within sets.

3. Observations within experimentally homogeneous sets should be from normally distributed populations. F is mathematically a ratio of two chi squares, each divided by its appropriate df. It will be recalled from Chap. 11 that chi square requires normally distributed populations.

4. The contributions to total variance must be additive. We have already seen that it was necessary to assume independence of the deviations between and within sets in order to say that the total variance is a simple sum of the two contributing variances.

Later, we shall consider what may happen when these assumptions are not satisfied. It was said before that the obtained F, significant at the .01 point, indicates that the means of sets are significantly different: i.e., somewhere among them, at least, there are significant differences. This is not to say that it is necessarily the means that are significantly different. In cases where the population variances are not equal, a significant F might be due in part to this fact. Conclusions about the means would then be in some doubt. But if we can eliminate the possibility of unequal variances, a significant F must indicate significant differences somewhere among the means.

SOME COMPUTATIONAL CHECKS

It will be noted in Table 13.2 that we have recorded the total sum of squares and the number of df for the same. These values have been found by summing the components in both instances, i.e., component sums of squares and component df. The total sum of squares is a composite of two independent factors—that derived from deviations of means and that derived from deviations within sets. From the additive feature of sums of squares, it follows that

$$\Sigma x^2 = \Sigma\Sigma x^2_s + n\Sigma d^2_s$$

where x = deviation from the grand mean $(X - M_t)$
    x_s = deviation of X from a set mean $(X_s - M_s)$
    d_s = the deviation $(M_s - M_t)$

The double summation sign before x^2_s indicates that the within-set deviations are squared and summed for each set and then these sums are summed over all sets.

If Σx^2 is computed from the complete data, it can be used as a check, for it should exactly equal the sum of the two component sums of squares. The number of df to be associated with Σx^2 is $N - 1$, which should equal the sum of the two different df values for between-sets and within-sets sums of squares. In Table 13.2 we find these checks satisfied.

FORMATION OF AN F RATIO

In analysis of variance generally, the numerator of the variance ratio is the estimate of variance that arises from variations whose sources we are testing. The denominator is the estimate that arises from variations whose sources are usually unknown. The latter variance is sometimes referred to as the *error term*. We assume that random sampling is the only source of the variations involved in this term. Sometimes the denominator is called the *residual term*, since its source is all that is left over after other sources have been accounted for.

It will almost always happen that the numerator term is larger, and that F is therefore greater than 1.0. We are thus dealing with the right-hand tail of the F distribution in our interpretation of F. We have a one-tail test. Should F on rare occasion turn out to be less than 1.0, the conclusion is merely that we do not reject the null hypothesis. There is no need to consult the F table for this kind of outcome, or even to compute an F ratio at all.

MAKING t TESTS FOLLOWING AN F TEST

A significant F tells us that there are nonchance variations among means somewhere in the list of sets; we do not know how many or which ones are significantly different. As a group they could not have arisen from a homogeneous list of samples. Further examination would be needed to tell us where the significant differences are and what sources in the form of experimental variation have probably determined them. Conclusions concerning the last point, of course, go beyond statistical decisions, but the latter may or may not call for the effort to find such conclusions.

There has been some difference of opinion as to how to make t tests following an F test and how to interpret the results. If F is insignificant, of course, we should not apply any t tests. Acceptance of the null hypothesis on the basis of an F test automatically accepts the null hypothesis for all pairs of means in the list, including the pairs with the largest differences.

The chief logical objection to making t tests after an F test is that if there is significance anywhere among the interset differences in means, as the F test has indicated, it is most likely to be found by making a t test among the largest differences. But the largest differences are known and are not obtained by random sampling from a population of differences. In a sense, we are "betting on a sure thing." At best, we can take the treatments that gave the largest differences as the ones to be given further tests in new experiments. But there is still the question of how many of the differences are sufficiently large to warrant further experiments.

A test of gaps between means.   Tukey has made a number of suggestions as to what might be done to meet this problem.[1] One of them will be mentioned here. The procedure starts by arranging the set means in rank order, giving attention to the pairs of neighboring values between which the large gaps occur. The expectation behind this procedure is that there is probably some clustering of means, as if two or more populations were represented. The gaps should indicate the areas of separation between such populations. A t test is applied at each gap that appears to indicate a separation.

A t test for difference between means requires a good estimate of population variance. One could use the mean squares from each pair of sets between which the t test is being made. But we can do better than that if the assumption of equal variances in different sets appears to be sound, i.e., the sums of squares from different sets are reasonably uniform. If there is reason to suspect that they are not uniform except for random errors, we could satisfy ourselves by taking the two most divergent estimations of within-sets variance, forming an F ratio, and making an F test, with $(n-1)$ and $(n-1)$ df. Having satisfied ourselves that this F is not significant, we can decide

[1]Tukey, J. W. Comparing individual means in the analysis of variance. *Biometrics*, 1949, **5**, 99–114.

that other pairs are not significantly different. We are then free to use the mean square for within sets as the best obtainable estimate of the population variance.

From Table 13.2 we see that the within-sets mean square is 4.325 – our best estimate of the population variance. What we need from this information is a standard error of a set mean and a standard error of a difference between two set means. The mean square $(MS)_w$ having been obtained by dividing the $(SS)_w$ by 16 df, what we actually have is an estimate of s^2_x. The SE of a set mean is to be estimated by the ratio $s_x / \sqrt{n}$. Now $s^2_x / n = 4.325/5 = .865$. The square root of this value is .93, the estimate for σ_{M_s}. From the fact that the SE of a difference between uncorrelated means can be estimated from $\sqrt{\sigma^2_{M_1} + \sigma^2_{M_2}}$, and the fact that the SE's of means are all equal in the t tests to be made in this problem, we can write the equation

$$\sigma_{d_M} = \sqrt{2\sigma^2_M} = \sqrt{\frac{2(MS)_w}{n}} \qquad \begin{array}{l}\text{(SE of any difference between}\\ \text{pairs of set means, estimated}\\ \text{from the mean square for}\\ \text{within sets)}\end{array} \qquad (13.4)$$

With 16 df applying to the σ_{d_M} here, Table D shows that t's of 2.12 and 2.92 are required for significance at the .05 and .01 levels, respectively. With $(MS)_w = 4.325$,

$$\sigma_{d_M} = \sqrt{\frac{2(4.325)}{5}} = \sqrt{1.73} = 1.32$$

Differences required for significance at the .05 and .01 levels may be found by use of the products $t_{.05}\sigma_{d_M}$ and $t_{.01}\sigma_{d_M}$, which give 2.80 and 3.85, respectively, i.e., 2.12 × 1.32 and 2.92 × 1.32.

Now let us look at the set means and the gaps between them when placed in order (from Table 13.1):

112.4   114.2   115.4   118.0

The largest gap is between the two highest means. It amounts to 2.6, but fails to achieve significance at the .05 level.

Significant deviations of set means from a population mean.   The writer suggests an alternative test that is simple and that does not depend upon tests of pairs of means. It asks whether any set means deviate significantly from an assumed population mean. Let M_t be the estimate of the population mean. Let the variance of the population be estimated from the mean square for within sets, as in the Tukey test. Assume a distribution of means with variance error of $(MS)_w/n$ and SE of the set means equal to $\sqrt{MS_w/n}$. In an earlier paragraph, the SE of the mean was estimated to be .93. For 16 df, the same t ratios are required, namely, 2.12 and 2.92. Deviations, d_s, significant at the .05 and .01 levels are $.93 \times 2.12 = 1.97$ and $.93 \times 2.92 = 2.72$.

Examination of the d_s values in Table 13.1 shows that the one for Set II is +3.0, which is significant at the .01 level, and the one for Set I is −2.6, which is significant at the .05 level. In view of the F significant at the .01 level, this kind of result is reasonable. The best policy is to adopt a level of significance for the t tests that has an alpha at least as small as that adopted for F. Perhaps it would be a good idea to use a .01 level generally in a two-tail test. This criterion applied to the illustrative problem leads to the decision that only one set mean deviates significantly. With F significant at the .01 level, it would seem reasonable that at least one of the set means would deviate significantly in a distribution whose dispersion is described by a σ_M based upon the within-sets mean square.[1]

The relation of t to F.   When we have only two sets of observations, as when we compare two means for significance of their difference, we can still make an F test. The between-sets variance has associated with it only 1 df. For this particular situation, when n_1 and n_2 are equal, $M_1 - M_2 = 2d_s$ and $d_s = (M_1 - M_2)/2$. Therefore, d^2_s, which is needed to find the $(SS)_b$, equals $(M_1 - M_2)^2/4$. The Σd^2_s, which is needed in formula 13.2, is equal to $2d^2_s$, or $(M_1 - M_2)^2/2$. Thus, for the between-sets mean square we have

$$(MS)_b = \frac{n(M_1 - M_2)^2}{2} \qquad \text{(Mean square for between sets when there are two sets)} \qquad (13.5)$$

To illustrate, let us take the largest difference between means in Table 13.1. Those two means are 112.4 and 118.0, with a difference of 5.6. Applying formula (13.5), we find 78.4 for the mean square for between sets. The within-sets sum of squares is a sum of 17.2 and 14.0, from Table 13.1. With 8 df, the within-sets mean square is 3.9. The F ratio is $78.4/3.9 = 20.10$. With 1 and 8 df, from Table F we see that F is significant beyond the .01 point.

It has been proven that with 1 df for the between-sets variance, $F = t^2$. In this same problem, then, $t = \sqrt{20.10} = 4.48$. If we compute t by means of formula (9.4), we arrive at the same value.

COMPUTATION OF MEAN SQUARES FROM ORIGINAL MEASUREMENTS

Just as we can compute standard deviations, and therefore variances, from original measurements without computing each deviation from the mean [see formula (5.11)], so we can calculate the necessary con-

---

[1]Although this test is simple and seemingly straightforward, it is possible that it gives only an approximation of the result of a more refined test such as Tukey's "test for stragglers" (Tukey, *op. cit.*).

stants for an analysis of variance. Such an approach requires squaring the original measurements as well as ΣX.

For pencil-and-paper calculations, it is convenient to reduce the observed numbers to a more workable size by coding them. The three-place numbers in Table 13.1 can be conveniently coded by deducting the constant 110, the lowest measurement, leaving the remainders shown at the left in the top half of Table 13.3. The mean squares are not in the least affected by this kind of transformation, as is easily proved (see Appendix A). Intuitively, one can see that the coded numbers maintain exactly the same distances from one another and from the means as before coding. The coded values are called X' in Table 13.3.

For the general solution, without knowing deviations x or d, the sums of squares we need are found by the following procedures. The between-sets sum of squares is given by the formula

$$(SS)_b = n\Sigma d^2{}_s = \frac{\Sigma(\Sigma X)^2{}_s}{n} - \frac{(\Sigma X)^2}{N} \qquad \text{(Sum of squares for between sets)} \qquad (13.6)$$

The within-sets sum of squares is given by

Table 13.3   Solution of an analysis of variance from original measurements (without determining deviations from means)

Measurements (reduced) (X')

	Set I	Set II	Set III	Set IV		
	4	9	2	7		
	5	10	6	7		
	1	9	6	4		
	0	6	5	2		
	2	6	2	7		
$(\Sigma X')_s$	12	40	21	27	100	$\Sigma X'$
					5.0	$M'{}_t$
$(\Sigma X')^2{}_s$	144	1,600	441	729	2,914	$\Sigma(\Sigma X')^2{}_s$

Squared measurements (X'^2)

	16	81	4	49		
	25	100	36	49		
	1	81	36	16		
	0	36	25	4		
	4	36	4	49		
$(\Sigma X'^2)_s$	46	334	105	167	652	$\Sigma(\Sigma X'^2)_s$

$$SS_w = \Sigma x^2{}_s = \Sigma(\Sigma X^2)_s - \frac{\Sigma(\Sigma X)^2{}_s}{n} \qquad \text{(Sum of squares for within sets)} \tag{13.7}$$

The total sum of squares is given by

$$\Sigma x^2 = \Sigma(\Sigma X^2)_s - \frac{(\Sigma X)^2}{N} \tag{13.8}$$

The steps called for in applying these formulas are:

Step 1. Sum the measurements X for each set, to obtain $(\Sigma X)_s$ for each set (see Table 13.3). Sum these values to obtain ΣX.

Step 2. Square the sums of the scores to obtain $(\Sigma X)^2{}_s$ for each set. Sum these values to find $\Sigma(\Sigma X)^2{}_s$.

Step 3. Square all measurements to find the X^2 values. Sum these values to obtain ΣX^2.

Applying the three formulas, by formula (13.6), we have

$$n\Sigma d^2 = \frac{2{,}914}{5} - \frac{10{,}000}{20} = 528.8 - 500 = 82.8$$

By formula (13.7),

$$\Sigma x^2{}_s = 652 - \frac{2{,}914}{5} = 652 - 582.8 = 69.2$$

and by formula (13.8),

$$\Sigma x^2 = 652 - \frac{10{,}000}{20} = 652 - 500 = 152$$

A check for accuracy of computations is to see that $n\Sigma d^2 + \Sigma x^2{}_s$ $= \Sigma x^2$. The check is satisfied, for $82.8 + 69.2 = 152$. A comparison of these values with those in Table 13.2 will show that we have arrived at the same sums of squares. From here on, the computation of mean squares and F is the same as before.

WHEN SAMPLES ARE OF UNEQUAL SIZE

The procedures described thus far apply to the special, but not unusual, case in which all set samples are of equal size. Experiments can be planned that way, but sometimes available data do not fit that specification. With a little modification of the formulas, we can take care of problems in which n varies.

For the between-sets sum of squares,

$$(SS)_b = \Sigma n_s(M_s - M_t)^2 = \Sigma \frac{(\Sigma X)^2{}_s}{n_s} - \frac{(\Sigma X)^2}{N} \qquad \begin{array}{l}\text{(Between-sets}\\ \text{sum of squares}\\ \text{when samples}\\ \text{vary in size)}\end{array} \tag{13.9}$$

where n_s = number of cases in a specified set

M_s = mean of that set

M_t = mean of all observations

For all expressions involving subscript s the summation is made over k sets.

For the within-sets sum of squares,

$$SS_w = \Sigma x^2{}_s = \Sigma\,(\,\Sigma X^2\,)_s - \Sigma\,\frac{(\Sigma X)^2{}_s}{n_s}$$

(Within-sets sum of squares when samples   (13.10) vary in size)

For the total sum of squares the formula is the same as when we have samples of equal size; hence formula (13.8) will apply for the general case.

The degrees of freedom are the same as in the case of equal n's for the total and between-sets sums of squares. The df for the within-sets sum of squares equal $\Sigma(n_s - 1)$.

Analysis in a two-way classification problem

In the preceding kind of problem the sets of data were differentiated on the basis of only one experimental variation. There was only one principle of classification, one reason for segregating data into sets.

In a two-way classification, there are two distinct bases of classification. Two experimental conditions are allowed to vary from trial to trial. There may be several trials or replications under each treatment. In the psychological laboratory different artificial airfield landing strips, each with a different pattern of markings, may be viewed through a diffusion screen to simulate vision through fog at different levels of opaqueness. In an educational problem, four methods of teaching a certain geometric concept may be applied by five different teachers, each one using every one of the four methods. There would therefore be 20 combinations of teacher and method, and let us suppose that an equal number of randomly chosen pupils receive learning scores under each combination.

TABULATION OF DATA IN A TWO-WAY CLASSIFICATION PROBLEM

For an illustration of the procedure in this type of problem, we shall assume an experiment on the relation of scores on a certain psychomotor test to the size of a target at which the examinee must aim. In conducting the experiment it is convenient to use three testing machines simultaneously in order to reduce the testing time. It is known that there are some, usually small, individual differences between machines, in this test, to the extent that it would be risky to attach one target size to one machine only throughout the tests. Under that arrangement, machine differences might make it appear that there were differences attributable to target differences or might by chance negate those differences. The target sizes were therefore combined with the machines systematically. There were therefore 12 target-machine combinations with five observed scores obtained with each combination. The scores (which are entirely fictitious for the sake of a good illustration) are tabulated in Table 13.4. This arrangement is typical and convenient for the operations of analysis of variance. The sums and means, as given, are also needed in the variance solution.

It should be emphasized that in the two-way problem to be illustrated, the observations within sets come from entirely different individuals selected at random from the same population. If the same individuals were used for more than one treatment, there would be some correlation introduced between sets of observations, and the two-way model as demonstrated would not apply. There are other models available to take care of data that involve correlated observations, such as the illustrative problem at the end of this chapter, in which each of several individuals is rated by each of several observers.[1]

DIFFERENT MODELS IN FACTORIAL DESIGNS

At this point one should know that in a two-way factorial experimental design different kinds of variables for classification introduce different models.[2] The main distinction of concern to us here is between fixed categories and randomly chosen categories.

Fixed categories are arbitrarily chosen by the investigator. Sometimes they are chosen for him because there are no other possibilities — the two sexes, the two political parties, right versus left arrangement of stimuli, and so on. If the variable is a quantitative one, such as amount of practice in learning, time of exposure, or hours of food deprivation, the investigator is likely to select a limited number of constant values, covering as much of the range as he thinks necessary. In the illustrative experiment, target size is one of those fixed-category variables, with four arbitrarily chosen target sizes.

Randomly chosen categories represent a sampling approach. Here the choice of machines is an example. The three selected were from a pool of possible machines that could have been used. Examples from other sources are selected individuals, picked at random, each person

[1]For more extensive treatment of the use of other models in experimental design, see Edwards, A. L. *Experimental Designs in Psychological Research*. New York: Holt, 1960.
[2]A factorial experimental design has two or more conditions varied systematically, such as age, method, or amount of practice.

Table 13.4   **Scores of 60 students earned on three different machines of a psychomoter test, each with the target size varied in four steps**

Target size		Machines			Sums for target size	Means for target size
		1	2	3		
A		6	4	4		
		4	1	2		
		2	5	2		
		6	2	1		
		2	3	1		
	Σ	20	15	10	45	
	M	4	3	2		3
B		8	6	3		
		3	6	1		
		7	2	1		
		5	3	2		
		2	8	3		
	Σ	25	25	10	60	
	M	5	5	2		4
C		7	9	6		
		6	4	4		
		9	8	3		
		8	4	8		
		5	5	4		
	Σ	35	30	25	90	
	M	7	6	5		6
D		9	7	6		
		6	8	5		
		8	4	7		
		8	7	9		
		9	4	8		
	Σ	40	30	35	105	
	M	8	6	7		7
Sums for machines		120	100	80	300	
Means for machines		6	5	4		5

to undergo the various kinds of treatment as determined by the second experimental variable. Each person might be given doses of a drug of different concentrations. There might be replications within treatments (several trials for each person) or there might be no replications, in which case there is only one experimental measurement for each cell of the two-by-two table of data from the two-way factorial experiment.

From the kinds of combinations of variables that are possible, we have three different models. With both variables having fixed categories, we have a *fixed model* or *fixed constants model*. Both sets of categories are arbitrarily chosen. When both variables have randomly selected categories, we have a *random model*. The latter offers the widest range of possible generalizations from the findings of the experiment, since the categories follow the statistical principle of random sampling from universes. With fixed categories, generalizations are restricted to the kinds of categories chosen. A third kind of model is called the *mixed model* because it has one fixed and one random set of categories.[1] Besides the experimental implications of random versus fixed categories that have just been touched upon, we shall see later that these differences in models are clearly related to the way in which F ratios are formed. The differences in models have no bearing upon how we extract information about mean squares from the data in a two-way analysis of variance, the operations of which we shall consider next.

THE SOURCES OF VARIANCE IN A TWO-WAY CLASSIFICATION PROBLEM

We could, if we chose, proceed to perform an analysis of variance based upon the model of the one-way classification problem already demonstrated. That is, we could take the 12 sets as if they represented categories based upon a single principle and test the 12 means collectively to see whether they could have arisen by random sampling from the same population. There are, however, logical objections to such a solution in a problem of this kind.

Suppose we did carry through the solution proposed and found an F ratio that indicated significance beyond the .01 point. We should not know whether this was due primarily or solely to the differences between targets or to the differences between machines, or to both possible sources. Suppose, on the contrary, the F ratio indicated no significant differences among sets. We should not be sure that one of the experimental variations, perhaps target size, was not actually

[1]For more detailed treatment of this subject, see McNemar, Q. *Psychological Statistics*. 3d ed. New York: Wiley, 1962; Lindquist, E. F. *Design and Analysis of Experiments in Psychology and Education*. Boston: Houghton Mifflin, 1953; Edwards, *op. cit.*

producing real variations that were either covered over or counteracted by the effects of the other experimental variations. We should have what is called a *confounding* of effects. We need some method that will segregate the variations associated with each of the experimental variables so that any significant differences at all will have a chance to emerge in the F test and so that we shall know to which source to attribute any significant differences found.

Interaction variance.   The procedure about to be described makes possible this kind of segregation of the sources of variations. As a result, we can then determine whether differences among means owe their divergencies to target size or to machine differences, or to both. Nor is that all; when there are two possible sources of variations, there is also a possibility of what is called *interaction variance*.

The phenomenon is well named. Interaction variations are those attributable not to either of two influences acting alone but to joint effects of the two acting together. If it turned out that the larger the target, the larger the scores tended to be, that would be one direct and isolable effect. It is one of the so-called *main effects*. If there were systematic machine differences so that among the three there was a most "difficult" one (i.e., one that yields lower mean scores) and an easiest one (i.e., one that yields higher mean scores), that is another distinct effect. This would be another main effect. There may be effects of target size and machine over and above these main effects. It is conceivable, but not very probable, that one machine, apart from its general difficulty, gains in difficulty by virtue of its having one size of target rather than others. It may be the coincidence of machine and target size that produces systematic variation in one direction from the general mean of scores. This would be an example of interaction variance.

Interaction variance might be more reasonably expected in a combination of teacher and instruction method, of kind of task and method of attack by the learner, and of kind of reward when combined with a certain condition of motivation. Interaction variance and main effects are illustrated in Fig. 13.1. The illustrative problem is one that could conceivably have been subjected to treatment as a three-way factorial design. Students in the fifth grade were given the same psychological test (Ravens Progressive Matrices) in city and country populations, composed of both boys and girls, at five socioeconomic levels. A 15-per-cent random sample was obtained from some Italian schools.[1]

If we hold one of the three variables constant at one of the cate-

[1]From data presented by Young, H. B., Taguiri, R., Tesi, G., and Montemagni, G. Influence of town and country upon children's intelligence. *Brit. J. Educ. Psychol.*, 1962, **32**, 151–158.

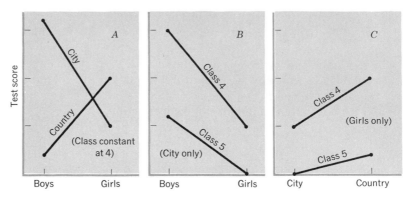

Fig. 13.1. *Illustrations of the phenomenon of interaction of variables. Note that in some instances the relation of one variable to another depends upon the influence of a third variable (especially in Case A) and in other instances the relation is very much the same (as in Case C).* (Based on data from H. B. Young, R. Taguiri, G. Tesi, and G. Montemagni. Brit. J. Educ. Psychol., 1962, **32**, 151–158, with permission of the authors.)

gories, we can have a two-way factorial problem of the kind with which we are at present concerned. If we concentrate on children of socioeconomic class 4, we have a study of mean differences of city versus country children and of boys versus girls. Part A of Fig. 13.1 shows a plot of the means so as to demonstrate relationships between scores and sex membership in city versus country children. It will be noted that the differences are in opposite directions, which illustrates a drastic interaction effect that might well prove to be significant in an F test. Whether or not boys are superior to girls on the average in the test depends very much upon whether the children in question are from the city or the country. If city and country children were treated in a combined sample, there would be practically no difference in means. In a two-way analysis the main effect for sex would very likely be insignificant. There would be a small main effect from city versus country (from city versus country means when boys and girls are combined), but it, too, might prove to be insignificant. The interaction effect here is dominant.

By contrast, parts B and C of Fig. 13.1 show some main effects but little interaction effect. In part B (city children only), the trends of sex differences in means are similar in direction, if differing slightly in slope. If they were parallel, the interaction variance would be nil. The lines need not run in opposite directions, as they do in part A, to indicate interaction variance. Difference in slope would suffice, provided the F ratio proved to be significant. In part B, there is a fairly obvious main effect for sex, from the downward slope of the lines, and also for class, from the general levels of the lines in the field. In part C, with sex constant for the category of girls, interaction is less than in B; the main effect for classes is fairly evident, but, from the slopes of the lines, the main effect for city versus country is of doubtful significance.

Although we could treat the total data as three two-way analysis problems, treatment as a three-way analysis not only reveals the three main effects and the three interaction effects, two at a time — sex by urban-rural, socioeconomic level by sex, and socioeconomic level by urban-rural — but doing so would miss the opportunity to test for a *triple interaction* effect — sex by urban-rural by socioeconomic level. Some of the deviations of means from the grand mean might be attributable to the combined effect of all three sources, over and above effects from two at a time, or of the variables taken singly. The principles demonstrated in the following two-way analysis apply, by extension, to more complex factorial designs.

Component sources in a two-way analysis. As in the one-way-analysis problem, we may write a basic equation for the two-way problem. It takes the form

$$X = M_t + d_a + d_b + d_{ab} + e_r$$

where an obtained measurement X is conceived as being made up of several independent components. M_t is the grand mean and contributes nothing to variance. d_a is a contribution to the deviation of the single observation from M_t owing to its membership in one of the categories of variable A. Similarly, d_b is a deviation due to variable B. d_{ab} is the source of interaction variance. In each observation, after accounting for main effects, membership in a certain combination of A and B categories determines another increment, positive or negative. As earlier, e_r is the random-error contribution. The sums of squares derived from the four different sources add up to the total sum of squares for all the X's.

ESTIMATION OF THE VARIANCE FROM DIFFERENT SOURCES

Two solutions will be described, one using deviations of observed values and of means of sets, from the various appropriate means, the other using original measurements and means. An attempt will be made to summarize the operations in terms of formulas, but some readers may find it easier to follow the examples as models rather than to apply the formulas. The system of symbols employed in the formulas is given in Table 13.5. This table provides only three columns and three rows, but it could be extended in the directions shown to take care of any number of columns and rows.

THE SOLUTION BASED UPON DEVIATIONS

In what follows, consistent with the symbols in Table 13.5, a subscript k stands for a particular column (we might have used c for column, but there would be danger of confusing this with a particular row — row C), and r stands for a particular row. There are three columns, 1, 2, and 3, in the psychomotor-test problem, and four rows, $A, B, C,$ and D. The symbol X_{ij} stands for any one observation in row r

Table 13.5 **Symbolic scheme for the values in a tabulation preparatory to analysis of variance in a two-way classification problem**

Row		Column 1	Column 2	Column 3	Sums of rows (ΣX_r)	Means of rows (M_r)
A	1	X_{a1}	X_{a2}	X_{a3}		
	2					
	3					
	4					
	5					
	Σ	ΣX_{a1}	ΣX_{a2}	ΣX_{a3}	ΣX_a	
	M	M_{a1}	M_{a2}	M_{a3}		M_a
B	1	X_{b1}	X_{b2}	X_{b3}		
	2					
	3					
	4					
	5					
	Σ	ΣX_{b1}	ΣX_{b2}	ΣX_{b3}	ΣX_b	
	M	M_{b1}	M_{b2}	M_{b3}		M_b
C	1	X_{c1}	X_{c2}	X_{c3}		
	2					
	3					
	4					
	5					
	Σ	ΣX_{c1}	ΣX_{c2}	ΣX_{c3}	ΣX_c	
	M	M_{c1}	M_{c2}	M_{c3}		M_c
Sums of columns (ΣX_k)		ΣX_1	ΣX_2	ΣX_3	ΣX_{ij}	
Means of columns (M_k)		M_1	M_2	M_3		M_t

Let X_{ij} = any one of the cell entries, $X_{a1}, X_{b1}, \ldots, X_{c3}.$
M_{rk} = any one of the set means, $M_{a1}, M_{a2}, \ldots, M_{c3}.$

and column k and M_{rk} stands for a mean of the five observations in a cell described as being in row r and column k. In the following, n stands for the number of observations within each set; in the illustrative problem $n = 5$. The number of rows is symbolized by r and the number of columns by k. The subscript t refers to the total distribution, all sets combined. Thus, M_t stands for the mean of the composite, and x_t stands for a deviation of any X from M_t.

The total sum of squares is given by the equation

$$\Sigma x^2_t = \Sigma(X_{ij} - M_t)^2 \tag{13.11}$$

Applied to the data of Table 13.4,

$$\Sigma x^2_t = (6 - 5)^2 + (4 - 5)^2 + (4 - 5)^2 \quad \text{(from first row of Table 13.4)}$$
$$+ \cdot \cdot \cdot \cdot \cdot \cdot \cdot \cdot \cdot \cdot \cdot \cdot \cdot \cdot \cdot \cdot \cdot \cdot$$
$$+ (9 - 5)^2 + (4 - 5)^2 + (8 - 5)^2$$
$$\text{(from last row of observations in Table 13.4)}.$$
$$= 1^2 + (-1)^2 + (-1)^2$$
$$+ \cdot \cdot \cdot \cdot \cdot \cdot \cdot \cdot \cdot \cdot \cdot$$
$$+ 4^2 + (-1)^2 + 3^2$$
$$= 374 \quad \text{(Total sum of squares)}$$

The sum of squares between rows is given by the equation

$$\Sigma d^2_r = nk[\Sigma(M_r - M_t)^2] \tag{13.12}$$

Applied to the same data,

$$\Sigma d^2_r = 5 \times 3[(3 - 5)^2 + (4 - 5)^2 + (6 - 5)^2 + (7 - 5)^2]$$
$$= 15[(-2)^2 + (-1)^2 + 1^2 + 2^2]$$
$$= 15 \times 10$$
$$= 150 \quad \text{(Sum of squares between rows)}$$

The sum of squares between columns is given by the equation

$$\Sigma d^2_k = nr[\Sigma(M_k - M_t)^2] \tag{13.13}$$

Applied to the data of Table 13.4,

$$\Sigma d^2_k = 5 \times 4[(6 - 5)^2 + (5 - 5)^2 + (4 - 5)^2]$$
$$= 20[1^2 + (-1)^2]$$
$$= 20 \times 2$$
$$= 40 \quad \text{(Sum of squares between rows)}$$

The interaction variance can be estimated in several ways. Perhaps the most common way is to derive it from the sum of squares between all sets, eliminating the sums of squares between columns and between rows. We already know the last two sums of squares. We proceed next to compute the sum of squares between sets. The formula is similar to the numerator of formula (13.2) but with different notation to fit the new system.

$$\Sigma d^2_{rk} = n\left[\Sigma(M_{rk} - M_t)^2\right] \tag{13.14}$$

The symbol d^2_{rk} refers to a squared difference between any set mean and the total mean M_t. The subscript rk implies that all rows and all columns are involved. Applied to the illustrative data,

$$
\begin{aligned}
\Sigma d^2_{rk} &= 5\left[(4-5)^2 + (3-5)^2 + (2-5)^2 \right. && \text{(from first row of means)}\\
&\quad + \cdots\cdots\cdots\cdots\cdots\cdots\cdots\\
&\quad \left. + (8-5)^2 + (6-5)^2 + (7-5)^2\right] && \text{(from last row of means)}\\
&= 5\left[(-1)^2 + (-2)^2 + (-3)^2 \right.\\
&\quad + \cdots\cdots\cdots\cdots\cdots\cdots\cdots\\
&\quad \left. + 3^2 + 1^2 + 2^2\right]\\
&= 5 \times 42\\
&= 210 && \text{(Sum of squares between means of sets)}
\end{aligned}
$$

If we remove from the entire sum of squares for the 12 set means the sum of squares attributable to columns and to rows, we have left the interaction sum of squares. By formula,

$$\Sigma d^2_{r\times k} = \Sigma d^2_{rk} - \Sigma d^2_k - \Sigma d^2_k \tag{13.15}$$

in which $\Sigma d^2_{r\times k}$ (the subscript reads r times k, for reasons that will be explained) stands for the interaction sum of squares. For the illustrative problem,

$$
\begin{aligned}
\Sigma d^2_{r\times k} &= 210 - 40 - 150\\
&= 20 && \text{(Interaction sum of squares)}
\end{aligned}
$$

Another, more direct, way of deriving interaction sums of squares utilizes the formula

$$\Sigma d^2_{r\times k} = n\left[\Sigma(M_{rk} - M_k - M_r + M_t)^2\right] \tag{13.16}$$

in which M_k is the mean of the column in which each particular M_{rk} appears and M_r the mean of its row. For the illustrative problem,

$$
\begin{aligned}
\Sigma d^2_{r\times k} &= 5\left[(4-3-6+5)^2 + (3-3-5+5)^2 \right. && \text{(from first row of}\\
&&& \text{means)}\\
&\quad + \cdots\cdots\cdots\cdots\cdots\cdots\cdots\\
&\quad \left. + (6-7-5+5)^2 + (7-7-4+5)^2\right] && \text{(from last row of}\\
&&& \text{means)}\\
&= 5\left[0^2 + 0^2 + \cdots + (-1)^2 + 1^2\right]\\
&= 5 \times 4\\
&= 20 && \text{(Interaction sum of squares; alternative solution)}
\end{aligned}
$$

The sum of squares within sets is computed by the formula

$$\Sigma x^2_s = \Sigma(X_{ij} - M_{rk})^2 \tag{13.17}$$

This formula, with new symbols, requires the same operations as formula (13.3) given in connection with the single-classification problem. Applied to the psychomotor problem,

$$\Sigma x^2_{\,s} = (6-4)^2 + (4-4)^2 + (2-4)^2 + (6-4)^2 + (2-4)^2 \quad \text{(from set } A1)$$

$$+ \cdots \cdots \cdots \cdots \cdots \cdots \cdots \cdots \cdots \cdots \cdots$$

$$+ (6-7)^2 + (5-7)^2 + (7-7)^2 + (9-7)^2 + (8-7)^2$$

$$\text{(from set } D3)$$

$$= 164 \quad \text{(Sum of squares within sets)}$$

We can now check the solution of this by deducting all previously computed sums of squares from the total sum of squares, and we have

$$374 - 40 - 150 - 20 = 164$$

We could compute $\Sigma x^2_{\,s}$ by this elimination process without going through the arduous arithmetic involved in using (13.17), but for checking purposes it is very desirable to derive all the component sums of squares separately and then check the results.

DEGREES OF FREEDOM

Before taking the next important step of estimating population variance from these different sources, we need, as usual, the degrees of freedom. Starting with the largest source, the total sum of squares, we have, as usual, $(N-1)$ df, or 59. This figure is to be subdivided among the contributing components. The sum of squares among the means of sets should have allotted to it the number of sets minus 1, or $12 - 1 = 11$ df. These 11, in turn, are to be allotted to three sources. Rows have the number of row observations (row means) minus 1, or

$$4 - 1 = 3$$

Columns have, by analogy, $3 - 1 = 2$. This leaves 6 out of the 11 for interaction. This 6 degrees is 3×2, the product of the df for rows and columns, each source taken separately. This is consistent with the idea of interaction itself, whose contributions to variations may be regarded as the products of two sources. This is why we use the subscript $r \times k$ when referring to interaction. Having taken care of the special sources of variations, we are left with a remainder, $59 - 11$, which gives the df left for within-sets sums of squares. This number of df may also be determined directly from a summation of df within sets. Since there are 12 sets and each contains 4 df, we have $12 \times 4 = 48$ df for the residual variance.

In terms of symbolic descriptions, the degrees of freedom may be given as follows:

Source	Degrees of freedom
Between rows	$r - 1$
Between columns	$k - 1$
Interaction	$(r - 1)(k - 1)$
Within sets	$N - rk = rk(n - 1)$
Total	$N - 1$

THE F RATIOS

We now face the question of how to constitute the three F ratios, F_k for main effect from columns (machines, in the illustrative problem), F_r for main effect for rows (target size), and $F_{r \times k}$, for interaction effect. In answering this three-part question, we must take into account the fact that we have a mixed model involved. Let us consider a systematic solution to the problem for all three kinds of models.

F ratios for different models. For the fixed model, the categories having been determined on a logical or experimental basis and not by sampling, the error term to use in all three F's is the residual or within-sets mean square. In other words, we extend to the two-way analysis the same kind of operation that was applied in the one-way analysis.

If the model is a random one, the categories in each variable having been obtained by random sampling from a universe of possible categories, the appropriate error term for testing the significance of *interaction effect* is the within-sets mean square. Whether or not the interaction F turns out to be significant, the appropriate error term and the denominator for F for testing both main effects is the interaction mean square. In so using the mean square from interaction, we wish to be sure that any significant main effect does not derive some of its possible significance from interaction effects themselves. We could not be sure about this if the within-sets mean square were used as the error term.

As we might expect, the mixed model presents some special questions. In the past, there has not been complete agreement on which error term to use in forming F ratios for the two main effects, but the present consensus seems to favor the following principles. There is only one error term that could be used in an F test for interaction, namely, the within-sets mean square. In testing the significance of the main effect that has the random categories, the mean square for within sets is considered to be the appropriate error term. But for testing the significance of the main effect with the fixed categories, the error term should be the mean square for interaction, regardless of whether or not the F for interaction has been found to be significant. The reason is that some of the interaction effects may have contributed to the variance of the main effect from the fixed-constants variable. Thus, if we used the within-sets mean square in connection with this variable's F test, and if the F were significant, we could not be sure that the significance is due only to the main effect. Since the interaction mean square is usually larger than the within-sets mean square, the use of the interaction mean square as the error term gives a smaller F, with less chance of being significant. But its use avoids the danger of having an ambiguous F to be interpreted.

F ratios for the psychomotor-test problem.   In the illustrative problem, as Table 13.6 shows, the F for interaction proved to be so near 1.0 that there was no question regarding its lack of significance. The F_k, for machines, was 5.85, which was larger than the F required for significance at the .01 level, with 2 and 48 df. Had this F been derived from genuine data, we could conclude that the suspicion that the machines present psychological tasks of different degrees of difficulty, regardless of the size of target, was well founded. As should have been expected in a genuine experiment, the F ratio for target size is well beyond the F required for significance at the .01 level. The insignificant F for interaction would indicate that a target's difficulty does not depend upon the machine upon which it appears.

*Table 13.6   **Sources of variance in the psychomotor-test data analysis, with F ratios***

Source	Sum of squares	Degrees of freedom	Mean squares
Target size (T)	150	3	50.0
Machine (M)	40	2	20.0
Interaction ($T \times M$)	20	6	3.33
Within sets	164	48	3.42
Total	374	59	

		Required F	
		$p = .05$	$p = .01$
F for interaction $= \dfrac{3.33}{3.42} = 0.97$		2.30	3.20
F for machines $= \dfrac{20.0}{3.42} = 5.85$		3.19	5.08
F for targets $= \dfrac{50.0}{3.33} = 15.00$		2.80	4.22

REMOVAL OF SOURCES OF VARIATION

It may illuminate the concepts of different kinds of variance and the way in which they contribute to total variance in the sample if we separate them in another way.

Table 13.7*A* shows the 12 means of sets for the psychomotor-test data. Variations among them are due to the three possible sources — target differences, machine differences, and the interaction of the two. The possible effects of target size are most apparent in the means of the rows — 3, 4, 6, and 7. The possible effects of machine differences are most apparent in the means of the columns — 6, 5, and 4. The possible interaction variance is obscured. It possibly contributes both to the means of rows and of columns; we do not know. Let us strip away first the variations attributable to machines and then that attributable to targets and see what variations are left. We have eliminated the contributions of random errors, e_r, by averaging within cells.

The mean of all observations is 5. Any deviation of a column mean from 5 indicates a constant error for a particular machine. Machine 1 gave a mean of 6, indicating that machine 1 had a constant error of +1. Machine 2 apparently had no constant error, while machine 3 had a constant error of −1. If we deduct from each cell or set mean in column 1 the amount of constant error involved for machine 1, we should presumably remove from the means in column 1 the influence of machine 1 as a source of variation. We can do likewise for column 3, deducting the constant error of −1, which is equivalent to adding +1 to each mean. We need do nothing for column 2. The results of these operations are shown in Table 13.7*B*. The means of the columns are now all 5, to agree with the composite mean, M_t. The means of the rows have been unaffected (they are still 3, 4, 6, and 7) because the changes in one column are compensated for by changes in reverse direction in another column. The cell values in Table 13.7*B* still have in them the variance attributable to targets and to interaction variance.

Next we remove the target variance. The constant errors for rows are −2, −1, 1, and 2, respectively. Deducting these from the values in their respective rows of Table 13.7*B*, we have the results in subtable *C*. The means of the rows as well as of the columns are now all 5. But within four cells there are departures from 5. These possibly are the interaction deviations, depending upon whether or not they prove to be significant. Machine 2 seems to favor high scores when coupled with target *B* and to favor low scores when coupled with target *D*. Machine 3 has a reverse tendency. But the *F* showed these deviations to be insignificant. There seem to be no good, logical reasons to expect any systematic coupling of target and machine. In other problems there may be significant interaction effects.

Table 13.7   Analysis of the between-sets sums of squares in the psychomotor-test data into three components by successive removal of contributing sources of variation

Row	Column 1	Column 2	Column 3	Σ	M

A. Original matrix of means of sets

Row	1	2	3	Σ	M
A	4	3	2	9	3
B	5	5	2	12	4
C	7	6	5	18	6
D	8	6	7	21	7
Σ	24	20	16	60	
M	6	5	4		5

B. With variations associated with machines removed

Row	1	2	3	Σ	M
A	3	3	3	9	3
B	4	5	3	12	4
C	6	6	6	18	6
D	7	6	8	21	7
Σ	20	20	20	60	
M	5	5	5		5

C. With variations associated with target size also removed; only interaction variance remaining

Row	1	2	3	Σ	M
A	5	5	5	15	5
B	5	6	4	15	5
C	5	5	5	15	5
D	5	4	6	15	5
Σ	20	20	20	60	
M	5	5	5		5

SOLUTION FROM ORIGINAL MEASUREMENTS

We now give the formulas and their applications for the solution of sums of squares without computing means and deviations. With small integral numbers to start with, or numbers coded to such magnitude, these procedures are often more convenient than those utilizing deviations. The first solution, with deviations, is more meaningful to the beginner. In the following exposition, each formula will be stated and then immediately applied to the psychomotor-test data.

Total sum of squares:

$$\sum x^2_t = \sum X^2_{ij} - \frac{(\Sigma X_{ij})^2}{N}$$

$$= 6^2 + 4^2 + 4^2 \qquad \text{(from first row of Table 13.4)}$$
$$+ \cdots \cdots \cdots$$
$$+ 9^2 + 4^2 + 8^2 \qquad \text{(from last row of Table 13.4)}$$
$$- \frac{(300)^2}{60}$$
$$= 1{,}874 - 1{,}500 = 374 \qquad \text{(Total sum of squares)} \qquad (13.18)$$

Sum of squares between sets:

$$\sum d^2_{rk} = \frac{\Sigma(\Sigma X_{rk})^2}{n} - \frac{(\Sigma X_{ij})^2}{N}$$

$$= \frac{1}{5}[\,(20^2 + 15^2 + 10^2$$
$$+ \cdots \cdots \cdots \qquad \text{(from first } \Sigma \text{ row of Table 13.4)}$$
$$+ 40^2 + 30^2 + 35^2)\,]$$
$$- \frac{(300)^2}{60} \qquad \text{(from last } \Sigma \text{ row of Table 13.4)}$$
$$= 1{,}710 - 1{,}500$$
$$= 210 \qquad \text{(Sum of squares between sets)} \qquad (13.19)$$

Sum of squares between rows:

$$\sum d^2_r = \frac{\Sigma(\Sigma X_r)^2}{nk} - \frac{(\Sigma X_{ij})^2}{N}$$

$$= [\,\tfrac{1}{15}(45^2 + 60^2 + 90^2 + 105^2)\,] - 1{,}500$$
$$= 1{,}650 - 1{,}500$$
$$= 150 \qquad \text{(Sum of squares between rows)} \qquad (13.20)$$

Sum of squares between columns:

$$\sum d^2_k = \frac{\Sigma(\Sigma X_k)^2}{nr} - \frac{(\Sigma X_{ij})^2}{N}$$

$$= [\,\tfrac{1}{20}(120^2 + 100^2 + 80^2)\,] - 1{,}500$$
$$= 1{,}540 - 1{,}500$$
$$= 40 \qquad \text{(Sum of squares between columns)} \qquad (13.21)$$

Sum of squares for interaction:

$$\Sigma d^2_{r\times k} = \Sigma d^2_{rk} - \Sigma d^2_r - \Sigma d^2_k$$
$$= 210 - 150 - 40$$
$$= 20 \quad \text{(Sum of squares for interaction)} \tag{13.22}$$

Sum of squares within sets:

$$\Sigma x^2_s = \Sigma x^2_t - \Sigma d^2_{rk}$$
$$= 374 - 210$$
$$= 164 \quad \text{(Sum of squares within sets)} \tag{13.23}$$

It will be noted that the correction factor $(\Sigma X_{ij})^2/N$ is the same in all the equations in which it appears, and need be computed only once.

The sums of squares by this method are seen to be identical with those found by the preceding method. The estimation of the population variance from each source and the application of the F test are the same as before (see Table 13.6).

A TWO-WAY CLASSIFICATION ANALYSIS WITHOUT REPLICATIONS

Occasionally there arises the kind of research problem in which there are two experimental variations but only one observation for each combination of conditions. This kind of problem will be illustrated by the use of ratings. The data in Table 13.8 will be utilized.

In these data, three raters have given their ratings of each of seven

Table 13.8   Application of analysis of variance in a two-way classification without replication

Ratee	Rater A	Rater B	Rater C	ΣX_r	$(\Sigma X_r)^2$
1	5	6	5	16	256
2	9	8	7	24	576
3	3	4	3	10	100
4	7	5	5	17	289
5	9	2	9	20	400
6	3	4	3	10	100
7	7	3	7	17	289
ΣX_k	43	32	39	114 ΣX_{ij}	2,010 $\Sigma(\Sigma X_r)^2$
$(\Sigma X_k)^2$	1,849	1,024	1,521	12,996 $(\Sigma X_{ij})^2$	

$$\Sigma(\Sigma X_k)^2 = 4{,}394 \qquad \Sigma X^2_{ij} = 720$$

individuals in a single trait. The procedure of analysis is much like that previously illustrated when there are replications. The main difference is that the interaction and error effects are not segregated from one another here, since there is no basis for doing so. The error term is derived from this combined source.

The total sum of squares is computed as in formula (13.18), and need not be repeated here. Applied to the data of Table 13.8,

$$\Sigma x^2_t = 720.00 - 618.86 = 101.14$$

The sum of squares between rows is given by the formula

$$\Sigma d^2_r = \frac{\Sigma(\Sigma X_r)^2}{k} - \frac{(\Sigma X_{ij})^2}{kr} \tag{13.24}$$

Applied to the data of Table 13.8, we have

$$\Sigma d^2_r = \frac{2,010}{3} - \frac{12,996}{21} = 670.00 - 618.86 = 51.14$$

The sum of squares between columns is given by

$$\Sigma d^2_k = \frac{\Sigma(\Sigma X_k)^2}{r} - \frac{(\Sigma X_{ij})^2}{rk} \tag{13.25}$$

Applied to the data of Table 13.8, this gives

$$\Sigma d^2_k = \frac{4,394}{7} - 618.86 = 8.85$$

The sum of squares for the remainder is obtained by deducting the last two sums of squares from the total sum of squares. We therefore have for the remainder sum of squares,

$$\Sigma x^2_e = 101.14 - 51.14 - 8.85 = 41.15$$

We are now ready to estimate variances and compute F ratios. The work is summarized in Table 13.9. Both F ratios prove to be insignificant. We therefore do not reject the hypothesis that there are no differences among raters and among ratees. There may be such real differences, but our F tests fail to indicate them. We should not be very surprised to find no significant differences among raters, except as some of them show marked errors of leniency in rating and some do not. We *should* be surprised, however, not to find significant differences among ratees, for individual differences in most traits are the almost universal finding. With a larger sample, the statistical test might have been sensitive enough to yield a significant F for ratees.

The smallness of sample, however, is not the whole story behind the insignificant F's. Note that it was stated at the beginning of this section that the error term includes contributions from interaction.

Table 13.9   **Estimated variances and F ratios from the data of table 13.8**

Source	Sum of squares	df	V	F	P
Ratees (rows)	51.14	6	8.52	2.48	>.05
Raters (columns)	8.85	2	4.425	1.29	>.05
Remainder	41.15	12	3.43		
Total	101.14	20			

If the interaction effects are of sufficient importance, they inflate the variance computed from the residual sum of squares and thus reduce the size of both F ratios. We know that there are often *halo errors*, which can be defined statistically as interaction effects — between rater and ratee. We should not be able to segregate this interaction effect without having independent replications, which would be difficult to obtain, or without having ratings made by the same raters of the same ratees on other traits.[1]

Another reason for the small variance among ratees is the lack of agreement among the raters. Some of this can be attributed to halo errors. In the extreme case, if there were zero correlations among the raters' ratings, the means of the ratees would tend toward equality, or no variance at all. The higher the intercorrelation of raters, the greater will be the variance estimated from among ratees. To this problem of inter-rater correlation we turn next.

INTRACLASS CORRELATION

From the data of Table 13.8 we can use the information already extracted about variances from which to compute correlations between raters. The average intercorrelation thus obtained is known as an *intraclass correlation*. This correlation is given by the formula

$$r_{cc} = \frac{V_r - V_e}{V_r + (k-1)V_e} \qquad \text{(Intraclass correlation among } k \text{ series)} \qquad (13.26)$$

where V_r = variance between rows, where each row stands for a person
V_e = variance for residuals (or error)
k = number of columns
For the data of Table 13.8,

$$r_{cc} = \frac{8.52 - 3.43}{8.52 + 2(3.43)} = .33$$

[1]For further treatment of ratings by analysis of variance, see Guilford, J. P. *Psychometric Methods.* 2d ed. New York: McGraw-Hill, 1954. Pp. 281–288.

This result indicates that the average of the intercorrelations of the three sets of ratings is .33. If we take the intercorrelations of raters to be an indication of reliability of ratings, we can say that the typical reliability of a single rater's ratings is of the order of .33. The actual correlations between single pairs might vary considerably from this figure because of sampling errors in such a small sample.

If we want to know the reliability of a sum or mean of these three raters' ratings in this population, a modified formula is available:

$$r_{kk} = \frac{V_r - V_e}{V_r} \qquad \text{(Intraclass correlation of a sum or average)} \qquad (13.27)$$

Applied to the same data,

$$r_{kk} = \frac{8.52 - 3.43}{8.52} = .60$$

From this we infer that if we averaged the three ratings for each ratee and could correlate the set of averages with a similar set of averages, the result would be about .60. Averaging reduces the relative importance of errors of measurement, leaving the relationships enhanced. This principle of reliability will be treated at some length in Chap. 17.

General comments on analysis of variance

ASSUMPTIONS TO BE SATISFIED IN APPLYING ANALYSIS OF VARIANCE

Like most statistics, those involved in analysis of variance have been derived on the basis of mathematical reasoning. Such reasoning starts with assumptions. If those assumptions are satisfied within certain limits of tolerance, the results in terms of F ratios may be interpreted as described in this chapter. If those assumptions are not sufficiently approximated, there is considerable risk that the conclusions may be faulty.

The four major assumptions to be satisfied in applying analysis of variance were presented earlier in this chapter. They include independent observations within sets (random sampling), equal variances within sets, normal distributions of population values within sets, and additivity of component contributions to variances.

Some extensive studies by Norton on sampling problems in analysis of variance have thrown considerable light upon what happens to F when distributions of populations are not normal and when variances are not equal.[1] With artificial populations of 10,000 cases, Norton varied the shape of distribution in various ways, making it leptokurtic, rectangular, markedly skewed, and even J-shaped. Other

[1] Cited by Lindquist, *op. cit.*

populations were normally distributed, but variances were 25, 100, and 225 in different cases—in other words, markedly differing—the standard deviations being 5, 10, and 15, respectively.

One general finding was that F is rather insensitive to variations in shape of population distribution. This is consistent with the known principle that distributions of means (sampling distributions) approach normality even though populations are not normally distributed. Another general finding was that F is somewhat sensitive to variations in variances of populations, but that only marked differences in variance are serious. Tests of homogeneity of variances in sets of data have been offered, but none is regarded as very satisfactory. A suggestion was made earlier in this chapter that a rough test would be in the form of applying an F test to any pair of variances suspected of being significantly different. Even if some pair shows a significant difference (which is not likely, with small samples), one may proceed with analysis of variance but should then discount significance levels somewhat. If F proves to be significant at the .05 level, this result may actually indicate significance at levels .04 to .07; one significant at the .01 level may actually be significant from the .005 to .02 levels. If anything, the significance is likely to be lower (probability higher) than that indicated by the F tables.

GENERAL USES AND LIMITATIONS OF ANALYSIS OF VARIANCE

There is insufficient space here to do more than give this introduction to the analysis-of-variance methods. There are many and varied applications of these basic procedures—the separation of sums of squares among a few sets of data into the "within" and "between" components—generally in the social sciences. Two additional applications will be seen in Chaps. 15 and 16.

Conditions affecting sets of measurements often vary in a number of ways in the same experiment. This complicates the analysis-of-variance solution in various ways. We have problems of three-way classification, four-way classification, and so on. We have triple and quadruple interactions. There are problems in which the sets of data are not independent, thus involving correlated means. There is a technique for analysis of covariance. Covariance and correlation are closely related, as will be seen later. For further descriptions of how to adapt analysis of variance to various kinds of experimental problems, the reader is referred to books that treat the subject at much greater length.[1]

Not the least of the merits of analysis of variance is the rather strict set of requirements it imposes in the designing of experiments.

[1]Edwards, *op. cit.;* Johnson, P. O. *Statistical Methods in Research.* Englewood Cliffs, N.J.: Prentice-Hall, 1949.

Experimental designs, particularly in psychophysics, have been the subject of thought and discussion for a long time. But they have not been generally so consciously considered or so well planned as when the experimenter knows that analysis of variance is to be used. Discussions of experimental designs will be found in extensive treatments elsewhere.[1]

EXERCISES

The values in Data 13 *A* represent measurements of the lower threshold for hearing the pitch of tones. Assume that they came from different groups of male and female observers, under each of four conditions, with 0, 4, 8, and 12 minutes of nearly complete relaxation just before each set of observations was made.

1. Using the four sets of observations made by the male observers only, apply an *F* test to determine whether there were systematic changes in threshold level associated with length of rest period. Estimate variances by using deviations from means. Interpret your results statistically and psychologically.

2. Make a similar *F* test of the data derived from the female observers, using the formulas for the original measurements. Make any $\bar{z}$ tests that seem called for.

3. Treat the entire table of data as a two-way-classification problem. Make *F* tests to determine the significance of the three special sources of variance. Defend your use of error terms. Interpret your results.

4. Remove each source of variance in Data 13 *A* step by step, as was demonstrated in Table 13.7.

5. Compute an *F* ratio for the analysis in Data 13 *B*. State your conclusions.

6. Compute an intraclass correlation between raters and also between averages of ratings, using Data 13 *B*.

[1]Cochran, W. G., and Cox, G. M. *Experimental Designs.* New York: Wiley, 1950; Maxwell, A. E. *Experimental Design in Psychology and the Medical Sciences.* New York: Wiley, 1958; Winer, B. J. *Statistical Principles in Experimental Design.* New York: McGraw-Hill, 1962; Lindquist, *op. cit.*

Data 13A **Data in a two-way classification**

Sex	Condition			
	I	II	III	IV
Male	24	19	21	24
	26	12	16	18
	21	17	17	22
	17	20	18	18
Female	18	15	16	15
	19	15	19	19
	18	14	17	16
	17	12	14	18

Data 13B **Ratings of seven individuals by three raters in a particular trait**

Ratees	Raters		
	A	B	C
1	3	4	5
2	5	5	5
3	3	3	5
4	1	4	1
5	7	9	7
6	3	5	3
7	6	5	7

ANSWERS

1. $n\Sigma d^2 = 62.76$; $\Sigma x^2_s = 125.0$; $F = 2.01$ (df = 3, 12).
2. $n\Sigma d^2 = 34.75$; $\Sigma x^2_s = 31.00$; $F = 4.48$ (df = 3, 12); t (for deviation of mean II from M_t) = 1.48 (insignificant); $\sigma_M = 1.61$, with df = 12.
3. $\Sigma x^2_t = 325.5$; $\Sigma d^2_{rk} = 169.5$; $\Sigma d^2_r = 72.0$; $\Sigma d^2_k = 90.5$; $\Sigma d^2_{r \times k} = 7.0$; $\Sigma x^2_s = 156.0$; F (between rows) = 11.08 (df = 1, 24); F (between columns) = 4.64 (df = 3, 24); F (interaction) = 1.08 (df = 3, 24).
4. Means of columns and rows constitute the necessary checks.
5. $\Sigma d^2_r = 61.14$; $\Sigma d^2_k = 3.71$; $\Sigma x^2_t = 79.14$; $\Sigma x^2_e = 14.29$; F (for rows) = 8.56 (df = 6, 12); F (for columns) = 1.56 (df = 2, 12).
6. $r_{cc} = .72$; $r_{kk} = .88$.

14 Special correlation methods and problems

PEARSON'S product-moment coefficient is the standard index of the amount of correlation between two variables, and we prefer it whenever its use is possible and convenient. But there are data to which this kind of correlation method cannot be applied, and there are instances in which it can be applied but in which, for practical purposes, other procedures are more expedient. The Pearson coefficient cannot or should not be computed, for example, unless the two variables X and Y are measured on continuous metric scales and unless the regressions are linear (see Chap. 15).[1] Many data are in terms of frequencies of cases having attributes—they are on nominal scales (see Chap. 2). Less often, two continuously measured variables bear to one another a relationship that is curved rather than linear. This chapter will describe some procedures that take care of these irregular situations and other situations where short-cut methods are used to advantage in estimating a Pearson r.

Even when we can apply the product-moment correlation method, however, there are many circumstances which may give rise to a somewhat atypical estimate of correlation or one that does not apply to the population in which we are interested. Samples may be heterogeneous or they may be restricted in variability or they may be forced into a smaller number of categories than we need for good estimates of correlation, estimates free from errors of grouping. These and other common irregularities in the sampling situation or in the data call for special corrective steps and for special interpretive action. It is impossible to anticipate all the peculiarities of data that the reader may encounter, but the more common exceptions to ideal correlation conditions will be touched upon.

[1] If X and Y are positively correlated, Y increases as X increases. If the rate of increase in Y, as related to X, is uniform, the regression is linear; if the rate changes, the regression is curved or nonlinear.

Spearman's rank-difference correlation method

When samples are small, a common procedure applied to regular data in place of the product-moment method is Spearman's rank-difference method. It is conveniently applied as a quick substitute when the number of pairs, or N, is less than 30. It is even more conveniently applied when the data are already in terms of rank orders rather than in terms of interval measurements.

THE COMPUTATION OF A SPEARMAN RHO

If we have data in terms of measurements or scores, it is first necessary to translate them into rank orders. The procedure will be demonstrated by means of the data in Table 14.1. There we have 15 pairs of scores for 15 individuals who responded to sets of cartoons and limericks by judging their humor values, each on a 5-point scale. The score in each case is the sum of the points each individual assigned to the set. We could correlate these scores in the usual manner, described in Chap. 6, but the rank-difference method will be found to be shorter. The following steps are necessary for the application of formula (14.1).

Table 14.1   **A rank-difference correlation between humor scores in reactions to cartoons and to limericks**

Cartoon score	Limerick score	R_1	R_2	D	D^2
47	75	11	8	3	9.00
71	79	4	6	2	4.00
52	85	9	5	4	16.00
48	50	10	14	4	16.00
35	49	14.5	15	0.5	0.25
35	59	14.5	12	2.5	6.25
41	75	12.5	8	4.5	20.25
82	91	1	3	2	4.00
72	102	3	1	2	4.00
56	87	7	4	3	9.00
59	70	6	10	4	16.00
73	92	2	2	0	0.00
60	54	5	13	8	64.00
55	75	8	8	0	0.00
41	68	12.5	11	1.5	2.25
					171.00
					ΣD^2

Step 1. Rank the individuals from the highest to the lowest in the first variable (here it is "cartoon score"), and call these ranks R_1. The highest score receives the rank of 1 (arbitrarily; we might have called it 15), the next highest 2, etc. The only difficulty is when we find tie scores. For example, in Table 14.1, two individuals have scores of 41. One of them comes at rank 12 and the other at rank 13. We do not know which, if either, is better, yet we must fill these two rank positions; therefore we take the average of the tied ranks and call them both 12.5. We make certain that the next ranking scorer is called 14, unless he also is tied. Here we find that he is tied with another who has a score of 35. We treat these two in a similar manner, and so they become each 14.5. If the lowest person is not tied with others, the last rank should be equal to N (in this case, 15). This serves as a check as to accuracy of ranking, though, of course, it will not detect inversions in rank order somewhere along the line. It merely shows whether any rank has been repeated, or any individuals have been overlooked, or ties have somewhere not been properly treated.

Step 2. Rank the second list of measurements in a similar manner, and call them R_2. In this problem, there are three scores of 75 for the individuals occupying places 7, 8, and 9. We call them all 8, leaving 7 and 9 out of the list. This treats the three alike, as required, and also gives a full set of 15 ranks.

Step 3. For every pair of ranks (for each individual), determine the difference in ranks. The smaller one can be subtracted from the larger one in each case, with no attention being paid to algebraic signs, for they are all going to be squared anyway.

Step 4. Square each difference to find D^2.

Step 5. Sum the squares of the differences (see the last column of Table 14.1) to find ΣD^2. The sum in our illustrative problem is 171.00.

Step 6. Compute the coefficient ρ (Greek letter rho) by means of the formula

$$\rho = 1 - \frac{6\Sigma D^2}{N(N^2 - 1)} \qquad \text{(Rank-difference coefficient of correlation)} \qquad (14.1)$$

where ΣD^2 = sum of the squared differences between ranks and N = number of pairs of measurements.

In this problem

$$\rho = 1 - \frac{6 \times 171}{15 \times 224}$$

$$= .695-$$

By this procedure, then, the estimate of the amount of correlation between the two sets of scores is .69.[1] How shall we interpret this correlation, as compared with a Pearson r?

INTERPRETATION OF A RHO COEFFICIENT

The rank-difference coefficient is rather closely equivalent to the Pearson r, numerically. There is a conversion formula by which the corresponding Pearson r can be estimated from rho. But this formula assumes large samples, which is precisely what we do not have when we compute rho. Results from the formula show, however, that on the average r is slightly greater than ρ and that the maximum difference, by the formula, is approximately .02, when both are near .50. We may therefore treat an obtained rho as an approximation to r.

Significance of a rho coefficient. There is no generally accepted formula for estimating the standard error of rho. We cannot, therefore, determine confidence limits. We can test the hypothesis that the population correlation is zero, in two ways. If N is as great as 25, the standard error of a zero rank-order correlation coefficient is estimated by the formula

$$\sigma_\rho = \frac{1}{\sqrt{N-1}} \qquad \text{(Standard error of rho when the population value is zero)} \qquad (14.2)$$

Under these conditions the sampling distribution may be assumed to be normal, and we may estimate a $\bar{z}$ ratio by the formula

$$\bar{z}_\rho = \rho \sqrt{N-1} \qquad (14.3)$$

When N is less than 25, the interpretation is best made by the aid of Table L, in which are given rho coefficients significant at the .05 and .01 levels of confidence. The rho of .69 obtained in the illustrative problem where $N = 15$ would be regarded as significant beyond the .01 level. It is thus highly unlikely that there is no correlation between the "cartoon" and "limerick" scores, but how close to .69 the population correlation is we cannot say.

A BRIEF EVALUATION OF THE RANK-DIFFERENCE CORRELATION

Although there is no good estimate of the standard error of a rho coefficient, there is reason to believe that rho is almost as reliable as a Pearson r of the same size in a sample of the same size. Consequently,

[1]The negative sign after the .695 in the solution to the rho coefficient indicates that the terminal digit 5 came by rounding upward from something above .6945. Further rounding takes this fact into account.

rho is almost as good an estimation of correlation as the Pearson r. If rho is used as a convenient estimate of r, the usual assumption of linear regression should be tenable.

In view of the fact that rho will ordinarily be computed only in small samples, in which low correlations cannot be accurately determined, its chief use, under these circumstances, would be to test the hypothesis of zero correlation. When correlations are high, we may have almost as much confidence in rho for indicating the amount of correlation as we have in r applied to samples of the same size.

Kendall has developed a ranking-method correlation coefficient called τ (tau), which rests on no special assumptions.[1] It has numerous applications, including the testing of hypotheses, but bears no direct relation to the traditional family of product-moment correlations.

The correlation ratio

The correlation ratio is a very general index of correlation particularly adapted to data in which there is a curved regression. Among test scores, linear relationships are apparently the almost universal type of regression. Normality, or near normality, in both distributions correlated is almost sufficient in itself to promote linearity. Outside the sphere of psychological and educational tests, however, or when nontest variables are correlated with test scores, we sometimes encounter curved trends in the scatter diagram. The means of the columns do not progressively increase as we go up the X scale. They may increase slowly at first, then rapidly later; or they may increase to a maximum in the center and then decrease; or other systematic divergencies from linearity may be apparent.

NONLINEAR REGRESSIONS

A common instance of nonlinear relationship is found when we correlate performance scores with chronological age. Typically, performance, as measured, increases most rapidly from ages five to ten and thereafter shows a slackening in upward trend through the teens. If we follow the progression still further, we find typically a maximal performance somewhere in the twenties, with slow decline to the forties and an increasing rate of decline thereafter. If we included all ages from five to seventy-five in our correlation study and if we computed the usual Pearson r between age and scores, the r would probably prove to be near zero. On such a correlation diagram, the scattering of points would be considerably dispersed from any straight line that we might try to draw through the data, slanting up-

[1]Kendall, M. G. *Rank Correlation Methods.* London: Griffin, 1948.

ward or slanting downward. Nevertheless, inspection would show a relationship between age and performance that takes into account the waxing and waning of ability within the span of ages studied.

We might break the chart in two and treat by themselves the years during which there is improvement and the years during which there is decline. We should be able to compute a positive correlation for the earlier span and a negative correlation for the later span by assuming straight-line trends. But these would be of doubtful significance and certainly would not do justice to the full strength of relationships, even within the two segments of life span. The reason is that the trends still deviate from straight lines. Curvature has been overlooked, and to that extent the index of correlation is perhaps markedly underestimated.

Two regression lines and two correlation ratios. The scatter diagram in Fig. 14.1 represents a sample of relationship between performance score in a form-board test and chronological age between five and fourteen years inclusive. Here the score is time required for completion; hence a high number indicates a poor performance, and the trend is downward. But the relationship obviously drops most rapidly during the first 3 years and settles down to slight changes from year to year during the last 3 years. Two regression lines are drawn in the diagram to show more clearly the trends. The regression of test score on age is shown by the solid line that is drawn connec-

Fig. 14.1. *A scatter diagram for a correlation-ratio problem.*

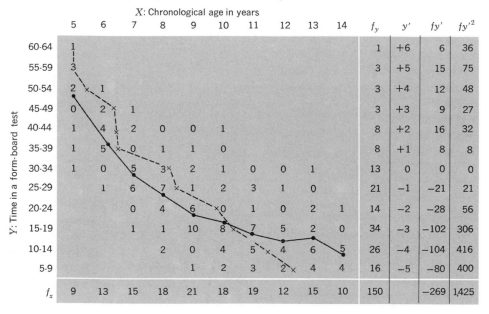

Y: Time in a form-board test	X: Chronological age in years										f_y	y'	fy'	fy'^2
	5	6	7	8	9	10	11	12	13	14				
60-64	1										1	+6	6	36
55-59	3										3	+5	15	75
50-54	2	1									3	+4	12	48
45-49	0	2	1								3	+3	9	27
40-44	1	4	2	0	0	1					8	+2	16	32
35-39	1	5	0	1	1	0					8	+1	8	8
30-34	1	0	5	3	2	1	0	0	1		13	0	0	0
25-29		1	6	7	1	2	3	1	0		21	−1	−21	21
20-24			0	4	6	0	1	0	2	1	14	−2	−28	56
15-19			1	1	10	8	7	5	2	0	34	−3	−102	306
10-14				2	0	4	5	4	6	5	26	−4	−104	416
5-9					1	2	3	2	4	4	16	−5	−80	400
f_x	9	13	15	18	21	18	19	12	15	10	150		−269	1,425

ting the points, which are plotted at the means of the columns. The regression of age upon test score is shown by the dashed line, and the means of the rows, by the x's.

Just as we find two regression lines (for an imperfect correlation) in Chap. 15, where linear regressions are involved, so here we find two regression curves, differing in shape as well as in slope. We have accordingly two correlation ratios, or eta coefficients, one for each of the regressions, and they will not necessarily be the same in value. This result differs from that in the case of linear correlation, where $r_{yz} = r_{xy}$.

The two correlations ratios are estimated by the formulas

$$\eta_{yx} = \frac{\sigma_{y'}}{\sigma_y} \qquad \text{(Correlation ratio for the regression of } Y \text{ on } X) \qquad (14.4a)$$

$$\eta_{xy} = \frac{\sigma_{x'}}{\sigma_x} \qquad \text{(Same, for regression of } X \text{ on } Y) \qquad (14.4b)$$

where $\sigma_{y'}$ = standard deviation of the values (Y') predicted from X

$\sigma_{x'}$ = standard deviation of the X values predicted from Y

σ_y and σ_x = standard deviations of the two total distributions

The manner in which $\sigma_{y'}$ and $\sigma_{x'}$ are determined will be explained next.

THE COMPUTATION OF A CORRELATION RATIO

In a prediction problem of this sort, the best prediction of Y for any column is the mean of the Y's in that column. This prediction will have the smallest sum of squared deviations from the observed Y's in that column. So Y' for each column is the mean of that column. We therefore first compute the means of the columns. These are listed in column 3 in Table 14.2. Now if there were no correlation, no relationship between Y and X, these Y' values would lie along the level of the mean of *all* the Y values, which in this problem is 23.0. No predictions could then be made on the basis of knowledge of X values. For every column with its X value (midpoint), the most probable corresponding Y would be 23.0 and our margin of error would be indicated by σ_y. It would be as large as if we had no knowledge of X for each individual (see Chap. 15 for a more complete discussion of this point).

The more the means of the columns deviate from the mean of all the Y's, relative to the overall deviations of Y's from their mean, the more accurate our predictions are. We are therefore interested in how far the Y' values do deviate from 23.0 here. Those deviations ($Y' - M_y$) are given in column 4 of Table 14.2. As usual, we square the deviations and find their mean as an indicator of how great is their average. The squared deviations ($Y' - M_y)^2$ are given in column 5 of Table 14.2. But

Table 14.2   **The computation of a correlation ratio for the regression of time score on chronological age**

(1) X' CA	(2) n_c	(3) Y' Time	(4) $Y' - M_y$	(5) $(Y' - M_y)^2$	(6) $n_c(Y' - M_y)^2$
14	10	11.0	−12.0	144.00	1,440.00
13	15	14.0	− 9.0	81.00	1,215.00
12	12	14.5	− 8.5	72.25	867.00
11	19	16.0	− 7.0	49.00	913.00
10	18	18.1	− 4.9	24.01	432.18
9	21	20.8	− 2.2	4.84	101.64
8	18	25.1	+ 2.1	4.41	79.38
7	15	31.3	+ 8.3	68.89	1,033.35
6	13	40.5	+17.5	306.25	3,981.25
5	9	49.8	+26.8	718.24	6,464.15
Sum	150				16,544.96 $\Sigma n_c(Y' - M_y)^2$
					110.2997 $\sigma^2 y'$
					10.50 $\sigma_{y'}$

before finding a mean of the squared deviations, we weight each one for a column by the number of cases in that column. The weighted, squared deviation for each column will be found in the last column of Table 14.2. Then the weighted, squared deviations are summed, and we divide by N, 150, to find $\sigma^2_{y'}$, which is 11.2997. The square root of this is 10.50, which is the σ of the deviations, $\sigma_{y'}$.

Remember that these are *not* the deviations of the observed points from the predicted Y values, because the larger these are, the *lower* the correlation. We are here interested in the size of deviations of predicted Y values from the mean of all the Y values, and the *larger* these are, the *higher* the correlation. When the correlation is perfect, $\sigma_{y'}$ is as large as σ_y, for then the ratio $\sigma_{y'}/\sigma_y$ equals 1.00. When $\sigma_{y'} = 0$, the ratio equals zero and eta is zero. In this problem, $\sigma_y = 12.535$. The correlation ratio is therefore

$$\eta_{yx} = \frac{10.50}{12.535} = .838$$

The steps in computing a correlation ratio may be summarized as follows.

Step 1. Determine the mean of all the Y values and also their standard deviation.

Step 2. Determine the means of the columns (Y').

Step 3. Determine the deviations of Y' from M_y, or $Y' - M_y$.

Step 4. Square the deviations.

Step 5. Multiply each squared deviation by the number of the cases in the column (n_c).

Step 6. Sum the weighted, squared deviations, and divide by N. This gives $\sigma^2_{y'}$. From this, find $\sigma_{y'}$.

Step 7. Solve the ratio $\sigma_{y'}/\sigma_y$, which is η_{yx}.

Remember that, for finding η_{xy}, we are dealing with *rows* rather than columns, so the steps will be the same except for the substitution of the word *row* for the word *column* in all these descriptions and the substitution of X for Y.

THE STANDARD ERROR OF A CORRELATION RATIO

The sampling variability of a correlation ratio, like that of r, is given by its standard error, and this is derived by a similar formula

$$\sigma_\eta = \frac{1 - \eta^2}{\sqrt{N-1}} \quad \text{(SE of a correlation ratio)} \quad (14.5)$$

The standard error of the eta coefficient that we have just obtained is .025. The amount of correlation is therefore rather close to the population correlation.

THE STANDARD ERROR OF ESTIMATE IN A NONLINEAR REGRESSION

The standard error of estimate here can be computed as from a Pearson r [see formulas (15.16a) and (15.16b)], but it can also be obtained from the knowledge that

$$\sigma^2_{yx} + \sigma^2_{y'} = \sigma^2_y$$

That is, the total variance in the Y distribution is made up of two components, the variance predictable from X (this is $\sigma^2_{y'}$) and the variance not predictable from X (which is σ^2_{yx}). Transposing, we have

$$\sigma^2_{yx} = \sigma^2_y - \sigma^2_{y'}$$

In solving for an eta coefficient, we must know both the terms on the right of this equation. For our illustrative problem, they are 157.1262 and 110.2997, respectively. The difference is 46.8265, which is the nonpredicted variance. The square root of this, which is 6.84, gives an estimate of σ_{yx}. The standard error of estimate tells us how much dispersion there is of the obtained values (Y values in this case) around the predicted values (Y' values in this case). The quantity 6.84 tells us that two-thirds of the time scores in the Form Board test may be expected to be within 6.84 units of the predicted values when the predicted values are the means of the columns of the scatter diagram. Such an estimate is useful, however, only when the variances within columns are fairly uniform, in other words, when the data approach homoscedasticity.

THE RELATION OF THE CORRELATION RATIO TO ANALYSIS OF VARIANCE

Those who have read Chap. 13 will find much that is familiar in the preceding paragraphs. Regarding the successive columns of data, which are really the result of a one-way classification on a quantitative variable, namely, chronological age, as sets, we have all the information we need to proceed with an analysis-of-variance solution (see Table 14.3). From Table 14.2, the sum 16,544.96 will be recognized as the sum of squares between sets, since it is based upon the squared deviations of set means from the mean. The quantity 7,023.97 is the grand sum of squares within sets. This sum is found most conveniently here from what we already know. It is given by the product $N\sigma^2_{yx}$, which in this problem is $150 \times 46.8265 = 7,023.97$. The sum of the two sums of squares makes up the total sum of squares for the composite sample in variable Y. All we need next are the numbers of degrees of freedom. For the between-sets variance (mean square) there are 9 (the number of sets minus 1). For the within-sets variance there are 140 (N minus the number of sets). The two estimates of the population variance are given in Table 14.3, also the F ratio, which is 36.6. Reference to Table F (Appendix B) shows that this F is well above the F required for significance at the .01 level of confidence, which is about 2.5.

The relationship discussed here is more of academic than of practical interest, for we already know that the eta coefficient is so high that there is little doubt of a relationship existing between chronological age and test score. Furthermore, the eta coefficient tells us a

Table 14.3 An analysis of variance based upon statistics derived in the solution of a correlation ratio

Component	Degrees of freedom	Sums of squares	Mean squares
Between sets	9	16,544.96	1,838.33
Within sets	140	7,023.97	50.17
Total	149	23,568.93	

$$F = \frac{1,838.33}{50.17} = 36.6$$

fact concerning the *degree* of relationship, which an *F* ratio does not convey. When the eta is near the lower margin of significance and a more rigorous test of significance is required, and when a decision is to be made as to whether or not there is *any* genuine relationship at all, then the *F* test has its advantages. Even then, however, an *F* test is not recommended unless *Y* is a *monotonic* (continuously increasing or continuously decreasing) function of *X*, i.e., the regression does not reverse its direction.

A TEST OF LINEARITY OF REGRESSION

Often the curvature in regression is so slight that we do not know if it is merely a chance deviation from linearity. We therefore want some statistical test to show whether or not the curvature is probably genuine. Several tests of nonlinearity have been proposed. The test currently most widely accepted is an *F* test based upon an analysis-of-variance approach. The computation of *F* in this instance is simple, requiring only the knowledge of eta and the Pearson *r* for the same scatter plot, and the number of degrees of freedom. The formula is

$$F = \frac{(\eta^2 - r^2)(N - k)}{(1 - \eta^2)(k - 2)} \qquad (F \text{ test of linearity}) \qquad (14.6)$$

where k = number of columns (or rows). For the problem discussed above, the correlation ratio was found to be .838 and the Pearson *r* was found to be .763. By formula (14.6) we have

$$F = \frac{(.702244 - .582169)(150 - 10)}{(1 - .702244)(10 - 2)}$$
$$= 7.06$$

In interpreting this *F*, the numbers of degrees of freedom are $(k - 2)$ and $(N - k)$. Reference to Table F shows that the obtained *F* is significant well beyond the .01 point. Thus, the difference between η_{yx} and r_{yz} is so great as to leave little doubt of nonlinearity.

The hypothesis tested here is that the regression of *Y* on *X* is linear. In more exact terms the hypothesis requires that the means of the columns all lie exactly on a straight line whose slope is determined by the Pearson *r*. Now if the actual form of regression were linear, sampling errors would cause the means of columns to deviate only slightly from the best-fitting straight line. The sampling distribution is of these deviations of the actual means of the columns, the *Y* values, from the regression line. These deviations are ordinarily sufficient to make the eta coefficient larger than the Pearson *r* computed from the scatter diagram. The question is whether the deviations are large enough to suggest that there is something over and above these chance deviations involved. That is what the F test here is supposed to tell us. The F test should be applied to this particular use only when N exceeds k considerably.

AN EVALUATION OF THE CORRELATION RATIO

The chief advantage and use of the eta coefficient has been indicated and illustrated—to determine the closeness of relationship between two variables when the regression is clearly nonlinear. Although very few nonlinear regressions have been found in the correlation of measures of ability with one another, there are probably many more such relationships in psychology and education than has been realized.

Correlation coefficients as indices of goodness of fit. Broadening the concept of correlation leads us to consider curves of learning and retention and many others. The eta coefficient assumes no particular type of functional relationship between Y and X. The type of relationship is defined by the actual, unsmoothed trend of the means of the columns (or rows). In this fact are both strength and weakness. Allowing the curvature of the regression to be as complex as the ups and downs in obtained class means make it, we find in eta the maximum size of correlation index for any set of data.

We might assume some kind of mathematical function for the data represented in Fig. 14.1—a hyperbola, parabola, logarithmic function, or some other. The goodness of fit, as indicated by some other correlation index of nonlinear correlation, would probably not be so high for any of these functions as the eta coefficient. Because the eta coefficient does allow the regression curve to follow the means of the columns, a certain amount of error or purely sampling variance undoubtedly gets into the deviations of column means from the general mean of the Y's; hence the eta is a somewhat inflated figure. When the actual regression is linear, the difference between eta and r computed for the same data tells us about how much inflation has occurred. When the regression is nonlinear, we have less ready evidence as to how much inflation there is. We should therefore discount any eta a little, particularly if the means of sets do not follow a smooth trend rather well. The smaller the sample, the more irregular the trend of the set means is likely to be, and therefore the greater the proportion of inflation in eta.

Examples of nonlinear regressions. In addition to the functional relationships involved in learning and other phenomena, it is likely that when more is known about human traits that are not abilities—temperament, interests, attitudes, and the like—and their interrelations, we shall find many more examples of nonlinear regression. In the validation of test scores against vocational or other criteria of adjustment, more such examples are coming to light. It has been known for some time that high "intelligence" may be just as bad prognostically as low "intelligence" in connection with proficiency in routine and repetitive job assignments. This result will probably be found more general than has been supposed. The reason it has not been more widely recognized before is that somewhat shortened ranges of ability have been related to proficiency criteria. If the total range, from lowest to the very highest, is studied in relation to proficiency indices on various kinds of jobs (except those requiring the highest abilities) we may find the optimal ability to be somewhat short of the top in most cases. This definitely means nonlinear regressions.

A number of instances have been called to the writer's attention in which scores on temperament tests bore a relation to rated proficiency in such a way that the optimal position on the trait score was barely above average. The application of the Pearson r method sometimes shows a near zero correlation in such instances whereas an eta coefficient might be as high as .30 or even .50. The straight line, in other words, was a very poor fit to the regression of the data. This should stress the importance of plotting scatter diagrams more frequently than is ordinarily done; otherwise important nonlinear regressions may be overlooked. It is possible that many a zero Pearson r reported in the literature conceals a significant nonlinear relationship.

The algebraic sign of eta.   Some writers regard it as a weakness of eta that its algebraic sign is always positive. The algebraic sign of r is meaningful in that it shows whether the general trend is upward or downward. In defense of eta it may be said that it tells us what we are most interested to know, the goodness of fit or closeness of relationship between two variables. If the overall trend is either upward or downward we can readily perceive it by inspection of the scatter plot, and we can attach whatever sign is appropriate if we wish to do so. Some curved regressions, for example, U-shaped or inverted U-shaped, may yield a significant eta without any general trend away from the horizontal. In this case no sign is meaningful for eta.

Dependence of eta upon the number of categories.   A more serious weakness of eta is that its size depends upon the number of columns (or rows). The minimum number of classes that would show any curvature at all is three, but three might give a much-smoothed and distorted view of the real relationship. With too small a number of classes, therefore, we run the chance of obtaining an estimate of correlation that is too small. On the other hand, as we increase the number of classes, we make the means of the classes less stable, and, as they fluctuate more, chance errors become more important in inflating eta. The limiting case would be classes so small that there was only one observation per class (assuming no duplicate measures on X), in which case the variance in the columns would be just as great as the overall variance in Y, and eta would equal 1.00.

Methods for correcting eta for number of classes have been proposed, but none can be recommended. The best rule is to keep the classes large enough so that means of classes are fairly stable and fall rather smoothly into line in the scatter plot and yet to have enough classes to bring out clearly enough the shape of the regression. The size of sample has some bearing on this. The larger the sample, the larger the number of classes that can be tolerated. Very small samples would be unsuitable for the computation of eta at all. With large samples (100 and above) it is suggested that the number of classes range between six and twelve.[1]

The use of mathematical functions.   Better than the correlation-ratio approach, in research studies, is an effort to establish the form of a regression as some mathematical function and then to test the goodness of fit of data to that function by methods which we cannot go into here. There are other texts that treat this topic in some detail.[2]

The biserial coefficient of correlation

The biserial r is especially designed for the situation in which both of the variables correlated are continuously measurable but one of the two is for some reason reduced to two categories. This reduction to two categories may be a consequence of the only way in which the data can be obtained, as, for example, when one variable is whether or not a student passes or fails a certain standard. We can well assume a continuum along which individuals differ with respect to achievement required to pass this standard. Those whose achievement is above a certain crucial point pass, and those whose achievement is below that point fail.

Let us assume the standard is graduation from pilot training. Although not all graduates are equal in achievement nor are all candidates eliminees, we know only whether each person belongs to one category or the other. It is as if the grouping were so coarse in this variable as to be confined to two class intervals rather than a dozen or so. If we are prepared to justify the assumption of normality of distribution in this dichotomized variable, we have a formula by which a coefficient of correlation can be computed.

Computation of a biserial r.   The principle upon which the for-

[1]For small samples, a statistic known as epsilon (a correlation ratio without bias) is recommended. See Peters, C. C., and Van Voorhis, W. R. *Statistical Procedures and Their Mathematical Bases.* New York: McGraw-Hill, 1940. Pp. 319*ff.*
[2]Lewis, D. *Quantitative Methods in Psychology.* New York: McGraw-Hill, 1960.

mula for a biserial r is based is that with zero correlation there would be no difference between means, and the larger the difference between means, the larger the correlation. The general formula for biserial r is

$$r_b = \frac{M_p - M_q}{\sigma_t} \times \frac{pq}{y} \qquad \text{(Biserial coefficient of correlation)} \qquad (14.7)$$

where M_p = mean of X values for the higher group in the dichotomized variable, the one having more of the ability on which the sample is divided into two subgroups

M_q = mean of X values for the lower group

p = proportion of the cases in the higher group

q = proportion of the cases in the lower group

y = ordinate of the unit normal distribution curve with surface equal to 1.00, at the point of division between segments containing p and q proportions of the cases (see Fig. 14.2)

σ_t = standard deviation of the total sample in the continuously measured variable, X

Table 14.4 presents typical data for computing a biserial correlation. The passing group and the failing group were distributed as shown. The proportions passing and failing are .65 and .35, respectively.[1] The y ordinate (from Table C) is .3704. The distribution of the total group is assumed to be as indicated in Fig. 14.2. The computation of the biserial r proceeds as follows:

$$r_b = \frac{98.27 - 83.64}{17.68} \times \frac{(.65)(.35)}{.3704} = .508$$

Table G (Appendix B) is designed, in part, to supply several of the constants needed in the computation of a biserial r, either by formula (14.7) or by formula (14.9), and the computation of its standard error. For given values of p, Table G supplies the corresponding values of pq/y, p/y, and $\sqrt{pq}/y$.

[1]It is good practice to compute p and q each to three significant digits, rather than two, as here.

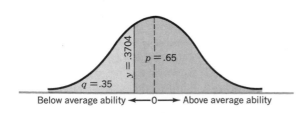

Fig. 14.2. *A normal distribution of the cases along the scale of ability to pass the course of training. The area to the right of the ordinate shown represents the 65 per cent who graduated and the area to the left represents the 35 per cent who failed to graduate.*

Table 14.4   Distribution of scores for two groups of students — those passing and those failing — also a combined distribution

	Scores										n	n/N
	40–49	50–59	60–69	70–79	80–89	90–99	100–109	110–119	120–129	130–139		
Passing students		1	3	10	27	30	26	21	7	5	130	.65 = p
Failing students	2	6	4	11	21	16	7	3			70	.35 = q
Total	2	7	7	21	48	46	33	24	7	5	200	1.00

THE STANDARD ERROR OF r_b

The standard error of a biserial r is estimated by the formula

$$\sigma_{r_b} = \frac{\dfrac{\sqrt{pq}}{y} - r^2_b}{\sqrt{N}} \qquad \text{(SE of a biserial } r) \qquad (14.8)$$

In this problem

$$\sigma_{r_b} = \frac{\dfrac{.4770}{.3704} - .258064}{\sqrt{200}} = .073$$

This standard error may be interpreted as usual, and we find that the obtained r_b is so large that we may infer, with a high degree of probability, that it did not arise from an uncorrelated population.

ALTERNATIVE FORMULA FOR BISERIAL r

In many situations, a more convenient formula for the biserial r is[1]

$$r_b = \frac{M_p - M_t}{\sigma_t} \times \frac{p}{y} \qquad \text{(Alternative formula for a biserial } r) \qquad (14.9)$$

where M_t is the mean of the total sample. The advantage of this formula over (14.8) is that formula (14.9) gives us one less distribution to deal with. A good type of work sheet for solution by this formula is shown in Table 14.5. It is convenient to use the same zero point for x' on both the component distribution and the total distribution.

[1]Dunlap, J. W. Note on computation of biserial correlations in item evaluation. *Psychometrika*, 1936, **1**, 51–60.

Table 14.5 **Solution of means and standard deviation
necessary for the computation of a biserial** r

Scores	x'	f_p	f_px'	f_t	f_tx'	$f_tx'^2$
130–139	+4	5	+20	5	+20	80
120–129	+4	7	+21	7	+21	63
110–119	+2	21	+42	24	+48	96
100–109	+1	26	+26	33	+33	33
90–99	0	30	0	46	0	0
80–89	−1	27	−27	48	−48	48
70–79	−2	10	−20	21	−42	84
60–69	−3	3	− 9	7	−21	63
50–59	−4	1	− 4	7	−28	112
40–49	−5			2	−10	50
Sums		130	+49	200	−27	629

$$M_{x'} = +.377 \qquad M_{x'} = -.135 \qquad \sigma_t = 10 \sqrt{629/200} - .135^2$$

$$iM_{x'} = +3.77 \qquad iM_{x'} = -1.35 \qquad = 10 \sqrt{3.1268}$$

$$M_p = 98.27 \qquad M_t = 93.15 \qquad = 17.68$$

AN EVALUATION OF THE BISERIAL r

Since the biserial coefficient of correlation is a product-moment r and is designed to be a good estimate of the Pearson r, the same require-ment as for the latter must be satisfied — linear regression — in addi-tion to the unique requirement that the distribution of the values on the dichotomous variable, when continuously measured, shall be normal. This requirement of normality applies to the form of popu-lation distribution. Even if the sample distribution is not quite nor-mal, the population distribution may still be normal.

The use of the quantities p, q, and y in formulas (14.7) and (14.9) directly implies the normal distribution of the dichotomized variable. Departures from normality, if marked, may lead to very erroneous estimates of correlation. With bimodal distributions, for example, it is possible that the computed r will prove to exceed 1.0. Bimodal and other nonnormal distributions are most likely to occur in heterogene-ous samples — for example, in variables in which there is a significant sex difference and both sexes are included in a sample.

Some attention must also be given to the distribution on the con-tinuous variable. Extreme skewness may indicate lack of linearity. The distribution need not be normal, but it should be unimodal and rather symmetrical. Odd-shaped distributions have been known to result in biserial r's greater than 1.00.

When to dichotomize distributions. There are instances in which the Y variable has been continuously measured, but there are irregularities that preclude computing a good estimate of the Pearson r. In such cases the biserial r may be brought into service. One example of this would be a truncated distribution;[1] another would be when there are very few categories for the Y variable and it is doubtful whether they are equidistant on a metric scale; another would be in the case of a markedly skewed sample distribution of Y values owing to a defective measuring instrument.

Before computing r_b, we of course need to dichotomize each Y distribution. In adopting a division point, it is well to come as near the median as possible. The reason for this will be made clear in the next paragraph. In all these special instances, however, we are not relieved of the responsibility of defending the assumption of the normal population distribution of Y. It may seem contradictory to suggest that when the obtained Y distribution is skewed we resort to the biserial r, but note that it is the *sample* distribution that is skewed and it is the *population* distribution that must be assumed to be normal.

Biserial r is less reliable than the Pearson r. Whenever there is a real choice of computing a Pearson r or a biserial r, however, one should favor the former, unless the sample is very large and unless computation time is an important consideration. The standard error for a biserial r is considerably larger than that for a Pearson r derived from the same sample. When $r_b = .00$, the standard error of r_b is at least 25 per cent larger than that for r for the same size of sample. As p approaches 1.0 or 0.0, the ratio becomes larger until, when $p = .94$, it is as large as 2. This is why in the preceding paragraph it was recommended that dichotomies have the division point as near the median as possible. It also suggests that, for the same dependability, we need larger samples of r_b than of r and that we should hesitate to compute r_b for very one-sided divisions of cases unless the sample is extremely large. This is reasonable from another point of view. Remember that prominent in the formula for r_b is the difference between means. This difference is not very stable unless each mean comes from a sample of sufficient size. Even if the sample totaled 1,000 cases, if only 1 per cent of the cases were in one of the two categories, its mean would be based upon only 10 cases. Such a condition is not favorable to a reliable estimate of a mean of differences.

[1] A truncated distribution is one that has been cut off at either end, with no cases with scale values beyond a certain limit.

Point-biserial correlation

When one of the two variables in a correlation problem is a *genuine* dichotomy, the appropriate type of coefficient to use is the point-biserial r. Examples of genuine dichotomies are male versus female, being a farmer versus not being a farmer, owning a home versus not owning one, living versus dying, living in Boston versus not living in Boston, and so on. Bimodal or other peculiar distributions, although not representing entirely discrete categories, are sufficiently discontinuous to call for the point-biserial rather than the biserial r. Examples of this type are color blindness versus normal color vision, being alcoholic versus nonalcoholic, and criminal versus noncriminal.

There are other variables, not fundamentally dichotomous and even normally distributed, which we should treat in practice as if they were genuine dichotomies. An outstanding example of this is a test item the response to which is scored as either right or wrong. No doubt those who answer the item correctly are not all equally capable in the trait or traits measured by the item. A total test score measuring the same trait would provide continuous gradations in trait levels. In testing practice, however, the kind of item described is limited to separating individuals into two groups, and only gross predictions can be made from responses to it. Such a variable is a good example with which to explain the basic nature of the point-biserial r.

If we gave a "score" of +1 to each person with a correct answer and a "score" of zero to each person with a wrong answer, in the item variable we would have only two class intervals and we would treat them as if they were genuine categories. A product-moment r could be computed with Pearson's basic formula. The result would be a point-biserial r. Computer programs for giving Pearson r's from score data automatically yield point-biserial r's between continuous and dichotomized variables.

A special formula, which does not resemble the basic Pearson formula, reads[1]

$$r_{pbi} = \frac{M_p - M_q}{\sigma_t} \sqrt{pq} \qquad \text{(The point-biserial coefficient of correlation)} \qquad (14.10)$$

where the symbols are defined as in the formula for the ordinary biserial r [formula (14.7)]. The only difference between this formula and the one for the ordinary biserial r is that the numerator contains $\sqrt{pq}$ rather than pq, and the constant y is missing from the denominator. For the same set of data, then, the ordinary biserial r would be $\sqrt{pq}/y$ times as large as r_{pbi}. In this ratio lies a feature of r_{pbi} to which we shall return soon.

[1] For a derivation of this formula, as well as formula (14.11), see Appendix A.

Let us apply formula (14.10) to some data on the relation of body weight to sex membership. In a sample of 51 sixteen-year-old high-school students, of whom 24 were male and 27 were female, the mean weights in kilograms were 67.8 and 56.6, respectively. The proportion of males is accordingly $^{24}/_{51}$ = .471 and q is .529. The standard deviation of the combined distributions is 13.2. Solving with formula (14.10),

$$r_{pbi} = \frac{67.8 - 56.6}{13.2} \sqrt{(.471)(.529)} = .42$$

The correlation between sex and body weight for sixteen-year-old high-school students is estimated to be .42.

SIGNIFICANCE OF A POINT-BISERIAL r

The hypothesis of zero correlation for the point-biserial r can be tested in two ways. Since r_{pbi} depends directly upon the difference between the means M_p and M_q, a significant departure from a mean difference of zero also indicates a significant correlation. A t test of the difference between means can therefore be used to test the significance of the departure of the correlation coefficient from zero.

A direct t test of the correlation coefficient can also be made, but only for the hypothesis of a correlation of zero. The t ratio can be computed for r_{pbi} in the same manner as for a Pearson product-moment r [see formula (8.13)] and the interpretation can be made with reference to Student's distribution.[1] For the illustrative problem, in which r_{pbi} = .42 and N = 51, t = 3.24, which indicates a correlation significant beyond the .01 level. Table D may also be used to determine whether an obtained r_{pbi} is significant.

When the population value of r_{pbi} is not zero, the mean of the t distribution is not zero; hence the determination of confidence limits for any obtained r_{pbi} is not a simple matter.[2]

ALTERNATIVE METHODS OF COMPUTATION FOR r_{pbi}

As for the ordinary biserial r, there is an alternative formula for computing r_{pbi} which may be more convenient in many situations. It reads

$$r_{pbi} = \frac{M_p - M_t}{\sigma_t} \sqrt{\frac{p}{y}} \qquad \begin{array}{l}\text{(Alternative formula for the} \\ \text{point-biserial } r)\end{array} \qquad (14.11)$$

[1] Perry, N. C., and Michael, W. B. The reliability of a point-biserial coefficient of correlation. *Psychometrika*, 1954, **16**, 313–325.
[2] For methods of estimating confidence limits in this situation, see Walker, H. M., and Lev, J. *Statistical Inference*. New York: Holt, 1953. P. 266; Perry, N. C., and Michael, W. B. A tabulation of the fiducial limits for the point-biserial correlation coefficient. *Educ. psychol. Measmt.*, 1954, **14**, 715–721.

Formulas for r_{pbi} making the computation of p and q unnecessary are

$$r_{pbi} = \frac{(M_p - M_q)\, \sqrt{N_p N_q}}{N \sigma_t} \qquad (14.12)$$

(Alternative formulas for
the point-biserial r)

$$r_{pbi} = \frac{(M_p - M_t)}{\sigma_t} \sqrt{\frac{N_p}{N_q}} \qquad (14.13)$$

where N_p and N_q are the frequencies in the two categories.

AN EVALUATION OF THE POINT-BISERIAL r

Since the r_{pbi} coefficient is not restricted to normal distributions in the dichotomous variable, it is much more generally applicable than is r_b. When there is doubt about computing r_b, the point-biserial r will serve. For this reason, it should probably be used more than it is. Although it is a product-moment r, in value r_{pbi} is rarely comparable numerically with a Pearson r, or even with an ordinary biserial r, when computed from the same data. Under special circumstances, to be described below, it may be used as a basis for making an estimate of the Pearson r. In regard to the continuous distribution, when r_{pbi} is computed, the same requirements apply as in computing the Pearson r or the biserial r—they include a rather symmetrical, unimodal continuous distribution.

Mathematical relation of r_{pbi} to r_b. If r_{pbi} were computed from data that actually justified the use of r_b, the coefficient computed would be markedly smaller than r_b obtained from the same data. Even if the one variable is actually continuous but not normally distributed (in which case we might better utilize r_{pbi}), the latter would give an underestimate of the amount of correlation. As was pointed out before, r_b is $\sqrt{pq}/y$ times as large as r_{pbi} when they are computed from the same data. This ratio varies from about 1.25 when $p = .50$ to about 3.73 when p (or q) equals .99 (see Table G). Figure 14.3 shows graphically the ratio of r_{pbi} to r_b for various values of p. The ratio of r_{pbi} to r_b is, of course, the reciprocal of the ratio of r_b to r_{pbi}; in other words, it is $y/\sqrt{pq}$. The diagram is designed in this manner to show maximum values of r_{pbi} that would arise from continuous, normal distributions. In terms of formulas,

$$r_b = r_{pbi} \frac{\sqrt{pq}}{y} \qquad \text{(Conversion of one biserial } r \qquad (14.14a)$$

into the other when normality

$$r_{pbi} = r_b \frac{y}{\sqrt{pq}} \qquad \text{of distribution exists)} \qquad (14.14b)$$

It is recommended that when the dichotomous variable is normally distributed without reasonable doubt, r_b be computed and inter-

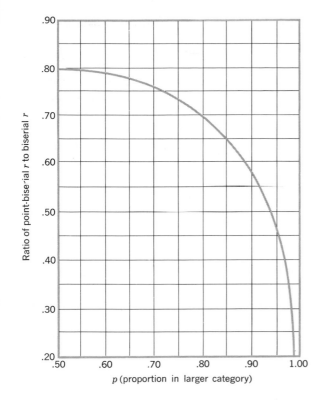

Fig. 14.3. *Ratio of the point-biserial r to the biserial r when the difference between means ($M_p - M_q$) and the standard deviation (σ_t) is constant and the proportion in the larger category (p) varies.*

preted. If there is little doubt that the distribution is a genuine dichotomy, r_{pbi} should be computed and interpreted. For doubtful situations, r_{pbi} should be computed but interpreted in the light of Fig. 14.3. That is to say, if the distribution in question is continuous but not normal, and if r_{pbi} approaches the limit described by Fig. 14.3, we can say that the genuine correlation approaches 1.00 more closely than the obtained r_{pbi} does. If the obtained r_{pbi} should exceed the limit, for the size of p involved, it probably means that the assumption of a genuine dichotomy is the correct one. In other words, when there is a point distribution, r_{pbi} can approach 1.00. Many distributions are in the doubtful class; they are neither dichotomous nor continuous. At least, if they are continuous, they may not be unimodal. It is to help take care of these twilight instances that Fig. 14.3 was designed.

If it develops after we have computed r_{pbi} that the situation justifies the use of r_b, we can convert the obtained r_{pbi} to the appropriate r_b by means of formula (14.14a). If we have computed r_b when it later develops that we should have used r_{pbi}, formula (14.14b) will provide the proper transformation.

Tetrachoric correlation

A tetrachoric r is computed from data in which both X and Y have been reduced artificially to two categories. Under the appropriate conditions it gives a coefficient that is numerically equivalent to a Pearson r and may be regarded as an approximation to it. It is sometimes the only way of estimating the correlation between two variables because the data could not be obtained in graded quantities. It is sometimes a quick and convenient method of estimating r from data that are in the form of continuous measurements, but when computation time is an important consideration and the sample is large.

ASSUMPTIONS UNDERLYING THE TETRACHORIC r

The tetrachoric r requires that both X and Y represent continuous, normally distributed, and linearly related variables. A problem in which the tetrachoric r may be computed is illustrated in Table 14.6, if we are willing to make the necessary assumptions. These data represent the numbers of students responding "Yes" and "No" to two questions in a personality inventory. Question I was, "Do you enjoy getting acquainted with most people?" and question II was, "Do you prefer to work with others rather than alone?" Out of 930 replies to both questions, we have the numbers who responded similarly (cells a and d in Table 14.6) and the numbers who responded differently to the two questions (cells b and c). It is obvious that in the case of a perfect positive correlation, all the cases would fall in cells a and d. In a perfect negative correlation, they would fall in cells b and c. In a zero correlation, the frequencies would be proportionately distributed in the four cells.

*Table 14.6 **Fourfold table from which a tetrachoric coefficient of correlation is computed***

| | | Question I | | | |
		No	Yes	Total	Proportion
Question II	Yes	167 (b)	374 (a)	541	.582 (p)
	No	203 (d)	186 (c)	389	.418 (q)
	Total	370	560	930	1.000
	Proportion	.398 (q')	.602 (p')	1.000	

The assumption of continuity and normality of distribution, in this particular example, can be defended as follows: It is unlikely that all who respond "Yes" to either question do so with equal degree of affirmation. It is similarly unlikely that those who respond "No" do so with equal degree of negation. It is most likely that the answers to either question represent a continuum of behavior extending from strong affirmation at the one extreme to strong negation at the other. Continuity, and not a real dichotomy, is thus the probable state of affairs. If a continuum is granted, the general law of unimodal distribution approaching normality in psychological traits may be cited in defense of the other requirement.

Figure 14.4 illustrates the situation in which two continuous, normally distributed variables are dichotomized. With a substantial degree of correlation between Y and X, in a scatter plot the cases would be distributed as in the ellipse. Drawing the dividing lines at the score levels of z and z' partitions the cases into four groups. The normal-curve values that appear in formula (14.15) are represented. We take advantage of those values in computing a coefficient of correlation. The diagram should indicate the importance of fulfilling the assumption of normal distributions in both X and Y.

THE EQUATION FOR THE TETRACHORIC r

The complete equation for the tetrachoric r is a long and complicated one, involving a series of terms many of which contain powers of r. With only the first few terms included, it reads

$$r_t + r^2{}_t \frac{zz'}{2} + r^3{}_t \frac{(z^2 - 1)(z'^2 - 1)}{6} + \cdots = \frac{ad - bc}{yy'N^2} \tag{14.15}$$

The symbols will be explained with reference to Table 14.6. The letters a, b, c, and d refer to the frequencies in the four cells of the four-fold table. r_t is given the subscript to indicate that it is a tetrachoric r. Numerically, under the appropriate conditions, it approximates a Pearson r.

In Table 14.6, it will be noted that the two-category distribution of all responses to question I is given in terms of proportions p' and q'. The distribution of all responses to question II is similarly given in terms of p and q. These proportions are required for finding the values for the y's and z's in formula (14.15). The symbols z and z' stand for the standard-score measurements on the base line of the unit normal distribution curve at the points of division of cases in the two distributions. The symbols y and y' are ordinates corresponding to z and z' in the unit normal distribution.

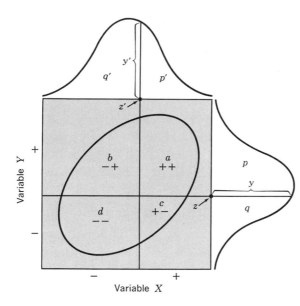

Fig. 14.4. *Theoretical normal bivariate distribution of cases divided into four categories by dichotomizing distributions on X and Y, illustrating the constants appearing in the equation for the tetrachoric r.*

METHODS OF ESTIMATING THE TETRACHORIC r

The solution for r_t by means of formula (14.15) is a formidable task and can be only an approximation at best. Consequently, a number of short cuts have been devised for estimating it. One of these will now be described.

The cosine-pi formula. One approximation formula for r_t is known as the cosine-pi formula. In mathematical form,

$$r_{\text{cos-pi}} = \cos\left(\pi \frac{\sqrt{bc}}{\sqrt{ad} + \sqrt{bc}}\right)$$

Since for purposes of computation π can be taken to be 180 deg, the practical form of the equation is

$$r_{\text{cos-pi}} = \cos\left(\frac{180°\sqrt{bc}}{\sqrt{ad} + \sqrt{bc}}\right) \qquad \text{(Cosine-pi approximation to a tetrachoric } r)} \qquad (14.16)$$

By dividing numerator and denominator by $\sqrt{bc}$, we have a formula that is more convenient for computation. It reads

$$r_{\text{cos-pi}} = \cos\left(\frac{180°}{1 + \sqrt{\dfrac{ad}{bc}}}\right) \qquad \text{(Cosine-pi formula in simpler form)} \qquad (14.17)$$

where a, b, c, and d are the frequencies as defined in Table 14.6.

It is well to remember that a and d represent the like-signed cases (Yes-Yes and No-No) and b and c the unlike-signed cases (Yes-No and

No-Yes). When numbers are substituted, the expression within the parentheses reduces to a single number, which is an angle in terms of degrees of arc. The cosine of this angle is the estimate of r_t. The angle will vary between zero, when either b or c, or both, is zero, to 180 deg, when either a or d, or both, is zero. In the first case, when the angle is zero, the correlation is +1.00, and in the second case, when the angle is 180 deg, r_t is −1.00. When the product bc equals ad, the angle is 90 deg, the cosine of which is zero, and r_t is estimated to be .0.[1]

Applying the cosine-pi formula to the data in Table 14.6, we have

$$r_{\text{cos-pi}} = \cos\left(\frac{180°}{1 + \sqrt{\dfrac{(374)\,(203)}{(167)\,(186)}}}\right)$$
$$= \cos 70.24°$$
$$= .343$$

In this method, if the angle should prove to be between 90 and 180 deg, the correlation is negative. This can be anticipated by noting that the product bc is greater than ad. Angles over 90 deg are not listed in Table J. For an angle between 90 and 180 deg, deduct the angle from 180 deg, find the cosine of this difference, and give it a negative sign.

Table M in Appendix B provides a quick solution for $r_{\text{cos-pi}}$ to two decimal places. Only the ratio ad/bc (or its reciprocal bc/ad) need be known; compute whichever gives a value greater than 1.0. For the illustrative problem above, ad/bc equals 2.444. This lies between the given ratios 2.4121 and 2.490, which indicates a correlation of .34.

Limitations to the use of the cosine-pi formula. It should be pointed out that formula (14.17) gives a very close approximation to r_t only when both variables X and Y are dichotomized at their medians.[2] As p and p' depart from .5, as p and p' differ from each other increasingly, and as r_t becomes very large, $r_{\text{cos-pi}}$ departs more and more from r_t and is systematically larger than r_t. For example, if $p = .5$ and $p' = .84$, when r_t is .79, $r_{\text{cos-pi}}$ is approximately .90. If both p and p' are within the limits of .4 to .6, however, when r_t is .50 the maximum discrepancy is approximately .02, and when r_t is .90 the maximum discrepancy is approximately .04, both in the direction of overestimation. In many situations we can control to a large extent the point of dichotomy and can see to it that p and p' are close to .5. When they are not, it would be best to use one of the graphic methods mentioned next.

[1] See Table J in Appendix B for cosines of angles.
[2] Bouvier, E. A., Perry, N. C., Michael, W. B., and Hertzka, A. F. A study of the error in the cosine-pi approximation to the tetrachoric coefficient of correlation. *Educ. psychol. Measmt.*, 1954, **14**, 690–699.

Graphic estimates of tetrachoric r.   When a large number of tetrachoric *r*'s must be computed, considerable saving of labor is provided by the Thurstone computing diagrams.[1] These are highly recommended since they yield two-place accuracy with little effort after the fourfold table is reduced to the status of proportions throughout, as in Table 14.7. From the computing diagrams, r_t for the data in Table 14.7 is estimated to be +.79. The correlation of the two questions of Table 14.6 is estimated as +.34, which checks with previous estimates. Another graphic procedure has been published by Hayes.[2]

THE STANDARD ERROR OF A TETRACHORIC *r*

The tetrachoric *r* is less reliable than the Pearson *r*, being at least 50 per cent more variable. r_t is most reliable (1) when *N* is large, as is true of all statistics; (2) when *r* is large, as is true of other *r*'s; but also (3) when the divisions into two categories are close to the medians. The complete formula for estimating σ_{r_t} is too long to be practical, and so it will be given here. But when $r_t = .0$, the formula is much simpler and reads[3]

$$\sigma_{r_t} = \frac{\sqrt{pp'qq'}}{yy'\sqrt{N}} \qquad (r_t = 0) \qquad \begin{array}{l}\text{(Standard error of a zero} \\ \text{tetrachoric } r)\end{array} \qquad (14.18)$$

For the 930 cases in the problem of Table 14.6,

$$\sigma_{r_t} = \frac{\sqrt{(.532)(.602)(.418)(.398)}}{(.3905)(.3858)\sqrt{930}}$$

$$= .053$$

Since the obtained r_t, .34, is more than 2.6 times this standard error, we can be quite confident that the two qualities represented by the two questions are really correlated in the population.

To attain the same degree of reliability in a tetrachoric *r* as in a Pearson *r*, one needs more than twice the number of cases in a sample. For very dependable results, when r_t is to be computed, it is recommended that *N* be at least 200, and preferably 300. In smaller samples than these, even less than *N* = 100, a tetrachoric *r* can be

[1]Chesire, L., Saffir, M., and Thurstone, L. L. *Computing Diagrams for the Tetrachoric Correlation Coefficient.* Chicago: University of Chicago Press, 1938.

[2]Hayes, S. P. Diagrams for computing tetrachoric correlation coefficients from percentage differences. *Psychometrika,* 1946, **11,** 163–172.

[3]For aids in estimating σ_{r_t}, see Guilford, J. P., and Lyon, T. C. On determining the reliability and significance of a tetrachoric coefficient of correlation. *Psychometrika,* 1942, **7,** 243–249; also Hayes, S. P. Tables of the standard error of tetrachoric correlation coefficient. *Psychometrika,* 1943, **8,** 193–203.

Table 14.7   **The reduction of a scatter diagram to a fourfold table preparatory to the computation of a tetrachoric coefficient of correlation***

IQ	Mark in schoolwork					Total
	F	D	C	B	A	
120 and above			12	32	40	84
110–119		4	23	66	23	116
100–109	1	10	67	77	15	170
90–99	1	22	133	40	3	199
80–89	8	71	125	21	2	227
70–79	36	92	24	1		153
Below 70	27	36	4			67
Total	73	235	388	237	83	1,016

IQ	In terms of frequencies			In terms of proportions		
	C, or below	A or B	Total	C, or below	A or B	Total
90 or above	273	296	569	.269	.291	.560
Below 90	423	24	447	.416	.024	.440
Total	696	320	1,016	.685	.315	1.000

*Adapted from Cobb, M. V. The limits set to educational achievement by limited intelligence. *J. educ. Psychol.*, 1922, **13**, 449. By permission of the publisher.

used to test the null hypothesis, but it cannot be depended upon to give very accurate estimates of the size of correlation unless r is very large.

REDUCING DISTRIBUTIONS IN CLASS INTERVALS TO FOURFOLD TABLES

Data need not be obtained in two categories each way in order to apply the tetrachoric solution for r. Any scatter diagram, in fact, can be reduced to two groups each way by making arbitrary divisions. Such a division should be made as nearly as possible at or near the median in each distribution. Table 14.7 shows a scatter diagram in which reduction to a fourfold table would be highly desirable. A Pearson r computed with so few class intervals each way would be highly influenced by errors of grouping. The very large number of cases renders the reduction in reliability of r by computing r_t of small

importance. The divisions suggested in Table 14.7 come between the
B's and C's for distribution of school marks and at an IQ between 89
and 90 for intelligence rating. The revised correlation distribution
is seen in Table 14.7.

SOME APPLICATIONS OF r_t TO BE AVOIDED

Many of the limitations of the tetrachoric r have already been pointed
out. There are others that should not go unnoticed. It is well to avoid
estimating r_t when the split in either X or Y is very one-sided—for
example, a 95-5, or even a 90-10, division of the cases. The standard
error is much larger in situations such as these.

Especially to be avoided is an attempt to estimate r_t when there is
a zero in only one cell. Table 14.8, A and B, illustrates two such examples. If r_t were computed for problem A, it would equal -1.0 (the
zero is in cell a); if computed for problem B, r_t would equal $+1.0$. This
is in spite of the fact that about one-fourth of the cases belie the
perfect correlations apparent by computation (90 cases out of 400 in
A are out of line with the finding and 80 cases in B).

These examples are perhaps somewhat rare, but zero frequencies
are certainly not unheard of. Even scatters like that in C would probably give a false estimate of correlation. There is no zero, but there is
an exceptionally small frequency (15) among much larger ones. In all
three fourfold tables the distributions are such as to suggest nonlinear regressions if these broad categories were broken down into
finer groupings. If the assumption of linearity is not satisfied, r_t may
well give a biased estimate of correlation. Such distributions as those
in Table 14.8 are not proof of nonlinear regression, but they strongly
suggest it. In general, a distribution in such a table should appear to
be rather symmetrical along one diagonal axis or the other, depending upon whether the correlation is negative or positive. This holds
true if the proportion p is somewhat near the proportion p', but even
if they differ very much, asymmetry cannot be taken necessarily to
mean curved regression.

*Table 14.8   Illustrations of some unusual fourfold contingency
tables in which computation of a tetrachoric r is questionable*

200	0	200
90	110	200
290	110	400

A

80	110	190
150	0	150
230	110	340

B

85	15	100
95	105	200
180	120	300

C

The phi coefficient

When the two distributions correlated are genuinely dichotomous, when the two classes are separated by a real gap between them and previous correlational methods do not apply, we may resort to the phi coefficient.[1] This coefficient was designed for so-called *point distributions*, which implies that the two classes have two point values or merely represent some unmeasurable attribute. Such a case would be illustrated by eye color (when limited to blue versus brown eyes), sex membership, "living versus dead," and the like. The method can be applied, however, to data that are measurable on a continuous variable if we make certain allowances for the continuity, by making appropriate corrections and in our interpretations. The phi coefficient is a close relative of chi square, which is applicable to a wide variety of situations.

THE COMPUTATION OF PHI

To illustrate the use of phi (ϕ), we shall use again some data that were previously employed with chi square (see Table 11.2). They are given here as we need them, in proportion form, in Table 14.9. The basic formula for the phi coefficient is

$$\phi = \frac{\alpha\delta - \beta\gamma}{\sqrt{pqp'q'}} \quad \text{(The phi coefficient)} \tag{14.19}$$

where the symbols correspond to the labeled cells in Table 14.9.[2]

[1]Also known as the Yule ϕ or sometimes as the Yule-Boas ϕ. See Yule, G. U. On the methods of measuring the association between two attributes. *J. Roy. Stat. Soc.*, 1912, **75**, 576–642.

[2]For a derivation of formula (14.19), see Appendix A.

Table 14.9 *A table to illustrate the correlation of attributes*

| | Intellectual status | | |
	Feeble-minded	Normal	Both
Married	.204 (β)	.269 (α)	.473 (p)
Unmarried	.296 (ϑ)	.231 (γ)	.527 (q)
Both	.500 (q′)	.500 (p′)	1.000

(*Marital status* is the row label)

The solution of ϕ for this table is

$$\phi = \frac{(.269)(.296) - (.204)(.231)}{\sqrt{(.473)(.527)(.5)(.5)}}$$
$$= .1302, \text{ or } .13$$

THE RELATION OF PHI TO CHI SQUARE

Phi is related to chi square computed from a 2×2 table by the very simple equation

$$\chi^2 = N\phi^2 \qquad \text{(Chi square as a function of phi)} \tag{14.20}$$

and phi is derived from chi square by the equation

$$\phi = \sqrt{\frac{\chi^2}{N}} \qquad \text{(Phi as a function of chi square)} \tag{14.21}$$

By formula (14.20), for the data of Table 11.2,

$$\chi^2 = (412)(.016952)$$
$$= 6.98$$

This checks with the solution of chi square by other methods (see Chap. 11).

Since phi can be derived directly from chi square, when the latter is applied to a 2×2 table, any of the formulas for chi square given for 2×2 tables in Chap. 11 will apply to its computation. Formula (11.8), especially, which is very similar to formula (14.19) above, is probably most convenient. Applied directly to the computing of phi, it becomes

$$\phi = \frac{ad - bc}{\sqrt{(a + b)(a + c)(b + d)(c + d)}} \qquad \begin{array}{l}\text{(Phi computed from}\\ \text{frequencies)}\end{array} \tag{14.22}$$

THE SPECIAL CASE OF PHI WHEN ONE DISTRIBUTION IS EVENLY DIVIDED

When one of the distributions, let us say the one for which we use p' and q' as total proportions, is evenly divided so that $p' = q' = .50$, the solution of ϕ is considerably simplified. The formula reads

$$\phi = \frac{\alpha - \beta}{\sqrt{pq}} \qquad \text{(Phi from evenly divided proportions)} \tag{14.23}$$

Applied to the data on marital status,

$$\phi = \frac{.269 - .204}{\sqrt{(.473)(.527)}} = .13$$

This particular case is useful in many an experimental situation where two separated groups are selected with equal numbers of cases.

THE RELIABILITY AND SIGNIFICANCE OF PHI

The formula for the estimation of the standard error of phi involves such laborious computations that it is impractical for general use, and it will not be given here. A test of the null hypothesis, fortunately, can be made through phi's relationship to chi square. If χ^2 is significant in a fourfold table, the corresponding ϕ is significant. The procedure, then, is to derive the corresponding χ^2 from the obtained ϕ by means of formula (14.20), and then examine Table E to find whether for 1 degree of freedom the required standard of significance is met. In the marital problem, we find that a chi square of 6.98 is significant beyond the .01 point; therefore the obtained phi of .13 is likewise significant.[1]

AN EVALUATION OF THE PHI COEFFICIENT

Phi is actually a product-moment coefficient of correlation. Its formula is a variation of Pearson's fundamental equation, $r = \Sigma xy/N\sigma_x\sigma_y$. The similarity may be seen, to some degree at least, if we break the denominator of formula (14.19) into two components, $\sqrt{pq}$ and $\sqrt{p'q'}$. These are the standard deviations of the two point distributions, in Y and X. If we give numerical values of +1 and 0 to the two categories in X and in Y, and if we carry through the computation of a Pearson r in a scatter diagram of four cells, we arrive at a correlation coefficient equal to ϕ.

Limitations to the size of phi. While ϕ can vary from -1.0 to $+1.0$, only under certain conditions can ϕ be as large as either of these extremes, even though a tetrachoric r computed for the same data would yield an r_t equal to 1.0. The reason for the reduced size of phi is that a 2×2 table places restrictions upon ϕ that do not affect r. The general principle is that ϕ can be as great as 1.0 only when $p = p'$, when p and p' refer to corresponding categories (both considered +, for example).

To illustrate, let us examine a few special cases in which $p = .5$ but p' is allowed to vary. Such instances are pictured in Table 14.10. With an even division of the cases in the two categories in Y, only when X is also evenly divided is it possible to have a perfect correlation, as shown in contingency tables A and B. With a division of 75-25 in variable X, the maximum ϕ would be .58 (contingency table C) and with a 90-10 division, the maximum ϕ would be .33. In contingency table E the division in X is again 75-25, but there is departure from maximal relationship. The obtained ϕ of .35 may be interpreted for size in the light of the maximal ϕ possible with the particular com-

---

[1]According to McNemar, we may use $1/\sqrt{N}$ as the standard error of ϕ (when $\phi = 0$) if N is not small (see *Psychological Statistics.* 3d ed. New York: Wiley, 1962. P. 198).

Table 14.10 **Some fourfold contingency tables illustrating the dependence of the size of phi upon the marginal totals**

		A			B			C			D			E	
		−	+		−	+		−	+		−	+		−	+
Y	+	0	50	50	50	0	50	0	50	50	0	50	50	5	45	50
	−	50	0	50	0	50	50	25	25	50	10	40	50	20	30	50
		50	50	100	50	50	100	25	75	100	10	90	100	25	75	100
			X			*X*			*X*			*X*			*X*	
		$\phi = +1.0$			$\phi = -1.0$			$\phi = .58$			$\phi = .33$			$\phi = .35$	

bination of marginal totals, if we are interested in the underlying strength of relationship between X and Y. If we are interested in making predictions from categories to other categories, however, the obtained ϕ is a more realistic figure. The problems of prediction will be taken up in the chapters to follow.

DETERMINATION OF A MAXIMAL PHI COEFFICIENT

Because of the importance of the phi coefficient, particularly in connection with test-item intercorrelations, it is desirable for the purposes of orientation to have some conception of the drastic limitations to the size of phi. In general, the maximal ϕ for any combination of marginal proportions can be calculated by means of the following formula[1]

$$\phi_{\text{max}} = \sqrt{\left(\frac{p_j}{q_j}\right)\left(\frac{q_i}{p_i}\right)} \qquad \text{where } p_i \lessgtr p_j \qquad \begin{array}{l}\text{(Maximal value for } \phi \\ \text{with different combi-} \\ \text{nations of } p_i \text{ and } p_j)\end{array} \qquad (14.24)$$

where p_i = largest marginal proportion in a 2×2 contingency table and p_j = the corresponding marginal proportion in the other variable. For example, in the correlation of two test items, if p_i is the proportion of the total sample who pass item A, p_j is then the proportion of all who pass item B. In other instances, p_i might be the proportion failing item K, in which case p_j would be the proportion who fail item L, when items K and L are being correlated. Where $p_i = p_j$, the maximal ϕ equals 1.0, which means that with the same corresponding marginal proportions, ϕ can be as high as 1.0. To apply formula (14.24) to Table 14.10, C and E,

$$\phi_{\text{max}} = \sqrt{\frac{(.50)(.25)}{(.50)(.75)}} = .58$$

[1]For proof of formula (14.24), see Ferguson, G. A. The factorial interpretation of test difficulty. *Psychometrika*, 1941, **6**, 323–333.

Computations by formula (14.24) are greatly facilitated by the use of Table G, where values of $\sqrt{p/q}$ and $\sqrt{q/p}$ are given. Formula (14.24) can be broken down into the two components $\sqrt{p_j/q_j}$ and $\sqrt{q_i/p_i}$, whose product gives the maximal phi.

Figure 14.5 provides a graphic solution to the same equation for values of p_i and p_j ranging from .50 through .98. These ranges will take care of many of the situations in which ϕ would ordinarily be computed. It is recommended that the maximal ϕ that applies to any given situation (combination of p_i and p_j) be considered when considering the size of an obtained ϕ.

Some investigators have used the *ratio* of the obtained phi to the maximal phi, that is, ϕ/ϕ_{max}, in place of the obtained phi, with the expectation that it would be a more realistic indicator of the *intrinsic* correlation: i.e., an estimate freed from the restrictions imposed by the inequality of means, p and p'. The writer knows of no mathematical justification for this practice and does not recommend it.

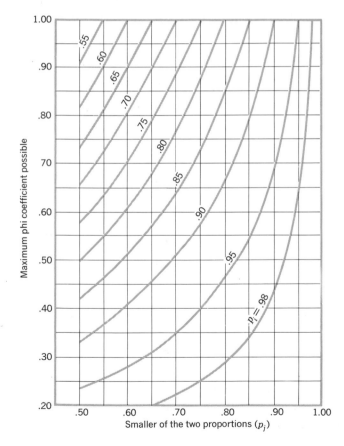

Fig. 14.5. *Maximal phi coefficients for different combinations of proportions of cases on the categories in X and Y having the largest marginal frequency p_i and its corresponding marginal frequency p_j.*

Furthermore, such a ratio would be absurd when the obtained phi is negative. For an obtained negative phi, we need to make a comparison with a minimal phi that could occur under the given conditions of the marginal frequencies. The minimal phi (or maximal negative phi) can be estimated by means of another formula, which reads

$$\phi = - \sqrt{\frac{q_i}{p_i}} \sqrt{\frac{q_j}{p_j}} \qquad \text{where } p_i \gtreqless p_j \qquad \begin{array}{c} \text{(Minimal phi, with differ-} \\ \text{ent combinations of} \\ p_i \text{ and } p_j) \end{array} \qquad (14.25)$$

where p_i = the smallest marginal proportion, p_j = the corresponding marginal proportion in the other variable, and q_i and q_j are their complements. From this equation, it can be seen that ϕ can reach a value of −1.0 only when $p_i = p_j$ and $q_i = q_j$.

Application of the formulas for $\phi_{\max}$ and $\phi_{\min}$ will show that the two values are not equidistant from zero, except under the special condition that $p_j = q_j = .50$. The range from $\phi_{\max}$ to $\phi_{\min}$ is not symmetrical about zero, under the usual circumstances. To say this in still another way, the amount of restriction in the size of phi is usually not the same in both positive and negative directions.

THE COEFFICIENT OF CONTINGENCY

It has been shown how a ϕ coefficient can be derived from chi square. When there are more than two classes in either X or Y, or in both, however, there is another correlation index, called the *coefficient of contingency*, designated by the letter C. C might be applied in correlating eye color with grades in a course, where there are three categories of eye color—e.g., blue, hazel, and brown—and four grade categories, A to D. The formula for deriving C from chi square is

$$C = \sqrt{\frac{\chi^2}{N + \chi^2}} \qquad \text{(Coefficient of contingency)} \qquad (14.26)$$

Like ϕ, the coefficient of contingency is restricted in size, but not to the same extent. When the number of categories is large (at least five each way), C approaches the Pearson r in size. If the categorized data represent continuous, normal distributions, if N is large, and if class intervals are of approximately equal size, the correction procedures applied to the Pearson r, described later in this chapter (Table 14.15), may be applied to the C coefficient. If the data are in genuine categories (point distributions, or nearly so), it is best to interpret C as it is. The maximum C for each given number of categories each way is shown in Table 14.11.

The standard error of C involves so much computation that it is hardly worth the effort to estimate it. A formula for this is given by

Table 14.11   **Maximal values attainable for a coefficient of contingency with different numbers of categories in both X and Y variables**

Number of categories	2	3	4	5	6	7	8	9	10
Maximum C	.707	.816	.866	.894	.913	.926	.935	.943	.949

Kelley.[1] For testing the hypothesis of zero correlation in a population, the chi square from which C is derived will serve very well.

Partial correlation

THE MEANING OF PARTIAL CORRELATION

A partial correlation between two variables is one that nullifies the effects of a third variable (or a number of other variables) upon both the variables being correlated. The correlation between height and weight of boys in a group where age is permitted to vary would be higher than the correlation between height and weight for a group at constant age. The reason is obvious. Because certain boys are older, they are both heavier and taller. Age is a factor that enhances the strength of correspondence between height and weight. With age held constant, the correlation would still be positive and significant, because at any age taller boys tend to be heavier.

If we wanted to know the correlation between height and weight with the influences of age ruled out, we could, of course, keep samples separated and compute r at each age level. But the partial-correlation technique enables us to accomplish the same result without so fractionating data into homogeneous age groups. When only one variable is held constant, we speak of a *first-order partial correlation*. The general formula is

$$r_{12.3} = \frac{r_{12} - r_{13} r_{23}}{\sqrt{(1 - r^2_{13})(1 - r^2_{23})}} \qquad \text{(First-order partial coefficient of correlation)} \qquad (14.27)$$

In a group of boys aged 12 to 19, the correlation between height and weight (r_{12}) was found to be .78. Between height and age, $r_{13} = .52$. Between weight and age, $r_{23} = .54$. The partial correlation is therefore

$$r_{12.3} = \frac{.78 - (.52)(.54)}{\sqrt{(1 - .52^2)(1 - .54^2)}}$$

$$= .69$$

With the influences of age upon both height and weight ruled out or nullified, then, the correlation between the two is .69.

[1]Kelley, T. L. *Statistical Method*. New York: Macmillan, 1923. P. 269.

As another example with three variables, the correlation between strength and height (r_{41}) in this same group was .58. The correlation between strength and weight (r_{42}) was .72. Although there is a significantly high correlation between strength and height, we wonder whether this is not due to the factor of weight-going-with-height rather than to height itself. Accordingly we hold weight constant and ask what the correlation would be then. Will boys of the same weight show any dependence of strength upon height? The correlation is given by

$$r_{41.2} = \frac{.58 - (.72)(.78)}{\sqrt{(1 - .72^2)(1 - .78^2)}}$$
$$= .042$$

By partialing out weight, it is found that the correlation between height and strength nearly vanishes. We conclude, therefore, that height *as such* has no bearing upon strength, but only by virtue of its association with weight does it show any correlation at all.

SECOND-ORDER PARTIALS

When we hold two variables constant at the same time, we call the coefficient a *second-order partial r*. The general formula is

$$r_{12.34} = \frac{r_{12.3} - r_{14.3}r_{24.3}}{\sqrt{(1 - r^2_{14.3})(1 - r^2_{24.3})}} \quad \text{(Second-order partial coefficient of correlation)} \quad (14.28)$$

In using this formula, the subscripts should be modified to suit the choice of variables. Here we are assuming that we want to know the correlation that would occur between X_1 and X_2 with the effects of X_3 and X_4 eliminated from both. It is clear that this formula requires the solution of three first-order partial correlation coefficients previously.

As an example of this partial, we may cite the correlation between strength and age with height and weight held constant. This would mean that if a group of boys having the same height and weight were taken, would older boys be stronger? The raw correlation between age and strength was .29. The second-order partial also turned out to be .29. This means that it seemingly makes no difference whether or not we allow height and weight to vary; the relation between age and strength is the same within the range examined.

SOME SUGGESTIONS CONCERNING PARTIAL CORRELATION

Needless to say, unless the assumptions necessary for computing the Pearson r's involved are fulfilled, there is little excuse for using them as the basis for computing partial correlations. There are relatively few occasions in psychology and education when a partial r is called for. The partialing out of such variables as chronological age is perhaps the most common instance in which it is useful. In a real sense, the use of partial correlation is a statistical substitute for experimental controls. The newer processes of analysis of variance and tests of significance of statistics from small samples make experimental planning seem more important and the treatment of results more satisfactory than resorting to partial correlations.

SIGNIFICANCE OF AN OBTAINED PARTIAL r

The standard error of a partial coefficient of correlation is the same as that for a Pearson r except that the number of degrees of freedom in the denominator of the formula for the standard error is a bit smaller. The general formula is

$$\sigma_{r_{12.34 \, \cdots \, m}} = \frac{1 - r^2_{12.34 \, \cdots \, m}}{\sqrt{N - m}} \qquad \text{(Standard error of a partial } r\text{)} \qquad (14.29)$$

where m is the number of variables involved.

Some special problems in correlation

THE RELATIVITY OF ALL COEFFICIENTS OF CORRELATION

It is apparent that the size of the coefficient of correlation depends to some extent upon how we compute it. More importantly, coefficients computed between the same two variables by the same procedure will vary not only from sample to sample but from population to population. It is therefore really meaningless to speak of *the* correlation between intelligence and character (even if it is assumed that we know what those variables are and have properly measured them) or even between age and height or any other common variables without at the same time specifying what kind of sample we measured and what kind of coefficient we used. In reporting coefficients of correlation, a writer should be very careful to state all the pertinent conditions that bear upon the size of his obtained correlation coefficients, and any reader should accept interpretations only when the significant circumstances are kept in mind. A few of the more common sources of variations of size of r will now be reviewed briefly.

THE VARIABILITY IN THE CORRELATED VARIABLES

The size of r is very much dependent upon the variability of measured values in the correlated sample. The greater the variability, the higher will be the correlation, everything else being equal. It should be easier to predict individual differences in academic achievement in a class with IQ's ranging from 50 to 150 than in a class where the range is restricted to 90 to 110. If the variability were zero (all IQ's being equal), there should be no correlation whatever—the limiting case in which, of course, no r could be computed at all. Often we know the correlation between some predictive index, such as aptitude-test score and achievement or some vocational criterion of success as derived from one group of individuals, but we shall often be applying the same index to other groups with different ranges of ability, larger or smaller. What will be the effectiveness of predictions in the new groups?

In the selection of personnel by means of tests, as during World War II, research on selective instruments was constantly beset with this very practical problem. New tests were put into use in the selection of personnel, and they correlated substantially with tests that were already being used in selection. The result was that the men who went into training represented only a higher segment of the population from which selection was to be made by the new tests. The validity of a test could be estimated only for this higher segment of restricted range. And yet it was the validity in the total tested population that it was important to know, for it is that validity which indicates the full selective value of the test. The coefficient of validity in a restricted group is almost invariably smaller than what it would be in an unrestricted group.

In a research program such as that on the selection and classification of aviation trainees during World War II, the problem of restriction of range becomes quite important. Near the end of the war, standards were set such that about 50 per cent of the applicants for air-crew training failed to pass the general qualifying examination, and of these as many as 75 per cent failed to qualify for a particular type of training. Furthermore, it was desired to correlate classification and experimental tests with advanced-training achievement criteria and even combat performance after many more men had been eliminated at various stages of training. The proportion of the original applicants who survived to these final stages was rather small. Restriction of range was very great.

Many years ago, Karl Pearson provided a solution that applies under certain conditions. The variables being studied must be normally distributed in the population and we must know certain parameters or estimates of them. We must know the relation of the dispersions in the restricted and unrestricted populations, either in terms of the variable on which selection occurred or on the basis of some variable correlated with it. We also must know the correlation in the restricted population between the variable we wish to validate and the criterion of success in training or on the job. There are three formulas of practical use in solving this problem, each of which recognizes the availability of certain information and the need for validation of a certain kind of variable.

Case I. Restriction is produced by selection on the basis of X_1, and there is knowledge of standard deviations in X_1 for both restricted and unrestricted groups. The correlation r_{12} is known in the restricted group. The correlation R_{12} for the unrestricted group is estimated by

$$R_{12} = \frac{r_{12}\left(\dfrac{\Sigma_1}{\sigma_1}\right)}{\sqrt{1 - r^2_{12} + r^2_{12}\left(\dfrac{\Sigma^2_1}{\sigma^2_1}\right)}} \qquad \text{(Correlation corrected for restriction of range, Case I)} \qquad (14.30)$$

where r_{12} = correlation between X_1 and X_2 in the restricted group
$\qquad \sigma_1$ = standard deviation in measurements on X_1 in the restricted group
$\qquad \Sigma_1$ = standard deviation in the same variable in the unrestricted group

In this and in the next two formulas, capital letters stand for values pertaining to the unrestricted population and lower-case letters refer to the restricted population.

The application of this formula is as follows: Suppose that the selection test (X_1) correlated .30 with the training criterion in the group selected on the basis of the test. The standard deviation in the unrestricted group (Σ_1) was 20 and that in the restricted group (σ_1) was 10. The solution is

$$R_{12} = \frac{.30\left(\dfrac{20}{10}\right)}{\sqrt{1 - .09 + (.09)\dfrac{20^2}{10^2}}}$$

$$= .53$$

Case II. Restriction is produced by selection on the basis of X_1, and there is knowledge of standard deviations for X_2 in both restricted and unrestricted samples and of the correlation r_{12} in the restricted group. The correlation in the unrestricted group is estimated by

$$R_{12} = \sqrt{1 - \frac{\sigma^2_2}{\Sigma^2_2}(1 - r^2_{12})} \qquad \text{(Correlation corrected for restriction of range, Case II)} \qquad (14.31)$$

where σ_2 = standard deviation on X_2 in the restricted group and Σ_2 = standard deviation on X_2 in the unrestricted group. This formula would apply when we correlate two selection tests, i.e., when we have selected on the basis of one test (X_1) but know the change of range from knowledge of variances in the other test (X_2). One or both of the "tests" might be a composite score derived from a combination of several tests. An example of this from aviation psychology was the correlation of an experimental test with the pilot stanine (composite aptitude score) when selection had been made on the basis of the stanine and it was more convenient to use the change in dispersion on the test. If we assume the same restricted correlation ($r_{12} = .30$)

as in the previous illustration, and that the restricted and unrestricted standard deviations are 10 and 20, respectively,

$$R_{12} = \sqrt{1 - \frac{10^2}{20^2}(1 - .30^2)}$$

$$= .88$$

Case III. Restriction is produced by selection on variable X_3, on which variable the restricted and unrestricted standard deviations are known. We wish to estimate the unrestricted correlation R_{12}, when we also know r_{12}, r_{13}, and r_{23}. The formula is

$$R_{12} = \frac{r_{12} + r_{13}r_{23}\left(\frac{\Sigma^2_3}{\sigma^2_3} - 1\right)}{\sqrt{\left[1 + r^2_{13}\left(\frac{\Sigma^2_3}{\sigma^2_3} - 1\right)\right]\left[1 + r^2_{23}\left(\frac{\Sigma^2_3}{\sigma^2_3} - 1\right)\right]}} \tag{14.32}$$

(Correlation corrected for restriction of range, Case III)

This formula would apply to the correlation of a new, experimental test X_1 with a practical criterion X_2, when selection had been made on the basis of a third variable (pilot stanine, for example) X_3.

The reader may have been somewhat surprised at the rather radical change in correlation that occurred as we corrected for restriction of range in the two hypothetical problems above. To show that these changes are not unreasonable, some data will be cited from the AAF results.[1] An experimental group of more than a thousand pilots had been permitted to enter training without any selection whatever on the basis of either qualifying or classification tests. We know, then, how the pilot stanine and certain classification tests correlated with the graduation-elimination criterion at the end of training. We can also arbitrarily pull out a high segment of the total sample and within that limited sample compute validity coefficients. The results are given in Table 14.12 for the instance in which a rather high, but not unknown, selection of the top 13 per cent occurred. It can be seen that where there were substantial correlations in the unrestricted sample the correlations in the selected group often shrank close to zero and, in one instance, to a trivial negative r. On the whole, those tests that correlated highest with the stanine lost most in validity correlation because of selection on the basis of the stanine.[2]

[1]Thorndike, R. L. (ed.). *Research Problems and Techniques. AAF Aviation Psychology Research Program Reports*, No. 3. Washington, D.C.: GPO, 1947.
[2]Abacs for application of the formulas for Cases I and II have been supplied by Michael, W. B., Jones, R. A., Gaddis, L. W., and Kaiser, H. F. Abacs for determination of a correlation coefficient corrected for restriction of range. *Psychometrika*, 1962, **27**, 197–202.

Table 14.12 **Validity coefficients for selective tests and a composite score for the selection of pilot students with and without restriction of range**

Variable	Correlation in the total group (N = 1,036)	Correlation in the selected highest 13 per cent (N = 136)
Pilot stanine	.64	.18
Mechanical principles	.44	.03
General information	.46	.20
Complex coordination	.40	−.03
Instrument comprehension	.45	.27
Arithmetic reasoning	.27	.18
Finger dexterity	.18	.00

Evaluation of the correction formulas for restriction.   It should be repeated that the problem of restriction is important, and that if one wishes to avoid wrong conclusions, when a substantial amount of selection has been made, one should apply correction procedures. Had we taken the second (restricted) set of coefficients in Table 14.12 seriously, without other knowledge to the contrary, we should probably have concluded that formerly valid tests, and even the stanine, had lost validities that were demonstrated early in the war when selection was a cause of little restriction.

It should be remembered that the formulas rest on the assumption of normal distributions of the population on the variables used, and the Pearson product-moment r is presupposed. The use of the biserial r or tetrachoric r as an estimate of the Pearson r in a restricted range raises considerable question when selection is severe. Experience tends to show, however, that when the biserial r is used as the validation coefficient, the formulas tend to underestimate the unrestricted correlation. The standard errors for these corrected coefficients are unknown, but it is probable that they are larger than those for Pearson r's of comparable size.

CORRELATIONS IN HETEROGENEOUS SAMPLES

Studies of validity of tests have frequently been faulty from a number of standpoints. The use of school marks as criteria of success in training has a number of faults, one of which will concern us here.

One factor working against accurate tests of validity is the indiscriminate pooling of marks from different subjects and from different instructors and treating them as if they were all the same. A cursory inspection of grade distributions in any school will show that marks are by no means of constant value when obtained from different sources. Means and variances differ from set to set of data. The data are *heterogeneous*. Much of this is caused by variations in ideas about marking from instructor to instructor. This variation among sets of marks when they are collectively correlated with other measures is very likely to affect the apparent amount of correlation.

As an example, in six sections of freshman English, *within* sections the correlation between quiz averages for the semester and a final comprehensive examination ranged from .63 to .92, with an overall correlation within sections, *when intersection differences had been eliminated*, of .83. Yet when the six sections were combined, *with intersectional differences left in*, the correlation was reduced to .71. It was interesting to find that *between* sections the correlation was −.17, which means that there was a very slight tendency for sections with average lower achievement to be given a higher average quiz mark! This fact accounts for the reduction in correlation from .83 to .71 when sections were combined.[1]

Figure 14.6 shows the situation just described, in somewhat exaggerated form, in diagram II. Diagram II is best understood by contrasting it with diagram I. In the latter we have a homogeneous combination of four subsamples drawn from the same population. The amount of correlation between X and Y within each subsample is indicated by the shape of a smaller ellipse. All the ellipses are of about the same shape, indicating about the same degree of correlation of X and Y *within* groups. The dots indicate the means of Y and X within each subsample. If we combine the four samples, we obtain a distribution described approximately by the large faint ellipse. Note in diagram I the proportions of the large ellipse are about the same as for each small ellipse, indicating the same level of correlation within the composite distribution as within each subsample. Note, also, that the distribution of the four means forms roughly an ellipse of similar proportions. If the correlation between means of Y and means of X differs from that within subsamples, the correlation of X and Y in the composite sample will differ from that within subsamples.

In diagram II of Fig. 14.6 we have a very different situation. While with each subsample the correlation between K and L is approximately the same, the subsamples did not arise from the same population so far as means are concerned. An ellipse drawn to enclose

[1]Further discussion of "within" versus "between" correlations when groups are combined will be found in Lindquist, E. F. *Statistical Analysis in Education Research*. Boston: Houghton Mifflin, 1940; Edwards, A. L. *Experimental Designs in Psychological Research*. New York: Holt, 1960.

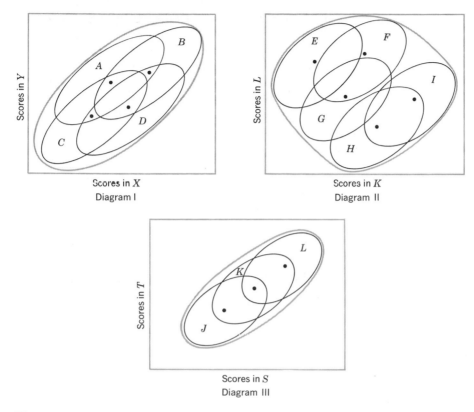

Fig. 14.6. *Illustration of bivariate distributions of cases in homogeneous and heterogeneous subsamples.*

just the dots would slant in the direction that would ensure a negative correlation between means of K and means of L. The effect of this can be seen in the faint line enclosing all subsamples. Its form suggests approximately zero correlation. Such situations are not uncommon. In general practice, if it is doubtful whether subsamples arose by random sampling from the same population, it would be best to compute correlations within subsamples separately and to average them, thereby obtaining a single value, or to apply equivalent procedures which we shall not take the space to describe here.[1] The hypothesis of homogeneity of samples can be examined by means of t tests or F tests as described in Chaps. 9 and 13.

THE CORRELATION OF AVERAGES

It was stated in an earlier chapter in connection with tests of significance of differences between statistics (Chap. 9) that the correlation between averages of samples is equal to the correlation between indi-

[1] See Lindquist, *op. cit.*

vidual pairs of measurements. *This statement assumes random samples from a homogeneous population.* Diagram I in Fig. 14.6 illustrates this kind of situation and shows how an *r* obtained within one sample can be used as an estimate of a correlation between means. Diagram II shows how a correlation coefficient obtained within a single sample might be very misleading about the amount of correlation between means. This example shows an instance in which the correlation between means is decidedly lower than that within samples, one perhaps even reversed in sign.

The correlation between means could also be higher than that within samples, as diagram III shows. An example of this would be the correlation between IQ and salary. Correlating *individuals*, we should find some positive correlation, but because of great variations in salary at any single IQ value, the correlation might not be very high. If we divided men into sets according to vocation and correlated *average* IQ with *average* salary, the coefficient would probably be very high. This is because people of different IQ levels gravitate to certain occupations, and occupations as such have established characteristic salary scales. Other factors that make for individual differences in salary *within* occupations are thus minimized in importance. The sampling is biased the moment we divide groups along occupational lines.

AVERAGING COEFFICIENTS OF CORRELATION

As stated earlier, one solution to the problem of correlations in some heterogeneous samples is to estimate the correlation between X and Y within each subsample and then average the coefficients in order to obtain a single estimate of the population correlation. This would presumably describe the relation between X and Y throughout the composite sample, free from whatever sampling biases there may have been in segregating the subsamples. Before averaging coefficients, however, we must make the assumption that the several r's did arise by random sampling from the same population – same with respect to the degree of correlation. It should go without saying, also, that we have correlated the same variables in all samples.

There are several procedures sometimes used in averaging r's. Coefficients of correlation are not values on a scale of equal metric units; they are index numbers. Differences between large r's are actually much greater than those between small r's. If the few sample r's to be averaged, however, are of about the same value and if they are not too large, a simple arithmetic mean will suffice. If the r's differ considerably in size and if they are large, it is best to use transformations to Fisher's **z** coefficients. This procedure is illustrated in Table 14.13. It consists in transforming each r into a corresponding **z** (Table H may be used for this purpose), finding the arith-

Table 14.13 **Demonstration of averaging coefficients of correlation when *r*'s differ in range and in size**

Sample A		Sample B		Sample C		Sample D	
Mean of r	z method	Mean of r	z method	Mean of r	z method	Mean of r	z method
.45	.48	.75	.97	.35	.37	.65	.78
.50	.55	.80	1.10	.55	.62	.85	1.26
.42	.45	.72	.91	.68	.83	.98	2.30
.38	.40	.68	.83	.50	.55	.80	1.10
.55	.62	.85	1.26	.58	.66	.88	1.38
Σ 2.30	2.50	3.80	4.75	2.66	3.03	4.16	6.82
M_z	.50		1.014		.606		1.364
M_r .46	.46	.76	.77	.532	.543	.832	.877

metic mean of the z's, and, finally, transforming the mean z back to the corresponding mean r.

The results of Table 14.13 show differences to be expected in the use of an arithmetic mean of r's and of corresponding z's. Samples A and B have the same range of r's, those in B being merely .30 greater than those in A. In sample A, agreement is perfect in the results from the two methods. In sample B, the mean r by the z method is .01 higher (.77 as compared with .76). In samples C and D there is much more spread in the r's averaged. For the r's of moderate size, sample C, the z method gives a result only .01 greater than the simple mean of r's. In the high coefficients, however, the difference is about .05.

There is serious question whether r's differing as much as these would satisfy the belief that they came from the same population by random sampling and hence would be candidates for averaging. When a few r's do satisfy this belief, the chances are that any discrepancy between a simple mean of r's and an average obtained by the z method would be small as compared with the standard error of r. If the r's did come from the same population, a mean of several would be a much more reliable estimate of population correlation. With the requirements satisfied, we could add degrees of freedom from the different subsamples to represent the degrees of freedom of the mean r and interpret its significance accordingly.

Weighting coefficients in averaging.   One more requirement should be mentioned, particularly if the last operation, combining degrees of freedom, is to be carried out—that is, to weight the obtained r's in averaging them. The weight for each sample is its number of degrees of freedom $(N - 2)$. In using the z method, the weights are applied to the z's. The weight to be applied to a z is its corresponding $N - 3$ [see formula (8.15)].

THE CORRELATION OF PARTS WITH WHOLES

We frequently want to correlate a part measurement, such as a part of a test battery, or a test item, with the whole of which it is a part. Since the variance of the total is in part made up of the variance of the component, that fact alone introduces some degree of positive correlation. The greater the relative contribution to the total variance made by the component, the more important is this "spurious" factor. Thus, a part-whole correlation is in part a correlation of a variable with itself. It is possible in a particular instance that the part is totally *uncorrelated* with the remaining parts and yet will be correlated with the total. If it is negatively correlated with the remaining parts, it will be less negatively correlated with the total.

If each part contributes about the same amount of variance to the total or if the part is one of a great many, so that its proportion of contribution is relatively small, we can compare correlations between parts and total with some confidence that they are compared on a very similar basis. But if these conditions do not obtain, we should do better to correlate each part with a composite of all other parts. When such a composite is unknown or is hard to obtain, we can still estimate the correlation by means of the formula

$$r_{pq} = \frac{r_{tp}\sigma_t - \sigma_p}{\sqrt{\sigma^2_t + \sigma^2_p - 2r_{tp}\sigma_t\sigma_p}}$$

(Correlation of part with a remainder, knowing correlation of part with total)   (14.33)

where p = part score

t = total score

$q = t - p$; in other words, the total with the part excluded

In the correlation of test items each with the total score of the test of which it is a part, it is important to know about how much a part would correlate with the total when there is really no relationship at all. We can estimate this, but only under the conditions that each part has the same variance and there is zero intercorrelation among all parts. Under these special conditions the average amount of correlation of a part with the total is given by the equation

$$r_{pt} = \frac{1}{\sqrt{n}}$$

(Average correlation of a number of parts, of equal variance and zero intercorrelation, with their total)   (14.34)

in which n = number of parts.[1]

If we should want to know the correlation of a part with a whole of

[1]An adaptation has been made of formula (14.33) to the correction of item-total correlations for spurious overlap. See Guilford, J. P. The correlation of an item with a composite of the remaining items of a test. *Educ. psychol. Measmt.*, 1953, **13**, 87 – 93.

which it is a part and we already know the correlation of the part with the remainder of the whole, the estimate is made by the equation

$$r_{pt} = \frac{\sigma_p + r_{pq}\sigma_q}{\sqrt{\sigma^2_p + \sigma^2_q + 2r_{pq}\sigma_p\sigma_q}}$$

(Correlation of part with whole, knowing correlation between part and remainder) (14.35)

in which the symbols have the same meaning as in formula (14.33). The utility of this formula is probably rather limited. It is given primarily to show what happens when two parts that correlate zero are combined. If r_{pq} is .0 in formula (14.35), the numerator reduces to σ_p. The denominator is actually the standard deviation of the composite $(p + q)$. The deduction is that if two parts correlate zero, when combined, the correlation of the part with the total will be equal to the ratio of the standard deviation of the part to that of the total.

INDEX CORRELATION

This is usually called *spurious index correlation* for the reason that when indices such as IQ, EQ (educational quotient), or AQ (achievement quotient) are correlated with each other, r is markedly influenced by the fact that these ratios have in common such factors as chronological age and mental age. IQ's from two different tests are derived from the MA's obtained from the two tests *each divided by the same* CA. If there is a range of CA in the group correlated, this fact in itself introduces some positive correlation.

Table 14.14 will show by means of fictitious and exaggerated data how this phenomenon works. For eight children who differ in chronological age from five to nine inclusive, mental-age ratings on two different tests are given. These are obviously selected children, since their mental-age values are all either seven or eight. Note, however, how the IQ's spread, from 160 through 78. The spread in IQ's is almost entirely due to the spread in chronological ages. Since each child has the *same* chronological age for *both* IQ's, that same denominator of the ratio of his MA to CA ensures that his IQ's will be about the same. Some IQ's go up together in the two tests for children of low CA and others go down together, for children with higher CA. The correlation computed between IQ's is .92.

All correlations are influenced by the conditions under which they were obtained. If one remembers what IQ's are and interprets correlations between them accordingly, no particular falsification of the facts is in question. The important thing is that one should correlate variables in the full knowledge of how the measurements were obtained, if possible, and should report to his readers the facts needed for wise interpretation, whether it be variability of the correlated group or range of CA's involved when IQ's have been correlated.

Table 14.14   Demonstration of how index numbers may acquire a high degree of correlation because of a common denominator: an extreme case

Child	CA	MA I	MA II	IQ I	IQ II
A	5.0	7	8	140	160
B	5.5	8	8	145	145
C	6.0	7	7	117	117
D	6.5	8	7	123	108
E	7.5	8	8	106	106
F	8.0	7	8	88	100
G	8.5	8	7	94	82
H	9.0	7	7	78	78

Correlation between mental ages I and II = .00
Correlation between IQ's I and II = .92

CORRECTION IN r FOR ERRORS OF GROUPING

If, in computing a Pearson r by means of grouping data in class intervals, a small number of classes either way has been used, the estimate of correlation is lowered to some degree. In the limiting case, of two classes each way, the computed r is about two-thirds of the r had there been no grouping. When the number of intervals is 10 both ways, r is about 3 per cent underestimated. For any number of classes in X or in Y, we can correct for the error of grouping by dividing r by a constant corresponding to that number of classes.

The correction is necessary because errors of grouping yield overestimates of the standard deviations, as was shown in Chap. 5. If Sheppard's correction has been applied to both standard deviations, no further correction is necessary in the coefficient of correlation.

Table 14.15 supplies the list of constants given by Peters and Van Voorhis to be used in making corrections in r.[1] Correction is made for the number of categories or intervals in Y as well as in X. The correction factors are used in the following manner. Suppose that we have an obtained r of .61 in a problem with eight intervals in X and nine in Y. The correction factors for these numbers of intervals are .977 and .982, respectively. The correction is made by dividing the obtained r by the product of the two correction factors. In terms of a formula,

$$r_c = \frac{r}{c_x c_y} \qquad \text{(14.36)}$$

(Coefficient of correlation corrected for coarse grouping)

[1] Peters and Van Voorhis, *op. cit.* P. 398.

in which c_x and c_y are the correction factors for variables X and Y, respectively, based upon the number of class intervals in each. Applied to the correlation of .61 with eight and nine categories in X and Y,

$$r_c = \frac{.61}{(.977)(.982)} = .626 \text{ (or .63)}$$

When there are the same number of intervals in both X and Y, the correction factor is the same for both, and the factor squared would be called for in the denominator of formula (14.36). The factors squared are given for this purpose in Table 14.15.

When the number of intervals in either X or Y is less than 10 it is good practice to apply this correction procedure, certainly when the number of intervals is eight or below. There is most to be gained in accuracy of estimate of r when the obtained r is large; little to be gained if r is small, particularly if the sample is small.

It should be remembered that the correction factors given in Table 14.15 are designed especially for the situation in which the midpoint of an interval is the index number for cases in that interval, the intervals are equal in size, and the distributions are normal. For other, less common situations, see the reference below.[1]

Correction of phi for coarse grouping. Since the phi coefficient is a product-moment estimate of correlation, the question arises as to whether it is ever subject to this kind of correction. This question should arise only when one or both variables are actually continuously measurable and we want a more realistic estimate of correlation that describes the relationship that exists when the variable is used in graded form. As to number of "intervals," we have two each way when ϕ is computed. The index number for each interval is not the midpoint, however, but is the mean of the cases in the interval.

If we can assume that the actual distributions of both X and Y in the population are continuous and normal, a Pearson r may be estimated from ϕ under limited conditions. Those conditions are that

[1]Peters and Van Voorhis, *ibid.*

Table 14.15   Correction factors for errors of grouping in the computation of Pearson's r when distributions are normal and midpoints of intervals stand for cases in the intervals

No. of intervals	2	3	4	5	6	7	8	9	10	11	12	13	14	15
Correction factor	.816	.859	.916	.943	.960	.970	.977	.982	.985	.988	.990	.991	.992	.994
Squared correction factor		.667	.737	.839	.891	.923	.941	.955	.964	.970	.976	.980	.983	.985	.987

ϕ is not greater than .4 and that p and p' are within the range .3 to .7. The formula is

$$r_\phi = \phi\left(\frac{\sqrt{pq}}{y}\right)\left(\frac{\sqrt{p'q'}}{y'}\right) \qquad \text{(Estimate of a Pearson } r \text{ from } \phi) \qquad (14.37)$$

where the symbols are as defined in Table 14.6.[1] It will be noted that the terms within parentheses are the same as in formula (14.14a). When a point-biserial r is wanted rather than a Pearson r, the estimate calls for only one of these terms—that corresponding to the one continuous variable.[2] If p and p' are .5, formula (14.37) may be applied when ϕ is as high as .6. When the specified conditions are not met, it is best to estimate the Pearson r by computing a tetrachoric r.

EXERCISES

1. By the rank-difference method:
a. Compute the correlations between the first 20 pairs of scores for variables I and II, and for variables V and VI, in Data 6A.
b. Interpret your results, and comment on the question of statistical significance of the two coefficients.

2. For Data 15A:
a. Compute a correlation ratio for the prediction of Y from X.
b. Find the standard error for the obtained eta.
c. Compute a standard error of estimate.
d. Apply the F test of linearity, with r_{xy} taken as .657.

3. a. Estimate a tetrachoric coefficient of correlation for Data 14A.
b. Determine whether or not the correlation is probably significantly different from zero.
c. If Thurstone's diagrams or any other computing aid are available, find another estimate of the tetrachoric r for the same data.

4. Preparatory to computing an estimate of r_t, reduce the following to a fourfold table:
a. The frequencies in Data 11B.
b. The frequencies in Data 6B.
c. Data 15A.

5. a. Compute a phi coefficient for Data 11A, using the different formulas provided in this chapter.
b. Estimate a chi square for the same data, using the obtained ϕ. Compare with the chi square obtained in connection with Exercise 2, Chap. 11.
c. Estimate a Pearson r for these same data, using the obtained phi coefficient.

[1]Guilford, J. P., and Perry, N. C. Estimation of other coefficients of correlation from the phi coefficient. *Psychometrika*, 1951, **16**, 335–346.
[2]Michael, W. B., Perry, N. C., and Guilford, J. P. The estimation of a point biserial coefficient of correlation from a phi coefficient. *Brit. J. Psychol., Stat. Sec.*, 1952, **5**, 139–150.

Data 14A **Relationship between failing in college and being above or below the median in high-school graduating class**

Status in high-school class	Failing in one or more courses	No failures in first semester	Total
Above the median	37	340	377
Below the median	49	71	120
Total	86	411	497

d. Estimate a Pearson r also by computing a cosine-pi r. Compare the two estimates just obtained.

6. *a.* Compute the following partial r's for Data 16A: $r_{34.2}$; $r_{41.2}$; $r_{51.2}$.
b. Interpret these results.
c. Which of these three coefficients has the most psychological or practical meaning? Which the least? Explain.

ANSWERS

1. a. $\rho_{12} = -.11$ (for parts I and II); $\rho_{56} = .65$.
   b. From Table L, ρ_{12} is insignificant; ρ_{56} is significant beyond the .01 level.
2. a. $\eta = .660$. *b.* $\sigma_n = .053$. *c.* $\sigma_{yx} = 5.06$. *d.* $F = 0.12$.
3. a. $r_{\text{cos-pi}} = .63$. *b.* $\sigma_{r_t} = .091$ (when $r_t = 0$).
   c. From Thurstone's diagrams, $r_t = .59$.
4.

a.

Yes ? +No		
D	117	133
ND	141	109

b.

	55–79	80–99
.140–.189	9	8
.100–.139	14	20

c.

	0–14	15–23
45	16	21–38
13	39	6–20

5. a. $\phi = .14$; *b.* $\chi^2 = 3.98$; *c.* $r_\phi = .22$; *d.* $r_{\text{cos-pi}} = .22$.
6. a. $r_{34.2} = .395$; $r_{41.2} = .466$; $r_{51.2} = .241$.
   c. $r_{41.2}$ is most practical and most meaningful psychologically; $r_{34.2}$ is least meaningful or useful.

15 *Prediction and accuracy of prediction*

ONE of the most important fruits of scientific investigation and one of the most exacting tests of any hypothesis is the ability to make predictions. So important is this topic that it deserves to have considerable space devoted to it. Particularly is this true for the reason that statistical reasoning applies to all predictions. Statistical ideas not only guide us in framing statements of a predictive nature but also enable us to say something definite concerning how trustworthy our predictions are—about how much error one should expect in the phenomenon predicted.

It is the purpose of this chapter and the next to illustrate the kinds of predictions the statistically oriented investigator makes and how he does not blind his eyes to his failures but brings them clearly into the light.

GENERAL TYPES OF PREDICTION

Although in this volume we have generally emphasized measurement, we have had to recognize from time to time that the highest types of measurements cannot be made (i.e., ratio and interval measurement, defined in Chap. 2), that data are sometimes merely classified in categories. With classification or nominal measurement, it is a matter of assigning attributes to cases rather than quantitative evaluations on a linear scale, for example, identifying individuals as to sex, race, political party, or criminality. Although such data are not allocated to linear-scale positions, we can still make predictions from them as well as predict them from other information. We thus have four cases of prediction:

1. Attributes from other attributes—as when we predict incidence of criminality from sex, race, or religious creed.

2. Attributes from measurements — as when we predict criminality from scores on tests of ability or of other behavior traits.

3. Measurements from attributes — as when we predict probable test scores from sex, socioeconomic status, or marital status.

4. Measurements from other measurements — as when we predict academic achievement from aptitude scores.

GENERAL WAYS OF EVALUATING ACCURACY OF PREDICTION

Predictions are obviously sound if they prove to be correct. The degree of correctness is indicated by *how often* or *how nearly* we hit the mark. In the case of predicting attributes, our success can be numerically indicated in terms of the percentages of "hits" or "misses." But a more accepted way is to ask how much better our predictions are than they would have been had we not used the information at our disposal — in other words, if we had not tried to predict one thing from the knowledge of another but merely from a knowledge of the predicted population itself.

In predicting measurements, whether from attributes or from other measurements, we ask a similar question. But whereas in predicting attributes for cases, we work in terms of the *number* of hits and misses, in predicting measurements, we work in terms of *how far* on the average we have missed the mark. We compare this average deviation between fact and prediction with the average of the errors we should make without using our knowledge as a basis of prediction. We shall begin with the case of predicting measurements from attributes.

Predicting measurements from attributes

THE PRINCIPLE OF LEAST SQUARES

What would be the most accurate prediction of the weight of a sixteen-year-old youth? By "most accurate" we mean a weight that, if chosen to predict the weight of each sixteen-year-old selected at random from a certain population, would be closer to the facts in the long run than any other estimate would be. In other words, we want a predicted weight that would give us the smallest average deviation from the actual weights. We should find the difference between the actual weight of each person and our prediction in order to learn how good our prediction is for that particular person.

Statisticians have good reason to deal here in terms of the *squares* of the deviations rather than in terms of the deviations themselves. They demand a predicted measurement from which the sum of the squared deviations is a minimum. The prediction that will satisfy this requirement is the mean of the distribution. In choosing the mean as the prediction, we are following the *principle of least squares.* Choosing the mean gives us the smallest set of squared deviations from the predicted value (see Chap. 4 for proof).

PREDICTIONS APPLY TO SELECTED POPULATIONS

In answer to the question with which we started this discussion, the best prediction of the weight of a sixteen-year-old, if we lack better knowledge, is the mean weight of the population of which he is a member. If we wanted this to cover *all* sixteen-year-olds, we should see to it that the distribution from which we derive the mean is made up of a large sample in which both sexes, all races, and all socioeconomic and geographic groups are proportionally represented. We might, however, confine the question to sixteen-year-olds from the United States. We might further confine it to high-school youths in one city, or, even further, to one particular high school. Whatever our restriction in population, the predicted weight would apply only (except by chance) to that kind of population. Whenever we extend predictions to samples beyond the known population, we always do so at the risk of enlarging errors of prediction.

ERRORS OF PREDICTION MEASURED BY THE STANDARD DEVIATION

In a certain high school in a certain city, a random sample of 51 sixteen-year-olds had weights distributed as shown in Fig. 15.1. For the sake of illustration, these sixteen-year-olds shall be our population. What we say concerning predictions within this group will hold by analogy to larger, more inclusive populations. The mean of the 51 students' weights is 61.9 kg, and the standard deviation is 13.2. If the

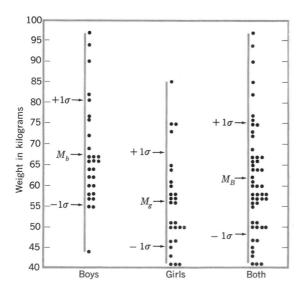

Fig. 15.1. *Distributions of sixteen-year-old high-school boys and girls for weight in kilograms. Each dot represents an individual.*

51 students were now listed in alphabetical order and without seeing them we used merely our knowledge of the mean, we should most nearly predict the actual weights if we wrote after each student's name "61.9 kg." The odds are about 2 to 1, as the interpretation of σ goes, that our errors would be no greater than 13.2 kg either way from the predicted weight. The σ of 13.2 kg may therefore be taken to measure our margin of error in predicting single cases within the sample, when prediction is based only upon knowledge of the mean.

According to the principle of least squares, any other prediction we might make for all the individuals would yield a larger margin of error. We should not be very proud of our accuracy of prediction in this instance, and for practical purposes of making decisions for individuals where their weights are important factors, we should be seriously in error in many cases. But we could do less well in predicting the individuals' weights if we did not even possess the knowledge of their mean. Even if we knew the mean of sixteen-year-olds in general and used that as the predicted value, we should do worse, unless the mean of this small population coincides (by chance) with that of all sixteen-year-olds. In other words, by knowing two attributes of our population – a specified age and being in a certain high school – and the mean weight associated with that attribute, we reduce the error of prediction to some extent.

PREDICTING WEIGHT FROM KNOWLEDGE OF SEX

Of the 51 cases in our population of sixteen-year-olds, 24 were boys and 27 were girls. Will it help to predict more accurately if we know each individual's sex? It should, since there is a sex difference in weights. Although many girls are heavier than many boys, the averages are distinctly different – 67.8 for the boys and 56.6 for the girls. Using the attribute of sex to assist in predicting individual cases and following the principle of least squares, for each boy we should predict his weight to be 67.8 kg, and for each girl, 56.6 kg.

How much will predictions now be improved? The margin of error of predictions for boys is given by the σ of their distribution, which is 12.6 kg, and the margin of error for the girls is given by a σ of 11.3. From this information, we see that both boys' and girls' weights have been predicted more accurately than before (when the margin of error was 13.2) and that the girls' predicted weights are more free from error than are the boys'.

To assess the gain in prediction from knowledge of sex membership, we may ask what the percentage of reduction in error of prediction is. For the boys, the change of .6 in the σ is 4.5 per cent, and for the girls, the change in σ is 1.9, or 14.4 per cent. Thus in predicting weight we gain more accuracy from knowledge that the student is a girl.

THE STANDARD ERROR OF ESTIMATE

There is a way of summarizing the margin of error for all cases combined. It requires the computation of a *standard error of estimate*, which is a kind of summary of all the squared discrepancies of actual measurements from the predicted measurements.[1] In terms of a formula, the standard error of estimate is

$$\sigma_{yx} = \sqrt{\frac{\Sigma(Y - Y')^2}{N}} \qquad \text{(Standard error of estimate)} \qquad (15.1)$$

where Y = measured value of a case we are trying to predict
Y' = predicted value for the case
N = total number of cases predicted

The subscript in σ_{yx} tells us that we are predicting variable Y from variable X. In the illustrative problem, Y is the variable of weight, and X is the variable of sex membership. The sum of the discrepancies squared (see Table 15.1) is 7,288.1, so

$$\sigma^2_{yx} = \frac{7,288.1}{51} = 142.90$$

$$\sigma_{yx} = 11.9$$

The standard error of estimate, in predicting weight on the basis of knowledge of sex, is 11.9. Using only the knowledge that this is a particular group of sixteen-year-olds with a mean of 61.9, the error of estimate was given by a standard deviation of 13.2. The margin of error using the information supplied by sex difference is 90.2 per cent as large as that without using this information. The reduction in size of error of prediction is 9.8 per cent, which is rather small but represents some gain.

In computing the standard error of estimate in this kind of problem, it is probably more natural to do so by finding the σ's of the two part distributions separately and then combining them. They cannot be combined directly by simple addition or averaging. It is the squared deviations in the two groups that must be combined. The sum of the squared deviations in each distribution can be found by the formula[2]

$$\Sigma x^2_a = N_a \sigma^2_a \qquad \text{(Sum of squares of discrepancies within one distribution)} \qquad (15.2)$$

where Σx^2_a = sum of the squared discrepancies between prediction and fact (or between measurements and the mean) in distribution A (one of the attribute distributions)

---

[1] A standard error of estimate is more meaningful and more representative of all errors of prediction when the variances within different distributions are homogeneous, a condition that is known as *homoscedasticity*.
[2] *Cf.* formula (5.7).

N_a = number of cases in distribution A

σ_a = standard deviation of distribution A

When these sums of squared deviations are obtained from all component distributions (distributions A, B, C, etc.), they may be combined by simple addition to give $\Sigma(Y - Y')^2$. In other words,

$$\Sigma(Y - Y')^2 = \Sigma N_k \sigma^2_k \qquad \text{(Sum of squares of discrepancies in all distributions)} \qquad (15.3)$$

where N_k = number of cases in any component distribution (distributions A, B, C, etc., in turn) and σ_k = standard deviation of the same distribution.[1]

The work of computing $\Sigma(Y - Y')^2$ for the problem on weights of sixteen-year-olds may be summarized as in Table 15.1. From here on the computation of σ_{yx} is exactly the same as previously demonstrated.

OTHER PREDICTIVE INDICES MAY BE INTRODUCED

Other attributes may be brought in as aids in prediction. For instance, if different glandular constitution has a definite bearing on body weight (for example, thyroid functioning), we could subdivide each sex group into two or three categories as to glandular condition. The mean of each new subgroup would then become the prediction for members of that group. The deviations of actual weights from these means would be smaller, and the new standard error of estimate would be reduced in size.

If we were successful in singling out all the significant factors correlated with weight and could predict from all of them at the same time, theoretically we could reduce errors of prediction to approximately zero. We can probably never know what all the significant factors are from which weight can be determined, and if we did it

[1] It will be recognized that $\Sigma(Y - Y')^2$ is essentially a sum of squares from which the *within-sets* variance would be estimated in analysis of variance (see Chap. 13).

Table 15.1 **Summary of the combinations of sums of squares from different subsamples**

Distribution	N_k	σ	σ^2	$N_k \sigma^2$
Boys	24	12.65	160.02	3,840.48
Girls	27	11.30	127.69	3,447.63
				7,288.11
				$\Sigma(Y - Y')^2$

might be impossible to assign all the attributes to each individual. We are here speaking of the hypothetical limiting case. Any improvement in predictions approaches that limit. From a practical standpoint, it is always a question of whether the trouble of uncovering and using new descriptive attributes is justified by the gains in predictive accuracy that result.

ESTIMATION OF ERRORS OF PREDICTION IN THE POPULATION

Strictly speaking, the standard error of estimate computed for the weight-prediction problem applies to the sample only. It is a biased estimate of the margin of error that would occur in making predictions beyond this particular sample but in the same population. To estimate the standard error of estimate for the population, we need, as usual, to consider degrees of freedom, unless the sample is large. The formula would be the same as (15.1) with the substitution of $N - m$ for N, where m is the number of categories predicted from:

$$_c\sigma_{yz} = \sqrt{\frac{\Sigma(Y - Y')^2}{N - m}} \quad \text{(Standard error of estimate corrected for bias)} \tag{15.4}$$

Applying this formula instead of formula (15.1), the corrected standard error of estimate is 12.2 rather than 11.9. The corrected value is the more realistic one to use in making predictions outside the sample but within the same population.

Predicting measurements from other measurements

When both known and predicted variables are measured on linear scales and there is some relation between them so that predictions are possible, we have a much more complicated problem. A complete treatment of it involves correlation methods, regression equations, and other procedures.

THE CORRELATION DIAGRAM

Our illustration of this kind of problem consists of two achievement examinations in a course on educational measurements. In Table 15.2, we have the two distributions grouped in class intervals and the measurements in each class interval broken down to form a distribution of its own in the other test. The class intervals for test X are listed along the top of Table 15.2 and the class intervals for test Y are listed along the left margin.

PREDICTION OF Y FROM X

As usual, we have here a double prediction problem: the prediction of a score in Y from a known score in X, and vice versa. Let us consider the prediction of Y from X first. For the individuals in any class

Table 15.2　**Predicting scores in one test from known scores in another test**

Test Y	Test X 60–64	65–69	70–74	75–79	80–84	85–89	90–94	95–99	f_y	M_{row}	σ_{row}
135–139								1	1	97.0	−*
130–134				1	1	0	1		3	83.7	6.61
125–129				1	0	2	1		4	85.8	5.45
120–124			1	4	4	6	2		17	83.2	5.67
115–119			7	5	7	2	1		22	78.6	5.72
110–114	1	4	2	9	4	2			22	75.9	6.56
105–109	1	1	2	5	1				10	74.0	5.56
100–104	1	3	0	1	1				6	70.3	6.87
95– 99		2							2	67.0	0.00
f_x	3	10	12	26	18	12	5	1	87 = N		
M_c	107.0	105.5	114.9	114.5	116.4	120.3	124.0	137.0			
σ_c	4.08	5.52	4.31	6.83	6.43	4.71	5.10	−*			

*The standard deviation of this array is indeterminate.

interval in test X, the best prediction is the mean of the Y distribution in that column, in other words, the mean of the column (M_c). For each column of Table 15.2, its mean is listed in the next to last row. For the first column, M_c is 107.0. Any person receiving a score from 60 to 64 inclusive in test X will probably earn a score of 107.0 in test Y. The other means of the columns are similarly interpreted. It will be noticed that there is a general upward trend in the M_c's as we go up the scale in test X, though there are two small inversions. In view of the small numbers of cases upon which these means are based, some inversions are not surprising.

The margin of error in predicting Y from X in each column is indicated by the standard deviation of that column. The σ_c's are listed in the last row of Table 15.2. They remain fairly constant, but the range is from 4.08 to 6.83. The significance of the variations in σ_c could be examined by making F tests (see Chap. 9).

The entire picture of predictions and their margins of errors within columns is shown graphically in Fig. 15.2. The dots indicate the positions of the column means, and the vertical lines running through them extend from $-1\sigma_c$ to $+1\sigma_c$. In each column, we expect two-thirds of the observed scores to lie within the limits of these lines.

STANDARD ERROR OF ESTIMATE

In order to obtain a single indicator of the goodness of the prediction of Y scores from X scores, we may compute a standard error of estimate as we did before when predicting measurements from attri-

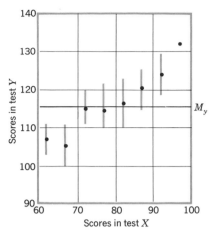

Fig. 15.2. *A chart showing the most probable score on test Y corresponding to each midpoint score on test X, also the range between plus and minus one standard deviation within each column.*

butes. The work is best organized as in Table 15.3. For every column, we list first N_c, the number of cases in that column. Second, we list σ^2_c, the squared σ of the distribution in that column. Next we find the product of these two values for that column. The sum of these products for all columns yields $\Sigma (Y - Y')^2$, which we need for computing σ_{yx}. This sum is 2,930.97. From here on the work follows formula (15.1).

$$\sigma^2_{yx} = \frac{2,930.97}{87} = 33.6893$$

$$\sigma_{yx} = 5.80$$

The σ of the entire distribution of Y scores is 7.85, so that there is a reduction in variability of 2.05, or 26.1 per cent, a marked improvement in prediction, as such tests go. We may say that the forecasting efficiency for predicting Y scores from X scores as we did is approximately 26 per cent.

PREDICTING X FROM Y

The predictions of X from Y are listed in Table 15.2 under M_{row} in the next to the last column. The most probable X score for any interval of Y scores is the mean of the row. The margin of error of the predictions is given in each case by σ_{row}, and these appear in the last column of Table 15.2. To complete the picture of these predictions and their σ's, Fig. 15.3 is presented. The standard error of estimate of the X scores, σ_{xy} (note the order of x and y in the subscript), is equal to 5.93. Since the total σ of the X scores is 7.60, the reduction in error of prediction is 1.67, which is 22.0 per cent. The forecasting efficiency in predicting X from Y in this problem is a bit lower than the forecasting efficiency (26.1 per cent) in predicting Y from X.[1]

[1]The σ's of the arrays were computed here without applying Sheppard's correction (see Chap. 5). Had this correction been used, the σ's would have been smaller and consequently σ_{yx} and σ_{xy} would have been smaller.

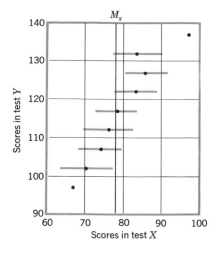

Fig. 15.3. *A chart showing the most probable score on test X for each midpoint score on test Y, also the range between plus and minus one standard deviation within each row.*

The procedure for predictions by using means of columns and rows is not used very much in practice. It was presented here because of the principles it illustrates, principles that underlie the regression methods to be described next. The reader will find that the main principle for making predictions of measurements still holds—the principle of least squares. He will also find that the principles for testing accuracy of prediction—the standard error of estimate and the percentage of reduction of errors—also still apply. New ways of estimating them will be shown and their relation to the coefficient of correlation will be explained. In addition, new ways of interpreting the usefulness of predictions will be demonstrated.

Table 15.3 **Computations of the standard error of estimate of Y scores from X scores**

N_c	σ^2_c	$N_c\sigma^2_c$
3	16.67	50.01
10	30.45	304.50
12	18.58	222.96
26	46.63	1,212.38
18	41.36	744.48
12	22.22	266.64
5	26.00	130.00
		2,930.97
		$\Sigma(Y-Y')^2$

Regression equations

THE MEANING OF A REGRESSION EQUATION

The main use of a regression equation is to predict the most likely measurement in one variable from the known measurement in another. If the correlation between Y and X were perfect (with a coefficient of $+1.00$ or -1.00), we could make predictions of Y from X or of X from Y with complete accuracy; the errors of prediction would be zero. If the correlation were zero, predictions would be futile. Between these two limits, predictions are possible with varying degrees of accuracy. The higher the correlation, the greater is the accuracy of prediction and the smaller the errors of prediction.

When we use the means of columns of a scatter diagram as the most probable corresponding Y values, we are actually predicting Y's only from the midpoints of intervals on X, or, stated in another way, we are predicting the same Y value for a certain range of values on X. If we desire to be more accurate than that, we have to be able to make predictions for *all* values of X. This the regression line and the regression equation enable us to do.

We found (see Figs. 15.2 and 15.3) that the means of the columns (and of the rows) tended to lie along a straight line, with some minor deviations from strict linearity. We shall now assume that the best predictions of Y from X lie along a line that best fits the means of the columns when those means are weighted according to the number of cases represented in each one. This is known as the *line of best fit*, or the *regression line*. When predicting X from Y, we have another such line for the regression of X on Y. The two regression lines for the achievement-test data are pictured in Fig. 15.4. Only when a correlation is perfect will the two lines coincide throughout their lengths. The higher the correlation, plus or minus, the closer together they lie. All such pairs of regression lines intersect at the point representing the means of Y and X; in this case, they cross at $X = 78.15$ and $Y = 115.28$.

THE REGRESSION EQUATIONS AND REGRESSION COEFFICIENTS

From elementary algebra, the student should remember that the equation for a straight line, in general form, is $Y = a + bX$. Such an equation completely describes a line when a and b are known; they are the *regression coefficients* and must be obtained from the data we have. Leaving out of account for the moment the coefficient a, we should have $Y = bX$, or Y equals b times X. We see from this that b is a ratio; *it tells us how many units Y increases for every increase of one unit in X*. If b were 2, then for every unit of increase in X, Y increases two units. If $b = 0.5$, then for every unit increase in X, Y in-

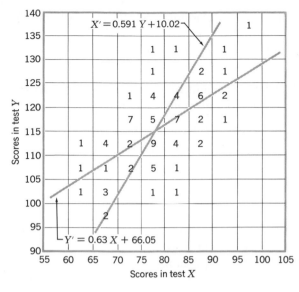

Fig. 15.4. *A scatter diagram for two examinations, with two regression lines represented and their equations.*

creases a half unit. The *b* coefficient gives us the *slope* of the regression line, and it depends upon the coefficient of correlation and the two standard deviations, as in the formula

$$b_{yx} = r_{yx}\left(\frac{\sigma_y}{\sigma_x}\right) \quad \text{(Coefficient for linear regression of } Y \text{ on } X) \quad (15.5)$$

where b_{yx}, with the subscripts in that order, implies that we are predicting Y from X.[1]

When we want to predict X from Y, we have a different regression equation with a different b, which is given by the formula

$$b_{xy} = r_{xy}\left(\frac{\sigma_x}{\sigma_y}\right) \quad \text{(Coefficient for linear regression of } X \text{ on } Y) \quad (15.6)$$

The coefficient of correlation is, of course, numerically the same in both cases, since $r_{yx} = r_{xy}$. But in each case, the b's are different and are equal to r times the ratio of the standard deviation of the *predicted* variable to that of the variable *predicted from*. We frequently speak of the predicted variable as the *dependent* variable and of the one predicted from as the *independent* variable. The reason for this is that, in predicting Y from X, we arbitrarily take any value of X that we wish at the moment, whereas the Y we predict from it *is* dependent upon what X we have chosen. Once we have selected a certain X, Y is immediately fixed by the regression equation.

The regression coefficient a is merely a constant that we must al-

[1]For a derivation of formulas for finding regression coefficients, see Appendix A.

ways add in order to ensure that the mean of the predictions will equal the mean of the obtained values. As b_{yx} determines the *slope* of the line, a_{yx} determines the general *level* of the line. It is given by the formulas

$$a_{yx} = M_y - (M_x) b_{yx} \qquad \text{(The } a \text{ coefficient in a linear} \qquad (15.7a)$$
$$a_{xy} = M_x - (M_y) b_{xy} \qquad \text{regression equation)} \qquad (15.7b)$$

where the first one is the equation for the regression of Y on X and the second is the equation for the regression of X on Y.

The derivation of the entire regression equation is more often accomplished by one composite formula, combining the derivations of a and b into one operation as follows:

$$Y' = r \left(\frac{\sigma_y}{\sigma_x}\right) (X - M_x) + M_y \qquad \text{(Complete statement} \qquad (15.8a)$$
of linear regres-
$$X' = r \left(\frac{\sigma_x}{\sigma_y}\right) (Y - M_y) + M_x \qquad \text{sion equations)} \qquad (15.8b)$$

We use Y' and X' here rather than Y and X to show they they are predicted rather than obtained values. Predictions and obtained values rarely coincide unless correlations are nearly perfect.

Applied to the data of Table 15.2, we have

$$Y' = .61 \left(\frac{7.85}{7.60}\right) (X - 78.15) + 115.28$$
$$= (.61) (1.03) (X - 78.15) + 115.28$$
$$= .630X - 49.23 + 115.28$$
$$= .630X + 66.05$$
$$X' = .61 \left(\frac{7.60}{7.85}\right) (Y - 115.28) + 78.15$$
$$= .591Y + 10.02$$

Interpreting these equations, we may say that Y' increases .630 unit for every unit increase in X and that X' increases .591 unit for every unit increase in Y. One way of checking the accuracy of the solution of regression equations is to substitute M_x in the first one to see whether Y' is the mean of the Y's and to substitute M_y in the second to see whether we obtain M_x as the prediction of X.

Another check as to the accuracy of computation of the b coefficients is the equation

$$b_{yx} b_{xy} = r^2 \qquad \text{(Relation of regression coefficients to } r^2) \qquad (15.9)$$

In other words, the product of the two b coefficients is equal to the square of the coefficient of correlation. In this instance

$$(.630) (.591) = .3723 = .61^2$$

THE CONCEPT OF REGRESSION

It may help in understanding the regression equations as given in formulas (15.8*a*) and (15.8*b*) to glance at their historical origin. The idea of regression came first and the correlation method followed. It began with Sir Francis Galton, who was making some studies of heredity suggested by implications of the theories of evolution put forth by his even more illustrious cousin, Charles Darwin.

When Galton studied the relation of heights of offspring to the heights of their parents, he began by preparing a scatter diagram, perhaps the first. In order to put parents and their children on a common measuring scale, he converted all heights to standard scores. As the reader already knows, this meant expressing each person's height as a ratio of his deviation from his group mean to the standard deviation of his group dispersion. The unit for the offspring's scale and also for the parents' scale was then 1σ. Figure 15.5 shows the type of figure Galton drew.

Galton next computed the means of offspring's heights (in z scores) corresponding to certain fixed parents' heights (in z scores). As we saw in the example earlier in this chapter when the same operations were performed (but with raw scores), he found that the means of columns fell along a straight-line trend. It struck him as remarkable that the means of offspring's heights did not increase as rapidly as did the parents' heights. Each mean height of offspring deviated less from their general mean than the height of the parents from which they came deviated from their mean. This "falling back" of heights of offspring toward the general mean has been called the *law of filial regression*. It is an illustration of imperfect correlation. Had the correlation between children and parents in height been perfect, the regression would have been as shown by the dotted line in Fig. 15.5. The correlation was actually about +.50, and the obtained regression line was as shown.

ORIGIN OF THE COEFFICIENT OF CORRELATION

Galton wanted a single value which would express the amount of this regression phenomenon in any particular relationship problem. Karl Pearson solved the problem with the formula to which his name is attached. The steps were somewhat as follows. Galton's own idea was to use the slope of the regression line as the index of relationship, because the steeper the slope, the closer the agreement between two variables. The slope of the regression line in Fig. 15.5, as in any coordinate plot, is the ratio of the increase in Y corresponding to a certain increase in X. From the plot we see that as X changes 2σ (from the mean to $+2\sigma$, as shown), Y changes only 1σ. The slope is $\frac{1}{2}$, or .5. This was Galton's coefficient of regression, which received the

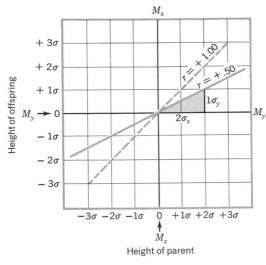

Fig. 15.5. *A diagram showing the relation of the Pearson product-moment coefficient of correlation to the slope of the regression line when scores in both X and Y are in standard-score units.*

symbol r for that reason. That symbol has remained. The Pearson r is the slope of the regression line when both Y and X are measured in standard-deviation units. In this case, it can be shown that

$$r_{yx} = \frac{\Sigma z_y z_x}{N} \qquad \text{(Pearson } r \text{ from standard measures)} \qquad (15.10)$$

In other words, r is an average of all the cross products of standard measures.

DERIVATION OF THE REGRESSION EQUATIONS

Since r is the slope of the regression line when standard measures are used, the equation for this situation is

$$z_{y'} = r_{yx} z_x \qquad \text{(Regression equation with standard measures)} \qquad (15.11)$$

Here we use $z_{y'}$, the prime denoting a predicted value as distinguished from the actual value. From this beginning, let us work toward the regression equations in raw-score form [formulas (15.8a) and (15.8b)]. The next step is to express these standard measures as deviations, y' and x. Since $z_x = x/\sigma_x$ and $z_{y'} = y'/\sigma_y$ (σ_y is the unit of the $z_{y'}$ values as well as of the z_y values), the equation becomes

$$\frac{y'}{\sigma_y} = r_{yx} \frac{x}{\sigma_x} \qquad (15.12)$$

If we multiply this equation through by σ_y, we have

$$y' = r_{yx} \left(\frac{\sigma_y}{\sigma_x} \right) \qquad \begin{array}{l} \text{(Regression equation} \\ \text{with deviation scores)} \end{array} \qquad (15.13a)$$

or

$$y' = b_{yx} x \qquad (15.13b)$$

Equation (15.13b) shows that the same b coefficient applies to deviation scores as that applying to raw scores [see formula (15.8a)]. It also
shows that since the means of x and y are zero, the regression lines
will pass through both of them without having an a coefficient in the
equation.

One more step is needed to arrive at the raw-score type of regression equations. Going back to equation (15.12), if we next convert x
to its equivalent, $X - M_x$, and y' to its equivalent, $Y' - M_y$ (M_y is the
mean of the Y' values as well as of the Y values), we have

$$\frac{Y' - M_y}{\sigma_y} = r_{yx} \left(\frac{X - M_x}{\sigma_x} \right) \tag{15.14}$$

Multiplying through by σ_y, we have

$$Y' - M_y = r_{yx} \left(\frac{\sigma_y}{\sigma_x} \right) (X - M_x)$$

And transposing M_y,

$$Y' = r_{yx} \left(\frac{\sigma_y}{\sigma_x} \right) (X - M_x) + M_y$$

which is identical to formula (15.8a).

REGRESSION COEFFICIENTS FROM UNGROUPED DATA

When data have not been grouped in class intervals, the derivation
of the b coefficient requires another formula, which reads

$$b_{yx} = \frac{N\Sigma XY - (\Sigma X)(\Sigma Y)}{N\Sigma X^2 - (\Sigma X)^2} \qquad \begin{array}{l}\text{(Regression coefficient directly}\\ \text{from data)}\end{array} \tag{15.15}$$

When this formula is applied to the data in Table 6.3, we have

$$b_{yx} = \frac{4{,}720 - 4{,}550}{6{,}240 - 4{,}900} = .127$$

The a coefficient is obtained by means of formula (15.7a) and is solved
as follows:

$$a_{yx} = 6.5 - (7.0)(.127) = 5.61$$

The regression equation is therefore $Y' = 5.61 + .127X$. The equation
for the regression of X on Y can be obtained by similar operations,
substituting Y for X, and vice versa, in formula (15.15). The solution
for the illustrative problem is

$$b_{xy} = \frac{4{,}720 - 4{,}550}{5{,}330 - 4{,}225} = .154$$

$$a_{xy} = 7.0 - (6.5)(.154) = 6.0$$

Checking the b coefficients, $b_{yx}b_{xy} = (.127)(.154) = .0196 = r^2$, which is in agreement with r^2 as previously known (see Table 6.3).

PREDICTIONS FROM REGRESSION EQUATIONS

As an illustration of how a regression equation is applied in prediction, let us assume some values of X and find the corresponding Y' values. Because in the preceding methods of prediction we predicted Y's corresponding to midpoints of the intervals of X, let us do the same here for the sake of comparison, remembering that we might have chosen any values of X that we pleased, within the range of obtained values of X. Table 15.4 gives the X values and their corresponding Y' values. When X is 62, Y' is 105.1, and when $X = 97$, $Y' = 127.2$, etc. It is interesting to compare these particular predictions with the means of the columns, which are given in the third row of Table 15.4. The discrepancies will be found very small as a rule. Granting that the column means are generally not very reliable because of small samples, we may feel more assurance in the Y' predictions because they are determined from the trend of the entire data rather than by small samples in separate columns. The predictions of X' from Y are given in the second section of Table 15.4 and are compared with the means of the rows as a matter of interest.

As a practical means of prediction, a graphic method will often be the most suitable procedure. If the regression lines are drawn as in Fig. 15.4 on cross-section paper, for any value of X on the base line, one can follow vertically up to the regression line and note the corresponding Y value at this point. One can read to the nearest unit with sufficient accuracy for practical work. The drawing of the

Table 15.4 **Predictions of Y from X and X from Y by means of regression equations***

$Y' = 0.630X + 66.05$

If $X =$	62	67	72	77	82	87	92	97
$Y' =$	105.1	108.3	111.4	114.6	117.7	120.9	124.0	127.2
$M_c =$	107.0	105.5	114.9	114.5	116.4	120.3	124.0	132.0

$X' = 0.591Y + 10.02$

If $Y =$	97	102	107	112	117	122	127	132	137
$X' =$	67.3	70.3	73.3	76.2	79.2	82.1	85.1	88.0	91.0
$M_{row} =$	67.0	70.3	74.0	75.9	78.6	83.2	85.8	83.7	97.0

*The data involved are from the two examinations correlated in Table 6.5. The means of the columns and rows are obtained from Table 15.2.

regression line is simple in that two points determine the position of a line. One point can be at the two means, which will serve for both regressions. Another point for the regression of Y on X might be at $X = 60$, $Y = 103.85$; a third point, for checking purposes, might be at $X = 100$ and $Y = 129.05$. For the regression of X on Y, points might be located conveniently at $Y = 100$, $X = 69.12$, and $Y = 130$, $X = 86.85$.

STANDARD ERRORS OF THE ESTIMATES

We previously saw (in Table 15.3) that the errors of prediction $(Y - Y'$ in the one case and $X - X'$ in the other) can be squared, summed, averaged, and then the square root extracted in order to obtain the standard error of the discrepancies between observed values and predicted values. There we computed the standard error of the estimate from the discrepancies themselves; here we shall see that it is not necessary to compute the errors of prediction.

When we have predicted on the basis of regression equations, we can estimate the margin of error of prediction, as given by σ_{yx} (or by σ_{xy}) from the coefficient of correlation. The formulas are

$$\sigma_{yx} = \sigma_y \sqrt{1 - r^2_{yx}} \qquad \text{(Standard error of estimate} \qquad (15.16a)$$

$$\sigma_{xy} = \sigma_x \sqrt{1 - r^2_{xy}} \qquad \text{computed from } r) \qquad (15.16b)$$

It will be seen that the two equations are the same except for the use of σ_y when we are predicting Y and of σ_x when we are predicting X (for $r_{yx} = r_{xy}$). The two standard deviations are multiplied by the common factor $\sqrt{1 - r^2}$. This factor is always less than 1.00 and *gives us an estimate of the reduction in errors of prediction from knowledge of correlated measurements as compared to errors of prediction without that knowledge.* When r is zero, this factor equals 1.00, and then $\sigma_{yx} = \sigma_y$ and $\sigma_{xy} = \sigma_x$. In other words, when $r = 0$, there is no basis for prediction. When $r = 1.0$ (or -1.0), the factor reduces to zero, and so does the standard error of estimate. This coincides with the expectation that the margin of error of prediction is zero when the correlation is perfect.

Interpretation of an obtained standard error of estimate. The interpretation of the standard error of estimate when r is neither zero nor 1.00 is somewhat as follows. Like any standard deviation, σ_{yx} can be referred to the normal curve of distribution, if the column and row distributions appear to approach the normal form. For the examination problem,

$$\sigma_{yx} = 7.85 \sqrt{1 - .3721} = 6.22$$

$$\sigma_{xy} = 7.60 \sqrt{1 - .3721} = 6.02$$

Unless there are obvious inequalities of variances within columns or rows, no matter in what part of the measuring scale we are predicting (within the range of obtained scores, naturally), we assume that the margin of error is the same. When we predict Y from X, the average dispersion of observed measurements about Y' is given by a σ of 6.22. We expect two-thirds of the observed cases to lie within the limits of plus and minus 6.22 from Y'. This situation is illustrated graphically in Fig. 15.6. There we have the regression line, along which the predicted Y's lie, and the dashed lines represent the limits of one σ_{yx} to either side of it. Had we plotted a point for every individual, we should have expected about two-thirds of them to fall between the two dashed lines. To make a particular prediction, when $X = 90$, $Y' = 122.8$. The odds are 2 to 1 that any individual whose X score is 90 will not fall below 116.6 or go above 129.0, these scores being one σ_{yx} below and above the predicted Y, respectively. We could state other odds for a divergence of two σ_{yx} either way or any other distance. It all depends upon our purposes.

We could prepare a similar diagram showing the limits of the middle two-thirds of the individuals about the line of regression of X on Y, and we could interpret the errors of prediction in a similar manner. It will be noted that the margin of error as given by σ_{xy} is 6.02, or 0.2 smaller in predicting in the other direction, i.e., X from Y, but this is merely because σ_x is smaller than σ_y. The *percentage of error is the same in the two cases.* The ratio of σ_{yx} to σ_y is exactly the same as the ratio of σ_{xy} to σ_x, and that ratio is given by the factor $\sqrt{1 - r^2}$. This factor we shall meet again with a name attached to it [see formula (15.21)].

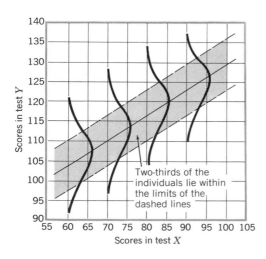

Fig. 15.6. *The line of regression of Y on X, showing the range of observed values expected in Y in separate categories of score values on X. Parallel dashed lines above and below the regression line at the vertical distance of one standard error of the estimate each way mark off the region within which we expect two-thirds of the observed values to be.*

THE REGRESSION LINE AS A MEAN

One way of looking at the regression line is to regard it as a moving average, a moving arithmetic mean. Like the arithmetic mean of any sample, the regression line satisfies the principle of least squares. The regression coefficients are so determined by the data that the sum of the squares of the deviations of observed points from the line is a minimum. Other lines might describe the trend of relationship nearly as well, but only the one line satisfies the principle of least squares. It is reasonable that, if the line is a mean, the deviations from it should be measured by a standard deviation. That standard deviation is the standard error of estimate.[1]

CORRECTION OF A STANDARD ERROR OF ESTIMATE FOR BIAS

In smaller samples (N less than 50) it would be well to make a correction in σ_{yx} (or σ_{xy}) before applying it to the population. The change can be made by the formula

$$_c\sigma_{yx} = \sigma_{yx} \sqrt{\frac{N}{N-2}} \qquad \text{(Correcting } \sigma_{yx} \text{ for bias)} \qquad (15.17)$$

where N is the number in the sample. The correcting can be done as well in the original computation, as follows:

$$_c\sigma_{yx} = \sigma_y \sqrt{(1 - r^2_{yx})\left(\frac{N}{N-2}\right)} \qquad (15.18)$$

THE ACCURACY OF A REGRESSION COEFFICIENT

Like all statistics, the b coefficient in the regression equation has its sampling error. Its standard error is estimated by

$$\sigma_{b_{yx}} = \frac{\sigma_{yx}}{\sigma_x \sqrt{N}} \qquad \text{(Standard error of a regression coefficient)} \qquad (15.19)$$

or by

$$\sigma_{b_{yx}} = \frac{\sigma_y}{\sigma_x} \sqrt{\frac{1 - r^2}{N}} \qquad \text{(Standard error of a regression coefficient)} \qquad (15.20)$$

The $\sigma_{b_{xy}}$ would be the same, except for changing the x and y subscripts around. For our examination problem

$$\sigma_{b_{yx}} = \frac{6.22}{(7.60)\,(9.3274)} = .088$$

---

[1] For an excellent discussion of regression effects in research problems see Thorndike, R. L. Regression fallacies in the matched group experiment. *Psychometrika*, 1942, **7**, 85–102.

We may say that the odds are 2 to 1 that the obtained b_{yx} of .63 does not deviate from the population b_{yx} by more than .088. There is very little chance that the true b coefficient here is zero.

The correlation coefficient and accuracy of prediction

The chief index of goodness of prediction of measurements thus far in this discussion has been the standard error of estimate. It has been shown how the latter is closely related to the coefficient of correlation. As r increases, the standard error of estimate decreases. There are other ways in which r and some of its derivatives can be used to indicate accuracy of prediction. Three of the common derivatives are the *coefficient of alienation*, the *index of forecasting efficiency*, and the *coefficient of determination*. Each has its unique story to tell about the closeness of correlation between two things and about the utility of predictions.

THE COEFFICIENT OF ALIENATION

Whereas r indicates the strength of relationship, the *coefficient of alienation*, k, indicates the degree of *lack* of relationship. By formula,

$$k = \sqrt{1 - r^2} \qquad \text{(Coefficient of alienation computed from } r) \qquad (15.21)$$

Squaring both sides of this equation, we have

$$k^2 = 1 - r^2$$

And transposing, we have

$$k^2 + r^2 = 1.00$$

Thus, although we might have expected k plus r to equal 1.00, it is rather the sum of their squares that equals 1.00. If r is .50, k is *not* also .50 but .886. When r is .50, then, the degree of relationship is less than the degree of *lack* of relationship. It is when $r = .7071$ that relationship and lack of relationship are equal, for k also then equals .7071. Then $r^2 + k^2 = .50 + .50 = 1.00$. Other values of k for different sizes of r can be found in Table 15.5. Figure 15.7 shows pictorially the functional relationship between k and r. Students of mathematics will recognize the relationship $r^2 + k^2 = 1.00$ as the equation for a circle with a radius of 1.00. The diagram shows only positive values of r and k.[1]

Sometimes we wish to stress the independence of two variables

[1]The relation of k to r is the same as that of the sine of an angle to the cosine of that angle. Values of k corresponding to known values of r can be found by using Table J in Appendix B.

Table 15.5   **Indicators of the importance of coefficients of correlation**

r_{xy}	k_{xy} Coefficient of alienation	$100(1 - k_{zy})$ Percentage reduction in errors of prediction of Y from X	$100\,r^2_{xy}$ Percentage of variance accounted for
.00	1.000	0.0	0.00
.05	.999	.1	0.00
.10	.995	.5	1.00
.15	.989	1.1	2.25
.20	.980	2.0	4.00
.25	.968	3.2	6.25
.30	.954	4.6	9.00
.35	.937	6.3	12.25
.40	.917	8.3	16.00
.45	.893	10.7	20.25
.50	.866	13.4	25.00
.55	.835	16.5	30.25
.60	.800	20.0	36.00
.65	.760	24.0	42.25
.70	.714	28.6	49.00
.75	.661	33.9	56.25
.80	.600	40.0	64.00
.85	.527	47.3	72.25
.90	.436	56.4	81.00
.95	.312	68.8	90.25
.98	.199	80.1	96.00
.99	.141	85.9	98.00
.995	.100	90.0	99.00
.999	.045	95.5	99.80

rather than their dependence. In such instances, we present k as well as r. Besides being related to r, k is also related to other indices of goodness of prediction to be mentioned next.

THE INDEX OF FORECASTING EFFICIENCY

In the formula for the SE of the estimate, $\sigma_{yx} = \sigma_y \sqrt{1 - r^2_{yx}}$, we can see that the factor with the radical, $\sqrt{1 - r^2_{yx}}$, is really the coefficient of alienation. We could rewrite the formula as $\sigma_{yx} = \sigma_y k_{yx}$. If we

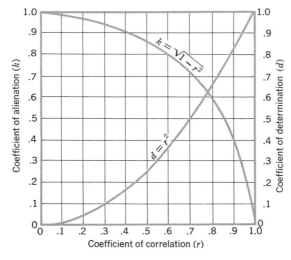

Fig. 15.7. *Chart showing k (coefficient of alienation) and d (coefficient of determination) as functions of r (coefficient of correlation).*

were to multiply k by 100, we should have the percentage σ_{yx} is of σ_y. When $r = .61$, as in our recent illustration, $k = .7924$. The SE of the estimate in this problem is 79.24 per cent of the observed dispersion of observations. Our margin of error in predicting Y *with* knowledge of X scores is about 79 per cent as great as the margin of error we should make *without* knowledge of X scores. For then we predict every Y to be the mean of the Y's, and the SE of the prediction then equals σ_y. The *reduction* of margin of error is 100 minus 79.24, or 20.76 per cent. The *index of forecasting efficiency* is defined as the percentage reduction in errors of prediction by reason of correlation between two variables. The general, simplified formula is

$$E = 100(1 - \sqrt{1 - r^2}) \quad \text{(Index of forecasting efficiency)} \quad (15.22)$$

or

$$E = 100(1 - k)$$

The calculation of E is facilitated by Table 15.5, where many of the E values are given for corresponding r's. Inspection will show that r must be as high as about .45 before E is 10 per cent. When a test has a validity coefficient of .45, the size of errors of prediction, on the whole, is only 10 per cent less than that we should have without knowledge of test scores but with knowledge of the mean criterion measure. Taken at its face value, this does not seem much of a gain. There are situations, however, in which, as will be shown later, an even smaller gain might be of practical importance.

Better tests, with validity coefficients of .60, have an E of 20 per cent, and still better tests, when $r = .75$, have an E of about 34 per cent. Although these efficiencies may also seem small, we must treat them in a relative, not an absolute, sense. It is probable that the efficiency of predictions based upon the average unsystematic interview is less than 5 per cent. With this as a base, the efficiency of tests looks much better.

Figure 15.8 shows graphically the functional relationship between E and r. The range of r's from .3 to .8 is marked off as representing the level of validity coefficients usually found for useful predictive instruments in psychological and educational practices. Tests rarely show correlations greater than .8 with practical criteria, and those correlating less than .3 are usually of very limited value when used alone. In a battery to which they make a *unique* contribution it may still be worth while to use them. The corresponding limits on the scale of E are 4.6 and 40.

THE COEFFICIENT OF DETERMINATION

Another mode of interpretation of r is in terms of r^2, which is called the *coefficient of determination*. This statistic is also sometimes symbolized as d. When multiplied by 100 the coefficient r^2 gives us the percentage of the *variance* (see Chap. 5) in Y that is associated with, determined by, or accounted for by variance in X. When $r = .50$, the percentage of the variance in Y that is accounted for by variance in X is 25, or one-fourth. To account for half the variance of any set of measurements, the r with another variable would have to be .7071. The proportion of the variance in Y *not* determined by or associated with variance in X is given by k^2, which is called the *coefficient of nondetermination*. These statements about determination of Y by X are reversible and apply equally well to determination of X by Y, when the regression is linear. We should speak of *determination* of one thing by another, however, only when a causal relationship can

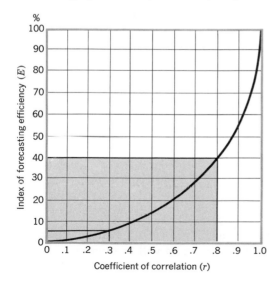

Fig. 15.8. E *(index of forecasting efficiency) as a function of r.*

be logically defended; otherwise the expression *associated with* or *accounted for* (by way of prediction) is better. In Table 15.5, several of the $100r^2$ values are given for corresponding r's. Figure 15.7 presents graphically the functional relationship between d and r.

Predicted and nonpredicted variances. The coefficient of determination, as well as its relations to r, k, and other statistics, can best be clarified by introducing another new idea. The total amount of variance in the predicted variable, Y, is denoted by σ^2_y. We can think of this variance as composed of two independent factors, the predicted and the nonpredicted portions. The predictions of Y, which we have called Y', have their dispersion and their variance which are denoted by $\sigma_{y'}$ and $\sigma^2_{y'}$, respectively. The standard deviation $\sigma_{y'}$ would be computed from the deviations of the predicted values about the mean of the Y values, M_y. The amount of nonpredicted variance is indicated by the square of the standard error of estimate, σ^2_{yx}. This statistic is computed from the deviations of the obtained Y values from the regression line (or from the predicted Y values). The two component variances of σ^2_y are therefore

$$\sigma^2_y = \sigma^2_{y'} + \sigma^2_{yx} \qquad \text{(Component variances in the predicted variable)} \qquad (15.23)$$

If we divide this equation through by σ^2_y, we have everything in terms of proportions:

$$\frac{\sigma^2_y}{\sigma^2_y} = \frac{\sigma^2_{y'}}{\sigma^2_y} + \frac{\sigma^2_{yx}}{\sigma^2_y} = 1.0 \qquad \text{(Total variance as the sum of two proportions)} \qquad (15.24)$$

The first term on the right, $\sigma^2_{y'}/\sigma^2_y$, is the proportion of the variance in Y that is predicted and the second term is the proportion of the variance that is not predicted. We have already defined r^2 as the proportion of predicted variance and k^2 as the proportion of non-predicted variance. This means that r^2 equals $\sigma^2_{y'}/\sigma^2_y$ and that k^2 equals σ^2_{yx}/σ^2_y, and that $r = \sigma_{y'}/\sigma_y$ and $k = \sigma_{yx}/\sigma_y$. We therefore have some new concepts of r and k. We can say that r is the ratio of the dispersion of predicted values to the dispersion of obtained values and that k is the ratio of the dispersion of errors to the dispersion of obtained values.

Prediction of attributes from measurements

We sometimes wish to decide, on the basis of known measurements, whether an individual should be expected to be in one category rather than another because he has one attribute rather than another. He will be happily married after 10 years or he will be divorced; he will vote for a Republican candidate or a Democratic candidate; he will develop a psychosis or he will not; he will commit a crime or he will not; and if he is on parole, he will succeed in keeping out of crime or he will fail. Sometimes it is a matter of placing individuals in different categories in order to help to bring about improved adjustment or success. We shall consider here the use of a single continuously measured variable as the predictor or independent variable and class membership as the criterion or dependent variable. We shall note two ways in which the predictions may be made, how the goodness of prediction may be evaluated, and some of the special problems encountered in this kind of prediction.

A SOLUTION BY LINEAR REGRESSION

One approach to the prediction of membership in two categories is to take a cue from the use of regression equations, as we have seen in the prediction of continuous variables. In this case, we arbitrarily assign values of 0 and 1 to the two categories and treat this dependent variable as if it were continuous. With the two categories representing a genuine dichotomy, the point-biserial coefficient of correlation applies.

As an example of the prediction of two alternative attributes from measurements, let us use some data on sex differences in strength of handgrip measurements for 417 high-school students, 171 boys and 246 girls. Prediction of sex membership is not a serious practical problem, but it will do for illustrative purposes. For deriving a regression equation, we need certain statistical information, which follows:

	Y *Sex* *membership*		*X* *Handgrip* *scores*
Mean	.410		27.51
Standard **deviation**	.492		10.74
Correlation **coefficient**		.763	

The mean of .410 for sex membership comes from arbitrarily assigning a value of 1 to being a boy and 0 to being a girl, from which the mean is the proportion of boys ($\Sigma X/N = {}^{171}/_{417} = .410$). The standard deviation of the distribution for sex membership is given by the expression $\sqrt{pq}$, where $p = .410$ and $q = 1 - p$.

For the regression equation we need to find two constants, b_{yx} and a_{yx}, using formulas (15.5) and (15.7a):

$$b_{yx} = .763 \left(\frac{.492}{10.74} \right)$$

$$= .035$$

$$a_{yx} = .410 - (.035)(27.51)$$

$$= -.552$$

The regression equation then reads $Y' = .035X - .552$. We could use this equation, substituting selected values of handgrip score to obtain a predicted Y. If Y' exceeds .5 the prediction is a boy; if it is smaller than .5 the prediction is a girl.

A simple operation makes it unnecessary to apply the equation more than once. That is, if we determine what handgrip score point yields a prediction of exactly .5, we know that all scores above that critical value predict boy and all scores below it predict girl. Substituting .5 for Y' in the obtained regression equation and solving for X, which is called X_c,

$$.5 = .035X_c - .552$$

Transposing and changing signs,

$$.035X_c = 1.052$$

and

$$X_c = 30.06$$

From this result we may say that scores of 31 and above predict boy and those of 30 and below predict girl.

Goodness of prediction in categories. Whereas the accuracy of prediction of measurements on a continuous scale is often evaluated in terms of a standard error of estimate, or something related to it, in prediction of cases within categories we are more concerned about misplacements of cases. When an error does occur it is to the extent of a whole point. One procedure, when there are two categories, is to set up a fourfold contingency table, in which the cases with scores above and below the critical score represent one dichotomous variable and the true dichotomy represents the other variable. In the handgrip problem, the predicted categories are scores of 31 and above versus scores of 30 and below. Remembering that the 1–0 distinction applies to boys versus girls, with the boy category positive, the girls who were predicted to be boys on the basis of handgrip scores are known as "false positives" and the boys who were likewise predicted to be girls are known as "false negatives." These two cells of the contingency table represent the "misses" in prediction. For the purpose of setting up such a contingency table we need score distributions for boys and girls separately, either ungrouped or finely grouped, so as to be able to apply the cutoff score accurately. We lack such distribution information here, and so we cannot apply this approach to assessing goodness of prediction in this particular example.

APPLICATION OF THE PRINCIPLE OF EQUAL LIKELIHOOD

Other methods for predicting attributes from measurements have been based on a principle pointed out by Louis Guttman.[1] Where two qualitatively different classes of individuals have different means but overlapping distributions on some continuous scale, there is a point on the scale at which the overlapping distribution curves intersect. At that point, which we shall call X_g, the probability of a case having the one attribute (let us call it attribute A) equals the probability of the case having the other attribute (B), where those having attribute B have a higher mean than those having attribute A. Above X_g, for any value of X, the probability of the case being in category B is greater than .5; below X_g the probability of a case being in category B is less than .5. Predictions of membership in categories A and B should be made accordingly. Figure 15.9 illustrates this principle.

    There are graphic methods for determining the best location of the critical score X_g, but the solution is naturally more accurate when carried out by means of computing formulas.[2] When the prediction is

[1] In *The Prediction of Personal Adjustment*. New York: Social Science Research Council, 1941. Pp. 271*ff*.
[2] See Guilford, J. P., and Michael, W. B. *The Prediction of Categories from Measurements*. Beverly Hills, Calif.: Sheridan Supply Co., 1949.

Fig. 15.9. *Distributions of two hypothetical groups possessing two different attributes, A and B, when measured on the same scale of another variable. For those with scores above X_g, attribute B is more likely; for those with scores below X_g, attribute A is more likely.*

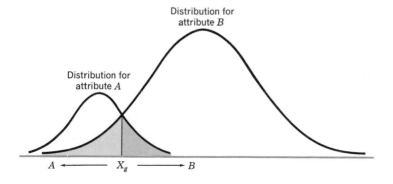

to a genuine dichotomy, the critical score can be computed by

$$X_g = M_x + \left(\frac{.5 - p}{pq}\right)\left(\frac{\sigma^2_x}{M_p - M_q}\right) \quad \begin{array}{l}\text{(Critical value on } X \text{ dividing} \\ \text{cases into more} \\ \text{probable categories)}\end{array} \quad (15.25)$$

where M_x = mean of all X values

$\quad\quad\quad p$ = proportion of the cases in the category having the higher mean of X values

$\quad\quad\quad q = 1 - p$

$\quad\quad\quad M_p$ = mean of X values for category higher on X

$\quad\quad\quad M_q$ = mean of X values for category lower on X

$\quad\quad\quad \sigma^2_x$ = variance in the total distribution of X

Applying formula (15.25) to the handgrip data, we need two additional items of information: $M_p = 37.35$ and $M_q = 20.68$. Then

$$X_g = 27.51 + \left[\frac{.5 - .41}{(.41)(.59)}\right]\left[\frac{115.38}{37.35 - 20.68}\right]$$
$$= 30.09$$

This result, in almost perfect agreement with the earlier one,[1] also tells us to predict that those with handgrip scores of 31 and above are boys and others are girls.

Close examination of formula (15.25) leads to some interesting inferences. First, note that the critical score is the mean of X plus an increment. This increment is positive, and X_g is above M_x when p is less than .5, so that the first expression in the incremental part of the equation is a positive quantity. The increment is negative, and X_g is below the mean, when p exceeds .5. In other words, in making predictions the division of scores is in the same direction as the actual division in the population. When $p = .5$, the increment becomes zero and the critical value equals M_x. This fact is true regardless of the amount of correlation existing between X and the dichotomized variable. When p deviates very far from .5, the ratio becomes quite large and so does the increment. The critical value may even go outside the distribution, which would mean that we would predict all cases to be within the category having the greater frequency. If 90 per cent of a population, let us say, is in the upper category, X_g might go very low on the scale. If we predicted all, or nearly all, the cases to be in the upper category, we should, of course, make a very small number of errors.

It is of interest to consider the relation of the increment to the amount of correlation between X and Y. The type of correlation

[1]The agreement should be very close, for formula (15.25) can be derived by substituting the formula for the point-biserial r in the linear regression equation.

appropriate here is the point biserial. The point-biserial r is directly related to $M_p - M_q$ and inversely related to σ_x. This being true, it appears that the increment is inversely related to the amount of correlation. The higher the correlation, the nearer X_g is to the general mean, M_x. When the correlation is perfect, predictions should be perfect. For predictions to be perfect, the position of X_g should be such that the proportion expected in the upper category coincides with p, the obtained proportion. As the correlation approaches zero, the critical value departs more and more from M_x and ensures the prediction of more and more cases in the more populous category. As r_{pbi} becomes zero, if p does not equal .5, the increment becomes very large and most, if not all, predictions fall in the more populous group. Thus, the prediction is determined relatively more by the knowledge of X when the correlation is large, and relatively more by the knowledge of which category is more populous when the correlation is small, as we should expect.

Prediction in artificial dichotomies. The same principles can be applied when the dichotomy is an arbitrary division of cases on some scale X. For example, the division may represent simply a decision of "pass" or "fail," where achievement is in reality measurable on a continuous variable. For determining a critical score X_h in such a problem, another formula has been derived:[1]

$$X_h = M_x + \left(\frac{zy}{pq}\right)\left(\frac{\sigma^2_x}{M_p - M_q}\right)$$

(Critical division point for maximal separation into two categories in a correlated variable)   (15.26)

where M_x = mean of all X values in the two categories combined

p = proportion of total distribution in the category having higher mean score on X

$q = 1 - p$

y = ordinate in the unit normal distribution at the point of division of the area under the curve with p proportion above it

z = standard measure of the point at which the division occurs

It will be noticed that while formula (15.25) resembles that for the point-biserial r [formula (14.10)], formula (15.26) resembles that for the biserial r [formula (14.7)]. The biserial r is the appropriate one to use under the circumstance of an artificial dichotomy, and the same assumption of normal distribution must be satisfied in connection with formula (15.26) as it applies to the biserial r.

[1]Guilford and Michael, *op. cit.*

Prediction of attributes from other attributes

Sometimes both the dependent and independent variables are in the form of category membership, and neither is in the form of continuous measurements. For example, this would be true in predicting marital adjustment from church membership, success on parole from marital status, or living versus committing suicide from membership in one racial group versus another. If both variables are dichotomies, we have a simple, fourfold table of frequencies. There are other contingency tables with more than two categories in one or both variables. We need to consider how predictions should be made and how they should be evaluated.

PREDICTING FOR MAXIMUM PROBABILITY

As an example of prediction of attributes from other attributes, let us consider the data in Table 15.6. There we have the numbers of persons in a "depressed" group who responded by saying "Yes," "?," and "No" to the question, "Would you rate yourself as an impulsive individual?" and also the numbers of a group described as "not depressed." The individuals in these two categories are the highest and lowest quarters of a sample of 1,000 students who were ranked in terms of a provisional score on a personality inventory. Although one can make an assumption of continuity of values on the response scale, all we have is information classifying the individuals into three categories; hence we may treat the responses as attributes. The separation of individuals in extreme quarters on the depression scale produces a definite break in continuity.

Table 15.6 provides us with two prediction problems. We can attempt to predict the verbal response to the question, knowing

Table 15.6 **Distribution of responses to the question, "Would you rate yourself as an impulsive individual?" as given by two extreme groups of students**

Group	Response			
	Yes	*?*	*No*	*Total*
Depressed	72	45	133	250
Not depressed	106	35	109	250
Both	178	80	242	500

whether the person is in the depressed or not-depressed group; or we can attempt to predict the group to which a person belongs, knowing what response he has made. Let us take the prediction of verbal response first.

Considering first the depressed group by itself, we find that the largest number of them respond with "No." Taking each member of the depressed group as he came along, we should predict for him the response "No." If all 250 came up for inspection, we should be correct 133 times out of 250, or 53.2 per cent of the time. For other samples from the same depressed population, we should expect a similar ratio of correct predictions. This illustration sets the pattern for all predictions of attributes from attributes. The prediction always observes the *mode* or most frequent attribute in the segment of the population chosen at the moment. For the not-depressed group, the mode is also at the response "No"; hence that is our prediction also for them, and our percentage of accuracy is 43.6 per cent, not so high as for prediction from depression but higher than if we had predicted either "Yes" or "?" for the not-depressed group. Such predictions follow the *principle of maximum probability*. Both depressed and not-depressed persons in this population are more likely to respond "No" than anything else, and so that is our prediction.

The second prediction problem here is to reverse matters and predict group membership from knowledge of the response. All persons responding "Yes" we should predict to be members of the not-depressed group, since 106 actually are, as compared with 72 who are not. Again the *modal* attribute is our prediction. For those responding "?" the prediction is membership in the depressed group, and so also for those responding "No." Altogether, there are 284 correct predictions, or 56.8 per cent. Without knowledge of which response each person made to the question, but with knowledge that half the total population are depressed and half are not, the expected number of chance successes is 250. Our predictions *with* knowledge of responses yield an excess of 34 or a *forecasting efficiency* of 13.6 per cent. We can say that predictions with knowledge of response to the question are 13.6 per cent better than those made without this knowledge would be, since 34 is 13.6 per cent of 250.

PREDICTION NOT EQUALLY GOOD IN THE TWO DIRECTIONS

It is now apparent that we can successfully predict group membership from knowledge of responses in this problem, whereas we cannot successfully predict response from knowledge of group membership. It is not always true, as it is here, that successful prediction is possible in one direction and *entirely* impossible in the other, but it is quite common that prediction is better in one direction than in the other when two variables are concerned, It will often clarify thinking about predictive problems to keep this fact in mind. This is a more serious matter in dealing with attributes than in dealing with measurements, for in the latter case, with linear regressions, the predictability of one measured trait A from a measured trait B is essentially as good as predictability of B from A.

CORRELATION INDICES AND THE PREDICTION OF ATTRIBUTES

Counting false positives and false negatives and estimating the forecasting efficiency in terms of percentage of gain from predictions provide approximations regarding the goodness of prediction, but we may also use correlation indices to provide another kind of information. The natural correlation coefficients to use would be the phi coefficient in the case of 2×2 contingency tables and the contingency coefficient, C, where the number of categories is greater. These coefficients were described in Chap. 14 and their relationships to chi square were mentioned.

A chi-square test would tell us whether or not there is any significant departure at all anywhere in the contingency table, but would not tell us where it is, unless we break down the table by rows or columns, or both, and compute chi squares for them separately or in any combination that seems meaningful. Since possibilities for predictions and goodness of prediction often vary for different directions and different sections of a contingency table, such statistical tests by sections are desirable.

The phi coefficient can also be used to determine the predictive value of different sections of a contingency table. For example, in the data of Table 15.6, we can test the predictive value for each response separately, "Yes," "?," and "No." When checking on the predictive value of response "Yes," we can combine the other two columns to form a "not-yes" category. The same may be done for each of the other two response categories. The phi's for the three responses prove to be .142, .055, and .095, respectively, corresponding to chi squares of 10.08, 1.49, and 4.61, respectively. From these results we may conclude that the correlation for response "Yes" is significant at the .01 level, that for response "No" is significant at the .05 level, and that for response "?" is insignificant. We could also conclude that the combination of "?" and "No" responses is significantly predictive, since it shares the correlation of .142 with the "Yes" response category. This information would be a basis for combining the "?" responses with the "No" responses in keying the question for assessment of depression.

Data 15A   **A scatter diagram for two mental tests**

Y (Opposites test in Army Alpha)	X (Mixed Sentences test in Army Alpha)								f_y
	0–2	3–5	6–8	9–11	12–14	15–17	18–20	21–23	
36–38								1	1
33–35							1	2	3
30–32				1	1	3	7	2	14
27–29						4	5	2	11
24–26			1	3	3	2	4	4	17
21–23			1		6	1	5	2	15
18–20		1	2	1	9	5	4		22
15–17	2	1	2	2	2	2	1		12
12–14	1	2	0	2	2	1			8
9–11	3	1	2	1	2				9
6– 8				1					1
f_x	6	5	8	11	25	18	27	13	113

EXERCISES

1. *a.* What is the most probable score for the passing and failing students represented in Table. 14.4?
b. What is the accuracy of prediction for each category?
c. How much improvement is there from knowledge of category?

2. For Data 15A:
a. Find the best prediction of score in the Opposites test corresponding to each midpoint score in the Mixed Sentences test.
b. Estimate the margin of error for each prediction and
c. For the predictions taken as a whole.

3. For the information in Data 15A, the following statistics have been computed: $M_x = 14.19$; $M_y = 21.65$; $\sigma_x = 5.71$; $\sigma_y = 6.73$; $r_{xy} = 6.57$.
a. Find the two regression equations for Data 15A.
b. Make a check for the accuracy of your b coefficients.

4. Using the appropriate regression equation:
a. Make a prediction of score in the Opposites test corresponding to each midpoint score in the Mixed Sentences test.
b. Compare these predictions with those obtained in Exercise 2.

5. *a.* Compute the two standard errors of estimate for Data 15A.
b. What are the *amounts* of predicted and nonpredicted variance in y?
c. What are the *proportions* of these two kinds of variance?

6. *a.* Draw a diagram like Fig. 15.4, showing the two regression lines.
b. Draw a diagram like Fig. 15.6, showing the limits set by the standard error of estimate σ_{yx}.

7. Derive the statistics k, E, and r^2 for Data 15A. Interpret these findings.

8. Using formula (15.15), compute a regression equation for the first 10 pairs of scores for parts V and VI in Data 6A.

9. For the data represented in Fig. 15.1, adopt the problem of predicting sex membership from known body weight. The predictor variable, X, is weight and the predicted variable, Y, is sex membership. The problem is to find a critical division point on X, called X_c, that will make the best discrimination of cases in the two sex categories. Solve the problem in two ways:
a. By means of the regression-equation approach, for which the following information is needed: $r_{pbi} = .424$; $M_x = 61.9$; $M_y = .4706$; $\sigma_x = 13.2$; $\sigma_y = .4991$, and
b. By use of formula (15.25), for which the following additional information is needed: $p = .4706$; $M_p = 67.8$; $M_q = 56.6$.

10. Using a critical score point of 63.7, estimate from Fig. 15.1 the frequencies of boys and girls above and below that point. Form a 2×2 contingency table.
a. From the table, report the numbers of false positives and false negatives.
b. Report the percentage of correct predictions and the phi coefficient.

11. In Data 15B, make predictions of whether a student will report "Yes," "?," or "No" to the question about talking in his sleep when he makes each of the same responses to the question about walking in his sleep.
a. What is the percentage of correct predictions for each of the predictor categories, and the overall percentage?
b. What is the percentage of correct predictions that could be made without knowledge of response to the question about talking? What is the percentage of gain in prediction *with* knowledge of category over that *without* knowledge?

		Walking in sleep			
		No	?	Yes	Total
Talking in sleep	Yes	400	9	88	497
	?	194	21	3	218
	No	1,069	3	7	1,079
	Total	1,663	33	98	1,794

Data 15B **Relationship between walking in one's sleep and talking in one's sleep as reported by 1,794 students**

c. Can you predict response to the question about walking in one's sleep from knowledge of response to the question about talking in one's sleep? Explain.

12. *a.* Compute a chi square for the 3×3 contingency table in Data 15B, and state the number of degrees of freedom involved. Compute the coefficient of contingency, C.

b. Combine the "Yes" and "?" categories for the variable of walking in sleep and compute a chi square and state its number of df. Compute C from this chi square.

ANSWERS

1. *a.* Means: 98.3; 83.6. SD's: 16.27; 16.19.
   b. Gains: for passing group, 8.0 per cent; for failing group, 8.4 per cent; for both combined ($\sigma_y = 17.68$ and $\sigma_{yx} = 16.22$), 8.3 per cent reduction in amount of error.
2. *a.* M_c: 12.5, 14.2, 17.1, 18.2, 19.5, 23.2, 25.7, 28.2.
   b. σ_c: 2.7, 3.1, 5.0, 7.1, 4.7, 5.7, 4.9, 4.6.
   c. $\sigma_{yx} = 5.07$.
3. *a.* $Y' = .774X + 10.67$; $X' = .557Y + 2.13$. *b.* $b_{yx}b_{xy} = .4316 = r^2_{xy}$.
4. *a.* Y': 11.4, 13.8, 16.1, 18.4, 20.7, 23.0, 25.4, 27.7.
5. *a.* $\sigma_{yx} = 5.07$; $\sigma_{xy} = 4.20$. *b.* $\sigma^2_{y'} = 19.55$; $\sigma^2_{yx} = 25.74$. *c.* $r^2_{xy} = .4316$; $k^2 = .5684$.
7. With $r = .657$, $k = .754$; $E = 24.6$; $r^2 = .4316$.
8. $M_5 = 22.9$, $M_6 = 27.7$; $X'_5 = .651X_6 + 4.87$; $X'_6 = .945X_5 + 6.06$; $b_{65}b_{56} = .6154$, $r^2_{56} = .6158$.
9. *a.* Regression equation: $S = .0159X - .5198$ (where S is sex membership); $X_c = 63.7$.
   b. By the equal-likelihood approach, $X_c = 63.7$.
10. *a.* False positives, 6; false negatives, 9.
    b. Percentage of correct predictions, 70.6; $\phi = .41$.
11. *a.* Percentages: 89.8 ($= 100 \times {}^{88}/_{98}$), 63.6 ($= 100 \times {}^{21}/_{33}$), and 64.3 ($= 100 \times {}^{1,069}/_{1,663}$), for predictions from "Yes," "?," and "No," respectively.
    b. Percentages: without knowledge, 60.1 ($= 100 \times {}^{1,079}/_{1,794}$); with knowledge, 65.7 ($= 100 \times {}^{1,178}/_{1,794}$); gain with knowledge, 9.3 ($= 100 \times {}^{5.6}/_{60.1}$).
12. *a.* For the 3×3 table, $\chi^2 = 287.95$, with 4 df; $C = .37$.
    b. For the 3×2 table, $\chi^2 = 178.75$, with 2 df; $C = .30$.

16 Multiple prediction

Multiple correlation

INDEPENDENT AND DEPENDENT VARIABLES

Thus far we have been dealing with correlations between two variables at a time and the prediction of some variable Y from another variable X, or vice versa. Actual relationships between measured variables in psychology and education are by no means so simple as that. One variable is found associated with, or dependent upon, more than one other variable at the same time. When we can think of some variables as being causes of another one, or even when we merely want to predict that one from our knowledge of several others correlated with it, we call the one variable the *dependent* variable and the ones upon which it depends the *independent* variables. The independent variables are so called because we can manipulate them at will or because they vary by the nature of things and, in consequence, we expect the dependent variable to vary accordingly.

Whether or not people like a certain color depends upon several factors: its hue (e.g., yellow, red, or purple, etc.), its brilliance (e.g., light, medium, or dark), and its chroma (saturation or density). The affective value of the color also depends upon its area, its use, and its background. We are here naming independent variables upon which the affective value of a color depends. In so far as each one is a determinant of agreeableness of color, it will exhibit some correlation individually with affective value. The size of any one of these correlations will depend upon the relative strength of that factor and also upon how well the other factors have been neutralized, as they should be in a good experimental situation.

A GRAPHIC PICTURE OF MULTIPLE DEPENDENCE

The idea of dependence of one variable upon two others can be illustrated by Fig. 16.1. That illustration shows how the dependent variable, success in pilot training, is related both to aptitude scores and to chronological age. It requires a three-dimensional figure to show

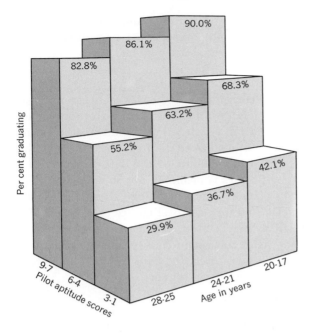

Fig. 16.1. *A multiple regression with percentage graduating from pilot training as a function of both chronological age and aptitude score (the latter variables measured in very broad categories).* (Adapted from an unpublished report of Headquarters, AAF Training Command, Fort Worth, Texas.)

these relationships. The vertical dimension represents the dependent variable. Here it is measured in terms of percentage of graduates — not an ordinary way of measuring, but one, nevertheless, that shows the principles involved. The two independent variables are represented as sides of the base, at right angles to each other. The scale of chronological age is shown reversed for convenience, since the correlation between age and the training criterion was negative. Both independent variables are shown here in very coarse categories for the sake of a simpler diagram.

By noting rows of blocks (left to right) we can see how graduation rate changes with age for a relatively constant level of aptitude. By noting the columns of blocks (front to back) we can see how graduation rate changes with aptitude score for a relatively constant age level. The term *constant* covers an unusual range in this illustration, but with finer grouping on age and aptitude we should expect similar trends. It is obvious that the regressions of the criterion on aptitude are much steeper than those of the criterion on age. The difference would be even more apparent if we had the criterion in terms of a properly graded measurement scale. The correlation between aptitude scores and the criterion was much higher (approximately .55) than that between age and the criterion (approximately −.10). A very rough appreciation of the joint predictive value of aptitude score and age can be seen by noting the change of height from the lowest block (29.9 per cent) to the highest (90.0 per cent). This change may be compared with those changes across columns alone or across rows alone. From this comparison we should expect better prediction from both independent variables than from either alone.

THE COEFFICIENT OF MULTIPLE CORRELATION

The coefficient of multiple correlation indicates the strength of relationship between one variable and two or more others taken together. The multiple correlation is related to the intercorrelations among independent variables as well as to their correlations with the dependent variable. The interdependency of the determinants suggested for affective value of colors is probably not so apparent as in the case of those related to achievement in college algebra. Here we can think of such predictive factors as intelligence-test scores and high-school marks, which, being related, duplicate one another to some extent in predicting achievement in college algebra. Hours of study and interest also are interrelated and thus are not completely independent determinants of success in algebra.

A MULTIPLE-CORRELATION PROBLEM

Table 16.1 presents some data that call for a multiple-correlation solution. Four of the variables (X_2, X_3, X_4, and X_5) are all measures of supposed determinants of academic success in college freshmen. X_1 is the dependent variable — average freshman marks. It is customary to designate the dependent variable by X_1.

An examination of Table 16.1 shows that the analogies test and high-school average mark have the highest correlations with X_1, whereas the interest score X_5 has the lowest. The highest *intercorrelations* are among X_2, X_3, and X_4. All represent abilities of one kind or another, and their correlations with X_5 (interests) are generally lower. This suggests that the interest scores will contribute something to the prediction of college marks that will not have been already contributed by the other variables; therefore it is worthwhile to include X_5 in the battery of predictive indices or predictors.

THE SOLUTION OF A THREE-VARIABLE PROBLEM

We first take the simplest case of multiple correlation, that between the dependent variable and two independent variables. In the general problem given by the data in Table 16.1, we may ask what is the correlation between freshman marks on the one hand and the two variables — analogies-test scores and high-school averages — on the other. The simplest general formula for this case is

$$R^2_{1.23} = \frac{r^2_{12} + r^2_{13} - 2r_{12}r_{13}r_{23}}{1 - r^2_{23}} \qquad \text{(16.1)}$$

(Square of coefficient of multiple correlation with three variables)

Table 16.1   Intercorrelations among five
variables, including one index of scholarship and
four predictive indices (N = 174)*

Variable	X_2	X_3	X_4	X_5	X_1
X_2		.562	.401	.197	.465
X_3	.562		.396	.215	.583
X_4	.401	.396		.345	.546
X_5	.197	.215	.345		.365
X_1	.465	.583	.546	.365	
M_x	19.7	49.5	61.1	29.7	73.8
σ_x	5.2	17.0	19.4	3.7	9.1

X_2 = arithmetic test in the Ohio State Psychological
Examination, Form 10
X_3 = analogies test in the same examination
X_4 = an average grade in high-school work
X_5 = student interest inquiry (measuring breadth of
interest)
X_1 = an average grade for the first semester in university
*These data were abstracted from the *Ohio State Coll. Bull.* 58, by L. D.
Hartson, and have been used in this chapter by permission.

where $R_{1.23}$ = coefficient of multiple correlation between X_1 and a
combination of X_2 and X_3. Notice that this formula gives R^2, the square
root of which is R.

The immediate example calls for finding $R_{1.34}$ rather than $R_{1.23}$. To
use formula (16.1), we need merely to substitute the subscripts 3 and
4 for 2 and 3. The solution is

$$R^2_{1.34} = \frac{(.583)^2 + (.546)^2 - 2(.583)(.546)(.396)}{1 - (.396)^2}$$

$$= \frac{.339889 + .298116 - .252108}{1 - .156816}$$

$$= .45766$$

$$R_{1.34} = .677$$

THE MULTIPLE-REGRESSION EQUATION

A multiple-prediction problem calls for a regression equation that
involves all three variables, in other words, a multiple-regression
equation. From such an equation, we can predict an X_1 value for
every individual. The correlation between these predicted values (X'_1)

and the obtained ones (X_1) will be .677. This is another interpretation of a coefficient of multiple correlation.

For the three-variable problem, the regression equation has the general form $X'_1 = a + b_{12.3}X_2 + b_{13.2}X_3$. As in previous regression equations, the coefficient a is a constant and must be calculated from the data. Its function is to ensure that the mean of the X'_1 values coincides with the mean of the X_1 values. The b coefficients serve the same purpose here as in the simple, two-variable equation. The coefficient $b_{12.3}$ is the multiplying constant, or weight, for the X_2 values, and $b_{13.2}$ is the weight for the X_3 values. The value of $b_{12.3}$ tells how many units X'_1 increases for every unit increase in X_2, when the effects of X_3 have been nullified or held constant. The value of $b_{13.2}$ tells how many units X_1 increases for every unit increase in X_3, with the effects of X_2 held constant.

The particular b weights, as computed by the formulas given below, are the *optimal* weights. They ensure the maximum correlation between predicted and obtained X values. The solution, with the obtained b weights, satisfies the principle of least squares in that the sum of the squares of discrepancies between the X_1 values and the X'_1 values will be a minimum.

Solution of the b coefficients. We do not find the b coefficients directly from the correlations but indirectly through the beta coefficients. Beta coefficients are called *standard partial regression coefficients — standard*, because they would apply if standard measures, $(X - M)/\sigma$, were used in all variables; *partial*, because, as in the case of the coefficient of partial correlation (see Chap. 14), the effects of other variables are held constant. The $b_{12.3}$ and $b_{13.2}$ are known as *partial regression coefficients*, because they, too, are weights that presuppose that other independent variables are held constant. They are given by the formulas

$$b_{12.3} = \left(\frac{\sigma_1}{\sigma_2}\right) \beta_{12.3} \tag{16.2a}$$

(Partial regression coefficients)

$$b_{13.2} = \left(\frac{\sigma_1}{\sigma_3}\right) \beta_{13.2} \tag{16.2b}$$

The betas are found by the formulas[1]

$$\beta_{12.3} = \frac{r_{12} - r_{13}r_{23}}{1 - r^2_{23}} \tag{16.3a}$$

(Standard partial regression coefficients)

$$\beta_{13.2} = \frac{r_{13} - r_{12}r_{23}}{1 - r^2_{23}} \tag{16.3b}$$

Similar equations apply, with change of subscripts, when the independent variables are X_3 and X_4 instead of X_2 and X_3. In our example

[1]The proof for these formulas is much like that for an ordinary regression coefficient (see Appendix A, Proof 10).

$$\beta_{13.4} = \frac{.583 - (.546)(.396)}{1 - (.396)^2} = .435$$

$$\beta_{14.3} = \frac{.546 - (.583)(.396)}{1 - (.396)^2} = .374$$

We can now solve for the b coefficients by means of formulas (16.2a) and (16.2b):

$$b_{13.4} = \frac{9.1}{17.0}\,(.435) = .233$$

$$b_{14.3} = \frac{9.1}{19.4}\,(.374) = .175$$

For the complete regression equation, the a coefficient is still lacking. It is given by the general formula

$$a = M_1 - b_{12.3}M_2 - b_{13.2}M_3 \tag{16.4}$$

Inserting the known values,

$$a = 73.8 - (.233)(49.5) - (.175)(61.1) = 51.58$$

The complete regression equation then reads

$$X'_1 = 51.58 + .233X_3 + .175X_4$$

To interpret the equation, we may say that for every unit increase in X_3, X_1 increases .233 unit and that for every unit increase in X_4, X_1 increases .175 unit. To apply the equation to a particular student whose X_3 score is 25 and whose X_4 score is 32, we predict that his X_1 score will be

$$X'_1 = 51.58 + 5.82 + 5.60 = 63.00$$

We use X'_1 to stand for his predicted average freshman mark, because he has an actual average mark that we call X_1. Some other examples of individual students are presented in Table 16.2 to show how various combinations of values for X_3 and X_4 point to corresponding values of X_1.

MULTIPLE PREDICTIONS BY A GRAPHIC METHOD

A graphic method of making predictions of scores in X_1 from different combinations of scores in X_3 and X_4 is shown in Fig. 16.2. The chart is drawn to apply to the prediction of average freshman grades from scores in the analogies test and high-school average. Diagonal lines are drawn in the figure, each representing locations of the same predicted value. These lines represent X'_1 scores at intervals of 5 units. Note, for example, the line for $X'_1 = 70$. A prediction of 70 may arise from many different combinations of X_3 and X_4. Choose several values, in turn, as possible scores in the analogies test, for example, 10,

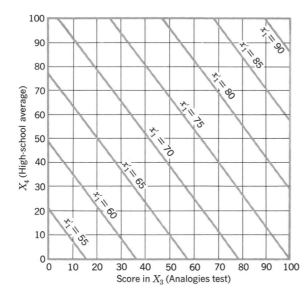

Fig. 16.2. *Diagram showing constant values in the dependent variable for different combinations of values in the two independent variables, each weighted as called for by the multiple-regression equation.*

30, 50 and 70. Corresponding values in high-school average needed to yield predictions of 70 are 92, 65, 38, and 12, respectively. The chief use of the chart, however, is to find X'_1 for two given values in X_3 and X_4. For an X_3 of 20 and an X_4 of 50, the prediction is 65. For an X_3 of 90 and an X_4 of 14, the prediction is 75.

When the prediction is not exactly on one of the diagonal lines, we interpolate, by inspection, between two lines. Thus, for $X_3 = 40$ and $X_4 = 70$, the most probable X_1 is 73. The proportion of the distance between two diagonal lines must be estimated by the perpendicular distance between them. The reader may obtain further practice in using the chart by verifying the predictions found by computation in Table 16.2.

CALCULATING THE MULTIPLE R FROM BETA COEFFICIENTS

If the beta coefficients are known, the shortest route to the multiple R is by way of the equation

$$R^2_{1.23} = \beta_{12.3} r_{12} + \beta_{13.2} r_{13} \tag{16.5}$$

Again, note that this gives R^2, from which the square root must be obtained. For the scholarship data and variables X_3 and X_4,

$$R^2_{1.34} = (.435)(.583) + (.374)(.546)$$
$$= .457809$$
$$R_{1.34} = .677$$

as was found by formula (16.1) previously.

INTERPRETATION OF A MULTIPLE R

Once computed, a multiple R is subject to the same kinds of interpretation, as to size and importance, as were described for a simple r. One kind of interpretation is in terms of R^2, which we call the *coefficient of multiple determination*. This tells us the proportion of variance in X_1 that is dependent upon, associated with, or predicted by X_3 and X_4 combined *with the regression weights used*. In this case, R^2 is .4578, and we can say that 45.78 per cent of the variance in freshman marks is accounted for by whatever is measured by the analogies test and by high-school marks taken together. The remaining percentage of the variance, which is 54.22 $(1 - R^2)$, is still to be accounted for. This remainder is given the symbol K^2 and is known as the *coefficient of multiple nondetermination*. This is consistent with the fact that $R^2 + K^2 = 1.0$, just as $r^2 + k^2 = 1.0$ in the simple correlation problem.

RELATIVE CONTRIBUTION OF INDEPENDENT VARIABLES

Since the coefficient of multiple determination, R^2, is composed of the two components in formula (16.5), and since each component pertains to only one of the independent variables, it seems reasonable to take each component as indicating the contribution of one independent variable to the total predicted variance of X_1. Following this line of reasoning, the first term, .2536 (from the product .435 × .583), would indicate that about 25 per cent of the criterion variance is accounted for by variance in the analogies-test scores and about 20 per cent (from the product .374 × .546) is accounted for by variance in high-school average.

The terms in equation (16.5) stand for both direct and indirect contributions of the two predictors, however. Each predictor makes a unique contribution and also a contribution indirectly through its

Table 16.2   **Some predictions of scholarship mark from measures in two variables**

	Student				
	A	*B*	*C*	*D*	*E*
X_3 **analogies score**	25	27	48	85	87
X_4 **high-school average**	32	61	65	90	52
$b_{13.4}X_3$	5.82	6.29	11.18	19.80	20.27
$b_{14.3}X_4$	5.60	10.68	11.38	15.75	9.10
X'_1 **(predicted mark)**	63.0	68.6	74.1	87.1	81.0

relation to the other predictor. The extents of the direct contributions are indicated by the two betas squared, which are $.435^2 = .1892$ and $.374^2 = .1399$, or approximately 19 and 14 per cent, respectively.[1] The amounts of indirect contribution are indicated by the beta-r products minus the betas squared, that is, $\beta_{13}r_{13} - \beta^2_{13}$ in the one case and $\beta_{14}r_{14} - \beta^2_{14}$ in the other, which give .0644 and .0643, or about 6 per cent indirect contribution in either case. An important limitation to the use of such estimates of components of prediction is that the β-r products must all be positive.

THE STANDARD ERROR OF ESTIMATE FROM MULTIPLE PREDICTIONS

The standard error of estimate is again brought in to indicate about how far the predicted values would deviate from the obtained ones. The formula is the same as previously, except that the multiple R is substituted for r. It reads

$$\sigma_{1.23} = \sigma_1 \sqrt{1 - R^2_{1.23}} \quad \text{(Standard error of multiple estimate)} \quad (16.6)$$

In the illustrative problem,

$$\sigma_{1.34} = 9.1 \sqrt{1 - .457809} = 6.7$$

We can now say that two-thirds of the obtained X_1 values will lie within 6.7 points of the predicted X_1 values. The margin of error *with* knowledge of X_3 and X_4 is 73.6 per cent as great as the margin of error would be without that knowledge. This is true because the radical term reduces to .736. These conclusions presuppose predictions made on the basis of the regression equation that was obtained, and predictions made for individuals belonging to the population and sampled at random.

The index of forecasting efficiency may also be used by way of interpretation and, because of its close relation to the standard error of estimate, may be mentioned at this point. The formula is the same as for a Pearson r [see formula (15.22)]. In the example of our three variables, $E = 26.4$ per cent, which means that predictions by means of the equation are 26.4 per cent better than those made merely from a knowledge of the mean of the X_1 values.

MULTIPLE CORRELATION IN SMALL SAMPLES

For small samples—and for multiple-correlation problems this means anything less than an N of 100—degrees of freedom should be considered in dealing with questions of sampling. If the multiple R and the other statistics derived from it are to be used for estimating pop-

[1]Chace, C. I. Computation of variance accounted for in multiple correlation. *J. exp. Educ.*, 1960, 28, 265–266.

ulation parameters, there is even more bias than for a simple correlation problem.

It was stated earlier that the multiple R represents the maximum
correlation between a dependent variable and a weighted combination of independent variables. The least-squares solution that is
represented in computing the combined weights ensures this result;
but it really ensures too much. It capitalizes upon any chance deviations that favor high multiple correlation. The multiple R is therefore an inflated value. It is a biased estimate of the multiple correlation in the population. If we were to apply the same regression
weights in a new sample and to correlate predicted X_1 values with
obtained X_1 values, we should probably find that the correlation
would be smaller than R.

It is desirable, therefore, to find some means of estimating a parameter $\bar{R}$ which gives a more realistic picture of the general situation. A common way of "shrinking" R to a more probable population
value is by the formula

$$_cR^2 = 1 - (1 - R^2)\left(\frac{N-1}{N-m}\right) \qquad \text{(Correction in } R \text{ for bias)} \qquad (16.7)$$

where N = number of cases in the sample correlated
$\qquad m$ = number of variables correlated
$\qquad N - m$ = number of degrees of freedom, one degree being lost for
$\qquad\qquad$ each mean, there being one mean per variable

For the illustrative problem above, where $R = .677$, the corrected R^2
would be

$$_cR^2 = 1 - (1 - .4579)\left(\frac{174-1}{174-3}\right) = .4515$$

from which $_cR = .672$. The correction does not make much difference
here because the sample was fairly large and the number of variables
small. There are problems in which the change would be very appreciable.

A similar correction is necessary for the standard error of estimate,
unless $_cR$ has been used in formula (16.6). The general formula is

$$_c\sigma_{1.23...m} = \sigma_{1.23...m}\sqrt{\frac{N-1}{N-m}} \qquad \text{(General correction of a}$$
$$\qquad\qquad\qquad\qquad\qquad\qquad\text{multiple standard error of} \qquad (16.8)$$
$$= \sigma_1\sqrt{(1-R^2)\frac{N-1}{N-m}} \qquad \text{estimate for bias)}$$

where the symbols N and m are as defined above. This correction also
makes the greatest difference when N is small and m is relatively
large.

SAMPLING ERRORS IN MULTIPLE-CORRELATION PROBLEMS

For an R derived from a number of variables, the standard error is

$$\sigma_R = \frac{1 - R^2}{\sqrt{N - m}} \qquad \text{(Standard error of a multiple } R) \qquad (16.9)$$

in which $N - m$ represents the number of degrees of freedom. Unless N is very large, and much larger than m, this formula underestimates the amount of sampling error. σ_R is subject to the same limitations as σ_r, and to an even greater extent.

When the null hypothesis is to be tested, Table D (in Appendix B) is most convenient. The R's meeting the 5 per cent and 1 per cent levels of significance are shown in columns headed by numbers of variables and rows headed by appropriate numbers of df. In the illustrative problem, $N = 174$, so the number of degrees of freedom is 171. The standard error of R is .041. The obtained R cannot very well be more than .11 from the population value of R (.11 being about 2.58 times σ_R). From Table D we find that with 150 degrees of freedom (the next lower and nearest to 171) and with three variables, an R of .198 is significant at the 5 per cent level and one of .244 at the 1 per cent level. We should have little room for doubt that a genuine multiple correlation exists in the population.

Standard error of a multiple-regression coefficient. For the beta coefficient the standard error is estimated by the formula

$$\sigma^2_{\beta_{12.34...m}} = \frac{1 - R^2_{1.234...m}}{(1 - R^2_{2.34...m})(N - m)} \qquad \begin{array}{l}\text{(Variance error of a} \\ \text{beta coefficient)}\end{array} \qquad (16.10a)$$

The new symbol here is $R_{2.34...m}$, which is a multiple R with X_2 as the dependent variable and all other variables except X_1 as independent variables. There would be one of these standard errors for each of the independent variables in turn, each being substituted for X_2. For a three-variable problem, the R in the denominator reduces to r_{23}. Note that this formula gives the *variance error*, i.e., σ^2.

For the b coefficient, the standard error is estimated by

$$\sigma_{b_{12.34...m}} = \frac{\sigma_{1.234...m}}{\sigma_{2.34...m}\sqrt{N - m}} \qquad \begin{array}{l}\text{(Standard error of a} \\ b \text{ coefficient)}\end{array} \qquad (16.10b)$$

Needed in the denominator for each independent variable in turn is the standard error of estimate of that variable from all other independent variables. Beyond a three-variable problem this becomes quite laborious, but in the latter the denominator term reduces to σ_{23}. Unlike the preceding formula, this gives the standard error *without* extracting a square root after it is solved.

The chief use of these standard errors is to test the null hypothesis, to determine whether each independent variable has anything at all to contribute to prediction when its relation to other variables is taken into account. If the obtained beta or b is not significantly different from zero, that variable might well be dropped from the regression equation, and a new equation derived.

Significance of a difference between multiple R's. We often want to know whether the multiple R with more independent variables included is significantly greater than the R with a smaller number of variables. There is available an F test for such a difference. The formula for computing F for this purpose reads

$$F = \frac{(R^2_1 - R^2_2)(N - m_1 - 1)}{(1 - R^2_1)(m_1 - m_2)} \tag{16.11}$$

where R_1 = multiple R with larger number of independent variables
$\qquad R_2$ = multiple R with one or more variables omitted
$\qquad m_1$ = larger number of independent variables
$\qquad m_2$ = smaller number of independent variables

In the use of the F tables, the df_1 degrees of freedom are given by $(m_1 - m_2)$ and the df_2 degrees of freedom by $(N - m_1 - 1)$.

Some principles of multiple correlation

Although multiple-correlation problems may be extended to any number of variables, before we consider the solution with more than three, it is desirable to examine some of the general principles that apply for any number of variables but which can be seen more clearly when there are only three.

The two main principles are (1) a multiple correlation increases as the size of correlations between dependent and independent variables increases and (2) a multiple correlation increases as the size of intercorrelations of independent variables decreases. A maximum R will be obtained when the correlations with X_1 are large and when intercorrelations of $X_2, X_3, \ldots, X_m$ are small. In building a battery of tests to predict a criterion, test makers should try to maximize the validity of each test and to minimize the correlations between tests. There are limitations to the application of these objectives, however, and in practice they tend to conflict, as we shall see. There are also apparent exceptions to the rules, as examples will show. The whole story is not contained in the two principles as stated.

SOME TYPICAL COMBINATIONS OF r_{12}, r_{13}, AND r_{23}

Table 16.3 provides some examples of various combinations of correlations among three variables that enter into a multiple-correlation problem. The mathematically wise student will be able to predict

Table 16.3 **Examples of multiple correlations in a
three-variable problem when intercorrelations vary**

Example	r_{12}	r_{13}	r_{23}	$R^2_{1.23}$	$R_{1.23}$
1	.4	.4	.0	.3200	.57
2	.4	.4	.4	.2286	.48
3	.4	.4	.9	.1684	.41
4	.4	.2	.0	.2000	.45
5	.4	.2	.4	.1619	.40
6	.4	.2	.9	.2947	.54
7	.4	.0	.0	.1600	.40
8	.4	.0	.4	.1905	.44
9	.4	.0	.9	.8421	.92
10	.4	.2	−.4	.3143	.56
11	.4	−.4	−.4	.2286	.48

the kind of outcome in each instance, from a general inspection of
formula (16.1). Repeated here for ready reference, it is

$$R^2_{1.23} = \frac{r^2_{12} + r^2_{13} - 2r_{12}r_{13}r_{23}}{1 - r^2_{23}}$$

If the correlation r_{23} is zero, the third term in the numerator is
zero, which has a tendency to make $R_{1.23}$ larger. On the other hand,
there is a distinct advantage in having r_{23} very large, because of its
role in the denominator. If r_{23} approaches 1.0, the denominator approaches zero. Even though the numerator may become small,
under these conditions R can be quite large. A large R is thus favored
by having r_{23} either very small or very large. This principle should be
added to the two mentioned above. But it should also be said that a
large r_{23} is more effective when the independent variables are unequally correlated with the dependent variable, and particularly
when one of the correlations is very small.

Note the first example in Table 16.3, in which $r_{23} = .0$. For this event,
formula (16.1) reduces to

$$R^2_{1.23} = r^2_{12} + r^2_{13} \qquad \text{(Multiple } R \text{ when} \qquad (16.12)$$
intercorrelation of two
independent variables is zero)

In other words, when independent variables have an intercorrelation
of zero, the proportion of variance predicted by their combination is
equal to the sum of the proportions of variance predicted by each
separately. This holds for any number of independent variables

whose intercorrelations are zero. A psychological interpretation of this is that when intercorrelations among predictive measures are zero, the total contribution of each to the prediction of a complex criterion containing all the things predicted is unique.

Note next the second and third examples and compare them with the first. In all three, the r_{12} and r_{13} correlations remain constant at .4, while r_{23} increases first to .4, then to .9. As this happens, R goes from .57 to .48 to .41. In the last instance r_{23} is so high that there is practically no gain from combining the two variables X_2 and X_3. We shall see a modified result in the next three examples.

In examples 4 to 6, r_{12} remains constant at .4 and r_{13} constant at .2, while r_{23} varies from .0 to .9. In the first of these three we find formula (16.12) verified. The two variances sum to .2000 and R is .45. As r_{23} increases to .4, R shrinks back to approximately .40. Thus we can conclude that if one test has a validity of .4, it may pay to add to it another with a validity of only .2, provided the two tests intercorrelate zero. But if there is any appreciable correlation between them, or only a moderate correlation, it would not pay.

What happens if we increase r_{23} still more? When it is as high as .9, R jumps to .54. This supports the third principle stated above: that r_{23} should be either very low or very high. One may ask why this principle does not appear to work in the first three examples. The answer is that it is obscured by the relation of r_{12} and r_{13}. In those examples r_{12} equals r_{13}, and in the next three examples these correlations are unequal. A better explanation is that one of them is very small. One may well ask what psychological meaning is involved in the increase in R when r_{23} is very large. This is best explained in connection with the next three examples.

In examples 7 to 9, r_{12} and r_{13} are still more uneven in size. They also have special interest because $r_{13} = .0$ in all three, while r_{23} varies from .0 to .4 to .9, as in the previous groups of three examples. It would seem, at first thought, that any test that correlates zero with a criterion would have no value in predicting that criterion. It is true that alone it has no value whatever for doing so. But it is not true if that test is combined with other tests with which it correlates. In example 7, the common-sense expectation is vindicated. The addition of an invalid test would offer no improvement. It would simply receive a regression weight of zero, which means it would not be included in the regression equation. But note that when r_{23} increases to .4, R becomes .44, and when r_{23} is .9, R becomes .92. Clearly a test with zero validity may add materially to prediction if it correlates substantially with another test that is valid.

Suppression variables.   The psychological significance of this state of affairs is best explained by factor theory (see Chap. 18). Roughly, the explanation is that variable X_2, in spite of its positive correlation with X_1, has some variance in it that correlates zero, or perhaps even negatively, with the criterion. This same variance prevents X_2 from correlating as highly as it might with X_1. Variable X_2 correlates with X_3 because they have in common that variance not shared by X_1. In this kind of situation we find that X_3 acquires a *negative* regression weight, although it may correlate only zero, and not negatively, with the criterion. Such a variable is a *suppression variable*. Its function in a regression equation is to suppress in other independent variables whatever variance is not represented in the criterion but which may be in some variable that does otherwise correlate with the criterion.

An example of this came to the author's attention in testing for pilot selection. It was a consistent finding that a vocabulary test, which is as pure a measure of the verbal-comprehension factor as we have, correlated zero or even slightly negatively with the criterion of success in pilot training. The same kind of test correlated substantially with a reading-comprehension test which also correlated positively with the pilot-training criterion. The reading test correlated positively with the criterion because it measured, besides verbal comprehension, such factors as mechanical experience and visualization which were also component variances in the criterion. The combination of a vocabulary test with the reading test, with a negative weight for the vocabulary test, would have improved predictions over those possible with the reading test alone.

The examples mentioned thus far have had only positive correlations involved. Generally, where human variables are measured we have only zero or positive correlations, if all measurement scales are aligned so that "good" qualities are given high numerical values. Where genuinely negative relationships do occur they are likely to be very small. Examples 10 and 11 in Table 16.3 are given more for their academic than for their practical interest. Example 10 should be compared with examples 4, 5, and 6. They differ only in the value of r_{23}. When r_{23} becomes negative, we see that the increase that occurs when r_{23} approaches zero appears to continue as r_{23} becomes increasingly negative. When r_{23} is $-.4$, R is even greater than when r_{23} is .9. It is doubtful whether situations like example 10 occur in nature, though they are theoretically possible. The trend could not go very far, however, for with r_{23} large enough in the negative direction we should come to a multiple R greater than 1.0, which would mean an impossible situation, even mathematically speaking.

Example 11 has two negative correlations, r_{13} and r_{23}. These simply mean that variable X_3 probably has a reversed scale, for X_3 is related to both X_1 and X_2 in the same direction. Note that the multiple R is the same as if both r_{13} and r_{23} were positive and of the same size numerically (example 2).

MULTIPLE-R PRINCIPLES IN LARGER BATTERIES

The principles illustrated above for the three-variable problems also apply in larger combinations of variables. The first two principles can be well illustrated by taking other hypothetical examples like those in Table 16.4. There we have a demonstration of how multiple R's behave as the number of independent variables increases from 2 to 20 and as intercorrelations increase from .0 to .6.

Following Thorndike's choices, we shall assume that each variable correlates with a criterion to the extent of .3. This is a rather low validity coefficient, and about the lower limit of usefulness for a single test or other predictive device. We shall see, however, how valuable such instruments may be when combined in a battery, provided their intercorrelations are not too high.

In the second row of Table 16.4, when two such tests are combined, we see how the multiple R decreases from .42 when r_{23} is zero to .34 when r_{23} is .60. In each row the same expected phenomenon occurs: a decrease in R as intercorrelations increase. Inspection of the columns shows how R increases as we add more tests, having similar correlations, to the battery and how the gain in R continues up to a battery of 20, except for the case of zero intercorrelations, for which the limit of $R = 1.0$ was passed when the number of tests exceeded 11. In this situation (zero intercorrelations) the principle of formula (16.12) still applies. The proportion of predicted variance contributed by each test would be .09, and 11 tests would yield an R^2 of .99 and a multiple R of .995. In other columns the increases of R are less drastic, but except in the last column, and perhaps in the one preceding, it would ap-

Table 16.4   Multiple correlations from different numbers of independent variables each correlating .30 with the dependent variable but with intercorrelations varying*

Number of independent variables	Intercorrelations			
	.00	.10	.30	.60
1	(.30)	(.30)	(.30)	(.30)
2	.42	.40	.37	.34
4	.60	.53	.44	.36
9	.90	.67	.48	.37
20		.79	.52	.38

*Adapted from Thorndike, R. L. *Research Problems and Techniques*, in *AAF Aviation Psychology Research Program Reports*, No. 3. Washington, D.C.: GPO, 1947.

parently pay to continue adding new tests until the 20 were included. Considerations of administrative effort would have to be balanced against gains in R.

Table 16.4 tells an even more important story. The value of having zero intercorrelation among tests in a battery is obvious. If one tries to achieve zero intercorrelations among tests, when each test measures a unique factor, however, he will often find that each test tends to correlate low with the criterion. This is because a practical criterion – e.g., training achievement or job performance – is usually a complex variable; it has a number of component variances, each component being a common factor (see the discussion of factor theory in Chap. 18). If one tries to increase the correlation of a single test with a criterion, the result is almost invariably an increase in the factorial complexity of the test, that is, more different factor variances are introduced. This automatically raises the correlation of this test with other tests, because they have more factors in common. This is the reason that in practice the two principles mentioned first lead to conflicting objectives.

Where there has to be a choice, it seems wisest to give less attention to the first principle (maximizing correlation of each test with the criterion) and greater attention to the second (minimizing intercorrelations). If there are 20 independent factors represented in a practical criterion, and if each is of equal importance, each would contribute .05 of the total variance. Each test, measuring only one of the factors, would need to correlate only $\sqrt{.05}$, which is .224, with the criterion. In this case, raising the correlation between any one test and the criterion would be of little use. There would be no objection to a higher correlation. Appropriate weighting would bring the test's contribution to prediction down to required proportions. Thus, it can be concluded that low correlations of tests with practical criteria can be tolerated, provided we can combine enough tests in a battery and provided their intercorrelations are near zero.[1]

Multiple correlation with more than three variables

With more than three variables, a good solution of a regression equation and of a multiple R may be carried out by means of the Doolittle method, which is one of a number of procedures for solving simultaneous equations. This procedure will be outlined step by step for a five-variable problem. We shall use all the variables represented in Table 16.1 and ask what regression weights would best predict X_1 from the other four combined and what the correlation of those predictions with obtained X_1 values would be.

[1]For a more detailed discussion of these problems, see Guilford, J. P. New standards for test evaluation. *Educ. psychol. Measmt.*, 1946, **6**, 427–438.

SOLUTION OF NORMAL EQUATIONS

As stated before, the Doolittle method solves simultaneous equations. The unknowns are the beta coefficients, and there are as many equations as unknowns. For a five-variable problem, in which there are four unknown betas, the equations are

$$
\begin{aligned}
\beta_{12} + r_{23}\beta_{13} + r_{24}\beta_{14} + r_{25}\beta_{15} &= r_{12} \\
r_{23}\beta_{12} + \beta_{13} + r_{34}\beta_{14} + r_{35}\beta_{15} &= r_{13} \\
r_{24}\beta_{12} + r_{34}\beta_{13} + \beta_{14} + r_{45}\beta_{15} &= r_{14} \\
r_{25}\beta_{12} + r_{35}\beta_{13} + r_{45}\beta_{14} + \beta_{15} &= r_{15}
\end{aligned}
$$

(Normal equations for the solution of beta weights)   (16.13)

The beta coefficients are symbolized in abbreviated form here to conserve space. β_{12}, in full, would be $\beta_{12.345}$, β_{13} would be $\beta_{13.245}$, and so on. The equations are systematic, the r coefficients being arranged as in the original table of intercorrelations (see Table 16.1) and each beta in its own column. The betas in the diagonal positions might be expected to have coefficients r_{22}, r_{33}, r_{44}, and r_{55} attached to them, but instead the coefficients attached to these betas are all +1.0, as the least squares solution requires.

THE DOOLITTLE-SOLUTION OPERATIONS

First we prepare a work sheet like that in Table 16.5. There is a column for every variable and the numbering corresponds. A last column is introduced for the purpose of checking the calculations, as will be explained. The rows are designated by letters, and in the first column a shorthand instruction is noted. These will be explained.

Step 1. Record in row A the correlations with X_2. These are obtained here from Table 16.1. In column 2, a coefficient of 1.0000 is inserted, because it is demanded by the Doolittle method. We are going to carry four decimal places throughout the solution (one more than those given in the r's), and so we record all numbers to four places.

Step 2. Sum the values recorded in row A, and give the sum in the last, or "check," column. This will be used later.

Step 3. Divide the numbers in row A each by −1.0000. In the table, the instruction reads "$A \div (-A2)$," which means that each number in row A is to be divided by the number that appears at $A2$ (row A, column 2) with sign changed. This includes the last column as well.

Step 4. Record in row C all the remaining correlations with X_3. We say "remaining," because one is already recorded, namely, r_{23}. The value of 1.0000 is recorded at $C3$.

Step 5. Sum all the correlations with X_3, including the .5620 in row A. Record the sum in the "check" column.

Step 6.   The numbers in row D are found by the instruction "$A \times B\,3$," which means to multiply all the numbers in row A (beginning in column 3) by the number that appears in row B and column 3. This number is $-.5620$ in Table 16.5.

Step 7.   Row E calls for the addition of all numbers in rows C and D.

Step 8.   Row F calls for the division of all numbers in row E by the number appearing in row E and column 3, with sign changed. This number, with sign changed, is $-.6842$.

Step 9.   We are ready for the first checking of calculations. Sum the values in row F, *not* including the last column. This should equal approximately -1.8720 in this particular problem, which was found by the steps already described. If there is a serious discrepancy here (other than in the fourth decimal place), check row E by adding values up to the check column. If this does not check, there is an error further back, and some recalculating is in order. All checks should be satisfied before proceeding.

Step 10.   In row G, record remaining correlations with X_4, with 1.0000 at $G\,4$.

Step 11.   Sum *all* the correlations with X_4, and record in the last column in row G.

Step 12.   Values in row H are the products of values in row A times the number at $B\,4$. This number is $-.4010$.

Step 13.   Values in row I are the products of numbers in row E times the number at $F\,4$, which is $-.2493$.

Step 14.   Sum the numbers in rows G, H, and I for each column.

Step 15.   Divide row J through by the number at $J\,4$, with sign changed; in other words, by $-.7967$.

Step 16.   Check by summing row K up to the last column. Does the sum agree with the number already found in that column?

Step 17.   and after. By now the abbreviated instructions for each row should be clear by analogy to those already given. The final check is made in row Q.

The illustrative solution is set up for a five-variable problem, but a larger number of variables would be treated in a similar manner simply by extending the table to more rows and columns. A smaller number of variables would mean fewer rows and columns. It will be noticed that the table is set up in terms of *blocks* of work, each one beginning with the entrance of correlations for a new variable and ending by dividing by a number that will ensure a -1.0000 as the first number in the last row of that block. The work is very systematic throughout. Any variable may be treated as the dependent variable, but it must then occupy the next-to-last column in the table.

Solution of the beta coefficients. The work represented in Table 16.5 is only part of the Doolittle solution. The end result gives the beta coefficients, which we find by means of a "back solution," so called because we work in a backward direction, as compared with the work in Table 16.5. This work can be tabulated, but it is probably clearest to the beginner in the form of equations. The first beta found is β_{15}, which can be located without further ado in Table 16.5. It is the number at the intersection of row Q and column 1, but with sign changed (in other words, it is described as $-Q1$). β_{15} is therefore +.1607. The other betas require more work, and so we shall follow the procedure step by step, including again the first step already taken, for the sake of completeness.

Step 1. $\beta_{15} = -Q1 = +.1607$
Step 2. $\beta_{14} = -K1 + \beta_{15}(K5) = .3506 + (.1607)(-.3012) = +.3022$
Step 3. $\beta_{13} = -F1 + \beta_{15}(F5) + \beta_{14}(F4)$
$\qquad = .4702 + (.1607)(-.1524) + (.3022)(-.2493) = +.3703$

Table 16.5   **Solution of a multiple-correlation problem by the Doolittle method**

Column number		2	3	4	5	1	Check
	Variable	X_2	X_3	X_4	X_5	X_1	Sum
Row	**Instruction**						
A	r_{2k}	1.0000	.5620	.4010	.1970	.4650	2.6250
B	$A \div (-A2)$	−1.0000	− .5620	− .4010	− .1970	− .4650	−2.6250
C	r_{3k}		1.0000	.3960	.2150	.5830	2.7560
D	$A \times B3$		− .3158	− .2254	− .1107	− .2613	−1.4752
E	$C + D$		.6842	.1706	.1043	.3217	1.2808
F	$E \div (-E3)$		−1.0000	− .2493	− .1524	− .4702	−1.8720
G	r_{4k}			1.0000	.3450	.5460	2.6880
H	$A \times B4$			− .1608	− .0790	− .1865	−1.0526
I	$E \times F4$			− .0425	− .0260	− .0802	− .3193
J	$G + H + I$			.7967	.2400	.2793	1.3161
K	$J \div (-J4)$			−1.0000	− .3012	− .3506	−1.6519
L	r_{5k}				1.0000	.3650	2.1220
M	$A \times B5$				− .0388	− .0916	− .5171
N	$E \times F5$				− .0159	− .0490	− .1952
O	$J \times K5$				− .0723	− .0841	− .3964
P	$L + M + N + O$				.8730	.1403	1.0133
Q	$P \div (-P5)$				−1.0000	− .1607	−1.1607

Step 4. $\beta_{12} = -B1 + \beta_{15}(B5) + \beta_{14}(B4) + \beta_{13}(B3)$
$= .4650 + (.1607)(-.1970) + (.3022)(-.4010)$
$$+ (.3703)(-.5620)$$
$= +.1039$

Before going further, it is well to check the calculations of the beta coefficients. This can be done by using the last equation in (16.13):

$$\beta_{12}r_{25} + \beta_{13}r_{35} + \beta_{14}r_{45} + \beta_{15} = r_{15}$$

Substituting known values,

$$(.1039)(.197) + (.3703)(.215) + (.3022)(.345) + .1607 = .3651$$

Since $r_{15} = .365$, the check is satisfied, and we may assume that there has been no error in computing the betas. This checking procedure can be summarized as in Table 16.6, which provides a convenient work plan.

THE SOLUTION OF REGRESSION WEIGHTS AND THE MULTIPLE R

Each b coefficient needed in the multiple-regression equation is found from its corresponding beta. Equations like those in formulas (16.2a) and (16.2b) apply. The b weight for X_2 should read in full $b_{12.345}$ to indicate that we are interested in the relation of X_1 to X_2, other variables, X_3, X_4, and X_5, being held constant. For the sake of brevity (as, indeed, we have already done for the betas), we denote the b's only by the first two subscript numbers b_{12}, b_{13}, etc. In the solution of a multiple R, equation (16.5) needs to be extended to include as many terms as there are variables. R^2 is the sum of the products of beta times its corresponding r, i.e.,

$$R^2 = \beta_{12}r_{12} + \beta_{13}r_{13} + \beta_{14}r_{14} + \beta_{15}r_{15} + \cdots$$
(General solution of R^2 from beta coefficients)   (16.14)

The a coefficient in the equation is also found by formula (16.4), extended with as many terms as necessary. It is the mean of the X_1

*Table 16.6   A check upon the computation of the
beta coefficients*

	β_{1k}	r_{k5}	$\beta_{1k}r_{k5}$
X_2	.1039	.197	.0205
X_3	.3703	.215	.0796
X_4	.3022	.345	.1043
X_5	.1607	1.000	.1607
			$\Sigma .3651 = r_{15}$

values minus the products of other means times their corresponding b weights, for

$$a = M_1 - b_{12}M_2 - b_{13}M_3 - b_{14}M_4 - \cdots$$

(Constant a in a multiple-regression equation) $\hspace{2cm}$ (16.15)

All these operations are conveniently carried out in a work sheet like Table 16.7, where R and the regression weights are systematically calculated. The second column contains the four betas. The third contains the original, or first-order, correlations of the four variables with X_1. The subscript k stands for variables 2 to 5 in turn. The fourth column contains the cross products of betas times the corresponding r's. Their sum is R^2, which here is .487855; by taking the square root we find R to be .698. This R, with full subscript, would read $R_{1.2345}$.

So much for the multiple R, the value of which we see is not very much higher when the equation includes two more variables (X_2 and X_5) than when it was obtained with only predictors X_3 and X_4. Then R equaled .677. The coefficient of determination is now .4879, or we have accounted for 48.8 per cent of the variance of freshman achievement, as compared with 45.8 per cent without using X_2 and X_5. The standard error of estimate (now designated as $\sigma_{1.2345}$ in full) equals 6.5, where before it was 6.7, a trifling change. The index of forecasting efficiency is now 28.4 per cent, where before it was 26.4 per cent. It is therefore questionable whether the trouble of measuring the two additional variables and using them in the regression equation is worthwhile.

For the solution of the b coefficients, we introduce in Table 16.7 first the column headed σ_1/σ_k. This is the ratio by which each beta is to be multiplied. The b coefficients follow in column 6. Each one tells how many units X_1 increases for every unit of increase in each of the other variables.

Table 16.7 **Solution of the regression coefficients for the multiple-regression equation**

(1)	(2) β_{1k}	(3) r_{1k}	(4) $\beta_{1k}r_{1k}$	(5) σ_1/σ_k	(6) b_{1k}	(7) M_k	(8) $(-M_k)b_{1k}$
X_2	.1039	.465	.048314	1.750	.182	19.7	-3.585
X_3	.3703	.583	.214885	.535	.198	49.5	-9.801
X_4	.3022	.546	.165001	.469	.142	61.1	-8.676
X_5	.1607	.365	.058655	2.459	.395	29.7	-11.732
			Σ .487855 $= R^2$			Σ	-33.794
			.698 $= R$			M_1	73.800
						$a =$	40.006

For the solution of the a coefficient, the last two columns are included. This coefficient turns out to be exactly 40.0. The entire regression equation now reads

$$X'_1 = 40.0 + .182X_2 + .198X_3 + .142X_4 + .395X_5$$

With this equation, we could predict an X'_1 for every student, knowing his four scores in the other variables.

As was said before, the addition of the terms involving X_2 and X_5 scarcely yields enough additional accuracy of prediction to justify their inclusion. One could try combinations of three predictive indices, variables $X_2, X_3,$ and $X_4,$ or $X_3, X_4,$ and $X_5,$ to see what happens. From the results in Table 16.7, it would seem that the latter combination is the more promising. One could determine by another Doolittle solution whether it increased R sufficiently above .677 to justify the introduction of X_5 with X_3 and X_4. An F test would make possible a statistical decision.

OBTAINING A SHORT, PREDICTIVE BATTERY

As in the three-variable multiple-regression problem, we can extract from the data in Table 16.7 some information concerning the relative contributions of the various predictors toward accounting for variance in the criterion. The β-r products, all being positive, give indications of both direct and indirect contributions combined, from which we can say that the proportions of "determination" are approximately 21 per cent for the analogies test (X_3), 16.5 per cent for high-school average (X_4), 6 per cent for the measure of interest (X_5), and 5 per cent for the algebra test (X_2).

Direct contributions of the predictors are estimated from the betas squared, which yield values of 14 per cent for the analogies test, 9 per cent for high-school average, 3 per cent for the measure of interest, and only 1 per cent for the algebra test. The indirect contributions are presumably indicated by the differences between these two sets of estimates. Again, it should be emphasized that these estimates of proportions of criterion variance accounted for pertain only to this particular combination of predictors.

Solution of a multiple-regression problem, even with the convenient Doolittle procedure, becomes energy- and time-consuming when the number of variables is large. The author has known of test batteries involving as many as 20 possible scores that could be combined, each with its appropriate weight. When there are more than four variables the situation calls for the use of high-speed computers, which are becoming more common.

The Wherry-Doolittle method. There is a modified Doolittle solution, which was introduced by Wherry.[1] The method was designed to meet the requirement of assembling a battery of tests to select personnel for some particular assignment. It takes particular cognizance of the fact that when a large number of tests are validated singly for the prediction of a certain criterion, only four or five when combined often seem sufficient. Indeed, adding tests beyond the point at which all the factors that the tests measure in common with the criterion are covered may merely contribute more error variance to the composite than anything useful. Even before the point has been reached where there is no *apparent* improvement in prediction, errors have been introduced which help determine the regression weights. This point was mentioned earlier in the discussion of shrinkage formulas [see formulas (16.7) and (16.8)].

The principles of the Wherry-Doolittle method are, briefly, as follows: One starts with the single test that seems to offer most in prediction of the criterion. The method then aids in selection of the second test that will have most to add to prediction when combined with the first. A third can be selected which will add most by way of prediction when combined with the first two, and so on. At each step a shrinkage formula is applied in order to determine whether the shrunken R is appreciably larger than the previous R. At the point where no further gain according to these standards is apparent, no more tests are added.

The method does undoubtedly offer an efficient way of assembling a battery of tests to meet a particular purpose. It results in a list of predictive instruments that, out of a larger number tried experimentally, is minimum for doing the job.

The author is inclined toward a quite different philosophy of development of test batteries, however, which would render the Wherry-Doolittle procedure unnecessary when there is sufficient information about the criterion and the tests.[2] For this reason the space that it would take to explain and demonstrate the Wherry-Doolittle method is not used here. The reason why only four or five tests have often seemed to be the limit in a useful battery is that only a limited number of the human abilities and other traits that are involved in a practical criterion have been represented in the tests. Although a dozen different tests may have been tried out, the same limited number of fundamental factors have been measured by them and the measurement is duplicated several times over. If a careful

[1]Described in full in Stead, W. H., Shartle, C. L., et al. *Occupational Counseling Techniques.* New York: American Book, 1940. Pp. 245–255.
[2]For a discussion of this at some length, see Guilford, J. P. Factor analysis in a test development program. *Psychol. Rev.*, 1948, **55**, 79–94.

study of the criterion is made, revealing *all* the factors that are worth trying to predict, and if there is sufficient variety in the tests to take care of all the factors, it will be found that more than four or five tests will probably be needed. If one knows that there are 10 traits involved in the criterion that are worth covering with tests, and if it takes 10 tests to do it, then one could put the 10 tests in a battery and expect that every one would have something unique to contribute toward prediction. A successive selection of tests by a method such as the Wherry-Doolittle would then be unnecessary.

Other combinations of measures

The regression equation is a means of combining different measures of the same object in order to derive a composite measure or score. The scores are summed, each weighted by its regression coefficient. There are other ways of combining scores to form a composite. For example, one might simply sum the raw scores for each person without applying differential weights. This is the common practice in deriving total scores of tests composed of subtests of different kinds, though in some cases there is some effort at weighting, for example, multiplying one score by 2, another by 3, and so on.

Actually, every test that is composed of items may be regarded as a *battery* of as many tests as there are items. The total score is usually an unweighted summation of the item scores, though in a few interest and temperament tests there may be differential weighting. Rarely does a test maker resort to the determination of regression weights for test items, but the same principle that applies to test batteries could be adapted to single tests composed of parts. More often than not, even in the case of test batteries, there are so many parts, or they are used to predict in such a variety of situations, that there is not sufficient incentive to work out all the regression weights that would be required.

Because there must be substitute weighting procedures in combining tests, it is important to know some of the better substitute procedures for the multiple-regression equation and to be able to evaluate the effectiveness of a composite derived by any method. The multiple R applies only when the optimal regression weights are used; other weights will yield a composite that is likely to correlate less with the criterion. There are other problems connected with composite scores that call for attention, including that of what mean and what standard deviation will result when measures are combined each with a certain weight. These problems will be dealt with in following paragraphs.

MEANS OF WEIGHTED COMPOSITES

When several measures of the same object are summed, each with its own weight, the mean of the same kind of composite for a sample of objects is given by the equation[1]

$$M_{ws} = \Sigma w_i M_i \qquad \text{(Mean of a sum of weighted measures)} \qquad (16.16)$$

where w_i = weight applied to each variable X_i, when i varies from 1 to n in a list of n variables, and M_i = mean for the same sample of objects in variable X_i.

If we apply this to the b weights computed for the regression equation in the prediction of average freshman grades (see p. 413), the solution would be

$$M_{ws} = (.182)(19.7) + (.198)(49.5) + (.142)(61.1) + (.395)(29.7)$$
$$= 33.8$$

Thus, the mean of the composite of four variables, including X_2 (arithmetic test), X_3 (analogies test), X_4 (high-school average), and X_5 (interest score), weighted with the coefficients .182, .198, .142, and .395, respectively, would be 33.8. This value is 40.0 units short of the mean for the criterion (freshman grades). By adding the difference (40.0), which is the a coefficient of the complete regression equation, we obtain a composite mean that coincides with that of the criterion. In other words, this discussion explains the need for the a coefficient in the complete regression equation. If we were not interested in achieving that mean, we could drop the constant 40.0 and be left with a mean of 33.8.

STANDARD DEVIATIONS OF WEIGHTED COMPOSITES

We can likewise estimate the standard deviation of a composite measure when each component has a multiplier or weight. The computation of this statistic may be clearer, however, if we consider the standard deviation of a simple unweighted sum first.

The standard deviation of sums when weights equal one. When scores from different tests are summed without applying differential weights, we may regard the weight for each test to be +1. When *two* scores are summed to make the composite, the variance of the composite scores is given by the equation[2]

$$\sigma^2_s = \sigma^2_1 + \sigma^2_2 + 2r_{12}\sigma_1\sigma_2 \qquad \begin{array}{l}\text{(Variance of a sum of two}\\\text{unweighted measures)}\end{array} \qquad (16.17)$$

[1]See Appendix A, Proof 11.
[2]See Appendix A, Proof 12.

where $\sigma^2{}_1$ and $\sigma^2{}_2$ = variances of the components and r_{12} = coefficient of correlation between the two components.

The expression $r_{12}\sigma_1\sigma_2$ is the *covariance* of the two components. Its relation to correlation can be better shown by relating it to the Pearson formula, in which

$$r_{12} = \frac{\Sigma x_1 x_2}{N\sigma_1\sigma_2}$$

If we multiply both sides of this equation by $\sigma_1\sigma_2$ we have

$$r_{12}\sigma_1\sigma_2 = \frac{\Sigma x_1 x_2}{N}$$

The parallel between the term at the right and the expression for a variance should be obvious. A variance is of the form $\Sigma x^2{}_1/N$ or $\Sigma x^2{}_2/N$. A covariance is the mean of the cross products of deviations; a variance is a mean of the squares of deviations. With this new information as background, we may translate equation (16.17) into English by saying that the variance of a composite is equal to the sum of variances of the components plus twice the covariances of all pairs of those components. This is a general principle that is important to remember.

From equation (16.17) it follows, by taking square roots, that

$$\sigma_s = \sqrt{\sigma^2{}_1 + \sigma^2{}_2 + 2r_{12}\sigma_1\sigma_2} \qquad \begin{array}{l}\text{(Standard deviation} \\ \text{of the sum of two} \\ \text{unweighted measures)}\end{array} \qquad (16.18)$$

A demonstration of how this works out in a particular sample is given in Table 16.8. Ten scores are given for the same individuals in X_a and in X_b between which the correlation r_{ab} equals zero. If $r = .0$, the third term in formula (16.17) drops out and the variance of the composite is merely the sum of the variances of the components.

In the illustration in Table 16.8, the variances of the two components are 4.2 and 6.6, respectively. Their sum is 10.8, which checks with the mean square found from variable X_c. The way in which variances combine is also demonstrated in Fig. 16.3, which pictures hypothetical distributions for X_a, X_b, and their sum X_c. The position of the scale for X_c is determined by the juncture of the lines erected at distances of 1σ from the means of X_a and X_b. The slanted scale of X_c is closer to that of X_b, consistent with the fact that X_b contributes more variance to it than does X_a and the fact that the composite correlates higher with X_b than with X_a. But these are incidental considerations here. The important demonstration is that when two variables like X_a and X_b are uncorrelated, we may regard the standard deviation of their composite X_c as the hypotenuse of a right tri-

Table 16.8 **The variance and variability of a composite score that is the unweighed sum of two uncorrelated scores**

Individual	X_a	x_a	x^2_a	X_b	x_b	x^2_b	X_c (X_a+X_b)	x_c	x^2_c
A	1	−4	16	6	0	0	7	−4	16
B	3	−2	4	7	+1	1	10	−1	1
C	4	−1	1	4	−2	4	8	−3	9
D	5	0	0	10	+4	16	15	+4	16
E	5	0	0	8	+2	4	13	+2	4
F	5	0	0	0	−6	36	5	−6	36
G	5	0	0	6	0	0	11	0	0
H	6	+1	1	8	+2	4	14	+3	9
I	7	+2	4	5	−1	1	12	+1	1
J	9	+4	16	6	0	0	15	+4	16
Σ	50	0	42	60	0	66	110	0	108
M	5.0		4.2	6.0		6.6	11.0		10.8
σ			2.05			2.57			3.29

angle of which σ_a and σ_b are the legs. The old, familiar Pythagorean theorem thus applies to the variance of the summation of two independent variables.

Relation of σ_s to the standard error of a difference.   The similarity between equation (16.18) and equation (9.3) for the standard error of a difference will probably have been noticed. The only difference is in the algebraic sign of the covariance term, $2r_{12}\sigma_1\sigma_2$, which is positive in the case of σ_s and negative in the case of σ_d. Of course, in the preceding discussion of σ_s we have been applying it to distributions of single observations, whereas σ_d has been applied to distributions of means (mean differences). The principles are the same, either with means or with single observations. Had we written the summation equation in the form $X_c = X_a - X_b$, instead of $X_c = X_a + X_b$, we should have been dealing with differences instead of sums. On the other hand, in the equation $X_c = X_a - X_b$, we can say that we actually have a summation of scores, those for X_a having a weight of +1 and those for X_b a weight of −1.

Variance of a composite of more than two components.   Equation (16.17) can be extended to include any number of unweighted components. For each component there would be a term for its variance but there would be as many covariance terms to include as there are *pairs* of components. With three components there would be three covariance terms: $2r_{12}\sigma_1\sigma_2$, $2r_{13}\sigma_1\sigma_3$, and $2r_{23}\sigma_2\sigma_3$. Where there are

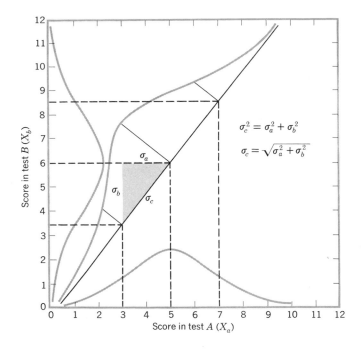

$$\sigma_c^2 = \sigma_a^2 + \sigma_b^2$$

$$\sigma_c = \sqrt{\sigma_a^2 + \sigma_b^2}$$

Fig. 16.3. *Illustration of the way in which the standard deviation of an unweighted sum of two scores is related to the standard deviations of those two scores taken separately, when the two are uncorrelated.*

n components, there are $n(n-1)/2$ pairs to consider. In terms of a general formula,

$$\sigma_s^2 = \Sigma\sigma_i^2 + 2\ \Sigma r_{ij}\sigma_i\sigma_j \qquad \text{(Variance of a sum of any number of unweighted components)} \qquad (16.19)$$

where σ_i^2 = variance of any one component, X_i

r_{ij} = correlation between any component X_i and any other component with a higher subscript number

σ_i and σ_j = standard deviations of the two components correlated

VARIANCE OF A COMPOSITE OF WEIGHTED COMPONENTS

When the components are weighted differently, the variance of the composite will reflect the weights. Let us begin with the special case of two components. If the summation equation is of the form

$$X_{ws} = w_1X_1 + w_2X_2$$

the variance of X_{ws} is given by the equation[1]

$$\sigma_{ws}^2 = w_1^2\sigma_1^2 + w_2^2\sigma_2^2 + 2r_{12}w_1\sigma_1w_2\sigma_2 \qquad \text{(Variance of a composite of two weighted components)} \qquad (16.20)$$

[1]See Appendix A, Proof 12.

where w_1 and w_2 = weights applied to components X_1 and X_2, respectively.

As an example of this type of problem, let us use the data on X_4 and X_5 in Table 16.1. If these two variables are used in a composite to predict X_1, the least-squares solution gives b weights of .224 and .491, respectively, and a multiple R, based upon these weights, of .578. The predicted X values based upon the equation $X_1' = .224X_4 + .491X_5$ would be expected to have a standard deviation equal to $R_{1.45}$ times σ_1 (since $R_{1.45} = \sigma_{x'_1}/\sigma_{x_1}$). This product is .578 × 9.1, which equals 5.26. Let us see whether formula (16.20) will lead to the same result. By substituting the appropriate values,

$$\sigma^2_{ws} = (.224^2)(19.4^2) + (.491^2)(3.7^2) + 2(.345)(.224)(19.4)(.491)(3.7)$$
$$= 27.6319$$

from which

$$\sigma_{ws} = 5.26$$

This agrees exactly with the expectation.

With weights of +1 for both X_4 and X_5, application of formula (16.17) would have given

$$\sigma^2_s = 19.4^2 + 3.7^2 + 2(.345)(19.4)(3.7)$$
$$= 439.5782$$

from which

$$\sigma_s = 21.0$$

Variance of a composite of any number of weighted components. When there are more than two components, each weighted differently, the variance of the composite is given by the general formula[1]

$$\sigma^2_{ws} = \Sigma w^2_i \sigma^2_i + 2\Sigma r_{ij} w_i \sigma_i w_j \sigma_j \qquad \begin{array}{l}\text{(Variance of a sum of} \\ \text{any number of weighted} \\ \text{components)}\end{array} \qquad (16.21)$$

where w_i = weight assigned to variable X_i, where i takes on values 1 to n in turn, there being n predictors

r_{ij} = correlation between X_i and any other variable X_j, where j is a subscript greater than i

σ_i and σ_j = standard deviations of X_i and X_j, respectively

We could apply formula (16.21) to the four components of the regression equation predicting freshman grades with the appropriate b

[1]See Appendix A, Proof 12.

weight substituted for w in each case. We should find that the standard deviation is equal to R times σ_1, which is $.698 \times 9.1 = 6.35$. The inclusion of variables X_2 and X_3 in the regression equation raises the dispersion of the predicted grades from 5.26, which it would be with X_4 and X_5 only, to 6.35.

ACHIEVING ANY DESIRED STANDARD DEVIATION IN A COMPOSITE

In using regression equations, the dispersion of the predictions falls short of that of the obtained values because in the product $R\sigma_1$, R is less than 1.0. This is all right and proper when we are interested in predicting an individual's most probable measure on the scale of obtained measures in X_1. The regression of predictions toward the general mean is a natural phenomenon of imperfect correlation, as was pointed out before (Chap. 15). There may be other uses of composites, however, that call for values other than those given by the regression equation. Suppose that we wanted predictions to spread just as much as the obtained values do. Or, suppose that we should want them to be dispersed with some standard variability, for example, with a σ of 10.0, as on a T scale, or a σ of 2.0, as on a C scale (see Chap. 19). The way that such a goal can be achieved will now be explained.

Fortunately for the solution of this problem, it is not the absolute sizes of the weights that matter, but their ratios to one another. So long as they bear the same relations to each other, the correlation of the composite with some criterion will remain the same. Consequently, we could double, triple, or otherwise change the regression weights by some common multiple, without affecting the predictive value, if all we want is to predict individuals in the same relative positions in a distribution.

The σ of the predictions is always related to the σ of the obtained values by the extent of the correlation (when optimal weights are used). In a multiple-regression problem, the σ of the predicted values equals R times the σ of the obtained values. We can therefore make the σ of the predictions equal the σ of the obtained values by dividing each regression coefficient by R. An adjusted b coefficient, then, would be computed by the formula

$$b'_{12.34...m} = \beta_{12.34...m} \left(\frac{\sigma_1}{\sigma_2 R_{1.23...m}} \right) \qquad \begin{array}{l} \text{(Regression coefficient} \\ \text{adjusted to make the } \sigma \text{ of} \\ \text{a composite equal } \sigma_1 \text{)} \end{array} \qquad (16.22)$$

If the σ desired in the composite is 10, or 2, or any other chosen quantity, this could be achieved by substituting that quantity for σ_1 in formula (16.22).

ACHIEVING ANY DESIRED MEAN FOR A COMPOSITE

In the optimally weighted regression equation, in order to make the mean of the predictions equal that of the obtained values, the a coefficient is introduced. The computation of a is given by formula (16.15). After one has determined any weights whatever to apply to the raw scores of the components of a composite measure, the same formula can be applied, putting in the place of M_y any desired quantity. This is true because of the reasoning involved in the computation of the mean of a composite [see formula (16.16)]. Thus, if we had wanted the mean of the grades predicted by the regression equation in Table 16.7 to be 50, we would have substituted 50 for 73.8, the actual mean of the grades. The only practical restriction would be to choose a mean such that no composite measures would be negative. This means that any chosen mean should be at least 2.5 to 3.0 times the standard deviation of the composite.

SUBSTITUTES FOR REGRESSION WEIGHTS

While regression weights derived from least-squares solutions, or weights proportional to them, yield the greatest accuracy of prediction from the variables available, it is often expedient in the practical situation to deviate from the refined solution. It can be shown that we may substitute weights that approximate the regression coefficients, even very roughly at times, and still not affect the degree of correlation very much. Instead of applying weights to three decimal places, one significant digit will often suffice, in other words, simple integral weights.

In predicting freshman grades from high-school average and interest score combined, for example, the optimal weights were found to be .224 and .491. We might in practice round these to .2 and .5, respectively. It will be shown later[1] that the change in correlation between X'_1 and X_1 in the two cases is from .578, with the three-digit weights, to .577, with the one-digit weights. This loss is quite trivial. We could use weights of 2 and 5 had we so chosen. Suppose we want even a simpler ratio of the two weights, such as $\frac{1}{2}$, rather than $\frac{2}{5}$. With weights of 1 and 2, also, the correlation of composites and grades would be .577. With equal weights the correlation would drop to .570. Even this much loss could be tolerated.

Before the reader draws the conclusion from this isolated example that all differential weighting is unnecessary, however, it is important to consider some points not yet brought out. There is no reason to believe that this is a typical example. Ordinarily, the larger the

[1]Methods for correlating composites or sums, either weighted or unweighted, will be described on pp. 427–428.

number of independent variables in a composite, the more can one depart from the weights demanded by least-squares solutions and yet maintain a high level of correlation between that composite and a criterion. This is why with a test composed of many items we may forget to bother with differential weighting. In a two-variable composite, however, we have the minimum of multiple predictors. We should therefore expect to find the validity of the composite to be rather sensitive to changes in weights.

Roughly, the explanation in this example is that X_4 (high-school average) has a beta weight about 2.4 times that for X_5 (interest score) and it has a standard deviation about five times as large as that for X_5. Even when X_4 and X_5 have the same weight in the composite, X_4 contributes to the composite in proportion to its standard deviation. This follows from equation (16.17), in which it is shown that *without differential weights (and with zero intercorrelations) each part's contribution to total variance is proportional to its own variance.* Without differential weighting of variables in the equation, then, X_4 is still weighted much more than X_5. This illustrates a fact that is not often realized. It is usually assumed that merely summing several scores weights those scores equally. As a rule, it does not; *it weights them in proportion to their standard deviations.* In everyday language, tests weight themselves.

Weighting measures inversely as their standard deviations. This discussion leads to the conclusion that if we really want to weight tests in a battery equally we should apply to each one a weight inversely proportional to its standard deviation. Without information as to the validities of the tests and of their intercorrelations, that would be a reasonable thing to do.[1] Table 16.9 shows how this end may be achieved. The four tests are the same as those used to predict freshman grades. The means and standard deviations are duplicates of those given in Table 16.1.

We could find a weight equal to $1/\sigma$ for every test, but these weights would be rather small decimal numbers in some cases. A good practical procedure is to select the largest σ in the list, in this case 19.4, and to compute the ratio $19.4/\sigma$ for each test. The test with the largest σ will thus achieve the smallest weight. With this particular ratio, the smallest weight will then be exactly 1.0. The ratio of any other weights to this one will be immediately apparent. It is recommended that all these ratios be rounded to the nearest integer, as shown in the fourth row of Table 16.9. The weights obtained by this process are 4, 1, 1, and 5, respectively. With these weights applied,

[1]Provided the tests are of the same general degree of reliability. In some tests, a small standard deviation suggests low reliability (see Chap. 17).

Table 16.9 **The process of weighting components inversely as their dispersions**

| | Variables | | | |
	A	B	C	D
M	19.7	49.5	61.1	29.7
σ	5.2	17.0	19.4	3.7
$19.4/\sigma$ (w_i)	3.73	1.14	1.00	5.24
Integral weight (W)	4	1	1	5
Estimated importance (I)	2	2	5	1
Combined weight (Iw')	7.46	2.28	5.00	5.24
Revised integral weight (W')	7	2	5	5
Simplified weight $(Iw'/2.28)$	3	1	2	2

all four tests would contribute approximately the same amount of variance to the total variance.

The principle of weighting each test inversely as its dispersion is involved in the b coefficient. Remember that b is equal to beta times σ_1/σ_i, where σ_i is the standard deviation of the test to be weighted. Using the procedure just described, therefore, is virtually equivalent to using an incomplete b coefficient. In a sense, it assumes equal validities for all tests and equal intercorrelations, conditions which would lead to equal betas.

From the solution in Table 16.9, measures X_4 and X_5 should receive weights of 1 and 5, respectively. The difference is in the same direction as for the two b weights, which are .224 and .491, respectively, but X_4 is given relatively about half as much importance as it should have if it is to be optimally weighted. The effect upon the correlation of the criterion with the composite, weighted this way, is to reduce it from the optimal R of .578 to a correlation of .558. The underweighting of X_4, which is more valid and has a larger beta than X_5, shows up in the lower validity of this composite.

Other principles of weighting. Common sense may suggest that component tests should be weighted in proportion to their lengths or their means or other obvious properties. To do so may lead the uninformed investigator astray. If two tests of unequal length are equally effective, in the sense that they produce dispersions in proportion to their lengths, when no weights are applied at all they are automatically weighted in proportion to their lengths. Attaching more weight to the long test thus merely exaggerates an effect we already have. There is no real justification for weighting tests in proportion to their means, and, when means are proportional to standard deviations, as they often are, the policy would again carry the weighting further in the same direction.

If parts are regarded as *really* of equal importance, then a correction such as was described above would be in order. If the traits measured by different tests are regarded as differing in importance, and if we can decide upon ratios of importance, we can combine weights based upon these ratios with whatever weights we already have. Suppose, for example, we thought that the four variables in Table 16.9 are important in the ratios 2, 2, 5, and 1 (see line 5 of the table). Two weights for a variable are combined by finding their product. In Table 16.9, it would be best to use the factor $19.4/\sigma$ for each test as the weight already established and to multiply it by the weight representing importance. The four products in row 6 of Table 16.9 are 7.46, 2.28, 5.00, and 5.24, respectively. Rounding these, we have 7, 2, 5, and 5. To simplify these still more, if we let the smallest weight equal 1, the others can be expressed as integral multiples of 1 (found by dividing every product by 2.28). The simplified, combined weights are then 3, 1, 2, and 2. These examples are given merely to illustrate several ways in which weights can be derived to meet different requirements and considerations.

Some investigators believe it important to consider reliabilities of measures in weighting them in combinations. By reliability here is meant consistency of scores as indicated by some kind of a self-correlation. If regression weights have been computed, reliabilities have been automatically taken into account and no modification of the weights for reliability would be necessary. But if some other method is used to arrive at weights and if the measures combined differ markedly in reliability, then some index of reliability should be considered. This tends to avoid giving "errors of measurement" in the less reliable instruments too much weight. If reliability coefficients have been computed, the weight contributed from this source should be the square root of each reliability coefficient, rather than the reliability coefficient itself. The type of reliability coefficient should be one indicating internal consistency, i.e., an odd-even type or a Kuder-Richardson type (see Chap. 17).

THE CORRELATION OF COMPOSITE MEASURES WITH OTHER MEASURES

The multiple R is only one index of correlation between a composite measure and some other measure. To test the predictive value for composites with other than optimal weights, we have procedures called collectively the *correlation of sums*. The components may be unweighted (i.e., each weight is +1) or differentially weighted.

Correlation of a composite of unweighted measures. The simplest case is solved by the equation[1]

$$r_{cs} = \frac{r_{c1}\sigma_1 + r_{c2}\sigma_2}{\sqrt{\sigma^2_1 + \sigma^2_2 + 2r_{12}\sigma_1\sigma_2}}$$

(Correlation of a sum of two un-weighted components with a third variable)   (16.23)

where σ_1 and σ_2 = standard deviations of the two components and r_{c1} and r_{c2} = correlation of each component with the third variable.

Let the illustrative summation equation be $X_s = X_4 + X_5$, where X_s stands for a sum of X_4 and X_5, which in recent illustrations have stood for high-school average and interest scores, respectively. What is the correlation of X_s with freshman grades, which here are symbolized by X_c? Applying formula (16.23),

$$r_{cs} = \frac{(.546)(19.4) + (.365)(3.7)}{\sqrt{19.4^2 + 3.7^2 + 2(.345)(19.4)(3.7)}}$$
$$= .570$$

When there are more than two components, the more general formula for the same kind of correlation is

$$r_{cs} = \frac{\Sigma r_{ci}\sigma_i}{\sqrt{\Sigma\sigma^2_i + 2\Sigma r_{ij}\sigma_i\sigma_j}}$$

(Correlation between a sum of un-weighted variables and another single variable)   (16.24)

where r_{ci} = correlation between any one component X_i and the out-side single variable (i varies from 1 to n)

σ_i = standard deviation of the same component

r_{ij} = correlation between X_i and any other component X_j, when j is a higher subscript number than i*

Correlation of a composite of weighted measures. When there are two components, each weighted differently, the correlation with a third measure is given by[2]

$$r_{c(ws)} = \frac{w_1 r_{c1}\sigma_1 + w_2 r_{c2}\sigma_2}{\sqrt{w^2_1\sigma^2_1 + w^2_2\sigma^2_2 + 2r_{12}w_1\sigma_1 w_2\sigma_2}}$$

(Correlation of a sum of two weighted measures with a third measure)   (16.25)

where w_1 and w_2 = weights attached to measures X_1 and X_2, respectively.

[1] See Appendix A, Proof 13.
*Here, as in similar formulas, $r_{ij}\sigma_i\sigma_j$ implies covariances of all possible pairs of variables.
[2] See Appendix A, Proof 13.

For the combination of high-school average and interest scores, let us assume weights of 2 and 5, respectively. These are closely proportional to the b coefficients of .224 and .491, respectively. Applying formula (16.25),

$$r_{c(ws)} = \frac{2(.546)(19.4) + 5(.365)(3.7)}{\sqrt{4(19.4^2) + 25(3.7^2) + 2(.345)(2)(19.4)(5)(3.7)}}$$
$$= .577$$

Thus, crude, integral weights of 2 and 5 would give as high a correlation of the combination of X_4 and X_5 with X_1 (freshman grades) as would the three-digit b coefficients .224 and .491.

For the general case, with more than two components, the correlation with an outside variable is

$$r_{c(ws)} = \frac{\Sigma w_i r_{ci}\sigma_i}{\sqrt{\Sigma w^2_i \sigma^2_i + 2\Sigma r_{ij}w_i\sigma_i w_j\sigma_j}} \qquad \text{(Correlation of a weighted sum with an outside variable)} \qquad (16.26)$$

Alternative summarizing methods

Summative equations represent only one way in which several measures may be combined in order to reach single predictions or decisions. There are alternative methods, some of which are better than regression equations in certain situations. The two chief contenders are the multiple-cutoff method and the profile method. These will be described and their variations discussed.

MULTIPLE-CUTOFF METHODS

In a multiple-cutoff method, a minimum qualifying score or measure is adopted for each variable used in making a joint prediction. A good example of the method is the medical examination in the qualification of individuals for military service, for life insurance, or for employment. Failure to meet the standard on any one test may disqualify the individual. Making a particularly good showing in one respect is not ordinarily allowed to compensate for a poor showing in some other. The phenomenon of compensation, which the regression-equation approach allows, is the chief difference between the two methods, in principle.

Multiple cutoffs contrasted with multiple regression. A geometric illustration of the difference between the two methods may be seen in Fig. 16.4. The two variables represented there (X_2 and X_3) are both independent variables, used jointly to predict some criterion X_1 which is not shown. A moderate correlation, of approximately .40, is assumed between X_2 and X_3, as represented by the familiar ellipti-

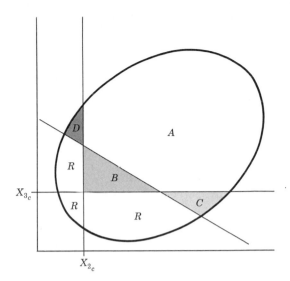

Fig. 16.4. *Geometric comparison of accepted and rejected personnel by the multiple-regression-equation method and the multiple-cutoff method, when approximately equal proportions are selected by either method.* (After R. L. Thorndike, AAF Report No. 3.)

cal distribution of the population. Let us assume a selection problem and that we have the alternatives of applying two cutoff scores X_{2c} and X_{3c} or of applying a single cutoff score based upon a weighted sum of X_2 and X_3. Assume also that we reject the same proportion of the applicants by either method.

The use of two cutoff scores would reject all individuals to the left of the point X_{2c} and a vertical line erected at that point, as well as all individuals below the point X_{3c} and a horizontal line drawn at that level. Some individuals would be rejected on the basis of either variable alone and some on the basis of failure to meet standards on both. The single cutoff on the weighted composite, however, would be represented by a slanted line. This is consistent with the slanted-line system shown in Fig. 16.2. All individuals below and to the left of this slanted line would be rejected.

It is now possible to see which individuals would be accepted by the one method and rejected by the other and on which ones the two methods agree. The individuals in area A of the ellipse would be accepted by either method. The individuals in area R would be rejected by either method. Individuals in area B would be rejected by the multiple-regression-equation method but would be accepted by the multiple-cutoff method. Individuals in areas C and D would be accepted by the regression method but rejected by the cutoff method, those in C for different reasons than those in D.

The crux of the comparison of values of the two methods lies in determining whether individuals in area B are any better in terms of the criterion than those in areas C and D. Individuals in area B are rejected by the one method because they combine low scores in

X_2 and X_3. They just succeed in meeting minimum standards in both variables and so would be accepted by the other method. Individuals in areas C and D, although below standards in one variable, are allowed to present compensating strong scores in the other variable and hence to be accepted by the multiple-regression method. They are regarded as doubtful risks by the cutoff method.

It can be argued that not enough is known about compensatory effects in performances that serve as criteria, and that is quite true. There is a need for experimental studies of this kind. A vindication of the regression method, however, is found in the consistency with which composite scores continue to correlate as they do in line with multiple-correlation coefficients that forecast those correlations. If compensatory effects did not occur, there would probably be much more shrinkage in correlation of sums with criteria than there is.

An evaluation of the multiple-cutoff method.   If all regressions are linear, theoretically, there should be no advantage in selection by multiple cutoffs over that by composites. This can be explained in general terms by the fact that in a linear regression there is a *continuous* improvement in criterion measures with increased score in an independent variable, and at a constant rate. Thus, so far as the relationship between the test and the criterion is concerned, there is no more reason for putting the cutoff at one point rather than another. The cutoff would have to be established on the basis of some other determinants, such as success ratio or validity. In using a number of tests for selection for a single purpose, presumably it would be best to make the most rejections on the basis of the most valid test. When a regression is definitely curved, there is a real basis for using a cutoff on a single test. The cutoff would be established in line with the region of transition between low and high rates of increase in the criterion measure.

There are some practical difficulties in the administration of multiple cutoffs which make the method less appealing than a regression equation. There is the difficulty of establishing several different cutoff points which will take full advantage of the differences in validity among the tests and which will yield the appropriate numbers of qualified applicants. Once the minimum standards are established, however, the method is simple to apply. Failure to meet any one of the minimal scores automatically means rejection.

Rejection of an applicant on the basis of a single test is somewhat risky as compared with rejection on the basis of a composite score, because of the fact that the reliability of a single test score is usually less than that for a composite. If the parts of a composite are positively intercorrelated, the total score is more reliable than the part scores.

PROFILE METHODS

For guidance work and clinical work in general there is a general preference for seeing an individual's scores represented in a pattern provided in a profile. A single summative score is unsuitable or may be unobtainable. A single composite score is unsuitable perhaps because the problem is not one of selection but of classification. In vocational guidance, clients are "sorted" into vocational categories. If there were single summative scores already established with satisfactory correlations with vocational criteria of many kinds, perhaps the profile method would be less important. Clinicians commonly express a desire to "see a personality in its totality," however, and a profile is one approach to this end.

There are several ways of using profiles. Some prefer to interpret an individual's profile intuitively, based upon a general impression of the plotted graph. Others prefer to match more definitely described job-requirement or adjustment-requirement patterns with individual trait patterns. It is possible, by means of careful research, to define certain adjustment requirements in terms of optimal scores in a number of different variables. This statement implies curved regressions, and that is precisely the condition which favors the choice of a profile method over a regression method.

Figure 16.5 demonstrates this kind of use of a profile. By experience, it was found that female workers in a certain kind of routine task tended to be most suited to the job if they had scores in certain regions on the 13 traits scored in the Guilford-Martin personality inventories. Such workers were likely to be best if somewhat shy or reclusive, a little on the depressed and emotional side, less active than average (the task was sedentary), less ascendant socially, somewhat beset with feelings of inferiority, somewhat subjective or hypersensitive, and perhaps none too agreeable or cooperative. In most respects the tendencies listed would seem to present a generally "poor" personality picture. Low extremes were unfavorable, however; the general tendency was just average or slightly below in most traits. This is understandable in that such an individual is probably lacking in aspirations for positions that require the better qualities and is contented with a routine type of work in which adjustments to social requirements are relatively easy. The profile is shown of a certain individual who was rated very high in performance at her task.

For selection purposes, a profile may be handled in various ways. That shown in Fig. 16.5 illustrates one procedure. The favorable zone is clear, and less favorable zones are shaded. The shading can be overprinted on the chart, or a plastic mask can be prepared to lay over individual charts. Decisions can be based upon the *number* of favorable scores or upon the trend of the individual's curve as

C-Score	Co	Ag	O	N	I	M	A	G	R	C	D	T	S	C-Score
10	97+	56+	71+	41+	48+	30+	35+	24	70+	0/5	0/1	0/10	0	10
9	96/89	55/53	70/68	40/38	47/45	29/28	34/33	23/22	69/64	6/9	2/5	11/14	1/3	9
8	88/81	52/47	67/62	37/35	44/43	27/26	32/30	21/20	63/58	10/13	6/9	15/19	4/6	8
7	80/72	46/42	61/55	34/32	42/40	25/24	29/26	19/17	57/51	14/18	10/13	20/25	7/11	7
6	71/65	(41/37)	54/49	31/28	39/36	23/20	25/23	16/14	(50/44)	19/24	14/18	26/31	12/17	6
5	(64/54)	36/32	48/42	27/24	35/33	19/18	22/19	13/12	43/38	25/31	19/25	32/37	18/23	5
4	53/45	31/27	41/36	(23/20)	32/28	17/13	(18/15)	11/9	37/30	32/38	26/31	(38/42)	(24/28)	4
3	44/35	26/22	(35/28)	19/16	27/22	12/11	14/12	8/7	29/23	(39/46)	(32/38)	43/47	29/33	3
2	34/27	21/17	27/20	15/11	(21/15)	(10/8)	11/8	(6/5)	22/16	47/52	39/45	48/53	34/39	2
1	26/20	16/12	19/13	10/7	14/11	7/6	7/5	4/3	15/10	53/58	46/53	54/61	40/46	1
0	19/0	11/0	12/0	6/0	10/0	5/0	4/0	2/0	9/0	59+	54+	62+	47+	0

compared with the trend of the optimal scores. If a single optimal score has been determined for every trait, and an "ideal" profile has been drawn, the departure of a single profile from the ideal profile can be determined in various ways, none of them highly satisfactory. The deviations of each person's scores from the ideal scores can be summarized in various ways. A way that meets common statistical principles would be to square the deviation, sum the squares, find a mean, and then a square root. This would give a single summarizing statistic that has some statistical sanction. There are many who would want more than such a number, however, for it does not tell us where the deviations are.

CLASSIFICATION OF PERSONNEL

Selection of personnel presupposes a supply of applicants and the possibility of rejecting a proportion of them. Attention is upon one kind of assignment to be filled. In the classification of personnel, there are two or more assignments that can be made and one might even consider rejecting none, provided proper assignments can be found for all. In some situations there is the double problem of selection and classification combined. The availability of more than one assignment, however, makes possible the utilization of many more applicants than would be true if there were only one kind of place to fill, for, presumably, personnel who do not qualify for one place might well qualify for some other. The more different kinds of places there are to fill, the smaller the chance of any applicant's being rejected for every kind.

Classification, broadly defined, means assigning each individual to the most appropriate category. This would include the operations in educational and vocational guidance. In vocational guidance, the number of kinds of "assignments" is almost infinite, though the number of major categories is limited. In selection we have an assignment with the need to find the person for it; in classification in general, we have a number of assignments with their requirements in terms of human resources, on the one hand, and a number of persons

Fig. 16.5. *An illustration of the profile method of selection applied to personality-inventory scores. The clear portion of the chart represents what is believed to be the most favorable score ranges for personnel who are assigned to a certain type of routine work. The scores of the worker shown all fell within the clear region.* (Courtesy of R. P. Kreuter, Hand Knit Hosiery Company, Sheboygan, Wis.)

who have the resources to satisfy or not to satisfy each assignment on the other. In vocational guidance, we have one individual, with a unique pattern of resources, on the one hand, and a large variety of possible occupations on the other.

As demonstrated in this and in preceding chapters, we have solved many of the statistical problems involved in selection of personnel. These are bound up with the problems of prediction and with the evaluation of goodness of prediction. By contrast, the problems of classification have been solved more slowly. Assignment to alternative classes requires a *differential prediction*, rather than a prediction on a single variable. We have to predict how much better the individual will adjust or perform if assigned to one category than if assigned to some other category.

When only two assignments are being considered and two predictive indices, we attempt to predict a *difference* in the criterion variable (or between criterion variables) from a *difference* in the assessment variable (or between assessment variables). It is reasonable that the more independence between two criterion variables (the less they intercorrelate), the more easily we can make a differential prediction. The more easily, also, can we find relatively independent assessment variables. Lack of correlation between both the criterion measures and the assessment measures seems to be very important for effective classification.[1]

Classification through selection. Regardless of the number of categories we have in which to place individuals, an approximate solution lies in the application of selection procedures. For each vocational category to be filled, we can derive a multiple-regression equation, where the criterion to be predicted is a measure of success in that vocation. The differences between composite scores would be the deciding factor in classification. If possible, each person would be assigned to that category for which he has the highest composite score. Profile methods could also be used. With an optimal profile developed for each category, and a method of comparing the extent to which an individual's profile approaches different profiles, decisions could be reached.

Use of the discriminant function in classification. A better procedure, that introduces more directly the principle of differential prediction, is to use the *discriminant function*. This is another statistic originated by Fisher. The general principle is that the different scores or measures will be weighted in such a way as to maximize the difference between the means of two composites derived from two criterion

[1]These problems have been discussed at greater length by Thorndike, R. L. *Personnel Selection*. New York: Wiley, 1949; and Brogden, H. J. An approach to the problem of differential prediction. *Psychometrika*, 1946, **11**, 139–154.

groups, relative to the variance within those groups. Suppose that we have two groups of successful individuals in two vocations – selling life insurance and piloting airplanes. We also have scores from individuals in the two groups from several tests. We want to weight the tests (with the same weights applying to both groups) so that the two means of the composite scores would differ as much as possible. The overlapping of the two distributions of composite scores would then be as small as possible. The result would be that an F ratio or a t ratio would be a maximum.

We can approach the problem from the point of view of correlation if we look at it in a different way. If we assign the criterion values of 1 and 0 to the two groups (which group is 1 and which is 0 does not matter), and if we treat the group differentiation as a genuine dichotomy, we have a multiple-point-biserial problem, as demonstrated by Wherry.[1] That is, the dichotomy is a criterion to be predicted by means of a multiple-regression equation, in which the components are optimally weighted. The information with which we start would be a point-biserial r between each measure and the criterion and a Pearson product-moment r (preferred) among the measures of assessment. The procedure for determining the weights in the regression equation would be the same as illustrated in this chapter. The standard deviation of the criterion would be $\sqrt{pq}$, where p = the proportion in one of the groups. A multiple-point-biserial R can also be computed to indicate the goodness of prediction afforded by this equation. A critical cutoff score could be found on the scale of X'.

When there are more than two classes to be predicted, the multiple-regression problem becomes quite complicated. There have been a number of attempts to solve the problem, of which one by Horst is a good example.[2]

EXERCISES

In connection with each exercise, state your conclusions and interpretations.

1. Using information obtained from Data 16A, derive a regression equation involving X_1 (dependent variable) with X_2 and X_4. Compute the multiple R and its standard error.

2. Do the same as in Exercise 1, substituting X_3 and X_5 as the independent variables.

3. Find a regression equation that includes all four of the independent variables in Data 16A, with a multiple R and its SE.

[1]Wherry, R. J. Multiple bi-serial and multiple point bi-serial correlation. *Psychometrika*, 1947, **12**, 189–195.

[2]Horst, P. A technique for the development of a differential prediction battery. *Psychol. Monogr.*, 1954, **68**, No. 380.

*Data 16A   Intercorrelations of scores from four
examinations and marks received in freshman
mathematics (N = 100)*

Variable	X_2	X_3	X_4	X_5	X_1
X_2		.70	.53	.39	.51
X_3	.70		.61	.29	.51
X_4	.53	.61		.28	.61
X_5	.39	.29	.28		.39
X_1	.51	.51	.61	.39	
M_x	4.10	5.44	5.37	4.95	5.70
σ_x	1.92	1.84	2.26	2.14	2.42

X_2 = **Ohio State psychological examination**
X_3 = **English-usage examination**
X_4 = **algebra examination**
X_5 = **engineering-aptitude examination**
X_1 = **marks in freshman mathematics**

4. Two students, A and B, have the following scores:

	X_2	X_3	X_4	X_5
A	8	5	2	7
B	2	4	9	3

Estimate their most probable marks in freshman mathematics, using the regression equations derived in Exercises 1, 2, and 3.

5. Compute the standard errors of multiple estimate, coefficients of multiple determination and multiple nondetermination, and indices of forecasting efficiency for the problems in Exercises 1 and 3.

6. Compute SE's of the regression coefficients in Exercise 1 and the $\bar{z}$ ratios.

7. Apply the shrinkage formulas to the multiple R's and the SE's of estimate in connection with Exercises 1 and 3.

8. Estimate the means of the combinations of scores by the regression weights found in Exercises 1 and 3.

9. Estimate the standard deviation of:
a. An unweighted combination of scores X_2 and X_4 in Data 16A.
b. A weighted combination of the same scores, using the regression weights found in Exercise 1. Check by using the product $\sigma_1 R_{1.24}$.
c. A weighted combination of the same scores, using weights of 2 and 5, respectively.

10. Find the correlation of:
a. An unweighted combination of X_2 and X_4 with X_1.

b. A weighted combination of the same variables with X_1, using weights of 2 and 5, respectively.

Compare these correlations with the multiple $R_{1.24}$.

ANSWERS

1. $X'_1 = .328X_2 + .505X_4 + 1.64$; $R_{1.24} = .649$; $\sigma_R = .059$.

2. $X'_1 = .570X_3 + .299X_5 + 1.12$; $R_{1.35} = .569$; $\sigma_R = .071$.

3. $\beta_{12} = .146$; $\beta_{13} = .096$; $\beta_{14} = .422$; $\beta_{15} = .187$; $X'_1 = .184X_2 + .126X_3 + .452X_4 + .211X_5 + .79$; $R_{1.2345} = .674$; $\sigma_R = .056$.

4. X'_1 (equation 1): 5.3; 6.8; X'_1 (equation 2): 6.1; 4.3; X'_1 (equation 3): 5.3; 6.4.

5. $\sigma_{1.24} = 1.84$; $\sigma_{1.2345} = 1.63$; $R^2_{1.24} = .421$; $R^2_{1.2345} = .454$; $K^2_{1.24} = .579$; $K^2_{1.2345} = .546$; $E_{1.24} = 23.9$; $E_{1.2345} = 32.6$.

6. $\sigma_{\beta12.4} = .091$; $\sigma_{\beta14.2} = .092$; $\sigma_{b12.4} = .115$; $\sigma_{b14.2} = .098$; $\bar{z}_{12.4} = 2.85$; $\bar{z}_{14.2} = 5.16$.

7. $_c\sigma_{1.24} = 1.86$; $_c\sigma_{1.2345} = 1.66$; $_cR_{1.24} = .639$; $_cR_{1.2345} = .656$.

8. M_{ws}: 4.06; 4.91.

9. (a) $\sigma_s = 3.66$; (b) $\sigma_{ws} = 1.57$ (check: $\sigma_1 R_{1.24} = 1.57$); (c) $\sigma_{ws} = 13.73$.

10. (a) $r_{cs} = .644$; (b) $r_{c(ws)} = .645$.

17 *Reliability of measurements*

THE IMPORTANCE OF RELIABILITY

By a perfectly reliable measurement we mean one that is completely accurate or free from error. The same "yardstick" applied to the same individual or object in the same way should yield the same value from moment to moment, provided that the thing measured has itself not changed in the meantime.

There are times, both in theoretical investigations and in practical work, when reliability is very important. Although numbers, as such, are exact, the fact that we amass a series of numbers attached to individuals or observations is no assurance that those numbers mean what they seem to mean concerning the things measured.

There is no way of simply looking at numbers and telling whether they stand for any real values or whether they have been "pulled out of a hat." Some samples of measurements actually approach the latter, chance condition. Others are not exactly "chance" collections of numbers, but there is a strong element of chance involved in them. Conclusions derived from statistical results might differ considerably depending upon how reliable we know the measurements to be. Thus, the matter of reliability merits considerable attention.

Reliability theory

It is impossible to appreciate the many problems that arise in connection with reliability and the several meanings of the term itself without an understanding of some of the mathematical ideas underlying the concept. There exists a rigorous definition of reliability from which it is possible to understand many of the peculiarities of measurements, particularly those called test scores. There are also several operational conceptions of reliability depending upon how it is estimated from empirical data — such as the internal-consistency, test-retest, and alternate-forms methods. Keeping in mind the several kinds of reliability and that operational definitions and logical definitions do not coincide will aid greatly in thinking about problems of reliability. We shall begin with some basic, theoretical conceptions of reliability.

A BASIC DEFINITION OF RELIABILITY

The reliability of any set of measurements is logically defined as the proportion of their variance that is true variance. Before elaborating upon the heart of this statement, which is the last part, attention should be called to the more incidental part. The statement begins with "the reliability of any set of measurements." Note that it is *measurements* that are said to have the property of reliability rather than the measuring instrument. That is because in psychological and educational measurement, and other behavioral and social measurements, reliability depends upon the population measured as well as upon the measuring instrument. It can rarely be said of any instrument, whether a test or some other device, that *the* reliability of that device is of a certain value (usually in the form of a coefficient of correlation). *One should speak of the reliability of a certain instrument applied to a certain population under certain conditions.*

The next comment on the definition, and a more important one, is in the definition of *true* variance. The idea of variance itself is not new. The total variance, which we shall now call σ^2_t, of a set of measurements is the mean of the squares of deviations from the mean of the measurements. The idea of separating total variance into components is also not new. That idea was emphasized in the chapter on analysis of variance (Chap. 13) and in the chapters on prediction of measurements (15 and 16). Here we make a new kind of segregation of variances. We think of the total variance of a set of measures as being made up of two sources or kinds of variance: *true* variance and *error* variance.[1] We think of each single measurement, also, as having two components: a true measure and an error. In terms of an equation,

$$X_t = X_\infty + X_e \qquad \text{(An obtained measure expressed as the sum of a true and an error component)} \qquad (17.1)$$

where X_t = obtained score or measure

X_∞ = true score or measure

X_e = error increment or component

Several assumptions are made in connection with this equation. The *true* measure is assumed to be the genuine value of whatever is

[1] An important distinction should be made here between error variance and sampling variance; the two are quite different. The development of test-measurement theory here ignores sampling errors.

being measured, a value we should obtain if we had a perfect instrument applied under ideal conditions. Another definition is that it is the mean value we should obtain for the object if we measured it a very large number of times. There is no inconsistency between these two conceptions. Any obtained measurement at a particular moment is determined in part by the true value and in part by conditions which bring about a departure, perhaps, from that value.

In measuring a series of objects, it is assumed that the error components occur independently and at random, that their mean is zero (they increase as often as they decrease a measurement), and that they are uncorrelated with the true values and with errors in other measurements. The assumption that the mean of the errors is zero is not essential but it is convenient. These conditions may not always be satisfied. Without evidence to the contrary we assume that they are satisfied. Knowledge of the instrument and of the other conditions of measurement is sometimes sufficient to lend support to these assumptions or to cause us to reject them in any particular situation.

Reliability was defined as the portion of the total variance that is true variance. The three variances, true, error, and total, are illustrated in Table 17.1. There we have a set of 10 hypothetical, true measures whose mean is 25 and whose variance is 105.0. For each true measure we have a corresponding error component that is to be added to it to form a total, or obtained, measure for the individual. The mean of these error components is zero, as assumed above. Their variance is equal to 15.2.

The variance of the total measures can be estimated from the component variances by using formula (16.17). With zero correlation between the true and error components, the variance of the total scores is merely the sum of the two component variances. In the new symbols,

$$\sigma^2_t = \sigma^2_\infty + \sigma^2_e \qquad \text{(A total variance as the sum of true and error variances)} \qquad (17.2)$$

The application of this equation in Table 17.1 gives a total variance of 120.2, which checks with that computed from the sum of squares of X_t.

To satisfy the definition of reliability, we need to find the proportion of total variance that is true variance. If we divide equation (17.2) by σ^2_t, we have proportions:

$$\frac{\sigma^2_t}{\sigma^2_t} = \frac{\sigma^2_\infty}{\sigma^2_t} + \frac{\sigma^2_e}{\sigma^2_t} = 1.00 \qquad \text{(Sum of proportions of true and error variance)} \qquad (17.3)$$

The reliability of these measurements is given by the ratio $\sigma^2_\infty/\sigma^2_t$ or, in another form, by $1 - \sigma^2_e/\sigma^2_t$. In other words, the reliability is

Table 17.1 Dispersion of true measures, error components, and their sums, the total measures, with means, variances, and standard deviations

True measures, X_∞	Error components, X_e	Total measures, X_t $(X_\infty + X_e)$
5	− 2	3
15	+ 2	17
20	− 4	16
25	− 2	23
25	+ 2	27
25	0	25
25	+10	35
30	− 4	26
35	− 2	33
45	0	45
Σ 250	0	250
M 25.0	0.0	25.0
Σx^2 1,050	152	1,202
σ^2 105.0	15.2	120.2
σ 10.2	3.9	11.0
σ_∞	σ_e	σ_t

measured by the ratio of true variance to total variance, or by one minus the ratio of error variance to total variance. Letting r_{tt} stand for the coefficient of reliability, we have two alternative equations:

$$r_{tt} = \frac{\sigma^2_\infty}{\sigma^2_t}$$

(Basic equations for the coefficient of reliability)   (17.4)

$$r_{tt} = 1 - \frac{\sigma^2_e}{\sigma^2_t}$$

For the problem of Table 17.1,

$$r_{tt} = \frac{105.0}{120.2} = .87$$

or

$$r_{tt} = 1 - \frac{15.2}{120.2} = .87$$

If we let e^2 stand for the proportion of error variance in the total, we have the equation

$$r_{tt} + e^2 = 1.00 \qquad \text{(Complementary nature of proportions of true and error variance)} \qquad (17.5)$$

The previous relationships are demonstrated pictorially in Fig. 17.1 and Fig. 17.2. In Fig. 17.1 dispersions of true measures and of total measures are shown. Both have the same mean because the mean of the errors is zero. The standard deviation σ_t is greater than σ_∞. This is always true, unless by some very remote possibility they happen to be equal. The effect of errors of measurement is always to increase obtained dispersions, never to decrease them, unless they should happen to be correlated with the true measures or with each other.

Figure 17.2 presents the picture in a somewhat different manner. Here the summative properties of variances are apparent. Without the assumption of zero correlations for the errors, such a simple picture would be impossible. This kind of representation of variances, in tests particularly, will be encountered with increasing frequency in this and the next chapter.

THE INDEX OF RELIABILITY

The reliability coefficient for a test, r_{tt}, as described thus far, is merely an abstract idea. Operationally, it is some kind of self-correlation of a test.

Before we go into the various operations for estimating r_{tt}, let us add more meaning to the fundamental idea of reliability. Let us think of the true score (X_∞) and the obtained score (X_t) as being two separate variables, the one dependent upon or predictable from the other. This is in spite of the fact that the one includes the other. Think of X_t as the dependent variable and of X_∞ as the independent variable. In a real sense, X_t is determined by or dependent upon X_∞. Figure 17.3

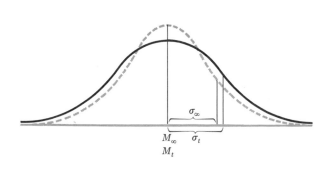

Fig. 17.1. *Distribution of obtained scores in a test (solid curve) and of the hypothetical true-score components (dashed curve). Means of obtained and true scores coincide on the assumption that the mean of the errors of measurement is zero. The standard deviation of the obtained scores is greater than that of the true scores.*

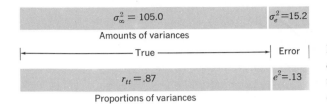

Fig. 17.2. *Amounts of true and error variance (first bar) in a test, and* proportions *of true and error variance (second bar).*

shows these two variables as coordinates and the line of regression of X_t upon X_∞. The correlation between the two, $r_{t\infty}$, is known as the *index of reliability*. The square of this correlation coefficient is an index of determination (see Chap. 14) and it indicates the proportion of variance in X_t that is determined by variance in X_∞. But this is precisely what the reliability coefficient (r_{tt}) tells us. Consequently, we have shown that

$$r^2{}_{t\infty} = r_{tt} \tag{17.6}$$

(Relation of an index of reliability to a coefficient of reliability)

$$r_{t\infty} = \sqrt{r_{tt}} \tag{17.7}$$

Nothing can correlate with obtained scores higher than their correlation with corresponding true scores. The statistic $r_{t\infty}$, then, is often used as an indication of the upper limit of correlation of any variable with another. Since $r_{t\infty}$ is the square root of the reliability coefficient, it is always numerically larger than r_{tt}. Do not be surprised, then, to find that a test may correlate higher with another test than it correlates with itself. We cannot compute $r_{t\infty}$ directly from data, but it can be estimated from r_{tt} or from other information. It is a seldom used statistic, but it has a definite meaning and could be used along with r_{tt} or in place of it.

THE STANDARD ERROR OF MEASUREMENT

Since we can estimate the correlation between obtained and true scores and can think in terms of prediction of one from the other, we can also inquire about the errors of prediction. We know the obtained scores and from them could predict true scores (assuming any mean and standard deviation we please for the true-score scale). But there is nothing to be gained by so doing, for the predictions would be no more accurate than the scores from which they were obtained. Nothing would have happened except a change of unit and zero point.

Suppose that we think in terms of prediction in the other direction, from true scores to obtained scores. This is impossible, practically, since we do not know the true scores from which to make predictions. Let us think rather in terms of determination: of true scores *deter-*

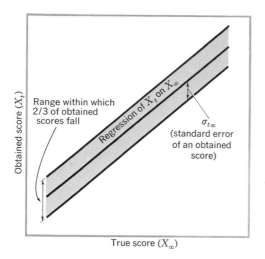

Fig. 17.3. *Regression of obtained scores on true scores, with parallel lines at vertical distances of one standard error ($\sigma_{t\infty}$) from the regression line. (Compare this illustration with Fig. 15.6. The standard error of measurement is also a standard error of estimate when obtained score is "predicted" from true score.)*

mining obtained scores. But errors of measurement also help to determine obtained scores. We are interested in the extent of the discrepancies caused by these errors of measurement, in other words, in the size of distortions produced in the otherwise true-determined measurements. The average of these discrepancies is estimated by the formula

$$\sigma_{t\infty} = \sigma_t \sqrt{1 - r_{tt}} \qquad \text{(Standard error of measurement)} \tag{17.8}$$

where σ_t = standard deviation of the distribution of obtained scores and r_{tt} = reliability coefficient.

The standard error of measurement is a standard error of estimate and may be interpreted as such.[1] Figure 17.3 shows the limits marked off at distances of plus and minus 1 $\sigma_{t\infty}$ from the regression line. In a certain test with a $\sigma_{t\infty}$ equal to 2.0 units, we may say that two-thirds of the obtained scores are within 2.0 units of the true scores that determined them. If a certain individual's true score were 35, for example, the odds are 2 to 1 that his obtained score would not exceed 37 or fall below 33. Allowing a margin of 2σ, we can say that the odds are 19 to 1 that his obtained score will not exceed 39 or fall below 31.

Any obtained score does not tell us what the corresponding true score is, but with knowledge of the $\sigma_{t\infty}$ we have a degree of confidence that the true score cannot be very far away. The same standard error gives us some basis for confidence as to whether the scores for two persons represent a real difference or whether we can tolerate the idea that they could have come from the same true score.

Reliability at different parts of the test scale.   Test users sometimes ask for the standard error of measurement rather than the reliability

[1]This statistic is also called the *standard error of an obtained score*.

coefficient because it tells them more directly what they wish to know. It tells them whether they should be concerned about differences of 2, 4, 8, or 12 points or whether any or all of these differences are within the probable range that could have been produced by errors of measurement. One could set up confidence intervals here for single scores as is done for means and other statistics (see Chap. 8).

It may happen, however, that because of a peculiarity of the test itself, discriminations are better at one part of the scale than at other parts. The $\sigma_{t\infty}$ statistic is a blanket index, implying approximately equal discriminating power all along the scale. If there is reason to suspect that discrimination is actually unequal along the scale, this can be examined by preparing a scatter diagram, showing the relationship between two forms (or halves) of the same test. The standard deviations of the columns or rows at different score levels will indicate where predictions have the greatest accuracy. If the score distribution approaches normality and if obtained scores do not extend over the entire possible range, the standard error of measurement is probably uniform at all score levels.

Computing the standard error of measurement from differences. Rulon has devised a way of computing $\sigma_{t\infty}$ directly from differences between scores made by individuals on odd and even pools of items from the same test.[1] The equation is

$$\sigma_{t\infty} = \sqrt{\frac{\Sigma d^2}{N}} \qquad \text{(Standard error of measurement computed from differences)} \qquad (17.9)$$

where d = difference between two scores of half tests for one individual. A rationale for the Rulon method is that a difference between one half score and the other half score for the same person is a measure of the error for that individual. Since errors are conceived as deviations, squaring, summing, and dividing by N should estimate the amount of error variance. That is precisely what $\sigma^2_{t\infty}$ signifies — the amount of error variance. Thus, $\sigma^2_{t\infty} = \sigma^2_e = \sigma^2_t - \sigma^2_\infty$. This fact will be used later as another way of estimating the reliability coefficient.

Methods of estimating reliability

We leave theory for a while and see how r_{tt} can be estimated from empirical data. There are many procedures, falling into three general categories: (1) internal-consistency reliability, or simply internal consistency; (2) alternate-forms reliability, or comparable-forms reliability, or parallel-forms reliability; and (3) retest reliability, or

[1] Rulon, P. J. A simplified procedure for determining the reliability of a test by split-halves. *Harv. educ. Rev.*, 1939, **9**, 99–103.

test-retest reliability. Cronbach has proposed that we speak of the second and third types of estimate as coefficients of equivalence and of stability, respectively.[1] It would be convenient, also, to speak of the first type as a coefficient of consistency.

There is no one best way of estimating r_{tt}. The method employed will depend upon one's purposes and the meaning and use one wishes to attach to r_{tt}. A secondary consideration is availability of data in the proper form. Other considerations are testing conditions and the kind of test or other measure.

The various procedures differ most in the kinds of things that may be considered as true variance and as error variance. What may be regarded as true variance in computing one kind of r_{tt} may be regarded as error variance in computing one of the others. For the sake of clarity, let us look at some examples.

CONTRIBUTORS TO TRUE AND ERROR VARIANCES

On the whole, sources that contribute to an examinee's making the same score in "repeated" applications of a test are contributors to true variance in the obtained scores. The word "repeated" is in quotation marks here because the repetition is broadly defined so as to include alternate forms or two halves of the same test. On the whole, things that contribute to varying evaluations of performance of an individual in a test are contributors to error variance. The sources of true and error variances are numerous. Certain of them appear clearly and frequently enough to be recognized and named.

Let the bar diagram in Fig. 17.4 represent the total variance in obtained scores of a test. Let c^2 be that proportion of the total variance that would be regarded as true variance no matter what method of estimating r_{tt} is employed. After all, such methods should have very much in common. Let e^2_a be regarded as those sources of error variance that are unique to the alternate-forms method but are regarded as sources of true variance for the other methods. The relative sizes of these portions will vary from test to test. Actual examples of e^2_a and of c^2 will be given shortly. Let e^2_i be sources of error variance particularly when some internal-consistency method is

[1]Cronbach, L. J. Test "reliability": its meaning and determination. *Psychometrika*, 1947, 12, 1–16.

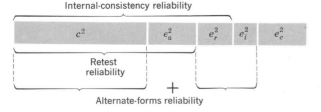

Internal-consistency reliability

Retest reliability

Alternate-forms reliability

Fig. 17.4. *Proportions of the total-score variance that can be regarded as true variance or as error variance, depending upon which type of reliability estimate is made.*

used. This portion is also represented as providing sources of errors for the retest method. Finally, let $e^2{}_r$ be more distinctly the source of error when the retest method is applied, but as being a source of true variance for the other methods. The actual situation is probably not so simple as this, but it is hoped that this much simplicity will contribute to clarity.

Now for some illustrations of actual determinants of the different kinds of variance. These determinants, it must be remembered, are to be thought of as contributing to individual differences between scores, either within a single application of a test or between applications or between forms. Among the determinants of individual differences that are consistent from time to time and from one form of a test to another is individual status in some enduring ability, skill, or other trait or traits. These are what we wish to measure. Incidental determinants that also belong under portion c^2 in the diagram (Fig. 17.4) are general skill in taking tests, skill in taking this particular kind of test, including the form of item used, and possibly the ability to understand test instructions. These additional sources of variance are only potential. For any given test, the task may require so little understanding or the type of item may be so well known to all examinees that they are practically on a par with respect to these determinants and they consequently would not contribute to individual differences in scores. If they do operate to affect variances, however, they would product effects in the same directions in odd and even scores, and, in so far as individuals do not change in these respects from one administration to another, they would contribute to true variance in all three types of reliability estimate.

Determinants that contribute to error variance in the retest method include temporary conditions, either of the examinee or of the testing environment, including the examiner. The examinee's state of health, fatigue, boredom, emotional condition, and the like may well change from one day to another. Environmental conditions can vary considerably without affecting scores materially, but, in so far as they do, such factors as temperature, humidity, lighting, audibility of instructions or signals, ventilation, and the like may differ enough to contribute to error variance.

There are probably more important changes in the examinee himself. Having taken a certain test, he is not the same individual when taking it again. The skills and knowledge acquired during the first administration and in the interval between administrations will have their effects upon the second performance. Memory of answers given on the first occasion may lead to repetitions of the same answers the second time and thus contribute to apparent true variance. Awareness of mistakes made in the first attempt, however, leads to changes in responses and hence to error variance. Besides possible improvement during the taking of the test the first time there is possible improvement resulting from transfer effects occurring during the interval between administrations. There are also possible maturational factors, particularly in young children. If learning and maturational effects were uniform for all individuals, or in proportion to their initial positions in the distribution, they would not contribute to error variance. But to the extent that learning and maturational effects differ from person to person, they do add much to error variance.

The longer the time interval between test administrations, the greater the error contributions. In some tests, continuous loss in reliability occurs as a function of time interval between test and retest. In some psychomotor tests, self-correlations of .90 to .96 may be found by the odd-even method (correlating two scores, one from odd-numbered items and one from even-numbered items), but test-retest correlations with a year interval between may give correlations of approximately .70. Results of this kind were found in testing aviation cadets in the AAF before training and again after air-crew training and perhaps some combat.

Error variance in the alternate-forms method is contributed chiefly by the change in content of the test. Knowledge and skill for dealing with one particular set of items may vary somewhat from the knowledge and skill for dealing with another set of items, and these variations differ from person to person. In addition, depending upon the time interval between administrations of the two forms, some of the causes of error variance just mentioned for the retest method may also apply to the alternate-forms method. An experiment in the AAF[1] in which the two forms were given in immediate succession and also with 4 hours of other testing intervening showed no appreciable change in the size of the self-correlation. Longer periods might well be expected to have some effect.

If the odd-even technique is used in the split-half method (using two scores from two halves of the same test, in the same administration), the changes in conditions that may occur during a single administration of a test are rather uniformly distributed over all items in both halves so that their effects would not show up as error variance. There are other ways of splitting tests into halves, however, which may allow more error variance to creep in. If the test is divided by blocks of items, as in odd and even half pages, or odd and even 2-min trials, or first half against second half, there is room for systematic shifting of conditions. The effects of learning, of temporary changes

[1]Guilford, J. P., and Lacey, J. I. (eds.). Printed classification tests. *AAF Aviation Psychology Research Program Reports*, No. 5. Washington, D.C.: GPO, 1947. Pp. 25–34.

in mental set (as for speed versus accuracy or as to mode of attack on the items), or of fatigue or motivation then might contribute to error variance. These are represented in section e^2_i in Fig. 17.4.

The sources of error that would affect all methods of reliability estimate alike, represented by e^2_c, are such phenomena as fluctuations of attention or memory or motivation that occur from moment to moment or from item to item. In some tests, guessing is an important contributor to error variance. If a test is so difficult that everyone does considerable guessing (in the extreme case assume that every examinee guessed on every item), the total scores for all examinees approach chance distributions whose variances are very largely error variance. If guessing is a feature in any test, the more difficult the test, the lower its reliability is likely to be. On the other hand, the easier the test, the lower the dispersion of scores and the lower the reliability. The smaller the number of alternative responses, the greater is the importance of guessing. True-false tests of the same material and the same number of items are less reliable than are four-choice tests, and these, in turn, are less reliable than tests of the completion form, other things being equal. The moral of this, of course, is to avoid items with too small a number of alternative responses or to compensate for the greater chance element by making the test longer.

WHEN DIFFERENT METHODS OF ESTIMATING r_{tt} ARE PREFERRED

Preference for one of the three types of reliability estimate depends mostly upon several considerations: type of test, meaning of the statistic, and the purpose for which the statistic will be used. These considerations will now be explained.

Homogeneous versus heterogeneous tests. Psychological tests can be divided roughly into two classes: homogeneous and heterogeneous. The former are functionally uniform or, in the extreme case, factorially unique. They measure one factor, i.e., one ability or trait. Very few tests satisfy this definition completely. Some examples are vocabulary, numerical-operations, and perceptual-speed tests. The great majority of tests are factorially complex. Each one measures at the same time a number of different abilities or traits.

So far as reliability is concerned, other tests may be considered homogeneous if the items are similar in factorial content. That is, if the test as a whole measures abilities P, Q, and R, and if each and every item also measures those three abilities, for operational purposes the test may be regarded as functionally homogeneous. An example of this would be an arithmetic-reasoning test or a figure-analogies test.

We expect that homogeneous tests shall be internally consistent—

we want all parts to measure the same thing, or things; consequently, some form of internal-consistency index is called for, unless the speed element is appreciable (many examinees do not complete the test).

If a test is heterogeneous, in the sense that different parts measure different traits, we should not expect a very high index of internal consistency. An example of such a test is a biographical-data inventory. This kind of test is composed of questions concerning the examinee's previous life and experiences. Each response to every item is usually validated by correlating it with some practical criterion, for example, success in pilot training. The reason one response is valid is not necessarily the same as the reason another is valid. They may both predict the criterion and yet correlate zero with each other. The parts of such a test, one randomly chosen half and another, will probably not correlate very high with each other. The test has low internal consistency. An r_{tt} computed in this manner would not do justice to the test. Neither would an alternate-forms r_{tt}, if the forms were developed without regard for item intercorrelations.

The only meaningful estimate of reliability for a heterogeneous test is of the retest variety. If, by chance, a heterogeneous test were developed, each item of which correlated with a criterion and yet did not correlate with any other item, the internal-consistency reliability would be zero. Yet, the retest reliability might be substantial or high. A biographical-data test of the type referred to above had a characteristic split-half reliability coefficient of about .35 and a retest reliability of about .65. Both these values are unusually low, but the test had a validity close to .40 for the selection of pilots and consequently was very useful.

It is clear from the discussion above that the internal consistency and the stability of the same test need not agree very closely. There can be very low internal consistency and yet substantial or high retest reliability. It is probably not true, however, that there can be high internal consistency and at the same time low retest reliability, except after very long time intervals. High internal-consistency reliability is in itself assurance that we are dealing with a homogeneous test, at least within the broad meaning of the term stated above.

Speed tests and power tests. Tests are also sometimes roughly categorized as speed tests and power tests. There is no sharp line of demarcation. A genuine power test is one that all examinees have time to finish. It is intended that every examinee shall attempt every item. Achievement examinations are in this category. Speed tests are those in which there is a time limit such that not all examinees can attempt all items. In this category are tests ranging all the way from those in which no one attempts all items to those in which 99 per cent may do so. The latter are so close to the power type that many examiners would be inclined to place them in the power category. As a general (rough) criterion, we may say that a power test is one finished by at least 75 per cent of the examinees.

It would be out of the question to use the odd-even method of self-correlation with a highly speeded test. If no examinee finished and if there were no errors, the correlation of halves would be +1.00, which would have no meaning except that the scorer had counted the numbers of reactions in the two halves correctly. If first and last halves were used, assuming everyone finished the first half and there were almost no errors, all scores for the first half would be about the same and those for the last half would depend upon the rate of work. The correlation would be near zero, for lack of dispersion of the first-half scores.

In fact, any internal-consistency estimate of r_{tt} would be misapplied to a speed test. The errors caricatured above are present to some degree no matter which one of the internal-consistency methods we apply. A retest method will be adequate for many speed tests, except where there is identity of items and hence learning and memory are sources of variance, both true and error, in unknown proportions. For most speed tests, and this includes those in which any appreciable number of examinees fail to reach the last item, an alternate-forms type of reliability estimate is usually best.

A good device to use in the development of new tests is to prepare two equivalent halves and to administer them in immediate succession as two separately timed tests. The correlation between the two halves, independently administered, can be treated as we treat the correlation of any other half scores by the Spearman-Brown formula (to be explained shortly) in order to estimate the reliability of the full-length test. The comparability of the halves can usually be accomplished by careful construction. Some check upon the adequacy of the efforts is in the comparability of means, standard deviations, and skewness of the two distributions.

Meaning and use of the indices of reliability.   The retest method yields information about the stability of rank orders of individuals over a period of time. A high r_{tt} from this source indicates that persons change very little in status within their population from the first to the second testing; also that the test measures the same functions before and after the interval. A low r_{tt} of this type may mean that individuals have changed in different directions or in the same direction at different rates. Changes of means and of standard deviations will help to interpret the kinds of systematic changes taking place. Plots of scatter diagrams may show whether systematic changes are uniform over the range. These changes we call *function fluctuations of individuals*. If the test measures something different after an interval than before, we have a *function fluctuation of the test*. These changes can be examined by means of correlations of the test with other tests before and after the interval; better yet, by factor analysis (see Chap. 18).

There may be some practical reasons for knowing the stability of scores over periods of time and, if so, the retest r_{tt} is the index to use. Usually, the length of time is a factor to be considered. The chief use of this information is in deciding whether to depend upon scores that were obtained in an earlier testing or to administer the same test or a new form to obtain some scores that better describe the individuals right now. As a general policy it would be desirable to establish the principles regarding what kinds of tests yield stable scores, with what kinds of populations, and over what periods of time, and what kinds of tests do not.

The meaning of internal consistency was covered in a superficial way in the discussion of homogeneous tests. We shall go more thoroughly into the matter shortly in treating the specific methods under this category. This concept probably comes closest to the basic idea of reliability. The methods make an estimate of reliability from a single administration of a single test form. The estimate is of an "on-the-spot" reliability. It tells us something of how closely the obtained score comes to the score the person would have made at this particular time if we had had a perfect measuring instrument. For some purposes this information will certainly not be sufficient. It is the kind of reliability that does have meaning in connection with factorial descriptions of tests. These descriptions (see Chap. 18) attempt to depict a test in terms of its component variances, some of which combine to make up its true variance. It tells us nothing about function stability of persons or of tests.

The alternate-forms estimate of r_{tt} tells us something about function stability in variations of the same test or in different items that have been designed to measure the same functions. It indicates how independent the measurements are of the particular items or content used. If the two forms happen to be two halves of the same test, then presumably the kind of items is the same in both (verbal, numerical, pictorial — matching, multiple-choice, completion); only the specific problems change. The alternate-forms r_{tt} may tend to be slightly lower than the internal-consistency r_{tt}, but this may mean that it gives a more realistic picture of how accurately the test measures the general traits, ruling out whatever variance is dependent upon the particular content of one form of the test. The two estimates will be almost identical, probably, in power tests of very closely matched content. In power tests, then, the two methods could be used almost interchangeably. In speed tests, as indicated above, the alternate-forms method is the most justifiable approach to reliability estimate.

Internal-consistency reliability

There are several operations by which an internal-consistency estimate of reliability may be made, and there is so much basic test
theory bound up with them that we need to give this approach special
attention. First, we shall consider some theory.

THE STATISTICAL NATURE OF A TEST COMPOSED OF ITEMS

Most tests are composed of items. Most tests are scored by giving
credit of +1 for a correct response to each item and a weight of 0 for
each wrong answer or omission. The theory about to be explained assumes that kind of test. Furthermore, it applies best to a power test,
in which omissions and wrong answers probably mean inability to
master the item. For the time being we shall not be concerned with
the problem of chance success by guessing. We might assume completion items in which chance factors resulting from guessing are
almost nil. The theory will probably apply to situations deviating appreciably from these specifications, enough so that the many conclusions to which it leads will have quite general application.

Item statistics.   It is convenient to think of each item as a subtest
in a larger composite. Each item, then, yields a distribution of scores,
with a mean and a standard deviation. The mean of such a distribution, where the measures are either 0 or 1, is equal to p, the proportion of all attempting the item who get the right answer; the variance
of the distribution is equal to pq, where $q = 1 - p$; and the standard
deviation is $\sqrt{pq}$.

The total score on such a test is the sum of part scores. In equation
form,

$$X_t = X_a + X_b + X_c + \cdots + X_i + \cdots + X_n \tag{17.10}$$
(The sum of item scores to make a total test score)

where $X_a, X_b, \ldots, X_n$ = scores in items $a, b, \ldots, n$, when there are
n items in the test.

The variance of the total test score can be derived from the variances and covariances of the items, according to the principles
brought out in the preceding chapter in connection with the variance
of sums. Equation (16.19) applied to this particular use would therefore read

$$\sigma^2_t = p_a q_a + p_b q_b + p_c q_c + \cdots + p_i q_i + \cdots + p_n q_n$$
$$+ 2r_{ab} \sqrt{p_a q_a p_b q_b} + 2r_{ac} \sqrt{p_a q_a p_c q_c} + \cdots$$
$$+ 2r_{(n-1)n} \sqrt{(p_{(n-1)} q_{(n-1)} p_n q_n} \tag{17.11}$$
(Total test variance as summation of item
variances and covariances)

where $p_a, p_b, \ldots, p_n$ = proportion passing items $a, b, \ldots, n$

$\qquad q_a, q_b, \ldots, q_n = 1 - p_a, 1 - p_b, \ldots, 1 - p_n$

$r_{ab}, r_{ac}, \ldots, r_{(n-1)n}$ = intercorrelations of items

In abbreviated, summational form, the equation reads

$$\sigma^2_t = \Sigma p_i q_i + 2\Sigma r_{ij} \sqrt{p_i q_i p_j q_j} \qquad \begin{array}{l}[\text{Same as formula (17.11) in}\\ \text{summation form}]\end{array} \qquad (17.12)$$

where $p_i = p_a, p_b, \ldots, p_n$, in turn and r_{ij} = correlation between item i and item j, where subscript j is numerically greater than i.

An example of item and test statistics. As an example of what has just been presented in terms of equations, let us take an artificial test of eight items, which has been administered to ten fictitious examinees, with resulting data as shown in Table 17.2. The tabulation is known as an item-score matrix because of the rows and columns of item scores, a column for each item and a row for each examinee. The items are arranged in order of increasing difficulty from left to right and the examinees are arranged in order of ability, from top to bottom, for the sake of convenience. The item score is 1 for a right answer and 0 for a wrong answer. All examinees attempted all items.

The sums of the rows of scores give total scores X_t for the individuals. The sums of the columns give the numbers of persons passing the various items. The sums of both sets yield the same overall sum,

Table 17.2   *An item-score matrix, listing eight item scores for each of ten examinees, with scores of 1 for right answers and 0 for wrong answers, along with odd and even scores and their differences*

		a	*b*	*c*	*d*	·	·	*i*	·	·	*n*	$\sum_{i=1}^{n} s_i = X_t$	X_o	X_e	*d*	d^2
								Items								
	1	0	0	0	0	0	0	0	0			0	0	0	0	0
	2	1	0	0	0	0	0	0	0			1	1	0	1	1
	3	1	0	1	0	0	0	0	0			2	2	0	2	4
	4	1	1	0	0	1	0	0	0			3	2	1	1	1
	5	0	1	0	1	0	0	1	0			3	1	2	1	1
	·	1	1	1	0	1	0	1	0			5	4	1	3	9
	·	1	1	1	1	1	1	0	0			6	3	3	0	0
	j	1	1	1	1	1	1	0	0			6	3	3	0	0
	·	1	1	1	1	0	1	0	1			6	2	4	2	4
	N	1	1	1	1	1	1	1	1			8	4	4	0	0
	$\sum_{j=1}^{N} s_i$	8	7	6	5	5	4	3	2			$40 = \Sigma X_t$	22	18		20
	p_i	.8	.7	.6	.5	.5	.4	.3	.2			$4.0 = M_t$			$\sigma^2_d =$	2.0
	$p_i q_i$	.16	.21	.24	.25	.25	.24	.21	.16			$1.72 = \Sigma p_i q_i$	$\sigma^2_t = 6.0$		$\sigma_t =$	2.45

Examinees (row label, left margin)

40, which is ΣX_t. Dividing the sums of the columns by N, we obtain the means for the items, where $M_i = p_i$, the proportion passing each item. The variance for each item is $p_i q_i$, giving values that appear in the last row of the table. The sum of the variances equals 1.72. The variance for the total scores X_t is equal to 6.0 (for which the computation is not shown). If we deduct the sum of the item variances from this quantity, we have $6.0 - 1.72$, which equals 4.28. From equation (17.12), it can be seen that this difference is the portion of the total-score variance that is contributed by the sum of the covariance terms (doubled). With eight item scores summed, there are $8(8 - 1)/2$, or 28, different covariance terms, each added in twice. We are not concerned with those covariance terms, as such, here. Each one, of course, contains a term for the correlation between a pair of items, a phi coefficient. We shall use the covariance values later, along with other information from Table 17.2. For the moment, we return to further consideration of formula (17.12).

DEDUCTIONS DERIVED FROM THE ITEM-VARIANCE EQUATIONS

There are many useful and enlightening inferences that can be deduced from equation (17.12). We shall consider only the most important ones here.

Relation of variance to item difficulty.   The first thing to be noted is the relation of variance to item difficulty. Remembering that variance means individual differences and that the greater the variance, the more we have dispersed individuals in measurement, it can be stated that the item that will produce the greatest dispersion is of median difficulty. It is an item passed by half of the group and failed by half of the group. When $p = q = .5$, the pq product is at a maximum. As p approaches 0 or 1 the variance decreases toward the vanishing point. This has a common-sense explanation. Let us suppose an item that 1 person out of 100 can answer correctly. This item discriminates 1 person from each of 99, or makes 99 discriminations. Then, suppose an item that can be passed by 2 out of 100. This item makes 2×98 discriminations, or 196. Continue this to 50, and we get 2,500 discriminations, each one of the 50 who pass it from each one, in turn, of the 50 who fail it. Items of moderate difficulty, then, yield the maximum variance.

Relation of reliability to item intercorrelations.   For the sake of internal consistency, however, large item variances by themselves would mean nothing. If equation (17.12) were limited to the item variance terms alone, the test would have zero internal consistency, zero reliability of the internal type. This kind of reliability comes entirely from the covariance terms, and these are composed of item intercorrelations as well as indices of dispersion. It is only by virtue of their entering into the covariance terms that the item variances contribute to internal consistency. The intercorrelations of the items are the essential sources of this kind of reliability. The larger the item intercorrelations, the greater is the internal consistency.

The effect of range of item difficulty upon reliability. Reliability will be higher when the items are nearly equal in difficulty. A wide range of difficulty of items is not favorable to reliability. The reason is that the appropriate index of item intercorrelation is the ϕ coefficient. Operationally, with items scored as either 0 or +1, their distributions are best conceived as point distributions. If two items differ much in difficulty, the proportions passing the two differ and ϕ is thus restricted in size. Only when the two items are equally difficult can the ϕ between them equal +1 as a maximum (see Chap. 14). Two items very far apart in difficulty might correlate less than .20 even when each measures the same thing and measures it well.

Effect of item intercorrelations upon total-score distributions. There is an interesting bearing of the internal consistency of a test upon the form of distribution of total scores on that test. Imagine a test of 10 items each of exactly median difficulty for the population ($p = q = .5$) and each correlated +1.0 with every other item. A person who passes one item would pass them all and a person who fails one item would fail them all. There would be only two scores possible, 0 and 10. If 20 examinees took this test, the chances are good that their frequency distribution would be like the first diagram in Fig. 17.5. There would be perfect and maximal separation of the two groups. The form of the distribution would be U-shaped. Examples of U-shaped distributions can be found in Hull's book on hypnosis and suggestibility, though they are not so extreme as the one in Fig. 17.5.[1] It appears that some tests of suggestibility are such that if the examinee responds in the suggestible manner in one trial he is likely to respond similarly in all trials.

If the item intercorrelations are not perfect but high, there will be some moderate scores but there will be a distinct tendency toward bimodality. The second distribution in Fig. 17.5 shows this type of test. With still further reduction in item intercorrelation, the distribution approaches rectangular form, as in the third diagram in Fig. 17.5. With still further reduction in correlation, the distribution approaches normal form, but is somewhat platykurtic. A test of zero internal consistency, and with all items of median difficulty, would probably yield a normal distribution. It should not be concluded, however, that a normal distribution indicates zero reliability. It might do so if all items were of equal difficulty at the level of $p = .5$ and are uncorrelated. Rarely do tests conform to this condition.

[1]Hull, C. L. *Hypnosis and Suggestibility.* New York: Appleton-Century-Crofts, 1933. P. 68.

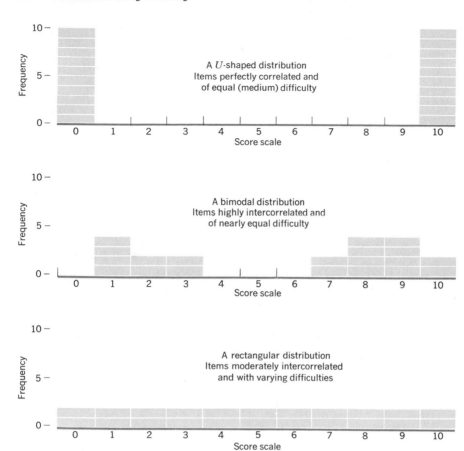

Fig. 17.5. *Illustration of the effects of item intercorrelation upon the form of the frequency distribution of total-test scores.*

THE SPEARMAN-BROWN FORMULA

The Spearman-Brown (S-B) formula was designed to estimate the reliability of a test n times as long as the one for which we know a self-correlation. Many times a split-half correlation is known for a test and the correlation of halves is an estimate of r_{tt} for the half test. The full-length test is not twice as reliable as the half test, but its reliability is greater and can be estimated by the special Spearman-Brown formula with $n = 2$. If we let r_{hh} stand for the correlation between halves of a test,

$$r_{tt} = \frac{2r_{hh}}{1 + r_{hh}}$$ (Reliability of a total test estimated from reliability of one of its halves)   (17.13)

An odd-even estimate of reliability.   To illustrate in a general way the application of this special case of the S-B formula, we use data from Table 17.2. For each examinee we have two split-half scores, one based on his item scores for odd-numbered items and the other on his item scores for even-numbered items. They are listed under the headings of X_o and X_e. The correlation between X_o and X_e was found to be .542. Applying formula (17.13),

$$r_{tt} = \frac{2(.542)}{1 + .542} = .70$$

The quantity .54 may be taken as an estimate of reliability of each of the two four-item tests, while .70 is the estimate of reliability of the total eight-item test.

When this estimation formula is used, comparability of the halves must be assumed. Comparability is indicated to some degree by the similarity of means, standard deviations, skewness of distributions, and, of course, content. If comparability is lacking, the reliability of the total test will be wrongly estimated. Since comparability is probably never perfect, an estimate by the use of the Spearman-Brown formula is probably conservative, that is, it tends to be an underestimate.

Because the split-half method and the alternate-forms method in the form of two separately timed halves of the same test are so commonly used in practice, the chart in Fig. 17.6 is supplied as an aid in the use of formula (17.13). Since the estimates are approximate, in any case, the graphic solution will probably serve for most purposes.

For the general case, in which n could be any ratio of test length to that for which r_{11} is known,

$$r_{nn} = \frac{nr_{11}}{1 + (n - 1)\, r_{11}}$$ (Spearman-Brown formula for reliability of a test of length n)   (17.14)

where r_{11} = reliability of the test of unit length.[1]

The ratio n in equation (17.14) could be fractional just as well as integral. If we knew the self-correlation for a test of 50 items, and we wanted to know the probable reliability for a similar test of 75 items, n would equal 1.5. If we knew the reliability of a test of 100 items and wanted to know approximately the reliability for a test of the same kind just half as long, n would be 0.5.

THE KUDER-RICHARDSON ESTIMATES OF RELIABILITY

In accordance with item theory, the Kuder-Richardson (K-R) formulas for estimating r_{tt} depend upon item statistics. They were developed because of dissatisfaction with split-half methods. A test can be

[1]For the derivation of formula (17.14) see proof at the end of this chapter.

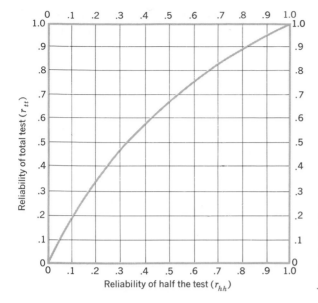

Fig. 17.6. *Reliability of a total-test score as a function of known reliability of a half-test score when the Spearman-Brown formula is applied.*

split into halves in a great many ways, and each split might yield a somewhat different estimate of r_{tt}. The use of item statistics gets away from such biases as may arise from arbitrary splitting into halves.

The Kuder-Richardson methods make the same assumptions as are involved in the use of the Spearman-Brown formula. Those assumptions call for items of equal, or nearly equal, difficulty and intercorrelation.

The most accurate of the practical Kuder-Richardson formulas (known as their formula 20) is [1]

$$r_{tt} = \left(\frac{n}{n-1}\right)\left(\frac{\sigma^2_t - \Sigma pq}{\sigma^2_t}\right) \quad \text{(General Kuder-Richardson formula for estimating reliability)} \quad (17.15)$$

where n = number of items in the test
$\quad p$ = proportion passing an item (or responding in some specified manner)
$\quad q = 1 - p$

It will be recognized, in comparing this formula with equation (17.12), that the numerator term $(\sigma^2_t - \Sigma pq)$ is the sum of the covariance terms in the summation of item variances and covariances used to express the total test variance. The expression Σpq is the sum

[1]Richardson, M. W., and Kuder, G. F. The calculation of test reliability coefficients based upon the method of rational equivalence. *J. educ. Psychol.*, 1939, **30**, 681–687.

of the variances of all items. Deducting this quantity from the total test variance, we have left the sum of the covariances. It is in these covariances that the source of *true* variance lies. The ratio of this quantity $(\sigma^2_t - \Sigma pq)$ to the total-test variance thus would seem to satisfy the basic definition of reliability given in the first part of this chapter. The factor $n/(n-1)$ is a correction to help take into account the fact that the numerator of the other fraction could never reach the quantity σ^2_t and hence equal 1.00, for Σpq would never be zero.

Having information on item variances in the data of Table 17.2, we can apply the Kuder-Richardson formula 20 to the eight-item test. Substituting the known values from that source,

$$r_{tt} = \left(\frac{8}{7}\right)\left(\frac{6.00 - 1.72}{6.00}\right)$$
$$= \frac{8(4.28)}{42}$$
$$= .81$$

The estimate here is higher than that from the odd-even approach, but this should not be surprising. The odd-even estimate is likely to be an underestimate. It is based on a division of a test in one arbitrary way, whereas the K-R formula 20 takes into account all possible ways of subdividing the test.

An approximation K-R formula. If we are justified in assuming that all items in the test have approximately the same degree of difficulty, we may use a formula that demands less information. It reads

$$r_{tt} = \left(\frac{n}{n-1}\right)\left(\frac{\sigma^2_t - n\overline{pq}}{\sigma^2_t}\right) \qquad \text{(An approximation formula for Kuder-Richardson reliability)} \qquad (17.16)$$

where $\overline{p}$ and $\overline{q}$ = average proportions of passing and failing examinees for each item, respectively. The equation is known as the Kuder-Richardson formula 21.

Applying the K-R formula 21 to the data from Table 17.2, where the mean p is .5 and therefore $\overline{pq}$ is .25, we have

$$r_{tt} = \left(\frac{8}{7}\right)\left[\frac{6.00 - 8(.25)}{6.00}\right]$$
$$= .76$$

This estimate is a bit lower than that from formula K-R 20, but a bit higher than the odd-even estimate. The estimate from K-R 21 is expected generally to be lower than that from K-R 20.

One advantage to formula K-R 21 is that we need not even make item counts, for the average p is equal to the mean of the total scores divided by n, and $\bar{q} = 1 - \bar{p}$. From these facts, the formula can be simplified to

$$r_{tt} = \frac{n\sigma^2_t - \overline{RW}}{(n-1)\sigma^2_t} \qquad \text{[Alternate to formula (17.16)]} \qquad (17.17)$$

where $\overline{R}$ = average number of right responses and $\overline{W}$ = average number of wrong responses (or $n - \overline{R}$). $\overline{R}$ is, of course, the mean of the total scores, where the total score is a sum of the item scores or number of right answers. Thus, for $\overline{R}$ and $\overline{W}$, we can substitute M and $(n - M)$, respectively.

It should be said that all the Kuder-Richardson formulas, indeed all the internal-consistency formulas that depend upon a single administration of a test, probably underestimate the reliability of a test, formula (17.17) most of all. Even formula (17.15) gives an underestimate when there is wide dispersion of item difficulties.

Horst's modification. More recently, Horst has suggested a modification of formula (17.15) which allows for variations of item difficulty.[1] The modification takes into account the extent to which the test approaches the maximum variance that a test with the same distribution of difficulties could have. That maximum variance is estimated by the formula

$$\sigma^2_m = 2\Sigma R_i p_i - M_t(1 + M_t) \qquad \begin{array}{l}\text{(Maximum variance a test}\\ \text{could achieve with its given}\\ \text{distribution of item}\\ \text{difficulties)}\end{array} \qquad (17.18)$$

where R_i is the rank position of an item in the test, where items are ranked for difficulty, the easiest item being ranked 1. p_i is the item mean and M_t the total-test mean. For the test represented in Table 17.2, the $R_i p_i$ products are summed as follows:

$$1(.8) + 2(.7) + 3(.6) + 4(.5) + 5(.5) + 6(.4) + 7(.3) + 8(.2) = 14.6$$

Applying formula (17.18),

$$\sigma^2_m = 2(14.6) - 4(5)$$
$$= 9.2$$

This value is to be compared with an obtained σ^2_t of 6. The modified K-R formula is designed to tell us how nearly the obtained variance approaches the maximum variance possible. The modified formula reads

$$r_{tt} = \left(\frac{\sigma^2_t - \Sigma pq}{\sigma^2_m - \Sigma pq}\right)\left(\frac{\sigma^2_m}{\sigma^2_t}\right) \qquad \begin{array}{l}\text{(Horst's modified Kuder-}\\ \text{Richardson formula)}\end{array} \qquad (17.19)$$

[1]Horst, P. Correcting the Kuder-Richardson reliability for dispersion of item difficulties. *Psychol. Bull.*, 1953, **50**, 371–374.

Substituting the values we have,

$$r_{tt} = \left(\frac{6 - 1.72}{9.2 - 1.72} \right) \left(\frac{9.2}{6} \right)$$
$$= \left(\frac{4.28}{7.48} \right) \left(\frac{9.2}{6} \right)$$
$$= .88$$

Assuming that the Horst formula gives the most nearly correct estimate of r_{tt}, we can see how much the other formulas fall short, in this particular instance. It is likely that in tests containing larger numbers of items and less dispersion of item difficulty, the variations among such estimates would be smaller.

It should be emphasized that the K-R formulas were designed for power tests, in which every examinee has a chance to attempt every item. They are entirely precluded for speed tests and for many others that depart very far from the power-test condition.

THE RULON METHOD OF ESTIMATING r_{tt}

It was mentioned earlier that Rulon had developed a method of computing the standard error of measurement, $\sigma_{t\infty}$, from differences in scores on two halves of a test. Because of the relations between r_{tt} and $\sigma_{t\infty}$, the same approach leads to another kind of estimate of reliability. It is usually applied to halves of the test in a single administration and hence comes under the category of an internal-consistency reliability, but it can also be applied to alternate forms.

Because $\sigma^2_{t\infty}$ measures the amount of error variance, an estimate of r_{tt} is given by the formula[1]

$$r_{tt} = 1 - \frac{\sigma^2_{t\infty}}{\sigma^2_t} \qquad \text{(Reliability by the Rulon formula)} \tag{17.20}$$

where $\sigma^2_{t\infty} = \Sigma d^2 / N$, as in formula (17.9). This formula can be conveniently applied to the odd and even scores in Table 17.2. What we need for the numerator term is the mean of the differences squared, which is 2.0. The estimated reliability by this method is

$$r_{tt} = 1 - \frac{2.0}{6.0}$$
$$= \frac{2}{3} = .67$$

This estimate is close to two others of .70 that were found for the same data, but very short of the best estimate by the modified K-R 20 formula. Since it is based upon the odd and even scores, we should expect it to be close to the odd-even estimate.

The Rulon method has the same restrictions as any split-half

[1] Rulon, *op. cit.*

procedure. It should be noted that *the formula gives the reliability of the total test scores and not of the halves,* and therefore the Spearman-Brown formula should not be applied. If the Rulon difference formula should be applied to differences between scores on two forms, the reliability coefficient thus estimated applies to a test of twice the length of either form. A correction to the reliability wanted for each form can be made by substituting .5 for n in formula (17.14).

RELIABILITY ESTIMATED FROM ITEM-TEST CORRELATIONS

If we know the size of the item intercorrelations for a test, and if they are uniform in size, or nearly uniform, we can apply the Spearman-Brown formula, letting n equal the number of items, to find an estimate of r_{tt}.

We would probably not want to take the trouble to determine the intercorrelations among items (although computers now make this a real possibility); their average can be estimated in a manner that is feasible. It has been shown that when item intercorrelations are of about the same magnitude and when items are of approximately equal difficulty, the average item intercorrelation is equal to the square of the average correlation of items with total score.[1]

In a formula,

$$\bar{r}_{ij} = \bar{r}^2_{it} \qquad \begin{array}{l}\text{(Relation of average item intercorrelation} \\ \text{to average item-test correlation)}\end{array} \qquad (17.21)$$

where the bars over the r's indicate that they are averages; r_{ij} = correlation between item I and item J, a ϕ coefficient; and r_{it} = correlation between item I and total test score, a point-biserial r. The item-test correlations are frequently known, as a by-product of item analysis. Their squared mean can be used in the Spearman-Brown formula, which would then read

$$r_{tt} = \frac{n\bar{r}^2_{it}}{1 + (n-1)\,\bar{r}^2_{it}} \qquad \begin{array}{l}\text{(Estimate of } r_{tt} \text{ from average} \\ \text{item-test correlations)}\end{array} \qquad (17.22)$$

where $\bar{r}_{tt}$ = mean of correlations of items with total test score.

A SUMMARY OF INTERNAL-CONSISTENCY RELIABILITY

Internal-consistency reliability is most appropriately applied to homogeneous tests, i.e., tests composed of equivalent units—equivalent in several respects. The parts (usually items) all measure the same trait, or traits, to about the same degree. The total variance of a test can be conceived as a sum of the variances and covariances of its parts. The true variance of a test is contributed by its covari-

[1]Richardson, M. W. Notes on the rationale of item analysis. *Psychometrika,* 1936, **1**, 69–76.

ances, to which both the item variance and item intercorrelations are important contributors. Internal-consistency reliability is the greatest when:

1. The item intercorrelations are greatest.
2. The variance of items is greatest. This is when the proportion passing an item is .50.
3. The items are of equal difficulty. Then the item intercorrelations can be at a maximum.

Some special problems in reliability

Like all coefficients of correlation, r_{tt}, however estimated, must be interpreted in a relativistic manner. Its size depends upon many conditions under which it is obtained experimentally. Some of the more important conditions and considerations will be mentioned in what follows.

RELIABILITY IN DIFFERENT RANGES OF MEASUREMENT

Like intercorrelations of different variables, self-correlations are affected by the range of ability or of a trait present in the population samples. The narrower the range, the smaller r_{tt} tends to be. This can be seen mathematically if one examines formula (17.2), where r_{tt} is given as equal to $1 - \sigma^2_{t\infty}/\sigma^2_t$. If the standard error of measurement remains constant and σ_t decreases, the denominator σ^2_t decreases, the ratio $\sigma^2_{t\infty}/\sigma^2_t$ increases, and r_{tt} decreases. This is why some test users prefer to know $\sigma_{t\infty}$ rather than r_{tt} concerning a test, since it is probably more stable from population to population. Figure 17.7 illustrates how in a restricted sample (small square) the same scatter of points gives a relatively wider spread and hence a lower correlation. Restriction is not ordinarily so clear cut or so severe as this in practice, but the principle is the same.

If we wish to estimate the reliability coefficient in one range from the known reliability in another range, the following formula may be used. It assumes the same standard error of measurement in both ranges.

$$r_{nn} = 1 - \frac{\sigma^2_o(1 - r_{oo})}{\sigma^2_n}$$

(Estimation of r_{tt} in a population of one dispersion from that in another similar population of different dispersion)   (17.23)

where σ_o = standard deviation of the distribution for which the reliability coefficient is known

σ_n = standard deviation of the distribution for which the reliability is not known

r_{oo} and r_{nn} = reliabilities in the two respective distributions

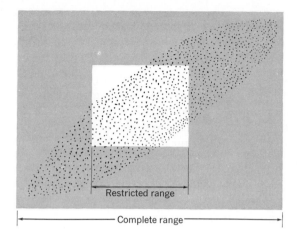

Restricted range

Complete range

Fig. 17.7. *Illustration showing an extreme instance of curtailment of range. The correlation for the cases within the smaller rectangle is much smaller than that for cases within the larger rectangle.*

If we know that a more limited group has a standard deviation of 8.0 and a reliability coefficient of .85 for a test, what will be the reliability coefficient in a more variable group whose σ is 10.0? Applying formula (17.23),

$$r_{nn} = 1 - \frac{8^2(1 - .85)}{10^2} = .904$$

RELIABILITY AND THE LENGTH OF TEST

It was indicated in connection with the split-half method that the whole test is more reliable than either half and that in general terms there is an increase in reliability with an increase in the length of the test. *This is true if the additional items added to a test are homogeneous with the ones to which they are added.* By homogeneous we mean that they have about the same intercorrelation with the items already in the test as those items have among themselves and possess about the same level of difficulty. If a test is lengthened to n times its present length under these conditions, we have a right to expect a change in reliability in accordance with the Spearman-Brown equation, which was given previously [formula (17.14)].

Lengthening a test to attain a certain desired reliablity. We can use the Spearman-Brown formula in reverse. If we know the reliability of a short test is .75, we can ask how long the test would have to be to attain a reliability of .90. If we solve the equation of the Spearman-Brown formula to find n, it becomes

$$n = \frac{r_{nn}(1 - r_{11})}{r_{11}(1 - r_{nn})} \qquad \text{(Estimation of length of test required for a given reliability)} \qquad (17.24)$$

Substituting the known values in this equation, we have

$$n = \frac{.90(1 - .75)}{.75(1 - .90)} = 3.0$$

The test with $r_{11} = .75$ would have to be three times as long to attain a reliability of .90.

Any other level of reliability, larger *or smaller*, in which we are interested can serve as r_{nn}, and the necessary n ratio can then be computed. Experience will show that some tests of low reliability cannot reach some desired high reliability without being made indefinitely long, or so long as to be impractical. Others will exhibit promising improvements in reliability with a moderate amount of extension. The formula is useful in this respect, that it helps decide upon rejection or extension of tests, or it is useful in cases in which a test is already too long for comfort and we need to decide whether shortening it would sacrifice too much in reliability.

RELIABILITY OF RATINGS AND OTHER JUDGMENTS

Many of the statistics described in connection with test scores also apply fairly well to human judgments of various kinds. The judgments may be in the form of rank order, rating-scale evaluations, pair-comparisons scaling, judgments in equal-appearing intervals, and the like. We can correlate the same observer's judgments obtained at two different times, or we can assume that similar judges are interchangeable and intercorrelate their evaluations (see discussion of intraclass correlation in Chap. 13). We can pool judgments for two comparable groups of observers and correlate them so long as they apply to the same objects or persons.

Experience has shown that, with the appropriate cautions exercised, these applications may be made with meaningful results. Every coefficient must, as usual, be interpreted in the light of the manner in which it was obtained. Even the Spearman-Brown formula has been shown to apply, as, for example, in the pooling of judgments from two observers, which yields increased reliability in a manner found for the doubling of a test in length. The comparability of judges must exist here, just as the comparability of items must exist in applying this formula to the change in length of test.

Derivation of the Spearman-Brown formula for the general case

Let us start with the equation that defines the reliability of a test of unit length:

$$r_{tt} = \frac{\sigma^2_\infty}{\sigma^2_t} \tag{1}$$

which represents the ratio of the true variance to the total variance of the test scores.

A test whose length is made n times as long can be conceived as a summation of n tests. The variance of a composite, as demonstrated earlier (p. 42), is the sum of the variances of the components plus twice the sum of the covariances. In this case there will be $n(n-1)/2$ covariances. We can take advantage of the assumption that the components are equivalent in every way, with equal variances and covariances. The true variance of a test n times as long is given by

$$\sigma^2_{n\infty} = n\sigma^2_{\infty} + 2\frac{n(n-1)}{2}r_{\infty\infty}\sigma_{\infty}\sigma_{\infty} \tag{2}$$

Now $r_{\infty\infty} = 1.0$ and may be dropped and $\sigma_{\infty}\sigma_{\infty} = \sigma^2_{\infty}$. Thus,

$$\sigma^2_{n\infty} = n\sigma^2_{\infty} + n(n-1)\sigma^2_{\infty}$$
$$= (n + n^2 - n)\sigma^2_{\infty}$$
$$= n^2\sigma^2_{\infty}$$

The last equation tells us that the true variance increases as the square of n. A test doubled in length has four times as much true variance; a test tripled in length has nine times as much true variance. Let us see how the total variance increases. For a test increased in length n times, by analogy to equation (2), we have

$$\sigma^2_{nn} = n\sigma^2_t + 2\frac{n(n-1)}{2}r_{tt}\sigma_t\sigma_t$$
$$= n\sigma^2_t + n(n-1)r_{tt}\sigma^2_t$$

Factoring out $n\sigma^2_t$,

$$\sigma_{nn} = n\sigma^2_t[1 + (n-1)r_{tt}]$$

For the test of length n, the ratio of the true to total variance is

$$\frac{n^2\sigma^2_{\infty}}{n\sigma^2_t[1 + (n-1)r_{tt}]}$$

Canceling n's and separating two components, we have

$$n_{nn} = \left(\frac{n\sigma^2_{\infty}}{\sigma^2_t}\right)\left[\frac{1}{1 + (n-1)r_{tt}}\right]$$
$$= nr_{tt}\left[\frac{1}{1 + (n-1)r_{tt}}\right]$$
$$= \frac{nr_{tt}}{1 + (n-1)r_{tt}}$$

EXERCISES

1. The following reliability coefficients were presented for a certain test:

Split half	.96	Retest after 1 month	.91
Alternate form	.94	Retest after 2 years	.86

Are these coefficients reasonable? Explain.

2. In six tests, the following correlations were found between halves composed of comparable items: .43, .55, .66, .74, .86, .94. Determine the reliability coefficient for the full-length tests.

3. In a certain test, the sum of the squared differences between scores on two comparable halves equaled 285. $N = 50$ and $\sigma = 8.5$. Find the coefficient of reliability for the total scores and the standard error of measurement.

4. In a test of 55 items, the SD of the total scores was 7.5. The sum of the variances of the items was 9.8327. Estimate the reliability of the scores.

5. Another test of 150 items has an SD of 24.4 and a mean of 94.2. Estimate the reliability of the scores, assuming that the items are approximately equal in difficulty and intercorrelation.

6. In four tests, the reliability coefficients were .65, .76, .87, and .94. Determine $r_{t\infty}$ and $\sigma_{t\infty}$ in each case, assuming an SD of 10.0.

7. Determine all the r_{nn} values lacking in Data 17A.

8. For the coefficients in the completed table in Data 17A, plot on graph paper the increase in r_{nn} (on the ordinate) as n (on the abscissa) increases, for each value of r_{11}. State some general conclusions.

9. Complete the table for Data 17B, computing the necessary n's.

10. A test has an SD of 7.2 and $r_{tt} = .86$. In another group the SD is 6.0. Assuming equal standard errors of measurement in the two samples, what should be the reliability in the second sample? In still another group, the SD is 9.0. What reliability should be expected in the third group?

11. As a mathematical exercise, assuming a constant standard error of estimate, derive formula (17.22).

12. Solving the Spearman-Brown equation for n, derive formula (17.23).

Data 17A   Reliability coefficients as n varies, for different values of r_{11}

| r_{11} | \multicolumn{6}{c}{n} | | | | | |
	1.5	2	4	6	10	20
.30	.39			.72		.90
.70		.82	.90	.93		.98
.90	.93	.95			.99	

Data 17B Lengths of
tests needed to achieve
certain levels of reliability

r_{11}	r_{nn}			
	.65	.75	.84	.95
.30	4.33		13.22	
.50		3.00		19.00
.70	0.80		2.43	
.90		0.33		2.11

ANSWERS

2. r_{tt}: .60; .71; .80; .92; .97.

3. r_{tt}: .92; $\sigma_{t\infty} = 2.39$.

4. $r_{tt} = .84$, by formula (17.15).

5. $r_{tt} = .95$, by formula (17.17).

6. $r_{t\infty}$: .81, .87, .93, .97; $\sigma_{t\infty}$: 5.9, 4.9, 3.6, 2.4.

7. When $r_{11} = .30$, r_{nn}: .46, .63, .81; when $r_{11} = .70$, r_{nn}: .78, .96; when $r_{11} = .90$, r_{nn}: .97, .98, .99.

9. When $r_{11} = .30$, n: 7.00, 44.33; when $r_{11} = .50$, n: 1.86, 5.25; when $r_{11} = .70$, n: 1.28, 8.14; when $r_{11} = .90$, n: 0.21, 0.58.

10. r_{nn}: .80; .91.

18 *Validity of measurements*

ALTHOUGH most of the comments in this chapter will be about the validity of tests, the problem of validity arises in connection with all kinds of measurements. Most of what is said about validity of tests applies, in a general way, to other methods of evaluation and measurement.

Problems of validity

It is usually easy enough to apply a measuring instrument and to obtain some numerical data. In the physical sciences the meaning of numbers that are used to describe phenomena is usually well established. The values stand for degrees of electrical resistance, pressure of a gas, or mass of a particle. In the behavioral sciences, however, the connection between a number and the thing, or things, for which it stands is not nearly so obvious.

Nor is the problem solved by dreaming up a name for the supposed variable for which the numbers stand. There is said to have been a country in which it was regarded as bad taste for anyone to question whether a certain test measures trait X if the distinguished psychologist who invented the test says it measures trait X. There are other places, unfortunately, in which similar attitudes exist to some degree. The problem would not be so serious if conclusion after conclusion about supposed underlying properties were not built upon the evidence of measurements which may not, after all, have much to do with those properties. There may even be considerable question about the possibility of demonstrating empirically those properties.

TYPES OF VALIDITY

The question of validity, of a test or of any measuring instrument, has many facets, and it requires clear thinking not to be confused by them. In crudest terms, we say that a test is valid when it measures what it is presumed to measure. This is, however, but one step

better than the definition that states that a test is valid if it measures
the truth.

This chapter will maintain that validity is a highly relative concept.
If the question is asked about any particular test, "Is this test valid?"
the answer should be in the form of another question, "Is it valid
for what?" Furthermore, just as we found in the preceding chapter
that we cannot, strictly speaking, state that any figure represents
the reliability of a test, so we cannot give a single number to indicate
the validity of a test.

There was a time, unfortunately still not entirely past, when each
test was supposed to measure some underlying variable that went by
a name. It was a test of intelligence, of introversion, or of neurotic
tendency. Those concepts, because of their fixed names, were supposed to be qualitatively stable, known, and have defined attributes.
In order to be valid, tests going by those names were expected to correlate highly with older, generally accepted criteria for those supposed entities. For example, new tests were "validated" by demonstrating a strong correlation with the Stanford Revision of the Binet
test or with Laird's test C2 or with Woodworth's inventory.

Factorial validity. Now that these areas of personality (intelligence, introversion, and neurotic tendency) have been shown to lack
unity and consensus as to their manifestations in behavior,[1] we are
properly more wary of attaching such names to tests. If we regard
intelligence as composed of a collection of functional unities, called
primary abilities for convenience, we find that the question of what
is a valid intelligence test has multiple meanings. The primary abilities, on the other hand, have been arrived at by means of well-defined
steps and can be verified by one who repeats those steps. If one ac-
quiesces in the procedures by which those functional unities are dis-
covered, he has no choice, if he still is concerned about the validity
of tests, but to ask whether test *A* is a valid one for measuring this
primary ability or that one.

The validity of a test as a measure of one of these factors is indicated by its correlation with the factor, which is its *factor loading.*[2]
It is recognized by those who adopt the factor-analytic approach that
scarcely any test is an unadulterated measure of any primary ability
or trait. Not only is it diluted by errors of measurement, as we saw
in the discussion of reliability, but it is also adulterated with vari-

[1]See in particular Thurstone, L. L. Primary mental abilities. *Psychometr.
Monogr.*, 1939, 1; Guilford, J. P., and Guilford, R. B. Personality factors D, R, T,
and A. *J. abnorm. soc. Psychol.*, 1939, 34, 21–36; Mosier, C. I. A factor analysis
of certain neurotic tendencies. *Psychometrika*, 1937, 2, 263–286; and Guilford,
J. P. Three faces of intellect. *Amer. Psychologist*, 1959, 14, 469–479.

[2]For a brief discussion of factor theory and methods, see Guilford, J. P. *Psychometric Methods.* 2d ed. New York: McGraw-Hill, 1954. Chap. 16.

ances in other primary abilities or traits. This situation is overcome to some extent by carefully combining tests, an exacting procedure that we cannot go into here. It is the author's belief that the best answer to the question, "What does this test measure?" is in the form of a list of the primary factors with which it correlates and their proportions of variance in the test.[1] This kind of validity may be called *factorial validity*. This idea will be explained more fully, and it will be shown that it is basic to the understanding of other kinds of validity and of many phenomena of correlation in general.

Predictive validity. The vocational counselor and the vocational selector face a different kind of problem when they inquire about validity of tests. They are concerned about predicting outcomes in specific tasks and situations—clerical ability, academic ability, salesmanship, and the like. A test is a valid one for clerical aptitude if its scores correlate highly with later clerical proficiency. Another test is a valid one for aptitude in selling because it correlates highly with later proficiency in selling. From this point of view, any test is valid for any sphere of behavior if it enables us to predict within that sphere, regardless of the name of the test or the supposed fundamental abilities that it measures. A test designed to predict the success of student aviators may prove also to be a valid test of academic aptitude in engineering or of aptitude for a military career in general. From the practical standpoint, the validity of a test is its forecasting efficiency in predicting any measurable aspect of daily living.

CRITERIA FOR VALIDITY

One of the most difficult of all aspects of the *predictive*-validity problem is that of obtaining adequate criteria of what we are measuring. The factor-analysis approach has a fairly good solution when it is primary traits or abilities that we wish to measure. If two or more tests or items are combined to measure the factor, the validity coefficient is the multiple correlation between the tests and the factor. But practical criteria for the operation of determining predictive validity are most in demand and are most difficult to obtain and to measure adequately. An example of this is the criterion of academic achievement.

It has often been assumed that academic achievement, like intelligence, is a unitary attribute of each individual. But this is far from the truth. Although there is generally a positive correlation between achievement in different school subjects, there is sufficient disagreement to permit an individual to receive marks all the way from *A* to *F* in different subjects. It is best, therefore, to examine the validity

[1]Guilford, J. P. Factor analysis in a test-development program. *Psychol. Rev.*, 1948, **55**, 79–94.

of each test used for guidance purposes in connection with *every* school subject taken by itself. Where a certain test of ability may possess only a moderate or low correlation with averages of school marks, it may correlate very highly with specific courses. The writer has data showing correlations all the way from .37 to .74 between the Ohio State Psychological Examination, Form 20, and marks in freshman courses at a certain university.

The point is that success in any sphere of life is ordinarily highly complex and is determined by many psychological factors (rather than one or a few) in the individuals. If we measure success in a complex activity by singling out as criteria one or more of its aspects and measuring them, we are checking upon the validity of the test or tests for predicting those chosen aspects. We should not identify those few aspects with the entire activity. We should, of course, attempt to single out the most significant aspects as criteria. Too often some inconsequential aspects are chosen because of their ready observability and measurability.

Having chosen the measurable variables of success in the area predicted, we have the problems of securing dependable measurements and perhaps of combining and weighting them in the wisest manner. With reference to measures of achievement, again, it should be emphasized that school marks as ordinarily assigned by teachers are rather poor as measurements. At best, letter marks are on a very crudely categorized ordinal scale. Variations in meaning and standards from teacher to teacher and from course to course are notorious. It can often be questioned whether sets of marks are very reliable or very valid indicators of achievement. The best measures of achievement in most courses are those obtained directly from good, comprehensive examinations. Marks otherwise obtained often have reliabilities in the range from .60 to .80, and their validities are unknown. When we attempt to find the predictive value of a psychological test, therefore, shall we reject tests that fail to correlate highly with such fallible criteria? We can allow for the unreliability of criteria statistically when we know a coefficient of reliability for them. We cannot so easily know or allow for lack of *validity* of criteria, though we can make interpretive allowances, knowing the kind of criteria we have.

A brief introduction to factor theory

Because so many of the facts of validity are explainable on the basis of factor theory, it is desirable for us to examine the basic features of factor theory in order to gain a better grasp of the problems and methods involved. There is not space here to describe the procedures for making a factor analysis of tests. These statistical procedures, if described in sufficient detail so they might be generally used, would take up a small volume in themselves.[1]

BASIC ASSUMPTIONS IN FACTOR THEORY

It is best to begin with basic theorems, two of which will give us the foundation we need for the logic of validity.

Theorem I. The total variance of a test may be regarded as the sum of three kinds of component variances: (1) that contributed by one or more common factors, *common* because they appear in more than one test; (2) that unique to the test itself and to its equivalent forms; and (3) error variance. We are now ready to partition what was called *true* variance in the preceding chapter into component variances. Both the common-factor variances and the specific variance in a test contribute to its internal-consistency reliability, and to its equivalent-forms reliability. It is not necessary to assume that the common-factor and specific-factor variances are all independent or uncorrelated. To do so relieves us of having to deal with covariance terms and thus simplifies the picture. What follows would be just as true, in general, if we did not add this specification to the assumption.[2] Theorem I may be stated in the form of an equation:

$$\sigma^2_t = \sigma^2_a + \sigma^2_b + \cdots + \sigma^2_n + \sigma^2_s + \sigma^2_e$$

(Sum of independent variances in scores on a test)   (18.1)

where σ^2_t = total variance of a test
$\sigma^2_a, \sigma^2_b, \ldots, \sigma^2_n$ = variances in common factors $A, B, \ldots, N$, respectively
σ^2_s = variance specific to this test
σ^2_e = error variance

If we now divide equation (18.1) by σ^2_t, we have

$$\frac{\sigma^2_t}{\sigma^2_t} = \frac{\sigma^2_a}{\sigma^2_t} + \frac{\sigma^2_b}{\sigma^2_t} + \cdots + \frac{\sigma^2_n}{\sigma^2_t} + \frac{\sigma^2_s}{\sigma^2_t} + \frac{\sigma^2_e}{\sigma^2_t} = 1.00$$

(18.2)

Substituting new symbols for these fractions, which are proportions, we have

$$1.00 = a^2_x + b^2_x + \cdots + n^2_x + s^2_x + e^2_x$$

(Proportions of factor variances in a test)   (18.3)

[1]The most profound book on factor analysis is Harman, H. H. *Modern Factor Analysis*. Chicago: University of Chicago Press, 1960. For other presentations, see Cattell, R. B. *Factor Analysis*. New York: Harper, 1952; and Fruchter, B. *Introduction to Factor Analysis*. Princeton, N.J.: Van Nostrand, 1954.
[2]This theorem and the second follow from the basic postulate that an obtained test score is a simple, linear summation of components from the sources indicated in theorem I.

where $a^2_x, b^2_x, \ldots, n^2_x$ = proportions of total variance contributed to test X by factors $A, B, \ldots, N$, respectively

s^2_x = proportion of specific variance in test X

e^2_x = proportion of error variance in text X

In the same notation, the reliability of test X can be written as

$$r_{tt} = 1 - e^2_x = a^2_x + b^2_x + \cdots + n^2_x + s^2_x \qquad (18.4)$$

(Reliability as a sum of proportions of nonerror variance)

This equation will be useful in discussions of the relation of validity to reliability later on.

Communality. A new concept that should be pointed out here, although we shall not have occasion to do much with it in this chapter, is the *communality* of a test. The communality of a test is the sum of the proportions of common-factor variances. In equation form,

$$h^2_x = a^2_x + b^2_x + \cdots + n^2_x \qquad \text{(Communality of a test)} \qquad (18.5)$$

The communality of a test contains all the nonerror variance except the specific variance. Communality is what gives any test the chance of correlating with other tests and with practical criteria. If there were no communality in a test it could be quite reliable and still not correlate with anything else. On the other hand, a test could have relatively low reliability, and yet if all its nonerror variance were in common with variance in other variables, its correlations with other things could be rather substantial; hence its validity could be good.

A numerical example of component variances. As an example, let us consider three tests and a practical criterion. Five common factors are represented in these four variables. Table 18.1 lists the proportions of common-factor, specific, and error variance for each variable. Test 1 has 36 per cent of its variance accounted for by factor A, and 36

Table 18.1   Proportions of common-factor, specific, and error variance in three tests and a practical criterion of proficiency

Variable	Common factors					Specific, S	Error, E	Communality, h^2	Reliability, r_{xx}
	A	B	C	D	F				
Test 1	.36	.00	.36	.00	.00	.10	.18	.72	.82
Test 2	.16	.00	.12	.00	.64	.00	.08	.92	.92
Test 3	.00	.49	.00	.25	.00	.09	.17	.74	.83
Criterion J	.16	.09	.16	.25	.00	.14	.20	.66	.80

per cent by factor C. The sum of these two components equals 72 per cent, which represents the communality of this test. Add the 10 per cent specific variance, and we have 82 per cent, which represents the test's true variance and a reliability of .82. The remaining 18 per cent is error variance. The other tests and criterion J can be interpreted in a similar manner. Figure 18.1 shows the component variances for these same four variables, each as a segment of a bar diagram.

Factor loadings. The proportion of a total variance contributed by one component may be regarded as a coefficient of determination of the total by the part. The square root of each proportion of variance contributed by a common factor may therefore be regarded as the correlation between the total variable and the factor. These square roots are correlation coefficients and are known as *factor loadings* or *factor saturations.* For the three tests and criterion J, the common-factor loadings are given in Table 18.2. Test 2 correlates .40 with factor A, .35 with factor C, and .80 with factor F. Factor F has no correlations with other variables in this list, but in order to be regarded as a common factor it must have some correlation with other variables not in this list.

The square roots of specific variance are not listed because it is not certain what the specific variances represent. A certain specific variance may indeed be unique to its own test, but it may be a composite of some kind, in which case each component of the specific variance would have its own correlation with the total. On the other hand, some specific variances might turn out in later analyses to be one or more unrecognized common-factor variances. Certain tests have been known to lack any specific variance at all, the entire true variance being composed of common-factor components and the communality equaling the reliability of the test.

Theorem II. The second major theorem of factor analysis is that the correlation between two experimental variables (such as tests and criteria) is equal to the sum of the cross products of their common-factor loadings. In equation form,

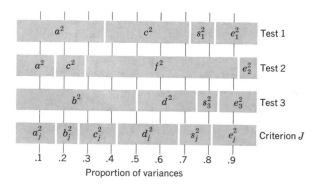

Fig. 18.1. *Proportions of common-factor, specific, and error variances in three hypothetical tests and a criterion.*

*Table 18.2 **Factor loadings (correlations of***
common factors with experimental variables) for
the three tests and a criterion

Variables	Common factors				
	A	B	C	D	F
Test 1	.60	.00	.60	.00	.00
Test 2	.40	.00	.35	.00	.80
Test 3	.00	.70	.00	.50	.00
Criterion J	.40	.30	.40	.50	.00

$$r_{jx} = a_j a_x + b_j b_x + \cdots + n_j n_x \qquad \text{(A correlation as a sum of factor-loading products)} \qquad (18.6)$$

where a_j and a_x = loadings of factor A in criterion J and test X, b_j and b_x = loadings of factor B in criterion J and test X, etc.

HOW FACTOR THEORY EXPLAINS PREDICTIVE VALIDITY

Applied to the loadings given in Table 18.2, the correlation between tests 1 and 2 would be

$$r_{12} = (.6)(.4) + (.0)(.0) + (.6)(.35) + (.0)(.0) + (.0)(.8) = .45$$

The correlation between test 1 and criterion J (its validity for predicting criterion J) would be

$$r_{j1} = (.4)(.6) + (.3)(.0) + (.4)(.6) + (.5)(.0) + (.0)(.0) = .48$$

The other intercorrelations and validity coefficients found in similar manner are listed in Table 18.3. In experimental practice we do not know the factor loadings first and derive from them the intercorrelations; we know the intercorrelations and by factor analysis arrive at the factor loadings. We have assumed that the factor loadings are known here for the sake of illustration.

Examination of the three validity coefficients in Table 18.3 shows that they are .48, .30, and .46, for tests 1, 2, and 3, respectively. The three validity coefficients are represented graphically in Fig. 18.2. The reasons for the validity of tests 1 and 2 are the same; their common ground with the criterion is in factors A and C. The reason test 3 is valid, however, is totally different from this. Test 3 is valid because of having factors B and D in common with the criterion. Test 2 has the lowest validity for predicting criterion J, but its unusually large loading in factor F offers strong possibilities for its validity in predicting some other criterion that has a substantial loading in factor F.

*Table 18.3   Intercorrelations of tests and criterion
J derived from their common-factor loadings*

Variables	Tests			Criterion J
	1	2	3	
Test 1		.45	.00	.48
Test 2	.45		.00	.30
Test 3	.00	.00		.46
Criterion J	.48	.30	.46	

HOW FACTOR THEORY EXPLAINS MULTIPLE-CORRELATION PRINCIPLES

The multiple correlations of some of these tests with criterion J can be nicely explained by the various factor loadings. The multiple correlation $R_{j.12} = .49$, which is only .01 higher than the correlation r_{j1}. Adding test 2 to test 1 in a battery to predict J is of little value because both bring to the composite a coverage of the same common factors in J. The multiple $R_{j.13}$, however, is equal to .66. Adding test 3 to test 1 to make a joint prediction of J is very effective because the two tests cover totally different components in J. The multiple $R_{j.23}$ is less than $R_{j.13}$, being .55. The reason for this is that test 2 does not cover factors A and C nearly so well as does test 1.

Optional weighting of factors in composites. We might well raise the question at this point as to whether tests 1 and 3, optimally weighted, with their multiple R of .66, have yielded the maximum amount of validity possible for a weighted composite that contains factors A, B, C, and D. Reference to equation (18.6) will show that the correlations r_{j1} and r_{j3} could have been higher if the tests' factor loadings a_1, c_1, b_3, and d_3 had been larger. The only limits to those factor loadings would be that the communalities should not exceed 1.0.

This, however, is not the whole story. We could make those loadings as large as the communalities would allow and they would still not yield the maximal correlation with criterion J unless they were in the right proportions. The right proportions would have to take into consideration the proportions of loadings a_j, b_j, c_j, and d_j in the criterion. With sufficient loadings of the four factors in the tests and with proper weightings, the maximum validity for the composite in predicting criterion J would be equal to the square root of the communality of that criterion. The square root of .66 is .81. This principle is reminiscent of the one mentioned in the preceding chapter regarding the index of reliability, which is the square root of the reliability

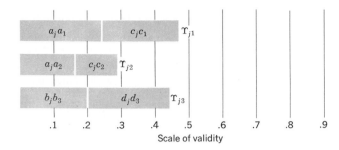

Fig. 18.2. *Segments of three intercorrelations of tests, each with a criterion, that are contributed by different common factors.*

coefficient. It gives the maximum possible correlation of anything with the variable in question. In this statement, however, is latent the assumption that all the true variance is common-factor variance; that $h^2 = r_{tt'}$.

It is doubtful whether tests 1 and 3 could ever be weighted appropriately to yield a validity for their composite equal to the maximum .81 with criterion J, even though their common-factor loadings were as large as possible. The reason is that factors A and C are tied together in the same test and factors B and D are tied together in the other test. Since factors A and C have equal loadings in criterion J and also in test 1, as long as they keep the same ratio in test 1 they would be properly weighted in a regression equation. This is merely a coincidence in this particular problem. Factors B and D, however, are weighted in reverse order in test 3 and criterion J. For optimal prediction of J, the loading d_3 should be greater than the loading b_3, to correspond with the fact that the loading d_j is greater than b_j. If we had loadings b_3 and d_3 in proportion to the loadings b_j and d_j and also 50 per cent larger (just as a_1 and c_1 are 50 per cent larger than a_j and c_j), they would be .45 and .75, respectively. These would yield [by equation (18.6)] an r_{j3} equal to .51 (where it was .46) and a multiple R of .70 (where it was .66).

The moral of this is that, for the freedom to weight each factor in a composite as it should be weighted to get the maximal prediction of a criterion, it is best to use unique, or univocal, tests, i.e., each test with but one common factor. In practice, a regression weight has to be applied to the test as a whole and all factors in it are weighted the same, in so far as external weights are applied.

Increasing validity by adding factors. We have just seen that increasing the predictive validity of a composite depends upon large factor loadings for factors represented in the criterion and an *optimal weighting of the individual factors*. There is another important way of increasing the validity of a composite, and that is to bring in a new test that covers a common factor in the criterion that is not already covered. Criterion J was reported to have 14 per cent of its variance devoted to specific sources. It is possible that this portion of the variance in J is really contributed by an unknown common factor. Further experimental work might identify it as stemming from one or more common factors. Suppose that it were found to belong entirely to one additional factor G. To contribute .14 to the total variance, the loading g_j would be about .37. With an additional test to measure this factor in the composite, the multiple R could be increased materially.

On the whole, there is much more to be gained in increasing R by discovery or identification of new factors than there is by increasing loadings for already known factors. With a large number of factors in a criterion, sizes of loadings will have to be small in order to stay within the limit of its communality, and their multipliers (loadings in the tests) can be correspondingly small, so as to produce a maximum validity coefficient, within the limit of the square root of that communality.

Conditions upon which validity depends

RELATION OF VALIDITY TO RELIABILITY

It has been a common belief that the predictive validity of a test, other things being equal, is directly proportional to its reliability — the more reliable a test, the more valid it is. There is much in the application of factor theory to support this idea, as we can see by reference to previous paragraphs. The greater the error variance in a test, the less room there is for common-factor variance, and common-factor variance is the source of validity. If we make a test more reliable and in so doing we increase variances in common factors, the possibilities for validity should be increased accordingly.

When validity and reliability are independent. There are important exceptions to this relationship between validity and reliability, however. If a test is heterogeneous, we might have a very low internal-consistency reliability and yet a high predictive validity. If a test is homogeneous, it would be possible to increase its reliability without affecting its validity. The increased reliability might mean added variance in a common factor that has no relation to the criterion. For example, a test measuring visualization is known to have validity for the selection of pilots. We might increase the reliability of this test by making it more difficult, thereby adding reasoning variance. If reasoning variance has no correlation with the pilot criterion, no improvement in pilot validity would follow such a change in this test. The added common-factor variance in a test will increase the practical validity of a test only when that new type of variance is also present in the criterion. If there were no valid variance in a test to begin with, no amount of increased reliability would give it validity unless the added variance is related to the criterion.

Goals of validity and reliability sometimes incompatible. When we seek to make a single test both highly reliable (internally) and also highly valid, we are often working at cross purposes. The two goals are incompatible in some respects. In aiming for one goal we may defeat efforts toward the other.

Maximal reliability requires high intercorrelation among items; maximal predictive validity requires low intercorrelations. Maximal reliability requires items of equal difficulty; maximal predictive validity requires items differing in difficulty. This point needs some explanation. Tucker has demonstrated this fact mathematically, but there is a simpler, common-sense rationale.[1] A range of difficulty is very desirable, of course, in order to obtain graded measures of individuals. It was shown in Chap. 17 how with perfect intercorrelation of items (which could occur with ϕ coefficients only when items are of equal difficulty) there were only two scores — perfect scores and zeros. For spacing individuals in fine enough graduations for measurement purposes it is necessary to have a continuous distribution, not a U-shaped one. It would be ideal, for fine measurements, to space items, each discriminating well between all those above a certain point on the scale and those below, rather evenly all along the range of ability in the population. With such spacings, intercorrelations could not be perfect, and some would, indeed, be very low.

There must be some compromising of aims; both reliability and validity cannot be maximal. Fortunately, the kind of moderate item intercorrelations usually obtained for well-constructed items are of the size that, according to Tucker's conclusions, will yield good validities. They will also yield satisfactory reliabilities, but those reliabilities will not often be above .90. To be more specific, the item-test correlations for well-constructed items range between .30 and .80, which means item intercorrelations approximately between .10 and .60. Items within these ranges of correlation should provide tests of both satisfactory reliability and validity. There is probably better reason for going below these limits than above them in constructing items. To do so would probably err on the side of validity, which, after all, is the more important.

Homogeneous tests; heterogeneous batteries. The relation of heterogeneity to validity deserves more attention. One way to make a test more valid for predictive purposes is to make it more heterogeneous. In factorial language this means adding new factors. If we succeeded in getting into the scores of the single test all the factors that are also

[1]Tucker, L. R. Maximum validity of a test with equivalent items. *Psychometrika*, 1946, **11**, 1–13.

in the practical criterion, and if we weighted them properly, we could achieve maximal accuracy of predictions from the single test.

Recall, in this connection, the principles of the multiple-regression equation. Maximal multiple correlation is achieved by minimizing the intercorrelations of the independent variables. If we apply this to test items, as separate variables, the principle still holds. The ideal test, from this point of view, would be one in which each item measured a different factor (and measured it consistently). This would mean a test of low internal reliability. It would also mean a test, which, though correlating well with the criterion, would make very crude discriminations for each factor. Each item would ordinarily differentiate only two categories—those who pass it and those who fail it—for each trait measured. If we brought in a number of items to measure each factor, with differences in difficulty to overcome this defect, we should have virtually a battery of tests within a single test.

The solution to the incompatibility of goals of reliability and predictive validity is precisely what has just been suggested: to use a battery of tests rather than single tests. Reliability should be the goal emphasized for each test; predictive validity the goal emphasized for the battery. Even in single tests some reliability should be sacrificed for the sake of well-graded measurements. It is strongly urged that, if possible, each test be designed to measure one common factor. It should be univocal, its contribution unique. In this way minimal intercorrelation of tests is ensured, which satisfies one of the major principles in multiple regression. It was also shown that when tests are univocal the various factors can be weighted in the best way to make each prediction. The univocal test will correlate less with a practical criterion than will a heterogeneous test, but what we lose in validity for the single test will be more than made up by forming batteries which cover the factors to be predicted and in a more manageable manner. For the sake of meaningful profiles also, a battery of univocal tests has no equal. The use of single-test scores in a profile, however, calls for high reliability for each test.

Reliabilities and test batteries.   If a composite score from a battery is be be used and not part scores from the components, as in a profile, it is likely that there is not much to be gained by achieving reliabilities for single tests higher than .60 or by having tests longer than 30 items each.[1] The reliability of the composite score of *independent* tests will be approximately a weighted average of the reliabilities of the components.[2] This means that if the components have a generally

[1] Dailey, J. T. Determination of optimal test reliability in a battery of aptitude tests. Technical memorandum No. 10, Lackland Air Force Base, 1948.
[2] Mosier, C. I. On the reliability of a weighted composite. *Psychometrika,* 1943, 8, 161–168.

low reliability, in such a battery the reliability of the composite will be low. This need not be disturbing, provided the validity of the composite is high. To the extent that the components are intercorrelated, the reliability of the composite will exceed the average reliability of the components. In general, if there is a choice between lengthening tests in a predictive battery to make them more reliable and adding more tests of different kinds that contribute unique valid variances, the decision should certainly go to the second alternative. If single-test scores are to be used separately, however, attention must also be given to reliability of components.

DISCRIMINATION VALUES OF ITEMS

Some of the points just discussed may be made a little clearer if we approach the item theory from a different aspect. Figure 18.3 is used to illustrate this approach. Imagine a scale of ability or of any other trait that we attempt to measure by means of a test. We want each item to correlate with that variable, to indicate the status of individuals with respect to the variable, to discriminate between individuals.

Suppose we already know the positions of large numbers of individuals on this scale. We apply to them an item that we will call item C. The item is of median difficulty, for of the entire group 50 per cent respond in the acceptable manner and 50 per cent do not. According to the requirements of good reliability, this knowledge about the difficulty of item C is promising, but not sufficient evidence that the item would contribute to a reliable test. We do not yet know whether it is at all related to the variable we want to measure. It could be of me-

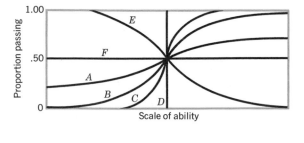

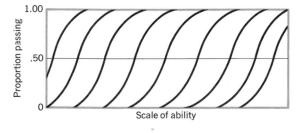

Fig. 18.3. *Proportion passing an item (responding correctly) as a function of ability level on the scale of the kind of ability (or weighted combination of abilities) required to pass the item.*

dian difficulty and still be uncorrelated with other items in the test. Let us subdivide the large sample into subsamples grouped in class intervals as if for known values along the scale. We are now interested in seeing whether those groups higher on the scale have any greater probability of passing the item than those lower on the scale. Theory states, and experimental evidence supports the idea, that the increase in the probability of passing the item follows the normal cumulative frequency curve. The regression of proportions passing the item upon ability is the S-shaped or ogive form. For item *C*, not very far below average ability we find a point below which none pass the item. Above a point just as far above the mean we find that all pass the item. The interval between is sometimes called the *transition zone*, a concept borrowed from psychophysics.[1]

Other items may have the same difficulty level as item *C*, but like items *B* and *A* in the diagram (Fig. 18.3) they have different degrees of discriminating power. Both *B* and *A* have much wider transition zones (they both actually go beyond the range of the given horizontal scale) and their curves have slopes that are less steep than that for *C*. The steepness of the slope is known as the curve's *precision*. The term applies well here because the steeper the precision of the curve, the greater is the precision of discrimination. A perfectly discriminating item is *D*, whose slope is infinite. A nondiscriminating item is *F*, whose slope is zero. There is a mathematical relationship between the precision of an ogive like these and the correlation between the item and a good measure of the trait.[2] Item *E* would have a negative correlation with the variable to be measured. This would be an unusual event and would probably mean that the item was keyed wrong in scoring. Items like *D* would seem to be ideal; they are perfectly discriminating. But it can be seen how only one such item used alone would be almost futile, for it discriminates at only one point. A set of such items, equally spaced as to difficulty, however, would make an ideal test.

The second diagram is more realistic and yet pictures a somewhat ideal situation. It shows a series of items about equally spaced as to difficulty and all with excellent discriminating power. With the extensive range of difficulty level, there could not be as high internal reliability as some might desire. But the possibility of accurately grading individuals on a continuous scale is greater because of that dispersion. To appreciate the full value of the items that depart from medium difficulty, one would need either to use a biserial *r* or a

[1]Woodworth, R. S. *Experimental Psychology*. New York: Holt, 1938. P. 401.
[2]For proof of this, see Richardson, M. W. Relation between the difficulty and the differential validity of a test. *Psychometrika*, 1936, **1**, 33–49.

tetrachoric r in correlating item with total score or to make allowance for the effect of divergencies in difficulty upon the phi coefficient.

VALIDITY AND THE LENGTH OF TEST

Since the homogeneous lengthening of a homogeneous test increases its reliability, in accordance with the Spearman-Brown formula, it will also increase its validity, either factorial or predictive. If the change in length is by some ratio n (the new length divided by the old) the new validity of the test is estimated by the formula

$$r_{y(nx)} = \frac{r_{yx}}{\sqrt{\dfrac{1 - r_{xx}}{n} + r_{xx}}} \qquad \text{(Validity of a homogeneous test increased in length } n \text{ times)} \qquad (18.7)$$

where r_{yx} = validity coefficient for predicting criterion Y from test X and r_{xx} = reliability of test X.

A certain line-drawing test developed to predict creative abilities of students in a course in designing had a reliability of .57 and a correlation with teacher's ratings of .65.[1] If this test were made twice as long, what validity could be expected? Applying formula (18.7),

$$r_{y(2x)} = \frac{.65}{\sqrt{\dfrac{1 - .57}{2} + .57}} = .73$$

It would thus definitely pay to make this test longer and more reliable in order to improve its validity.

If we wanted to know how much homogeneous lengthening is needed in order to achieve a desired level of validity, we could do this by solving formula (18.7) for n, which gives

$$n = \frac{1 - r_{xx}}{\dfrac{r_{yx}^2}{r_{y(nx)}^2} + r_{xx}} \qquad \text{(Ratio of new length of test for a required validity)} \qquad (18.8)$$

If we wanted a validity of .80 for the line-drawing test, the ratio of the revised length to the former length would have to be

$$n = \frac{1 - .57}{\dfrac{.4225}{.64} - .57} = 4.8$$

Whether it would be practical to devote nearly five times as much effort to this test is a question of policy that goes beyond statistical answers.

[1]Guilford, J. P., and Guilford, R. B. A prognostic test for students in design. *J. appl. Psychol.*, 1931, **15**, 335–345.

RELATION OF VALIDITY COEFFICIENTS TO ERRORS OF MEASUREMENT

When two measured variables are correlated, the errors of measurement, if uncorrelated among themselves, always serve to lower the coefficient of correlation as compared with what it would have been had the two measures been perfectly reliable. We say that the degree of correlation has been attenuated. If we want to know what the correlation would have been if the two variables were perfectly measured, we must resort to the *correction for attenuation*, for which we have a formula

$$r_{\infty w} = \frac{r_{xy}}{\sqrt{r_{xx} r_{yy}}} \qquad \text{(An intercorrelation corrected for attenuation)} \qquad (18.9)$$

where r_{xx} and r_{yy} = reliability coefficients of the two tests.

The correlation obtained between a figure-classification test and a form-perception test was .36. The reliability coefficients for the two tests were .60 and .94, respectively. Applying formula (18.9),

$$r_{\infty w} = \frac{.36}{\sqrt{(.60)(.94)}} = .48$$

We should therefore expect the correlation between true scores in these two tests to be .48 rather than the obtained one of .36.

Rather commonly, when making this correction for attenuation in two fallible tests, we are dealing with two forms of the same test for purposes of finding reliability. There is a possibility of determining four intercorrelations between the two tests, i.e., each form of the one correlated with the two forms of the other. In this case, it is well to use all the information available concerning the intercorrelation of the two tests by computing the four coefficients and using their arithmetic mean as a better estimate of the numerator of the fraction in formula (18.9).

Factorial explanation of attenuation and its correction. It may not be clear to the reader why errors of measurement always lower intercorrelations, and why, when the corrective formula is applied, correlations should not be perfect. The answers to both these questions can best be given by reference to factor theory.

Consider test 1 and criterion *J* of the illustration used above when factor theory was introduced. Error variance made up 18 per cent of the total variance of test 1 and 20 per cent of criterion *J*. Let us suppose that we could rid each variable of all errors of measurement, all error variance. In doing so, let us further suppose that the remaining true variance is expanded with all its components in proportion to their original amounts. Figure 18.4 demonstrates what happens when the error components are "squeezed out" of variables and the true-

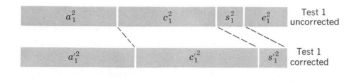

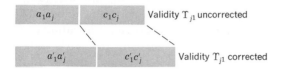

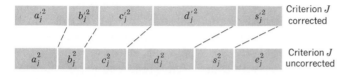

Fig. 18.4. *Proportions of variance in a test and a criterion after correction for attenuation (elimination of error variance statistically), also the contributions of factors to the validity coefficient before and after correction.*

variance components expand to take their places. Variances that were .36 and .36 for factors A and C in test 1 before correction become .439 and .439 after correction. The new factor loadings are .663 on each factor. In the criterion the corresponding loadings become .447 in place of .40. By equation (18.6), the new correlation r_{j1} becomes .59, whereas it was .48. The use of formula (18.9) applied to the original r_{j1} gives

$$r_{\infty w} = \frac{.48}{\sqrt{(.82)(.80)}} = .59$$

The change in validity from .48 to .59 is shown graphically in Fig. 18.4.

CORRECTION FOR ATTENTUATION IN THE CRITERION ONLY

The correction procedure of formula (18.9) has limited application except in theoretical problems. In practice, we are compelled to deal with fallible tests. If the tests from which we wish to predict something else are not perfect, that fact must be faced, and our predictions are reduced in accuracy accordingly. But we should hardly expect to be asked to overlook the fallibility of the criterion we are trying to predict. If it measures success inaccurately, this lack of accuracy should not be permitted to make it appear that the test is less valid than it really is. It is desirable, therefore, to correct predictive validity coefficients for attenuation in the criterion measurements but not in the test scores. This one-sided correction is made by the formula

$$r_{xw} = \frac{r_{xy}}{\sqrt{r_{yy}}} \qquad \text{(Validity coefficient corrected for attenuation in the criterion only)} \qquad (18.10)$$

As an application of this formula, we cite the line-drawing test previously mentioned that correlated with a teacher's rank-order judgments of creative ability in her students in design to the extent of .65. The reliability of the teacher's ratings (combined from two rank orders a month apart) was found to be .82. Had the teacher's ratings been perfectly reliable measures of the thing she was judging, the correlation with test scores would have been $.65/\sqrt{.82} = .72$. The correlation of .72 is accordingly taken as the genuine validity of the test, unless we are concerned about predicting teacher's judgments, contaminated by flaws as they obviously are, rather than genuine ability as evidenced by those ratings.

Many a validity coefficient reported in the literature is of very uncertain meaning because errors of measurement in the criterion were not taken into account. The reliability of ratings, even of the better ones, is characteristically about .60. With such criteria, validity coefficients are about 25 per cent underestimated. Too often the reliability problem of a criterion is entirely ignored. The writer has known of purported criteria of a performance criterion (bombing errors of bombardiers in training) which at best had reliabilities of only approximately .30. What is even more important, but incidental to the discussion here, is the *validity* of the criterion. An investigator who hopes to develop successful selective instruments is often beaten before he starts, if he does not first ensure reliable and valid criteria, or if he does not estimate these features and make allowances for their shortcomings.

Limitations to the use of correction for attenuation. The correction of a correlation for attenuation requires that we have a rather accurate estimate of reliability for each variable that enters into the situation. If either r_{yy} or r_{xx} is underestimated, the corrected r_{yx} will be overestimated. If either reliability coefficient is overestimated, the corrected r_{yx} will be underestimated. It is probably best, if one wishes to be on the conservative side, that, if anything, a reliability estimate should be too large when used for this purpose. On the other hand, it is likely that most estimates of internal-consistency reliability are too low, which is in the wrong direction for conservatism.

There is also the question as to which of the three main types of reliability coefficient is desirable in correcting for attenuation. There are proponents for the use of each type in this connection. It is best to decide what kind of errors of measurement should be ruled out in the particular situation or particular use of r_{tt}. Once this decision is made, the type of reliability will be selected accordingly, since it was shown in the preceding chapter that each type emphasizes certain sources of variance as error. The tendency of underestimation of r_{tt} by internal-consistency methods is against their use where there is a reasonably good alternative. In general, the alternate-forms approach is probably best.

VALIDITY OF RIGHT AND WRONG RESPONSES

Many tests are scored with a formula score in which the wrong responses are given a negative fractional weight and the right responses a weight of +1.

A priori scoring formulas. One of the reasons behind such scoring formulas is a priori reasoning about chance success and the need for correcting for it. In a true-false test we have a two-alternative situation and the assumption is that when the examinee does not know an answer he will guess at random. When he guesses, his probability of getting the right answer is .5. When there are three alternatives, the theoretical proportion of right answers in guessing is .33; in a four-choice item the probability is .25, and so on. This has led to the stock scoring formula of the form

$$S = R - \frac{W}{k-1} \qquad \text{(A test score with a priori correction for guessing)} \qquad (18.11)$$

where R = number of right responses

W = number of wrong responses (not including omitted items)

k = number of alternative responses to each item

In a true-false test this reduces to the familiar $R - W$. In a five-choice-item test it becomes $R - W/4$. Incidentally, a similar correction could be made by the general formula

$$S = R + \frac{O}{n} \qquad \text{(Alternative scoring formula with correction for guessing)} \qquad (18.12)$$

where O = number of omissions (including items not attempted). This score is not numerically identical to that from formula (18.11) but is perfectly correlated with it.

It should be emphasized that neither of these formulas will tend to reduce the error variance introduced by guessing unless there are an appreciable number of omissions or failures to attempt items. If every examinee attempts all items, the correlation between R and W will be a perfect -1.0, which offers no freedom for improvement by scoring formula. The formula scores would then correlate $+1$ with R and the correction operation would be of no value for the purposes of measurement. In a speed test, however, and in a power test in which the examinees voluntarily omit many items, such a scoring formula may help to eliminate some of the error variance and thus promote better reliability and validity. The more difficult the test, the more important it is to apply the correction formula, for as difficulty increases the amount of guessing increases.

If a scoring formula of this type is to be used in a test, and particularly if it is a power test, there should be explicit instructions to the examinees that there will be a deduction of a fraction of a point for each wrong answer (or a bonus of a fraction of a point for an omission). The second formula is naturally more palatable to examinees. But there are usually better scoring formulas than those based upon a priori reasoning about guessing, as we shall see next.

It might be pointed out, incidentally, that when examinees do not know the answer to an item, their habits of taking tests are such that they do not choose among the alternatives entirely at random. Certain positions in a list of five responses may be favored by habits of reading or of attention. This is probably not sufficiently important in itself to overthrow the usefulness of "chance" scoring formulas. In the long run, if the position of the right answer is randomized, the correction may work well enough. More serious, however, is the fact that many test writers, in preparing four- or five-choice items, do not provide "misleads" or "distractors" that are equally attractive. It is easy, perhaps, for the test writer to think of one good wrong answer to an item, but to think of more than one and to make all equally attractive is a trying art. Many a four- or five-choice item reduces virtually to a three- or two-choice item because of this fact. The a priori scoring formula as given above then undercorrects; we do not know by how much.

Empirical weighting of right and wrong answers.   When R and W scores are not too highly intercorrelated, and when there is a practical criterion, it often pays to treat the two as if they were two different variables, as if they had arisen from two different tests. One then applies multiple-regression procedures and derives optimal weights which will maximize the correlation of a weighted combination of R and W scores and the criterion. Since, as was pointed out before (Chap. 16), it is the *relative* sizes of the weights that are important and we do not care whether the formula scores have the same mean as the criterion or represent predictions in proper sizes, we can let the R score have a weight of +1 and find what weight the W score must then have. We should expect it to have a fractional negative weight, though it might differ markedly from the weight given by formula (18.11). For this purpose, Thurstone has given the following equation to determine the weight for the W score:[1]

$$v = \frac{\sigma_r(r_{cr}r_{wr} - r_{cw})}{\sigma_w(r_{cw}r_{wr} - r_{cr})} \qquad \begin{array}{l} \text{(Optional weight for error scores} \\ \text{when weight for rights} \\ \text{scores is +1)} \end{array} \qquad (18.13)$$

[1]Thurstone, L. L. *The Reliability and Validity of Tests.* Ann Arbor, Mich.: Edwards, 1931. P. 80.

where the subscripts c, r, and w stand for criterion, rights, and wrongs scores, respectively. The correlation between these formula scores and the criterion is given by the usual multiple-R formula for three variables. In symbols that apply here,

$$R^2_{c.rw} = \frac{r^2_{cr} + r^2_{cw} - 2 r_{cr} r_{cw} r_{wr}}{1 - r^2_{wr}}$$

(Correlation of optimally weighted formula score with a criterion)   (18.14)

Note that this gives R^2.

The application of these formulas sometimes leads to surprising results. A two-choice numerical-operations test, a fairly simple and unique measure of the factor known as facility with numbers, should have had a scoring formula of $R - 3W$ to yield maximal validity for the selection of navigators in the AAF. Another, five-choice, numerical-operations test should have had a weight of -2 for wrong answers. Thus the importance of accuracy was much greater than the a priori weights would have provided for. For the selection of bombardier students, the weight for wrong responses should have been about $-.5$ for the two-choice items and about zero for the five-choice items, for maximal validity of the test. For the bombardier criterion, accuracy was of relatively less importance than for the navigator.

For still other tests, there were results deviating from a priori weighting, for example, one test involving estimations of lengths or distances on a map seemed to require a *positive* weight for wrong answers, for maximal validity for pilots, indicating that speed was of great importance in this test, even at the expense of accuracy.

On the whole, the experience with scoring formulas tended to show that empirical formulas give validities slightly better than a priori weighting of wrong responses, with gains of the order of .02 to .03 being typical. On the whole, optimal weighting of wrongs gives increases of the order of .03 to .06 over validities for the rights scores used alone. There are some instances when the optimal weight for W is zero.

In Fig. 18.5 are shown the relationships between validities of formula scores in three different tests and different weights for wrongs scores in those tests when the rights scores are weighted $+1$. Not only can we see that there is an optimal weight for the wrongs scores for each test (.0 for test 1, -1 for test 2, and approximately -3 for test 3) but also that some weights would be detrimental to validity. These various validities can be estimated by using the correlation-of-sums formulas given in Chap. 16. The validity of each test when scored for number of right responses only can be noted at the place where $v = 0$. The amount of gain by optimal weighting can be noted by comparing this validity with the peak of the curve. There is no very marked

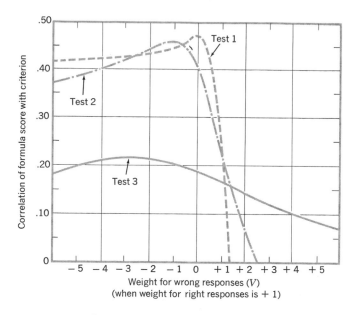

Fig. 18.5. *Predictive validity of each of three tests as
a function of the weight
applied to the wrong re-
sponses in scoring the test.
Especially to be noted are
the weights offering optimal validity for each
test and the sensitivity
of the validity coefficient to
changes in weight.*
(Adapted from informal
AAF report, Headquar-
ters, Training Command.)

change in validity for various negative weights up to −.5. An error in
weighting in the negative direction would apparently not be very serious. But validity drops much more rapidly if the error in the weight
is in the other direction — precipitously, sometimes, if the weight goes
on the positive side. Common-sense reasoning would ordinarily not
permit us to choose a positive weight for the wrongs.

Empirical scoring formulas should not be derived unless samples
are quite large. In some combinations of correlations among C, W,
and R, the weight is very sensitive to minor errors in any one of the
three correlations involved and may be unreasonable on the face of
it. When in doubt, it is best to be conservative. It may help to plot a
curve for a test, after assuming different weights for W and solving
the correlation $r_{c.rw}$ by the formula for correlation of sums (16.25).

Factorial validity of rights and wrongs scores. The procedure for
maximizing predictive validity for a test by using the proper scoring
weights can also be applied to maximizing the correlation of a test
with a factor; in other words, in increasing its loading in a factor.
Recent experience shows that error scores might well be given much
attention as sources of certain kinds of variance that it is worth our
while to measure. Some AAF findings indicated that a trait of care-
fulness was quite measurable by using wrongs scores in several tests,
whereas the number of right responses usually failed to measure it.[1]

Fruchter has more recently found by factor-analyzing rights scores
and wrongs scores in the same tests that while the two scores in the

[1]Guilford and Lacey, *op. cit.* Chap. 25.

same test may measure the same factors (in reverse), they do so to different degrees. He also found that some factors are more measurable by wrongs score than others.[1] In fact, it is possible that a certain kind of reasoning should be measured by errors rather than by correct solutions. These results have not been verified as yet, but they are suggestive of the rich possibilities that may exist in the fuller use and weighting of wrong responses.

Item analysis

Many of the statistical operations in dealing with tests, particularly during test construction, have to do with item analysis, wherever tests are composed of items or other small parts. The major goals of item analysis are the improvement of total-score reliability or of total-score validity, or both, and the achievement of better item sequences and types of score distributions. We want to be sure that all items in a test are functioning; that they do something for us in the way of measurement, or at least make some contribution toward that end. Item-analysis procedures, including appropriate statistical methods, enable us to differentiate between the better and the poorer items.

RATIONAL AND EMPIRICAL APPROACHES TO TEST DEVELOPMENT

The basic philosophies of test makers differ considerably. On the one hand, there are those who prefer to develop tests that measure recognized, basic psychological traits or variables. In other words there is much concern with construct validity. This school of thought is generally divided between those who regard factor analysis, properly used, as the best means of demonstrating construct validity and those who do not. Supporters of factor analysis point out that it both isolates the trait involved and also ascertains which tests measure it best. Their opponents depend upon intercorrelations of tests and other variables for evidence of construct validity, but balk at going further in the way of factor analysis.

The empirical school of thought is commonly represented among those who face practical problems of measurement. Their immediate concern is to make testing instruments that will help to solve pressing everyday problems. For example, if he wishes to be able to identify individuals with high aptitude for creative production in science or in management, the test maker may adopt the specific approach of predicting a criterion of success in creative performance from a very large list of items containing biographical information. Any item that

[1]Fruchter, B. Differences in factor content of rights and wrongs scores. *Psychometrika*, 1953, **18**, 257–265.

is found correlated significantly with the criterion is retained in the test; there may be little or no concern regarding the personality traits involved in what is measured by the total test scores. Of course, this does not mean that those who primarily adopt the empirical view are behaving irrationally or that they necessarily have no interest in basic concepts. There is quite a range of dispositions toward the rational school on the part of the empiricists. Both groups make much use of empirical steps of item analysis in test development.

COMMON ITEM STATISTICS

Of the descriptive statistics commonly used in item analysis, three kinds stand out. For one thing, we want to know about the difficulty level of an item, if the test is one of ability, or the "popularity" level of an item, if it is designed to measure a nonaptitude trait. In this context, "popularity" does not mean "social desirability"; it refers to the extent to which the individuals of a population answer the item in the keyed direction. In both aptitude and nonaptitude tests, the basic index of difficulty and of popularity is the proportion of the individuals passing the item (answering in the keyed direction). The proportion "passing" item I, p_i, is the item mean, as was pointed out in the preceding chapter. We shall see that there are more meaningful indices of difficulty or popularity, but they are based upon p_i.

The other two statistics of common interest in item analysis are r_{it}, the correlation of an item with the total score from the test of which it is a part, and r_{ic}, the correlation of the item with some outside criterion. The criterion may be a recognized measure of a trait, when construct validity is of primary interest, or some measure of success in everyday life, when predictive validity is of primary interest. We shall see that these two kinds of correlation may take different forms and that there are statistics that have been proposed as substitutes for them.

ITEM DIFFICULTY AND INDICES OF DIFFICULTY

When the term "difficulty" is used in an item-analysis context, it also covers the concept of "popularity," mentioned above in connection with difficulty. There are two things wrong with using the item mean as an index of difficulty for an item. One is that the larger the p_i the *easier* the item, i.e., the scale of difficulty is reversed. The other is that the scale of proportions is not an interval scale. Neither of these objections is fatal. A correct rank ordering of items can be achieved and items having the same p_i may be assumed to be of equal difficulty for the same population. One can also get used to a reversal of direction of the scale. But for certain purposes a better scale is desirable.

A rational scale for item difficulty. A rational scaling of difficulty of items is achieved by making a transformation from proportions to corresponding standard-score values, z_i. To illustrate, let us use some data on six words from a vocabulary test, as represented in Table 18.4. A test including many other words had been given to 360 elderly people, many of them in various stages of senility, so that a wide range of ability was involved.[1] The total sample was divided into upper and lower halves based on a standardized interview that asked questions designed to assess immediate memory, remote memory, knowledge of current events, and other common knowledge. Six words, representing a wide range of difficulty, were selected for this illustration. For each word we have the two proportions giving fully satisfactory answers in the upper and lower groups (designated by p_u and p_l) and in the two groups combined (p_i).

The rational scaling procedure assumes that the proportions represent areas under the normal distribution curve. A given proportion p_i is taken to represent the proportion of the area under the normal distribution *above* a certain corresponding z_i value on the base line of the curve. Thus, the greater the proportion, the lower the z_i value. Items with proportions above .50 receive negative z_i values and proportions below .50 receive positive z_i values (see Fig. 18.6). The relationship between p_i and z_i in a coordinate system is that of a descending cumulative frequency curve. In Fig. 18.6 the curve is shown, with a point on the curve for each of the six items. Two of the words are shown with special information. The z_i values seen in Table 18.4 are found from Table C of Appendix B.

It will be noted that the z values for the upper and lower groups are numerically different. Naturally, the same items should be more difficult for the lower group than for the upper one, so we should expect systematically higher z values for the lower group. There is also

[1]The writer is indebted to Dr. Oscar J. Kaplan for the use of these data.

Table 18.4   ***Means and standard-score values for six vocabulary-test items****

	p_u	p_l	p_i	z_u	z_l	z_i
Hat	.993	.723	.853	−2.46	−0.59	−1.05
Forest	.903	.500	.701	−1.30	0.00	−0.53
Middle	.747	.333	.540	−0.66	+0.60	−0.10
Prefer	.550	.173	.362	−0.13	+0.94	+0.35
Adept	.267	.060	.164	+0.62	+1.55	+0.98
Coherent	.050	.027	.038	+1.64	+1.93	+1.77

*Adapted from item-analysis data provided by Dr. Oscar J. Kaplan, with his permission.

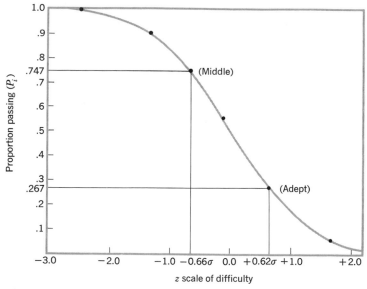

Fig. 18.6. *Diagram representing the determination of a z-scale value for each of six vocabulary-test items from their proportions of correct responses in a certain population.*

another difference in the ranges of the two sets of z values: those for the upper group have a greater range. The difference in range is due to a difference in actual range of ability in the two groups.

If we plot the two sets of z values, z_u and z_l, on a pair of coordinates, we find that there is a linear relationship with near-perfect correlation. There is merely a difference in unit and mean in the two sets. By making a linear transformation (explained in Chap. 19) it is possible to modify the scale values in the one set to make them coincide in mean and standard deviation with those in the other set. The two transformation equations are

$$z'_u = 1.42z_l - 1.48$$
$$z'_l = .714z_u + 1.05$$

depending upon whether we wish to adopt the upper-group scale or the lower-group scale as the common measuring stick for difficulty of these items. Although the zero point on such a z scale is a meaningful quantity, being the point of median difficulty for the group, if we wished to be rid of negative signs in the z values, we could add a constant of 5.00 to each of them.

Scaling items for difficulty on z scales is, of course, not always necessary. Doing so, however, makes feasible a number of things that would otherwise not be possible. Having equal-unit, or interval-scale, values for items, we find it possible to talk about functional relationships between difficulty of the items and some other properties. For example, if the items are sounds to be judged for differences in pitch or in loudness, stimulus properties can be related to item difficulty. Relations to chronological age and other variables also become possible in quantitative terms.

Item difficulty when there is chance success. Many frequently used tests are composed of items to each of which one response is to be chosen from several (commonly two to five) possible answers. In such cases, the proportion of right answers is inflated by an increment due to chance success. The smaller the number of alternatives, the greater is the chance contribution. A formula has been provided for correcting for this chance element, giving a proportion that would probably have been obtained had there been no possibility for the examinee to guess.[1] The formula reads

$$cp = \frac{kp - 1}{k - 1} \qquad \text{(Proportion of correct responses to an item, with chance success eliminated)} \qquad (18.15)$$

where cp = the corrected proportion of correct answers

p = the obtained proportion

k = the number of alternative answers to each item

The all-important assumption is that when the examinee does not know the right answer he guesses completely at random among the alternatives. It is probable that in some items the examinee knows that one or two alternatives are incorrect, so his guessing actually lies among a number of alternatives smaller than k. Thus the formula undercorrects where there is a bias.

To illustrate how much difference the correction for guessing makes, let us assume an obtained p of .75. With 5 alternatives, cp becomes .69; with 4 alternatives, .67; with 3 alternatives, .625; and with 2 alternatives, .50. The corresponding z values would be changed, ranging after correction from a z of −0.67 when p is .75 to a z of 0.00 when p is .50. The use of corrected proportions is especially desirable when difficulties of items having different numbers of possible responses are being compared.

ITEM CORRELATIONS

More important than the matter of item difficulty are the questions of whether a test item discriminates individuals in line with other items in the test, whether responses to the item predict some criterion, and whether the criterion is total score on the test of which it is a part or some outside evaluation of individuals. The problem is

[1]Guilford, J. P. The determination of item difficulty when chance success is a factor. *Psychometrika*, 1936, **1**, 259–264.

often known as that of *item validity;* a case of construct validity when the criterion is the total score, and a case of predictive validity when the criterion is an outside measure, particularly when it is a practical variable of some kind. Of course, raising the correlations of items with total score has the effect of increasing homogeneity of the test, which is a matter of reliability. But, as just stated, it is also a matter of construct validity, i.e., ensuring that the psychological variable measured be uniform for all items.

Discrimination value of items. One principle of item validation, less commonly utilized than others, is the discrimination value of items. In this connection, the question is how sharply the item segregates persons higher on the scale of the criterion from those lower on the scale. Figure 18.3 shows some ogive functions, each presenting the increase in proportion passing an item as a function of the ability that it measures.[1] The more steeply the curve rises, the better the discrimination and the fewer false positives and false negatives predicted by the item. An index indicating the degree of steepness of the curve would serve as a measure of the discrimination value of the item. The discrimination principle is a good one, but the procedures for applying the principle require considerable computational effort, and hence they have lost out in popularity to correlation methods, which will be discussed next. It can be readily inferred that the higher the discrimination value of an item the greater its correlation with the criterion; hence the one approach is a real alternative to the other and both yield about the same conclusions regarding the goodness of an item.

Item correlations with an external criterion. For an illustration of item-criterion correlations, r_{ic}, let us use data from the same source as those represented in Table 18.4, the six words from a vocabulary test. We should consider, first, what particular kind of correlation coefficient is most appropriate. If we have the appropriate information regarding results with an item and the criterion, a number of coefficients can be computed — biserial r, point-biserial r, tetrachoric r, and the phi coefficient — all are possible and meaningful.

The choice of correlation depends upon what kind of question we want to answer. If we want to know whether the attribute or attributes measured by the criterion are also measured by the item, and the extent to which the item measures them, we should use a biserial r or a tetrachoric r. If we want to know how much predictive power the item has and how it would contribute to predictions, we should use a point-biserial r. With the item giving information in only one of two categories, when scored 0 or 1, its predictive power is accordingly limited. The point-biserial r takes this into consideration. If the

[1]An ogive function is a normal cumulative distribution of proportions.

prediction to be made is in one of two categories only, for example, predicting whether an individual will succeed or fail, a phi coefficient is to be preferred.

Actually, if the only use to be made of the correlation coefficients is to select and to reject items in making up a test, one coefficient is about as good as another. They are generally interrelated by ratios such that for the same items the coefficients of different kinds would come in about the same rank order. Other considerations, then, have some bearing: the amount of information needed for computing the coefficient, the amount of labor (and availability of laborsaving aids), and whether or not there is a good statistical test of whether the obtained coefficient differs significantly from zero.

If one were to apply the most convenient formulas for the two biserial coefficients, reference to Chap. 14 will show that the information required includes M_p, the mean total-test score for those individuals who passed the item (which changes from item to item); M_t, the mean of the entire sample (which is the same for all items); p, the proportion passing the item, and other normal-curve values derived from it; and σ_t, the standard deviation of the total-score distribution.

Fortunately, all four kinds of coefficients can be estimated with much less information required. In each case the crucial information includes p_u and p_l, when the division of cases on the criterion variable is at $p' = q' = .50$. For example, the formula for the phi coefficient then reduces to

$$\phi = \frac{p_u - p_l}{2 \sqrt{pq}} \qquad \text{(Phi coefficient for an item with a variable on which the mean is .5)} \qquad (18.16)$$

where p_u and p_l = proportions of individuals passing the item in upper
and lower criterion groups, respectively
p = proportion of total sample passing the item

With an equal division of cases, $p = (p_u + p_l)/2$. The terms p_u and p_l are readily obtained in the process of counting the number of passing individuals.

To determine whether an obtained ϕ is significantly divergent from zero, we make use of the relation of ϕ to chi square: $N\phi^2 = \chi^2$. Phi coefficients significant at the .05 and .01 levels can be estimated by the equations

$$\phi_{.05} = \frac{1.960}{\sqrt{N}}$$
$$\text{(Phi coefficients significant at the .05 and .01 levels, respectively)} \qquad (18.17)$$
$$\phi_{.01} = \frac{2.576}{\sqrt{N}}$$

where N is the number of cases in the two groups combined.

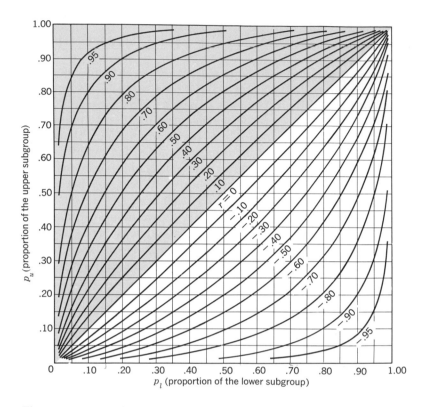

Fig. 18.7. *An abac for graphic estimates of the tetrachoric r when one variable has been dichotomized at the median of the distribution.* (Prepared from the Pearson Tables of r_t by Harvey F. Dingman.)

For convenience in estimation of item-criterion correlations, abacs like those in Figs. 18.7 and 18.8 have been developed for all four kinds of coefficients. Only those for r_t and ϕ are given here, since they represent all four directly or indirectly.[1] The biserial r would presumably be very similar to r_t in value, and one can be taken as an estimate of the other. The point-biserial r is related to both the biserial r and to ϕ by certain ratios, provided the proportion p is not extreme:

$$r_{pbi} = r_b \frac{y}{\sqrt{pq}} \qquad (18.18)$$

(Estimation of r_{pbi} from r_b and from ϕ)

$$r_{pbi} = \phi \frac{\sqrt{pq}}{y} \qquad (18.19)$$

[1]For the other abacs and for further details on item-analysis methods, see Guilford, J. P. *Psychometric Methods, op. cit.*

We are now ready to examine the data in Table 18.5. For each item the values p_u and p_l are given. Using the abacs, we find the r_t and ϕ estimates given in the fourth and sixth columns of numbers. The r_{pbi} values have been estimated from the r_t values by means of formula (18.18). By checking, the reader may see how close the r_{pbi} values would come to those estimated from the ϕ coefficient, using formula (18.19). With $N = 360$, use of formula (18.17) tells us that it takes a ϕ of .103 to be significant at the .05 level, and a ϕ of .135 to be significant at the .01 level. Five of the six ϕ's are significant beyond the .01 level. Using formulas for the standard errors of r_t and r_{pbi} (the SE for the latter being essentially the same as for the Pearson r), with $r = 0$, we could also determine which of those coefficients are significantly different from zero.

Item-total-score correlations. For an illustration of correlation of items with total scores, let us use data from Table 17.2, where we have item scores of ten fictitious examinees on eight hypothetical items. Dividing the ten cases into the highest five and lowest five on total

Fig. 18.8. *An abac for graphic estimate of the phi coefficient when one variable has been dichotomized at the median.*

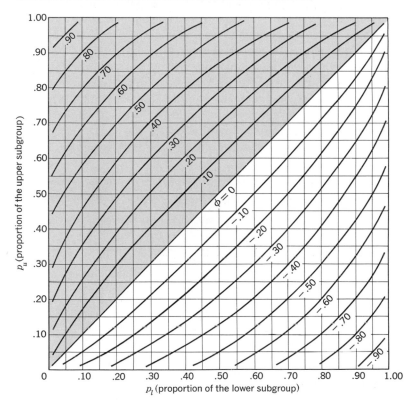

score, we can determine the proportions in each group who pass each item. The p_u and p_l values are given in Table 18.6. Such information would be the basis for entering the abac in Fig. 18.7 or Fig. 18.8. But it will be noted that so many of the proportions are 0 or 1.0 that the utility of graphic estimates of correlations is often very dubious for these data. On the other hand, enough information is available in Table 17.2 to compute either a biserial r or a point-biserial r. Let us compute the latter. We can do so, for we know the mean M_t to be 4.0, the standard deviation to be 2.45, and M_p can be readily computed for each item, as well as p, the mean of p_u and p_l. The point-biserial r's, thus computed, are listed in the third row of Table 18.6. We could also have computed the phi coefficients, preferably by means of formula (18.16). It would be unwise to estimate tetrachoric r's from these data by computation, because in so many of the 2×2 tables there are zero frequencies, which lead to estimates of $+1.0$ and -1.0 for r_t, as pointed out in Chap. 14.

Correction of an item-total correlation for overlap.   An item-total correlation is a part-whole correlation and is thus spuriously high, because the item's specific and error variances contribute to the correlation as well as its common-factor variance, where only the latter should be tolerated for complete accuracy. The smaller the number of items in a test the more serious is the inflation of r from this source. As pointed out in Chap. 14, where there are n components of a total, all with equal variance and mutually independent (uncorrelated), each component would correlate with the total to the extent of $1/\sqrt{n}$. In this eight-item test, such a value would be $1/\sqrt{8}$, or .35. It will be noted that one of the obtained r's in Table 18.6 is about that size; all are larger than the actual relationships would warrant.

One solution to this problem would be to adapt formula (14.23),

Table 18.5   **Item-criterion correlations for six vocabulary-test items, derived from proportions of correct answers in two criterion groups of elderly subjects***

Item	p_u	p_l	p_i	r_t	r_{pbi}	ϕ
Hat	.993	.723	.853	.80	.52	.40
Forest	.903	.500	.701	.70	.52	.44
Middle	.747	.333	.540	.62	.49	.41
Prefer	.550	.173	.362	.59	.46	.39
Adept	.267	.060	.164	.55	.39	.29
Coherent	.050	.027	.038	.20	.09	.05

*Adapted from item-analysis data provided by Dr. Oscar J. Kaplan, with his permission.

Table 18.6   *Correlation of eight items with total scores derived from those items, with correction for part-whole overlap*

	a	b	c	d	e	f	g	h
p_u	1.0	1.0	1.0	.8	.8	.8	.4	.4
p_1	.6	.4	.2	.2	.2	.0	.2	.0
r_{pbi}	.51	.78	.75	.73	.65	.83	.36	.61
$_{ir}r_{pbi}$	.37	.68	.64	.62	.51	.75	.21	.48

which gives the general equation for the correlation of a part (in this case an item) with the sum of the remainder of the parts in the total composite. This formula could be adapted to an item-total, point-biserial r, using the information that the standard deviation of the item distribution is given by $\sqrt{pq}$. The writer has provided such a formula.[1]

But it is now possible to do better. The main objection to the above procedure is that for every item the remainder is a slightly different criterion. Another objection, a rather minor one, is that the correlation obtained is between the item and a composite of $n - 1$ items rather than n items. Some new formulas developed by Henrysson provide for the estimation of the correlation of an item with the same total composite of n items, with the spurious overlap effect removed.[2] For the point-biserial correlation the formula is

$$r_{pbi} = \left(\sqrt{\frac{n}{n-1}}\right)\left(\frac{r_{pbi}\,\sigma^2_t - \sqrt{pq}}{\sqrt{\sigma^2_t - \Sigma pq}}\right)$$

(Point-biserial r between a test item and the total-test score, corrected for part-whole overlap)   (18.20)

where n = number of items in the test

$\quad r_{pbi}$ = obtained item-total-score correlation

$\quad \sigma^2_t$ = total-score variance

$\quad p$ = proportion passing the item and $q = 1 - p$

For the biserial correlation, the formula is

$$r_b = \left(\sqrt{\frac{n}{n-1}}\right)\left[\frac{r_b\sigma^2_t - (pq/y)}{\sqrt{\sigma^2_t - \Sigma pq}}\right]$$

(Biserial r between a test item and the total-test score, corrected for part-whole overlap)   (18.21)

[1]Guilford, J. P. The correlation of an item with a composite of the remaining items in a test. *Educ. psychol. Measmt.*, 1953, **13**, 87–93.
[2]Henrysson, S. Correction of item-total correlations in item analysis. *Psychometrika*, 1963, **28**, 211–218.

The usefulness of these corrections for part-whole overlap is most apparent when obtained correlations are small. Such (uncorrected) r's might well be almost entirely due to the spurious part-whole component. The statistical significance of small, uncorrected item-total correlations should be questioned. If they do not reach the required level of significance after correction, they are not to be regarded as significant before correction.

Assuming statistical significance, uncorrected r's are still useful, for they are probably in approximately correct order as to size. Correction would probably not change the order materially. Correction is usually of little importance when tests exceed 20 items in length, but the investigator who is concerned about the statistical significance of the r_{it} correlations should consider whether the quantity $1/\sqrt{N}$ is of about the same order of magnitude as the r required for significant departure from zero, in deciding whether or not to apply a correction.

Some general considerations on item correlations.   For most purposes of item correlations, it does not matter much which kind of coefficient is used, as shown by experience.[1] A minor point in favor of phi is that it does not require an assumption of normal distribution, as is true of r_b and r_t. Although ϕ does not apply logically to the case of a continuous criterion measure, where upper and lower halves of the cases are used in a dichotomy, it does apply logically when a certain proportion of the middle scores are omitted—the middle half, 46 per cent (when the two extreme 27 percentages of the cases form the criterion groups), or any arbitrarily chosen portion.

On the practice of eliminating central cases the writer is rather negative. On the one hand, this procedure does not use all the available data; it throws away information. In addition to the loss of power of statistical tests that is involved, one loses the opportunity to determine whether there are nonlinear relationships between items and criterion. In aptitude items it is probably safe to assume linear relationships, in which case the loss of middle cases is immaterial from this point of view. But in the case of nonaptitude variables, instances of nonlinear relationships are more common. The middle third of the cases might behave much like the upper group or like the lower group, and not lie between them in the proportion passing. There are even cases in which the two extremes are alike in responding to an item, both different from the middle. Such information would be missed if only extreme groups were utilized.

One weakness of the phi coefficient in item correlations, a weak-

[1]As demonstrated by Guilford and Lacey, *op. cit.* Pp. 28–33.

ness shared to some extent with the point-biserial r, is the fact that it favors items of median difficulty. Recall that phi can be maximum when the means p and p' are equal. When p' is arbitrarily fixed at .5, as is usually the case, items with p near .5 can correlate higher with the criterion. Items with extreme means have little chance of significant correlations. In one sense this is not a fault but a virtue, in that items of median difficulty mean greater internal-consistency reliability. But a test composed of items all of near-median difficulty would fail to be a good discriminating measure of cases near the extremes of the range. For discriminating among the very highest and lowest on the score scale, we need items of high and low difficulties.

If we are looking for valid items at extreme levels of difficulty, there is one thing we can do. A second item analysis could be done in which the cases are subdivided into the highest one-fifth against the second one-fifth (or even the lowest four-fifths). Phi coefficients could be computed with this new division of criterion cases. A similar item analysis could be done with the lowest one-fifth of the cases in a criterion group. Items at means of .8 and .2 would then be favored by the use of a ϕ coefficient in these two analyses, respectively.

ITEM COMPOSITES FOR PREDICTIVE VALIDITY

If the test maker's objective is to produce a test instrument with maximum validity for predicting some practical criterion, his item-analysis procedures differ somewhat from those described. A practical criterion is likely to be factorially complex, with a number of common factors involved. Different items will be needed to represent each of the common factors, except where the items themselves are factorially complex in favorable ways, i.e., having the same combinations of factors represented as in the criterion. Multiple-regression principles apply to this situation, which calls for items that correlate strongly with the criterion but low with one another. Thus, in item analysis for constructing a test of this nature, we need both correlations of items with the outside criterion and with one another. The alternative to information on item intercorrelations is in item-total correlations. Selecting items with higher r_{ic}'s and lower r_{it}'s should accomplish the kind of heterogeneous test that is required for maximum validity. The optimal validity would be achieved by means of a multiple-regression equation, with optimal weights for the items.

Weighting items for reliability. The mention of weighting items differentially, which means other than the usual 0 or 1 weights, to achieve maximum validity, raises the question of whether the same kind of practice might not also be applied when the construct to be measured is a fundamental trait. After all, items do not correlate equally with a total-score criterion. It seems reasonable to suppose that items correlating higher with this kind of criterion should be given more voice in the composite score. Methods of weighting items in such scales have been devised and used.[1] But the general experience is that, if many items are scored for a trait score, differential weights contribute very little to increasing its reliability. When a test is very short, containing 10 to 15 items, let us say, differential weighting may contribute enough to reliability to make the practice worthwhile.

A need for cross validation. Where methods are used to achieve good differential weights for items, as in applying multiple-regression principles to derive optimal weights, a cross-validation study becomes very important in order to check on the applicability of the weights in new samples, even from the same population. As pointed out in connection with multiple-regression procedures in Chap. 16, the solution for optimal weights capitalizes upon all favorable chance effects available. A cross validation would involve applying the same weights in scoring in a new sample and determining the correlation between predicted criterion values and obtained criterion values. Much shrinkage of validity is ordinarily expected. Indeed, the mere selection of the more valid items in item analysis should also be followed by a cross validation in a new sample, where possible.

EXERCISES

Give your conclusions and interpretations in connection with the solution to each of the following problems:

1. For the data in Data 18*A*, compute: (*a*) communalities; (*b*) proportions of specific variance; and (*c*) intercorrelations.

2. Test *X* has a reliability coefficient of .92 and a criterion *Y* has a

[1] For methods of weighting items, see Guilford, J. P. *Psychometric Methods, op. cit.*

Data 18A **Loadings for four uncorrelated common factors and reliability coefficients in two tests and a criterion**

Variable	Factors				r_{tt}
	A	*B*	*C*	*D*	
Test 1	.10	.60	.40	.00	.80
Test 2	.20	.30	.50	.70	.87
Criterion *J*	.20	.50	.10	.00	.65

Data 18B **Reliability coefficients
and validity coefficients for four tests**

Coefficient	Test			
	X_1	X_2	X_3	X_4
r_{xx}	.80	.80	.60	.80
r_{yx}	.70	.50	.50	.30

reliability of .65. Assume that the coefficient for predictive validity in connection with four different samples has values of .35, .48, .61, and .72.

a. Determine the probable correlation between the "true" test scores and the "true" criterion measures in each of the four situations.

b. Determine the validity of the fallible test for predicting the "true" criterion in each situation.

3. In connection with Exercise 2, assume that $\sigma_y = 15.0$. Compute the standard error of estimate of the "true" criterion from the fallible test score for the four instances.

4. Using the information given in Data 18B:

a. Estimate the validity coefficient in each case, assuming that each test is doubled homogeneously in length.

b. Do the same, assuming that each test is made five times as long.

c. Do the same, assuming that each test is made half as long.

5. How long (in ratio to original lengths) would it be necessary to make tests X_1 and X_2 in Exercise 4 in order to achieve a validity co-efficient of .60?

6. Assume the following data for a certain test:

$$\sigma_r = 10.0 \qquad \sigma_w = 4.0 \qquad r_{cr} = .3 \qquad r_{cw} = -.2 \qquad r_{wr} = -.4$$

(where the subscripts stand for "right," "wrong," and "criterion" scores, respectively).

a. Compute the optimal weight for the wrong responses (W), when the right responses (R) are weighted +1.

b. Compute the correlation of scores obtained by use of these weights with the criterion (C).

c. Assume, in turn, arbitrary weights of −2.0 and +1.0 for the wrong responses (with a weight of +1 for the right responses), and estimate the correlation with C for such weighted combinations.

7. For the items in Data 18C, determine the z-scale values for difficulty of the items.

a. What can you conclude concerning the relative levels of ability of the two groups and concerning their dispersions in ability measured by the test?

b. Plot points representing the z_I values and the corresponding z_{II} values and fit a straight line to the points by inspection.

8. For the items represented in Data 18*D*, give the difficulty values *z* for the corrected and uncorrected proportions, taking into account the number of alternative responses in each case.

9. For the information in Data 18*E*:
a. Compute the phi coefficients by formula; also look them up in the abac given in the chapter.
b. Look up the tetrachoric correlations for the items in the abac.
c. Estimate the corresponding point-biserial *r*'s from both ϕ and r_t and compare them.
d. Determine which coefficients are significantly different from 0.

Data 18C   **Proportion of examinees passing each of five items in two groups**

Group	Item				
	A	B	C	D	E
I	.02	.10	.33	.71	.96
II	.09	.31	.54	.84	.97

Data 18D   **Items differing in number of alternative responses and in proportions of examinees passing them**

Alternatives	2	2	3	3	5	5
Proportion passing	.85	.55	.85	.55	.85	.55

Data 18E   **Proportions of examinees from upper and lower halves on a total-test score who passed each of four items (N = 100)**

Group	Item			
	G	H	I	J
Upper	.75	.95	.40	.57
Lower	.35	.80	.05	.43

ANSWERS
1. h^2: .53, .87, .30; s^2: .27, .00, .35; $r_{12} = .40$; $r_{1J} = .36$; $r_{2J} = .24$.
2. *a.* $r_{\infty\omega}$: .45, .62, .79, .93.
   b. $r_{\omega x}$: .43, .59, .76, .89.
3. $\sigma_{\omega x}$: 10.9, 9.7, 7.9, 5.4.
4. *a.* .74, .53, .56, .32.
   b. .76, .55, .61, .33.
   c. .64, .46, .42, .27.

5. *n*: 0.36; −1.82 (the negative sign may be disregarded).
6. *a.* $v = -0.91$; *b.* $R = .31$; *c.* r_{cs}: .30, .24.
7. z_I: +2.05, +1.28, +0.44, −0.55, −1.75.
   z_{II}: +1.34, +0.50, −0.10, −0.99, −1.88.
8. z (without correction): −1.04, −0.13, −1.04, −0.13, −1.04, −0.13.
   z (with correction): −0.52, +1.28, −0.76, +0.45, −0.89, +0.16.
9. Computed ϕ: .40, .22, .42, .14.
   $\quad\quad\quad r_t$: .60, .48, .72, .20.
   Estimated r_{pbi}: .48, .30, .52, .16.

19 Test scales and norms

IN this chapter we consider in some detail the problems of measurement by means of test scores. In previous chapters where test scores played a role, it was usually assumed that they approximated scales with equal units and that equal increments of numbers correspond to equal increments of psychological quantity. Such an assumption is necessary for the meaningful application of most statistical operations. When a test is composed of many items and when it is of an appropriate level of difficulty for the population examined, this assumption is fairly sound.

In the following pages we shall consider some ways of transforming raw-score scales into other scales for various reasons. One objective is to effect a more reasonable scale of measurement. Another important objective is to derive comparable scales for different tests. The raw scores from each test yield numbers that have no necessary comparability with numbers from another test. There are many occasions for wanting not only comparable values from different tests but also values that have some standard meaning. These are the problems of test norms and test standards.

WHY COMMON SCALES ARE NECESSARY

Aside from a few tests that yield scores in terms of physical-stimulus values (such as tests of sensory acuity) or of response values (such as time, distance, or energy values), most tests yield numerical values that have no unique significance. There was a time when scores were given in terms of percentages. The tradition of grading examinations in terms of percentage of right answers still has popular appeal, in spite of the many experimental demonstrations that such percentages are neither accurate nor numerically meaningful. The method gives a feeling (definitely fallacious) of having some kind of an "absolute" measure of the individual.

If modern psychology and education have taught anything about measurement, they have amply demonstrated the fact that there are few, if any, absolute measures of human behavior. The search for absolute measures has given way to an emphasis upon the concept of individual differences. The mean of the population has become the reference point, and out of the differences between individuals has come the basis for scale units. Even when the test happens to yield such objective scores as those in time, space, or energy units, it is sometimes doubted that such units, though unquestionably equal from a physical point of view, really represent equal psychological increments along scales of ability or talent. These considerations, among others, send us in search of more rational and meaningful scales of measurement for behavior events.

In addition to the theoretical demands just mentioned, there is the very practical consideration that scales for different tests should be comparable. The most obvious need for comparable scales is seen in educational and vocational guidance, particularly when profiles of scores are utilized. A profile is intended to give a psychological picture of an individual. We should hardly bother to prepare one for an individual if we did not expect to make very direct comparisons of the person's levels in different traits. The comparisons of trait positions for the same individual would be misleading, if not worthless, if there were not at least reasonable comparability of levels for different scores with the same numerical value.

No informed person would think of using raw scores as a basis of making direct comparisons among an individual's scale values with respect to trait variables. Conversion of raw scores to values on some other common scale is essential. Centile-rank positions were mentioned earlier (in Chap. 4). Centile ranks are suitable to the extent that they do make possible some comparable values for different tests; they do use the mean (or median) as the main reference point; and they are easily understood by the layman. They serve their best purpose when measurements must be interpreted to the layman. But centile values have limitations which give them less than full usefulness to those who expect something more of measurements. Centiles, after all, are rank positions and do not represent equal units of individual differences. It is possible to have scales that probably provide units approximating equal size as well as comparability of means, dispersions, and form of distribution.

SOME COMMON DERIVED SCALES

The chief interest in what follows will be in such scales—those that achieve comparability of means, dispersions, and form of distribution. We shall not go into the subject of the very popular mental-age concept or the IQ scale. As simple as those ideas may be, making a battery of tests that meet the requirements of age equivalents and appropriate distributions of IQ involves statistical problems of an intricate nature which we cannot go into. Treatment of these problems may be found by referring to McNemar and to Marks.[1] The three kinds of scales to be discussed here are the standard-score scale, the *T* scale, and the *C* scale. Their application to derivation of test norms and profile charts will be examined. The treatment will be kept at a rather elementary level, emphasizing basic concepts. For a more advanced treatment of some of these problems the reader is referred to a discussion by Flanagan.[2]

Standard scores

AN EXAMPLE OF THE NEED FOR COMPARABLE SCORES

A concrete example will illustrate some of the ideas expressed above. A student earns scores of 195 in an English examination, 20 in a reading test, 39 in an information test, 139 in a general academic-aptitude test, and 41 in a nonverbal psychological test. Is he therefore best in English and poorest in reading? Could he perhaps be equally good in all the tests? From the raw scores alone, we can answer neither of these questions nor many others that could be legitimately asked. This student's five scores are listed in column 4 of Table 19.1 (student I). Knowing the means of students in the five tests helps to some extent, since they serve as norms or comparable reference points. The means are listed in column 2. We now see that the student is well above average in English and in academic aptitude and is somewhat below average in reading and information, just as the numbers seem to indicate at their face value. The second student, whose raw scores are also in column 4, is numerically highest in the same two and lowest in the same three. When we consider the averages again, however, we find that student II is only about average in English, in academic aptitude, and in the psychological test, but he is above average in reading and in the information test.

When a student is above the mean in two tests, in which one is he actually superior? Student I is 39.3 points above the mean in English and 16.2 points above the mean in the psychological test (see column 5 of Table 19.1). Is his superiority in English really greater than his superiority in the psychological test? Student II is 20.3 points above the mean in reading and 17.5 points above the mean in information. Is he about equally superior in the two tests?

[1]McNemar, Q. *The Revision of the Stanford-Binet Scale.* Boston: Houghton Mifflin, 1942; Marks, E. S. Sampling in the revision of the Stanford-Binet scale. *Psychol. Bull.,* 1947, **44**, 413–434.
[2]Flanagan, J. C., in Lindquist, E. F. (ed.). *Educational Measurement.* Washington, D.C.: American Council on Education, 1951. Chap. 17.

Table 19.1   **A comparison of standard scores with raw scores earned by two students in five examinations**

(1)	(2)	(3)	(4) X Raw scores		(5) x Deviations		(6) z Standard scores	
Examination	Mean	Standard deviation	I	II	I	II	I	II
English	155.7	26.4	195	162	+39.3	+ 6.3	+1.49	+0.24
Reading	33.7	8.2	20	54	−13.7	+20.3	−1.67	+2.48
Information	54.5	9.3	39	72	−15.5	+17.5	−1.67	+1.88
Academic aptitude	87.1	25.8	139	84	+51.9	− 3.1	+2.01	−0.12
Psychological	24.8	6.8	41	25	+16.2	+ 0.2	+2.38	+0.03
Sums			434	397			+2.54	+4.51
Means							+0.51	+0.90

And how do the two students compare? The superiority of student I is apparent in three tests (English, academic aptitude, and psychological) and that of student II in the other two tests. This we can tell from the raw scores. But suppose the two were competing for a scholarship at a university; which one, if there is to be a choice between the two, should win? The totals of the five scores are 434 and 397, in favor of student I. Assuming that the five different abilities are equally important, have we done justice by comparing sums of raw scores? Are we justified in finding a sum or an average of each student's five raw scores?

Suppose that we were interested in determining which student is the more consistent in his abilities, as shown by these five tests, and which one has the greater variability within himself. Would a comparison of the average deviations or standard deviations of the five raw scores give us the answer? As the reader has probably guessed, the reply to most of these questions is in the negative. We are extremely limited in making direct comparisons in terms of raw scores for the reason that raw-score scales are arbitrary and unique. We need a common scale before such comparisons as we have called for can be made. Standard scores furnish one such common scale.

THE NATURE OF A STANDARD-SCORE SCALE

A standard-score scale has a mean of zero and a standard deviation of 1.0. An illustration of the conversion of a raw-score scale into a standard scale is shown in Fig. 19.1, *A*, *B*, and *C*. Distribution *A* is

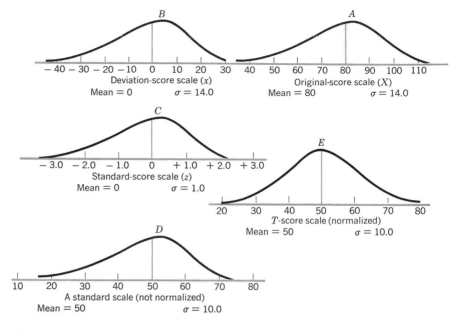

Fig. 19.1 *Distributions before and after conversion from a raw-score scale to a standardized-score scale with a desired mean and standard deviation, with and without normalizing the distribution.*

based upon the original, or raw, scores. The mean is 80 and standard deviation is 14.0. The distribution is obviously somewhat negatively skewed.

As we have previously seen, a standard score z is derived from a raw score X by means of the formula

$$z = \frac{X - M}{\sigma} = \frac{x}{\sigma} \qquad \text{(Standard score } z \text{ corresponding to a raw score } X \text{ and to a deviation } x) \qquad (19.1)$$

An intermediate step between the raw-score scale and the standard-score scale is to find the deviation $X - M$, or x. This step is illustrated in Fig. 19.1B. Deducting the mean from every raw score has the effect of shifting the entire distribution down the same scale so that the mean becomes zero. The final step, arriving at the z scale, is shown in Fig. 19.1C. Distribution C is drawn so that the mean is directly beneath that in distribution B, both at zero, so that deviations of 14 units on the original scale correspond with deviation of 1o on the standard scale. Note especially that the form of distribution has not changed; it is still skewed exactly as it was originally. This procedure *does not* normalize the distribution as some other scaling procedures do.

APPLICATION TO COMPARISONS OF SCORES

The two students represented in Table 19.1 will now be compared in terms of their standard scores. Before we take these comparisons very seriously, however, we must consider two possible limitations to this procedure. Applying formula (19.1), we arrive at the standard scores in column 6 of Table 19.1. For accurate comparisons between different tests, there are two necessary conditions to be satisfied. The population of students from which the distributions of scores arose must be assumed to have equal means and dispersions in all the abilities measured by the different tests, and the form of distribution, in terms of skewness and kurtosis, must be very similar from one ability to another.

Unfortunately, we have no ideal scales common to all these tests, with measurements which would tell us about these population parameters. Certain selective features might have brought about a higher mean, a narrower dispersion, and a negatively skewed distribution on the actual continuum of ability measured by one test, and a lower mean, a wider dispersion, and a symmetrical distribution on the continuum of another ability represented by another test. Since we can never know definitely about these features for any given population, if we want to achieve communality of scales at all (standard or any other), we often have to proceed on the assumption that actual means, standard deviations, and form of distribution are uniform for all abilities measured. In spite of these limitations, it is almost certain that derived scales, such as the standard-score scale, provide us with more nearly comparable values than do raw-score scales. The recognition of these limitations, however, should be admitted, and interpretations based upon the use of standard scores should be made with appropriate reservations in line with those limitations.

Returning to Table 19.1, with the standard scores we have for the two students, we can now give more satisfactory answers to the questions raised above about these students. Student I is most superior in the psychological test, next in academic aptitude, and third in English. Had we judged this by his deviations from the mean, we should have decided that his order of superiority was academic aptitude first, English second, and psychological third. We find that in terms of standard scores he is equally deficient in reading ability and information, whereas the deviations would have placed him lower in information than in reading. Student II's five standard scores come in about the same rank order as do his deviation scores but certainly not in the same order as his raw scores.

When comparing the two students in terms of raw scores, we should conclude that student I has the greatest advantage in number of points in academic aptitude; in terms of deviations, this would be the same, but in terms of standard scores it is in the psychological test that the advantage is greatest. Student II has about the same superiority over student I in the reading and information tests in terms of raw scores and deviations but has decidedly greater superiority in reading ability in terms of standard scores. When we compare the two students as to total or average score, whereas the raw-score total gives student I the distinct advantage of 37 points, or an *average* superiority of about 7 points, the standard-score averages reverse the order and give student II a 0.39σ lead. In a scholarship contest, we should conclude that student II has the greater all-round ability as indicated by these tests, when students are compared on a standard-score basis.

DISADVANTAGES OF STANDARD SCORES

Although standard scores will do for us all that we have said and more, under the proper conditions, there are several things about them that make them less convenient than some others. One shortcoming is the fact that half the scores will be negative in sign, which makes computation awkward. Another disadvantage is the very large unit, which is one standard deviation.

We could, of course, overcome the first shortcoming by adding a constant to all the scores to make them all positive, and we could multiply them by another constant, preferably by 10, to make the unit smaller and the range in total units greater. If we did both of these, we could achieve almost any mean and standard deviation we wanted, depending upon the choice of constants. If we wanted a mean of 50 and a standard deviation of 10, we would multiply every standard score by 10 and add 50.

DIRECT SCALING TO A DESIRED MEAN AND STANDARD DEVIATION

This brings us to a more general procedure. If we knew from the time we had acquired the distribution of raw scores that we were to convert them to a common scale with a certain mean and standard deviation, we should not go to the trouble of converting first to standard scores, then to the new scale. We can do the operation in one step by the equation[1]

[1]For the derivation of this type of equation, see Appendix A, Proof 14.

$$X_s = \left(\frac{\sigma_s}{\sigma_o}\right) X_o - \left[\left(\frac{\sigma_s}{\sigma_o}\right) M_o - M_s\right]$$

(Conversion of scores in one scale directly to comparable scores in another scale; a linear transformation) (19.2)

where X_s = a score on the standard scale, corresponding to X_o
X_o = a score on the obtained scale; a raw score
M_o and M_s = means of X_o and X_s, respectively
σ_o and σ_s = standard deviations of X_o and X_s, respectively

If the desired mean is 50 and the desired standard deviation is 10, with these substitutions the equation becomes

$$X_s = \left(\frac{10}{\sigma_o}\right) X_o - \left[\left(\frac{10}{\sigma_o}\right) M_o - 50\right]$$

Knowing σ_o and M_o from the particular distribution of raw scores, the equation reduces to the very simple form describing a straight line. Taking the illustration of Fig. 19.1, where M_o = 80 and σ_o = 14.0,

$$X_s = \left(\frac{10}{14}\right) X_o - \left[\left(\frac{10}{14}\right) 80 - 50\right]$$
$$= .714 X_o - 7.12$$

By this formula a raw score of 100 would become a scaled score of 64. A raw score of 50 would become a scaled score of 29. We can see a graphic exhibition of this transformation by relating distributions A and D in Fig. 19.1. A score of 100 in A is in a position comparable to a score of 64 in D, and a score of 50 in A is in a position similar to 29 in D.

Scaling by this procedure, as by the standard-score method, assumes that the obtained form of distribution is the same as the population distribution. If this is true, then it is probable that units on the derived scale are equal if they were equal on the raw-score scale. So far as improving the equality of units is concerned, then, nothing has been gained, nor was anything to be gained. We know, however, that the form of distribution of a sample is not necessarily the form of distribution of the population. The discrepancy need not be, and probably is not, due to sampling errors, particularly if the sample is large. There are many reasons for radical departures of sample distributions from genuine population distributions of the trait measured: difficulty level of the test, intercorrelation of the items (see Chap. 17), and the variations in difficulty and intercorrelation. We should not, therefore, feel obligated to retain the same form of distribution in scaled scores as in the raw scores. If there is a real discrepancy between population distribution and sample distribution, there is much room for improvement of the scale in terms of equality of units. The next methods to be described have the probable advantage that by normalizing distributions they also achieve better metric scales.

The T scale and T scaling of tests

The well-known *T* scale overcomes the objections raised against standard scores and adds besides an advantage peculiar to itself.[1] It adopts as its unit one-tenth of a standard deviation, so that an ordinary distribution with a range of 5 to 6σ on its base line yields 50 to 60 integral *T*-scale scores. In addition, the *T* scale goes beyond any ordinary distribution, extending over a spread of 10 standard deviations, or 100 units in all.

Any age or grade group would yield its own distribution extending 5 to 6σ. A group just higher in ability would overlap this one and yet would need an extension over new units beyond the limit of the first group. A third group of lower ability would need an extension of the measuring stick at the other end. When all groups from lowest to highest are taken into account, considerable extension is required. The result, with these extensions, is a single common scale on which all groups, over a wide range, have a common unit and a common zero point. It has been found in practice that a scale with 100 units (or 10σ) will be extensive enough. It is based upon a normal curve whose tails extend from -5σ to $+5\sigma$ (see Fig. 19.2). Besides making the unit equal to 0.1σ, the *T* scale also has the zero point at the extreme left, which places it at -5σ. The mean becomes 50, and the other *T*-scale points are spaced as in Fig. 19.2.

[1]It is of interest to note that the "*T*" stands for E. L. Thorndike, an early leader in measurement, the symbol having been applied by one of his students.

Fig. 19.2. *The T scale and its relation to the standard-score scale extending over a total range of* 10σ.

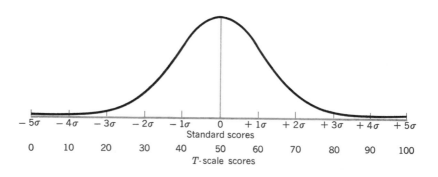

Table 19.2   **The calculation of T scores for a distribution of English-examination scores**

(1) Scores	(2) Upper limit of interval	(3) Frequency	(4) Cumulative frequency	(5) Cumulative proportion	(6) T score (from Table 19.3)
225–229	229.5	1	83	1.000	
220–224	224.5	0	82	.988	72.6
215–219	219.5	1	82	.988	72.6
210–214	214.5	5	81	.976	69.8
205–209	209.5	5	76	.916	63.8
200–204	204.5	7	71	.855	60.6
195–199	199.5	6	64	.771	57.4
190–194	194.5	6	58	.700	55.2
185–189	189.5	6	52	.627	53.2
180–184	184.5	11	46	.554	51.4
175–179	179.5	9	35	.422	48.0
170–174	174.5	5	26	.313	45.1
165–169	169.5	5	21	.253	43.3
160–164	164.5	6	16	.193	41.3
155–159	159.5	5	10	.120	38.2
150–154	154.5	2	5	.060	34.5
145–149	149.5	1	3	.036	32.0
140–144	144.5	1	2	.024	30.2
135–139	139.5	0	1	.012	27.4
130–134	134.5	1	1	.012	27.4

HOW TO DERIVE T-SCALE EQUIVALENTS FOR RAW SCORES

A college or university or a single school system may wish to use the T-scale idea as its common yardstick for all its tests. The freshmen entering a large university, for example, may be taken as the standard group for this purpose. As an illustration, let us use the data in Table 19.2. Here is a distribution of 83 scores obtained by freshmen in an English examination of the objectively scored type. The procedure will be described step by step:

Step 1. List the class intervals as usual. Here a large number of class intervals is desirable.

Step 2. List the exact upper limits of class intervals; cumulative frequencies are to be used.

Step 3. List the frequencies.

Step 4. List the cumulative frequencies (see Chap. 3 for instructions).

Step 5. Find the cumulative proportions for the class intervals.

Step 6. Find the corresponding T scores from Table 19.3. These are then listed in the last column of Table 19.2, given to one decimal place. We usually want finally a ready means of reading directly the T score corresponding to any integral raw score. It is recommended that the remaining steps be taken to satisfy this objective.

Step 7. Plot a point to represent each T score in Table 19.2 corresponding to the upper limit of the class interval, as in Fig. 19.3. If the original distribution of raw scores is normal, the points should fall rather close to a straight line. The reason that they are not perfectly in line is that there are some

Table 19.3 **A table to aid in the calculation of T scores**

Proportion below the point	T score	Proportion below the point	T score	Proportion below the point	T score
.0005	17.1	.100	37.2	.900	62.8
.0007	18.1	.120	38.3	.910	63.4
.0010	19.1	.140	39.2	.920	64.1
.0015	20.3	.160	40.1	.930	64.8
.0020	21.2	.180	40.8	.940	65.5
.0025	21.9	.200	41.6	.950	66.4
.0030	22.5	.220	42.3	.960	67.5
.0040	23.5	.250	43.3	.965	68.1
.0050	24.2	.300	44.8	.970	68.8
.0070	25.4	.350	46.1	.975	69.6
.010	26.7	.400	47.5	.980	70.5
.015	28.3	.450	48.7	.985	71.7
.020	29.5	.500	50.0	.990	73.3
.025	30.4	.550	51.3	.993	74.6
.030	31.2	.600	52.5	.995	75.8
.035	31.9	.650	53.9	.9960	76.5
.040	32.5	.700	55.2	.9970	77.5
.050	33.6	.750	56.7	.9975	78.1
.060	34.5	.780	57.7	.9980	78.7
.070	35.2	.800	58.4	.9985	79.7
.080	35.9	.820	59.2	.9990	80.9
.090	36.6	.840	59.9	.9993	81.9
		.860	60.8	.9995	82.9
		.880	61.7		

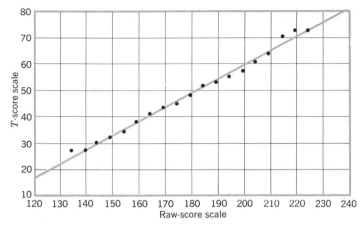

Fig. 19.3. *A smoothing process applied in deriving T-scale equivalents for English-examination scores (see Table 19.2).*

irregularities in the original data. With a ruler, draw through the points a line that will come as close to all the points as seems possible. Among those that do not touch the line, as many of them should be above it as below it. The line may be extended beyond the ends of the points at both ends. If the raw-score distribution is skewed, the trend in the points when plotted will show some curvature. It is best, then, to attempt to follow the curvature but with a smooth trend. If the curvature is not followed, the distribution of the population on the scaled scores will not be normalized.

Step 8. For any integral raw-score point, find the corresponding *T*-score points. For example, in Fig. 19.3, a raw score of 220 corresponds to a *T* score of 70, and a raw score of 150 corresponds to a *T* score of 33. In this we favor integral *T* scores but at times have to resort to half points when we cannot decide upon the nearest unit.

Step 9. Prepare a table in which every integral raw score, or every second, third, or fifth one, appears in one column and the corresponding *T* scores in the other, such as Table 19.4. It will serve for all future purposes of translation where the original tested group remains the standard. Many test users prefer to list *every* raw score and its *T*-score equivalent so as to avoid the need for interpolation.

A NORMAL GRAPHIC PROCEDURE FOR *T* SCALING

It is possible to do more of the *T* scaling graphically by the use of normal-probability paper. This graph paper is especially designed with spacing for cumulative proportions along one axis in a manner

Table 19.4   Rectified scaling with T scores for the distribution of English-examination scores

Examination score	T score	Examination score	T score	Examination score	T score
240	81	195	57	155	35.5
235	78	190	54	150	33
230	75.5	185	51.5	145	30
225	73	180	49	140	27.5
220	70	175	46	135	25
215	67.5	170	43.5	130	22
210	65	165	41	125	20.5
205	62	160	38	120	17
200	59.5				

consistent with the cumulative normal-curve function. Figure 19.4 shows how the English-examination data can be so treated. Using the cumulative proportions appearing in Table 19.2, column 5, we plot each one against its corresponding raw-score value given in column 2. The trend of the points will be in a straight line if the distribution of raw scores is normal. If that distribution is skewed there will be some curvature in the trend which one should try to follow in smoothing. To find the T equivalent for any raw score, we find that raw score on the base line, follow it up to the line drawn through the points, locate the equivalent proportion, then go to Table 19.3 for the corresponding T.

AN EVALUATION OF THE *T*-SCALE PROCEDURE

The T scale is one of the most widely used derived scales.[1] Its advantages are many, its disadvantages few. When the scaling is carried out, as described, the procedure normalizes distributions. This effect is pictured in Fig. 19.1. Compare distributions D and E in that illustration. Both have a mean of 50 and a σ of 10. The one is skewed like the original distribution, the other is normal. The normalizing process comes about through the conversion to centiles and then to corresponding deviations from the mean in a normal distribution. Table 19.3 is based upon the normal curve. For a given proportion (area below a given point) a T-score equivalent is given instead of a standard-score equivalent.

The normalizing process may be pictured as in Fig. 19.5. In that

[1]College-aptitude tests are commonly scaled to a variant of the T scale, with mean and SD ten times as great (500 and 100).

diagram, an obtained distribution, seriously skewed, is given below, and the normalized distribution on the derived scale above. The process ensures that the *areas A, B, C, . . . , M* correspond, in the proportions that they occupy, to *areas A', B', C', . . . , M'*. The correspondences of scale distances are also shown, by connecting dashed lines. If the units on the derived scale (not shown) represent genuinely equal increments of the measured variable, then obviously those on the original scale do not. We may not know that the population is normally distributed on a trait, but by normalizing distributions, where there is no inhibiting information to the contrary, we achieve more common and meaningful scores.

Other advantages of the *T* scale have been mentioned – the possibility of extending it beyond limited populations, its convenient mean, unit, and standard deviation, and its general applicability. It has some limitations which should be pointed out. In much practical

Fig. 19.4. *A graphic solution to scaling, which utilizes normal-probability graph paper.*

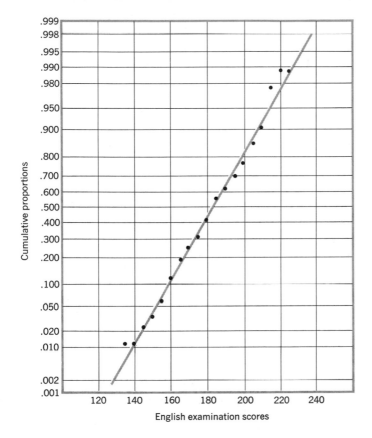

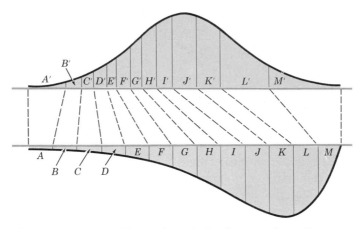

Fig. 19.5. *A graphic illustration of what happens in scaling so as to normalize a distribution. Intervals are matched so as to equate corresponding* areas *under the curves.*

use of tests, as fine a unit as .1σ may be an overrefinement. Much coarser discriminations may be all that are necessary. Furthermore, the unit may give quite a false sense of accuracy of the measurement that is actually being made. If the original scores had a standard deviation much smaller than 10—for example, one of five score units—then the substitution of a unit of .1σ is in a sense "hairsplitting." Two whole units on the *T* scale are then as fine a distinction as we could actually make between individuals.

Furthermore, every test, even the best of them, has an error of measurement whose size is indicated by its "standard error of measurement" (see Chap. 17). This stems from the fact that the test is not perfectly reliable. If the error of measurement is as much as two units on the raw-score scale, it might be even larger on the *T* scale. If the error is such that the best practical discriminations we can make between individuals are of the order of one-half σ, it is rather presumptuous to apply a scale that pretends to distinguish to one-tenth σ. For this reason, particularly, and because many test users require less refinement than the *T* scale offers, the writer has proposed the *C* scale, which will be described next.

The C scale and C scaling

THE *C*-SCALE SYSTEM

The principles of the *C* scale and the derivation of *C*-scale equivalents for raw scores are illustrated in Table 19.5. The *C* scale is so arranged that the mean will be exactly at 5.0, with the two limiting classes being 0 and 10. Column 2 gives the exact limits of the 11 units in terms of standard scores. The corresponding centile limits (derived from Table B) are given in column 3. The percentage of cases within each unit is found by subtracting neighboring pairs of centile limits. Thus, in the middle unit, the difference $59.9 - 40.1 = 19.8$, etc. Since it is more convenient to think in terms of whole numbers, the approximate percentages of the cases falling in the different classes are given as nearest whole numbers in column 5. These can be used either as a guide in thinking of the make-up of the standard distribution or even in subdividing lists of scores of individuals when

Table 19.5 **The eleven-point scaled-score system and its application to the memory-test data**

(1) C-scale score	(2) Standard-score limits	(3) Centile-rank limits	(4) Percentage within each interval	(5) Percentage in whole numbers	(6) Corresponding score points in the memory test	(7) Memory-test scores in each scaled-score interval
	+2.75	99.7				
10			0.9	1		41+
	+2.25	98.8			40.5	
9			2.8	3		38 – 40
	+1.75	96.0			37.6	
8			6.6	7		35 – 37
	+1.25	89.4			34.6	
7			12.1	12		31 – 34
	+0.75	77.3			30.8	
6			17.4	17		28 – 30
	+0.25	59.9			27.8	
5			19.8	20		25 – 27
	−0.25	40.1			24.4	
4			17.4	17		21 – 24
	−0.75	22.7			20.8	
3			12.1	12		18 – 20
	−1.25	10.6			17.7	
2			6.6	7		15 – 17
	−1.75	4.0			14.5	
1			2.8	3		12 – 14
	−2.25	1.2			11.8	
0			0.9	1		0 – 11
	−2.75	0.3				

arranged in rank order. Thus, if we had 100 persons lined up in rank order in a test, the highest person would be given the score of 10, the next three a score of 9, the next seven a score of 8, etc., until the last in line is given a score of 0.

STEPS IN DERIVING A *C* SCALE

The operations for deriving a *C* scale are much the same as those for deriving a *T* scale. There are some differences in the steps to be recommended, however, and so all the steps will be listed here.

Step 1. List the class intervals.
Step 2. List the exact upper limits of the intervals.
Step 3. List the frequencies.
Step 4. List the cumulative frequencies.
Step 5. Find the cumulative proportions for the intervals.
Step 6. From here on the steps differ from those for *T* scaling. Next, plot the cumulative proportions on the ordinate corresponding to *X* values (exact upper limits) on the abscissa of ordinary coordinate paper.
Step 7. Draw by inspection a smooth S-shaped curve through the trend of the points. If the distribution is obviously skewed and one tail of the S is short, or even if it vanishes, follow the general trend of the points anyway. At this stage one sees the advantage of having a liberal number of classes.
Step 8. Look for each of the centile limits (from column 3 of Table 19.5) on the ordinate, find the intersection of that centile-rank level with the curve, and drop down to the abscissa to locate the corresponding raw-score point. Avoid arriving at a point exactly at integers, so that it is clear whether each integral raw score goes above or below the division point. The values thus obtained are like those in column 6 of Table 19.5.
Step 9. Determine within which *C* intervals the various integral score values lie and write the limiting scores as in column 7 of Table 19.5.

Alternative graphic C-scaling steps. If one already has drawn a figure like Fig. 19.3 that is used in *T* scaling, one could use it to accomplish steps 6 and 7 in the following manner. The σ for the *T* scale is 10 and that for the *C* scale is 2. The means are 50 and 5, respectively. An interval of one unit on the *C* scale corresponds to five units on the *T* scale. A *C* score of 5, therefore, occupies a range from 47.5 to 52.5; a *C* score of 6 corresponds to a range 57.5 to 62.5, and so on. All the *T*-score limits of the *C* intervals can be seen represented in Table 19.6. The *T*-score limits, therefore, can be located in Fig. 19.3 and from them the corresponding points of division on the raw-score scale.

Table 19.6   T scores equivalent to C-score intervals

C score	T-score limits	Middle T score
10	72.5 – 77.5	75
9	67.5 – 72.5	70
8	62.5 – 67.5	65
7	57.5 – 62.5	60
6	52.5 – 57.5	55
5	47.5 – 52.5	50
4	42.5 – 47.5	45
3	37.5 – 42.5	40
2	32.5 – 37.5	35
1	27.5 – 32.5	30
0	22.5 – 27.5	25

These mark off the raw-score ranges corresponding to all C scores.

The normal-graphic procedure described in connection with T scaling can also be applied here; in fact, it is even more convenient in this connection and is to be recommended in preference to steps 6 and 7. Since the centile ranks are marked on probability paper (see Fig. 19.4), one would locate the centile-rank limits (column 3 of Table 19.5) and from the plot, usually a straight line, find the corresponding raw-score division points.

AN EVALUATION OF THE C SCALE

The C scale has many of the advantages of the T scale. It refers obtained scores to a common scale that is related to the normal distribution. If the population distribution on a measured trait is normal, then the distribution of C scores properly represents that population and the units of measurement may be regarded as equal. It lacks the refinement of a small unit such as that provided by the T scale. On the other hand, it probably more nearly represents the accuracy of discrimination actually made by means of tests, and its broader categories will do for guidance purposes.

There is a handicap in selection of personnel in that a change of minimum qualifying score of only one C-scale unit may result in quite a difference in percentage of cases selected. For example, if the cutoff score were changed from 5 to 6, 20 per cent more rejections would have to be made. For selection purposes, however, raw-score cutoffs would be just as feasible as derived scores. The reference of any chosen raw-score cutoff to equivalent C-score limits or centiles would add meaning to that particular value.

For guidance and counseling purposes, the use of a zero C score may be unwise. Unless he is more sophisticated than most people, a counselee would hardly relish being told that he earned a score of zero. To meet this contingency, one could let the scores range from 1 through 11 instead of 0 through 10. Or one could resort to a condensed scale, to be described next.

THE STANINE SCALE

There are several reasons for condensing the C scale to some extent by giving it a nine-unit range. This is usually done by combining the two categories at either end, with 4 per cent of the distribution in categories 1 and 9. Such a scale was standard for the Army Air Force Aviation Psychology Program during World War II. All test scores and composites were eventually scaled to this system, called "stanine" as a contraction of "standard nine." The mean of such a norm distribution is 5.0, as in the C scale, but the standard deviation is a trifle lower — 1.96 — because of the contractions at the tails of the curve.

Perhaps the chief practical benefit to be derived from nine units rather than 11 is that such scores occupy only one column on computer punched-card records. For research purposes, however, a slight grouping error (see Chap. 5) is thus introduced, calling for corrections of various sorts when precise dispersion statistics are wanted. In guidance work, many counselors would probably not like to have the rare one person in a hundred at either extreme submerged with the other 3 per cent next to him. There is presumably as much discrimination between the hundredth person and the next 3 per cent as there is between any other neighboring categories. This loss of discrimination in the stanine scale might not be tolerable and is unnecessary in the use of profiles in guidance.

Some norm and profile suggestions

Suggestions were made in Chap. 3 concerning the derivation of centiles and centile points, and concerning how to interpolate to find the latter. Here we shall find use for centile values. We shall present a profile chart, in which raw scores can be interpreted in terms of the C scale, T scale, and centile rank.

A PROFILE CHART WITH THREE INTERPRETIVE SCALES

Figure 19.6 shows an example of a profile chart by means of which raw scores on several tests may be readily translated into C-scale, T-scale, or centile equivalents. The seven tests are the parts of the Guilford-Zimmerman Aptitude Survey.

Centile	T score	C score	Norms for college men — Parts of the survey						
			I VC	II GR	III NO	IV PS	V SO	VI SV	VII MK
99.7			67	26	128	72	50	60	53
	75	10	65	25	123	71	47	59	52
99			63		119	69		57	51
				24		67	44		
	70	9	60	23	114	65	42	54	50
			57	22	109	63	40		49
95					105		38	51	
	65	8	54	21	101	61	36	48	48
			51	20	98	59	34		
90				19				45	45
	60	7	48	18	93	57	32	42	42
80			45	17	88	55	30		
			42	16		53	28	39	39
	55	6	39	15	82	51	26	36	36
			36	14	77	49	24	33	33
60				13		47	22	30	30
50	50	5	33	12	71	45	20	27	
			30	11	66		18	24	27
40			27	10	63	43	16	21	24
30	45	4	24	9	61	41	14	18	21
					58	39			
20			21	8	54	37	12	15	18
	40	3	18	7	49	35	10	12	15
				6	45	33	8		
10			15	5	42	31	6	9	12
	35	2	14	4	38	29	4	6	
5			13	3	35	27	2	3	10
			12	2	31	25			8
	30	1	11	1	27		0	1	6
			9		23	23		0	5
1			7	0	19	20	−3		
	25	0	6		15	17	−5	−2	4
0.3			5	−1					

Fig. 19.6. *A profile chart for the seven parts of the Guilford-Zimmerman Aptitude Survey, based upon norms for college men. The key to the part names is as follows: VC = Verbal Comprehension; GR = General Reasoning; NO = Numerical Operations; PS = Perceptual Speed; SO = Spatial Orientation; SV = Spatial Visualization; and MK = Mechanical Knowledge.*

Such a chart is most conveniently prepared by using a plot of the cumulative distribution on probability paper, as described earlier in this chapter. In the chart, the spacing of centile ranks is made to conform to the spacings of T and C scales, whose units are at equal intervals. The location of the raw scores for each test is made to conform to the appropriate centile levels as read from the plot on probability paper. As many of the raw-score integers are included as space will permit.

EXERCISES

1. *a.* Determine the standard scores for the two hypothetical students in Data 19 *A.*
   b. Give a rank order to each student in the five tests, first in terms of raw scores, then in terms of standard scores. Explain discrepancies in rank order.

2. *a.* Derive a conversion equation for transforming scores in the syllogism test into a scale that would give a mean of 50 and an SD of 10.
   b. Using the equation, determine the scores for students A and B on the new scale.

3. Determine the equivalent T scores for the upper-category limits of the form-perception scores in Data 19*B.*

4. By a graphic smoothing process, find a modified set of equivalent T scores for the same category limits.

5. Using the results of Exercise 4, find equivalent T scores for the following raw scores in the form-perception test: 8, 12, 16, 22, 37, 42.

6. Determine for the form-perception test the exact score limits (to one decimal place) corresponding to the C-score categories. Use a smoothing process, on regular or probability graph paper.

7. Determine C-score equivalents for the six raw scores listed in Exercise 5.

8. Through the relationship of either T scores or C scores to centiles, determine the centile equivalents to the raw scores listed in Exercise 5.

Data 19A **Means and standard deviations in five parts of an engineering-aptitude examination and scores of two students**

Test	Figure classification	Cube visualizing	Syllogism	Paper folding	Form perception
Mean	22	15	28	33	26
SD	4	6	8	5	7
Student A	28	26	30	17	35
Student B	15	32	15	32	41

Data 19B **Frequency**
distribution of scores for
engineering freshmen in
the form-perception test

Scores	Frequencies
40–44	2
35–39	16
30–34	42
25–29	52
20–24	55
15–19	26
10–14	13
5–9	1
	Σ 207

ANSWERS
1. a. *A*: +1.50; +1.83; +0.25; −3.20; +1.29.
      B: −1.75; +2.83; −1.62; −0.20; +2.14.
2. a. $X_s = 1.25 X_o + 15$.
   b. X_s: 52.5; 33.75.
3. *T*: 73.3; 63.6; 55.5; 48.9; 41.3; 35.1; 24.2.
4. *T*: (79); 72; 64; 56; 49; 41; 34; 26.
5. *T* scores: 23; 30; 36; 45; 68; 75.
6. *C*-score limits: 39.9; 36.2; 32.8; 29.6; 26.4; 23.2; 19.9; 16.7; 13.3; 9.7.
7. *C* scores: 0; 1; 2; 4; 9; 10.
8. Centiles: 0.5; 2.5; 9.0; 33.5; 97.0; 99.6.

Appendix A
Some Selected
Mathematical Proofs
and Derivations

A LIST OF BRIEF TITLES

1. *Effect upon a mean of adding a constant*
2. *Effect upon a mean of multiplying by a constant*
3. *The mean of a simple linear function*
4. *Effect upon the standard deviation of adding a constant*
5. *Effect upon the standard deviation of multiplying by a constant*
6. *The standard deviation of a simple linear function*
7. *Variances and standard deviations in combined frequencies*
8. *Derivation of the formula of the point-biserial r*
9. *Derivation of the phi coefficient from r_{pbi}*
10. *Regression coefficients in a two-variable linear equation*
11. *The mean of a sum of measures*
12. *The variance and standard deviation in a sum of measures*
13. *The correlation of sums*
14. *Linear transformation equation*

This Appendix presents a few derivations or proofs of equations. Selection has been determined by several considerations: (1) Their relative simplicity enables certain of the proofs to be followed by most students; (2) the proofs are illustrative of the manner in which formulas in general are derived; (3) the proofs should help to give insight into some fundamental statistical concepts; and (4) the proofs are not commonly found elsewhere. Footnote references in the preceding chapters often indicate sources of derivations of other formulas.

1. *The effect upon a mean of adding a constant to every observed value*

Let X = any observed value in a set of measurements
C = a constant value added to every X
M_x = arithmetic mean of all the X values
$M_{(x+c)}$ = arithmetic mean of all values $(X + C)$
N = number of observations in the sample

Then

$$M_{(x+c)} = \frac{\Sigma(X + C)^*}{N}$$
$$= \frac{\Sigma X}{N} + \frac{NC}{N}$$
$$= M_x + C \tag{A.1}$$

In other words, the mean of X values, each augmented by the addition of a constant C, is equal to the mean of the X's plus the same constant. C may have a negative value as well as a positive one.

2. *The effect upon a mean of multiplying each observed value by a constant*

Let M_{cx} = arithmetic mean of all values $C \times X$, and other symbols be defined as in 1 above.

$$M_{cx} = \frac{\Sigma CX}{N}$$
$$= \frac{C\Sigma X}{N}$$
$$= CM_x \tag{A.2}$$

*In these equations and those following throughout this Appendix, the summation sign is given without showing the range over which summation is made. Strictly speaking, ΣX should be written here as

$$\sum_1^N X$$

to show that the N values of the sample are included. The omission makes for easier reading, particularly where formulas become complicated. It is believed that in all instances the range of summation will be clear, if not directly from the formula, at least from the context.

In other words, the mean of X values all multiplied by the same constant is equal to the mean of those values times the constant.

3. *The mean of a linear function of a value*

Let the linear function of X be the regression equation $Y' = a + bX$ (see Chap. 15). We want to find the mean $M_{(a+bX)}$. Here we have a combination of a product of a constant times X, namely, (bX), and also a constant increment (a).

$$M_{y'} = M_{(a+bX)} = \frac{\Sigma(a + bX)}{N} = \frac{Na + b\Sigma X}{N}$$
$$= \frac{Na}{N} + \frac{b\Sigma X}{N}$$
$$= a + bM_x \tag{A.3}$$

In other words, the mean of a linear function of X is that same function of the mean of X. This principle is useful in connection with regression equations in general.

4. *Effect upon the standard deviation of adding a constant to each observed value*

Using the same symbols as above, with the addition of:

$\sigma_x =$ standard deviation of the X values
$\sigma_{(x+c)} =$ standard deviation of all values $(X + C)$
$x =$ a deviation of X from M_x
$x_{(x+c)} =$ deviation of $(X + C)$ from the mean $(M_x + C)$

We find that

$$x_{(x+c)} = (X + C) - (M_x + C)$$
$$= X - M_x$$
$$= x$$

From this it follows that

$$\Sigma x^2_{(x+c)} = \Sigma x^2$$
$$\sigma^2_{(x+c)} = \sigma^2_x$$
$$\sigma_{(x+c)} = \sigma_x \tag{A.4}$$

In other words, adding a constant to every observed value has no effect upon the standard deviation.

5. *Effect upon the standard deviation of multiplying each observed value by a constant, C*

Let $\sigma_{cx} =$ standard deviation of the products CX. From (A.2) above, $M_{cx} = CM_x$. Therefore,

$$x_{cx} = CX - CM_x$$
$$= C(X - M_x)$$
$$= Cx$$
$$\sigma^2_{cx} = \frac{C^2\Sigma x^2}{N}$$
$$= C^2\sigma^2_x \tag{A.5}$$

Taking square roots of both sides of (A.5),

$$\sigma_{cx} = C\sigma_x \tag{A.6}$$

6. *Standard deviation of a linear function of X*

If the function of X is $a + bX$, the mean of this function, from (A.3) above, is equal to $a + bM_x$. Each deviation of this function (Y) from its mean is, therefore,

$$
\begin{aligned}
y_{(a+bX)} &= (a + bX) - (a + bM_x)\\
&= bX - bM_x\\
&= b(X - M_x)\\
&= bx
\end{aligned}
$$

From (A.6), we deduce that $\sigma_{bx} = b\sigma_x$. Therefore,

$$\sigma_{(a+bx)} = b\sigma_x \tag{A.7}$$

Thus, wherever we use a simple regression equation of the form $Y' = a + bX$, the standard deviation of Y' equals $b\sigma_x$.

7. *Variances and standard deviations of combined distributions*

Assume two sample distributions A and B, whose frequencies are summed to form a total distribution T.

Let M_a, M_b, and M_t = means of distributions A, B, and T, respectively

n_a, n_b, and N = numbers of cases in corresponding distributions

X_a, X_b, and X_t = measures in the three distributions, respectively

x_a, x_b, and x_t = deviations of measures from the means of their respective distributions

x_{at} and x_{bt} = deviations of measures in distributions A and B, respectively, from M_t

d_a and d_b = deviations of means of distributions A and B, respectively, from M_t

From the preceding,

$$d_a = M_a - M_t \qquad \text{and} \qquad d_b = M_b - M_t \tag{A.8}$$

Transposing,

$$M_t = M_a - d_a \qquad \text{and} \qquad M_t = M_b - d_b \tag{A.9}$$

By definition given above, and from (A.9) and (A.8),

$$
\begin{aligned}
x_{at} &= X_a - M_t = X_a - M_a + d_a = x_a + d_a\\
x_{bt} &= X_b - M_t = X_b - M_b + d_b = x_b + d_b
\end{aligned}
$$

Squaring both sides of these equations,

$$
\begin{aligned}
x^2_{at} &= (x_a + d_a)^2 = x^2_a + d^2_a + 2x_a d_a\\
x^2_{bt} &= (x_b + d_b)^2 = x^2_b + d^2_b + 2x_b d_b
\end{aligned}
$$

Summing for all measures in either distribution,

$$
\begin{aligned}
\Sigma x^2_{at} &= \Sigma x^2_a + n_a d^2_a + 2d_a \Sigma x_a\\
\Sigma x^2_{bt} &= \Sigma x^2_b + n_b d^2_b + 2d_b \Sigma x_b
\end{aligned}
$$

Now both Σx_a and Σx_b equal zero, which eliminates the last terms from the last two equations. The sum of squares in the total distribution is the combination of Σx^2_{at} and Σx^2_{bt}; in other words,

$$\Sigma x^2_t = \Sigma x^2_a + n_a d^2_a + \Sigma x^2_b + n_b d^2_b \tag{A.10a}$$

Or, by combining terms,

$$\Sigma x^2_t = (\Sigma x^2_a + \Sigma x^2_b) + (n_a d^2_a + n_b d^2_b) \tag{A.10b}$$

This proof has involved the combination of only two sample distributions. It can readily be generalized to include any number of samples, by adding, by analogy, additional equations in each step taken above.

8. *Formula for the point-biserial coefficient of correlation, r_{pbi}*
Let X be a continuous variable, continuously measured.
Let Y be a genuine dichotomy, with point values of 0 and +1.
    The cases in the favored category have values of +1.
    N = total number of cases
    N_p = number of cases in the favored category ($N_p = pN$)
    N_q = number of cases in the other category ($N_q = qN$ and
        $N_p + N_q = N$)
    M_x = arithmetic mean of the X values
    σ_x = standard deviation of the X values
    M_p = mean of the X values in the favored category on Y
    M_q = mean of the X values for the remaining category
    p = proportion of the cases in the favored category ($p = N_p/N$)
    $q = 1 - p$; q also equals N_q/N
    M_y = mean of the point values in variable Y. It can be shown to
        equal p
    σ_y = standard deviation in the point values. It can be shown to
        equal $\sqrt{pq}$

The point-biserial r is a product-moment correlation coefficient. There are several ways of deriving the formula for r_{pbi}. Let us start with the basic formula for the Pearson r,

$$r_{yx} = \frac{\Sigma xy}{N\sigma_x\sigma_y} \tag{A.11}$$

where $x = X - M_x$ and $y = Y - M_y$. Therefore,

$$\Sigma xy = \Sigma(X - M_x)(Y - M_y) = \Sigma XY - M_y\Sigma X - M_x\Sigma Y + NM_xM_y \tag{A.12}$$

Substituting NM_x for ΣX and NM_y for ΣY in (A.12),

$$\Sigma xy = \Sigma XY - NM_xM_y - NM_xM_y + NM_xM_y = \Sigma XY - NM_xM_y \tag{A.13}$$

Substituting (A.13) in (A.11),

$$r_{yx} = \frac{\Sigma XY - NM_xM_y}{N\sigma_x\sigma_y} \tag{A.14}$$

Making some other substitutions,

$$\Sigma XY = N_p M_p \qquad NM_x M_y = NM_x p = N_p M_x \qquad \text{and} \qquad \sigma_y = \sqrt{pq}$$

we get

$$r_{yx} = \frac{N_p M_p - N_p M_x}{N\sigma_x \sqrt{pq}} \tag{A.15}$$

Dividing numerator and denominator of (A.15) by N,

$$r_{yx} = \frac{pM_p - pM_x}{\sigma_x \sqrt{pq}} = \frac{(M_p - M_x)\, p}{\sigma_x \sqrt{pq}} \tag{A.16}$$

Dividing numerator and denominator of (A.16) by $\sqrt{p}$,

$$r_{yx} = \frac{M_p - M_x}{\sigma_x} \sqrt{\frac{p}{q}} \tag{A.17}$$

This is one form of the equation for the point-biserial r. If we want the form involving M_q rather than M_x, some further proof is required.

$$M_x = pM_p + qM_q$$

so that

$$
\begin{aligned}
M_p - M_x &= M_p - pM_p - qM_q \\
&= (1 - p)\, M_p - qM_q \\
&= qM_p - qM_q \\
&= q\, (M_p - M_q)
\end{aligned}
\tag{A.18}
$$

Substituting (A.18) in (A.17),

$$r_{pbi} = \frac{(M_p - M_q)\, \sqrt{pq}}{\sigma_x} \tag{A. 19}$$

9. *Derivation of the formula for phi from* r_{pbi}

Phi is a product-moment correlation in a 2×2 contingency table where both variables are genuine dichotomies and the distributions are point distributions, with values of +1 and 0. Let the symbols used be defined in the two following tables, one based upon frequencies and the other upon corresponding proportions.

Frequencies

	+1	0	Both
+1	a	b	N_p
0	c	d	N_q
Both	$N_{p'}$	$N_{q'}$	N

Proportions

	+1	0	Both
+1	α	β	p
0	γ	δ	q
Both	p'	q'	1.00

In these point distributions,

$$M_p = \frac{a}{N_p} = \frac{\alpha}{p}$$

$$M_q = \frac{c}{N_q} = \frac{\gamma}{q}$$

$$\sigma_x = \sqrt{p'q'}$$

Substituting these values in (A.19), we have

$$r = \phi = \frac{\left(\frac{\alpha}{p} - \frac{\gamma}{q}\right)\sqrt{pq}}{\sqrt{p'q'}} \tag{A.20}$$

Now

$$\frac{\alpha}{p} - \frac{\gamma}{q} = \frac{\alpha q - \gamma p}{pq} \tag{A.21}$$

And since $p = \alpha + \beta$ and $q = \gamma + \delta$, the right side of (A.21) becomes

$$\frac{\alpha(\gamma + \delta) - \gamma(\alpha + \beta)}{pq} = \frac{\alpha\gamma + \alpha\delta - \alpha\gamma - \beta\gamma}{pq} = \frac{\alpha\delta - \beta\gamma}{pq} \tag{A.22}$$

Substituting (A.22) in (A.20),

$$\phi = \frac{(\alpha\delta - \beta\gamma)\sqrt{pq}}{pq\sqrt{p'q'}}$$

$$\phi = \frac{\alpha\delta - \beta\gamma}{\sqrt{pqp'q'}} \tag{A.23}$$

10. *Regression coefficients in a two-variable linear equation*
Let the general regression equation for a straight line be

$$Y' = a + bX$$

Problem: To find for any set of data involving corresponding X and Y those values of a and b which will make $\Sigma(Y - Y')^2$ a minimum.
We first set up an equation involving the expression $(Y - Y')$:

$$(Y - Y') = Y - a - bX$$

Squaring both sides, we have an expression for the discrepancy squared:

$$(Y - Y')^2 = (Y - a - bX)^2$$
$$= Y^2 + a^2 + b^2X^2 - 2aY - 2bXY + 2abX$$

Summing for all observations,

$$\Sigma(Y - Y')^2 = \Sigma Y^2 + Na^2 + b^2\Sigma X^2 - 2a\Sigma Y - 2b\Sigma XY + 2ab\Sigma X \tag{A.24}$$

The partial derivatives of (A.24) are

$$\frac{\partial[\Sigma(Y - Y')^2]}{\partial a} = 2Na - 2\Sigma Y + 2b\Sigma X \tag{A.25}$$

$$\frac{\partial \left[\Sigma (Y - Y')^2 \right]}{\partial b} = 2b\Sigma X^2 - 2\Sigma XY + 2a\Sigma X \tag{A.26}$$

Setting derivative (A.25) equal to zero, we have

$$2Na - 2\Sigma Y + 2b\Sigma X = 0$$

or

$$Na - \Sigma Y + b\Sigma X = 0$$

Transposing, we have

$$Na + b\Sigma X = \Sigma Y \tag{A.27}$$

Setting derivative (A.26) equal to zero, we have

$$2b\Sigma X^2 = 2\Sigma XY + 2a\Sigma X = 0$$

or

$$b\Sigma X^2 - \Sigma XY - a\Sigma X = 0$$

Transposing, we have

$$a\Sigma X + b\Sigma X^2 = \Sigma XY \tag{A.28}$$

(A.27) and (A.28) provide us with two *normal equations* which, solved simultaneously, give us formulas for deriving a and b from the observations X and Y. Dividing (A.27) by N, we have

$$a + \frac{(\Sigma X)b}{N} = \frac{\Sigma Y}{N}$$

$$a + M_x b = M_y$$

Transposing,

$$a = M_y - M_x b \tag{A.29}$$

Substituting (A.29) in (A.28), we have

$$(\Sigma X) M_y - (\Sigma X) M_x b + (\Sigma X^2) b = \Sigma XY$$

Collecting terms and transposing,

$$\left[(\Sigma X^2) - (\Sigma X) M_x \right] b = \Sigma XY - (\Sigma X) M_y$$

Solving for b,

$$b = \frac{\Sigma XY - (\Sigma X) M_y}{(\Sigma X^2) - (\Sigma X) M_x} \tag{A.30}$$

Multiplying numerator and denominator by N,

$$b = \frac{N\Sigma XY - (\Sigma X)(\Sigma Y)}{N\Sigma X^2 - (\Sigma X)^2} \tag{A.31}$$

11. *The mean of a sum of measurements*
a. For equally weighted measurements:

Let X_1 and X_2 be two independently derived measures of the same individual. Let X_1 and X_2 be summed for each individual, giving a composite measure $X_1 + X_2$. The problem is to find the mean of the composite, $M_{(x_1+x_2)}$.

$$M_{(x_1+x_2)} = \frac{\Sigma(X_1 + X_2)}{N}$$
$$= \frac{\Sigma X_1 + \Sigma X_2}{N}$$
$$= \frac{\Sigma X_1}{N} + \frac{\Sigma X_2}{N}$$
$$= M_1 + M_2 \tag{A.32}$$

where M_1 = mean of X_1 values and M_2 = mean of X_2 values.

For the general case, in which there are n measurements of each individual, it can be similarly shown that

$$M_{(x_1+x_2+\,\cdots\,+x_n)} = M_1 + M_2 + \cdots + M_n \tag{A.33}$$

If we let the symbols M_s = mean of an unweighted sum of n measures as M_i = the mean of any one of the measures X_1 to X_n inclusive, we may write equation (A.33) in more economical form as

$$M_s = \Sigma M_i \tag{A.34}$$

In other words, when measures are summed without weighting, the mean of the sums is equal to the sum of the means.

b. For differentially weighted measurements:

When the measurements X_1 and X_2 are weighted by multipliers w_1 and w_2, respectively,

$$M_{(w_1 x_1 + w_2 x_2)} = \frac{\Sigma(w_1 X_1 + w_2 X_2)}{N}$$
$$= \frac{w_1 \Sigma X_1 + w_2 \Sigma X_2}{N}$$
$$= \frac{w_1 \Sigma X_1}{N} + \frac{w_2 \Sigma X_2}{N}$$
$$= w_1 M_1 + w_2 M_2$$

To describe the general case, with n measurements,

$$M_{(w_1 x_1 + w_2 x_2 + \,\cdots\, + w_n x_n)} = w_1 M_1 + w_2 M_2 + \cdots + w_n M_n \tag{A.35}$$

If M_{ws} symbolizes the mean of a weighted composite, and M_i symbolizes the mean of any one measurement that enters into it, we may write equation (A.35) in abbreviated form:

$$M_{ws} = \Sigma w_i M_i \tag{A.36}$$

12. *Variance and standard deviation of a sum*

a. When measurements are equally weighted:

Let X_1 and X_2 be two independently derived measures of the same individual, summed without weighting to obtain a composite measure. The variance of the composite measures is given by the following equation

$$\sigma^2_{(x_1+x_2)} = \frac{\Sigma (x_1 + x_2)^2}{N} \tag{A.37}$$

where $(x_1 + x_2) =$ a deviation of $(X_1 + X_2)$ from $M_{(x_1+x_2)}$.* Expanding the binomial in (A.37),

$$\sigma^2_{(x_1+x_2)} = \frac{\Sigma (x^2_1 + x^2_2 + 2x_1 x_2)}{N}$$

$$= \frac{\Sigma x^2_1}{N} + \frac{\Sigma x^2_2}{N} + 2\frac{\Sigma x_1 x_2}{N} \tag{A.38}$$

The most meaningful interpretation to make of (A.38) in this development is to say that the first term on the right of the equality sign is the variance in X_1, the second term is the variance in X_2, and the third term is twice the covariance between X_1 and X_2. It will be helpful, next, to relate the covariance term to the correlation between X_1 and X_2. By the Pearson product-moment formula,

$$r_{12} = \frac{\Sigma x_1 x_2}{N \sigma_1 \sigma_2} \tag{A.39}$$

Multiplying both sides of (A.39) by $\sigma_1 \sigma_2$,

$$r_{12} \sigma_1 \sigma_2 = \frac{\Sigma x_1 x_2}{N} \tag{A.40}$$

Substituting σ^2_1, σ^2_2, and $r_{12} \sigma_1 \sigma_2$ in (A.38), we have

$$\sigma^2_{(x_1+x_2)} = \sigma^2_1 + \sigma^2_2 + 2r_{12} \sigma_1 \sigma_2 \tag{A.41}$$

Taking square roots of both sides of (A.41),

$$\sigma_{(x_1+r_2)} = \sqrt{\sigma^2_1 + \sigma^2_2 + 2r_{12} \sigma_1 \sigma_2} \tag{A.42}$$

In other words, the variance of an unweighted sum of two measures is equal to the sum of the variances of the components plus two times their covariance. To generalize to any number of unweighted components, and remembering that we shall have as many covariance terms as there are *pairs* of components,

$$\sigma^2_{(x_1+x_2+\cdots+x_n)} = \sigma^2_1 + \sigma^2_2 + \cdots + \sigma^2_n + 2r_{12} \sigma_1 \sigma_2 + 2r_{13} \sigma_1 \sigma_3 + \cdots$$
$$+ 2r_{1n} \sigma_1 \sigma_n + \cdots + 2r_{(n-1)n} \sigma_{(n-1)} \sigma_n$$

Let $\sigma^2_s =$ variance of an unweighted sum of any number of measures

$\sigma^2_i =$ variance of any measure from 1 to n, inclusive

*The deviation of a composite of two values from the mean of the composite equals $x_1 + x_2$, for

$(X_1 + X_2) - (M_1 + M_2) = (X_1 - M_1) + (X_2 - M_2) = x_1 + x_2$

Then

$$\sigma^2_s = \Sigma\sigma^2_i + 2\Sigma r_{ij}\sigma_i\sigma_j \qquad \text{(where } i < j) \tag{A.43}$$

By square roots, the standard deviation of a sum is given by

$$\sigma_s = \sqrt{\Sigma\sigma^2_i + 2\Sigma r_{ij}\sigma_i\sigma_j} \qquad \text{(where } i < j) \tag{A.44}$$

b. When measurements are differentially weighted:

Let the weights to be applied to $X_1, X_2, \ldots, X_n$ be $w_1, w_2, \ldots, w_n$, respectively. For the variance of the sum of two weighted measurements:

$$\sigma^2_{(w_1x_1+w_2x_2)} = \frac{\Sigma(w_1x_1 + w_2x_2)^2}{N}$$

$$= \frac{\Sigma(w^2_1x^2_1 + w^2_2x^2_2 + 2w_1w_2x_1x_2)}{N}$$

$$= \frac{w^2_1\Sigma x^2_1}{N} + \frac{w^2_2\Sigma x^2_2}{N} + 2w_1w_2\frac{\Sigma x_1x_2}{N}$$

Making substitutions similar to those made in (A.38),

$$\sigma^2_{(w_1x_1+w_2x_2)} = w^2_1\sigma^2_1 + w^2_2\sigma^2_2 + 2r_{12}w_1w_2\sigma_1\sigma_2 \tag{A.45}$$

In other words, the variance of a weighted sum of two measures equals the sum of the component variances, each weighted by its weight squared, plus twice the covariance multiplied by the product of the weights. The standard deviation, by taking square roots, is

$$\sigma_{(w_1x_1+w_2x_2)} = \sqrt{w^2_1\sigma^2_1 + w^2_2\sigma^2_2 + 2r_{12}w_1w_2\sigma_1\sigma_2} \tag{A.46}$$

Generalized to include n components and to apply the symbols as defined in (A.43),

$$\sigma_{ws} = \sqrt{\Sigma w^2_i\sigma^2_i + 2\Sigma r_{ij}w_iw_j\sigma_i\sigma_j} \qquad \text{(where } i < j) \tag{A.47}$$

13. *Correlation of sums*

a. Correlation between one variable, C, and an unweighted sum of two other variables, X_1 and X_2:

Applying the Pearson product-moment formula to this problem,

$$r_{c(x_1+x_2)} = \frac{\Sigma c(x_1 + x_2)}{N\sigma_c\sigma_{(x_1+x_2)}}$$

$$= \frac{\Sigma cx_1 + \Sigma cx_2}{N\sigma_c\sigma_{(x_1+x_2)}} \tag{A.48}$$

Now $\Sigma cx_1 = Nr_{c1}\sigma_c\sigma_1$ and $\Sigma cx_2 = Nr_{c2}\sigma_c\sigma_2$. Substituting in (A.48),

$$r_{c(x_1+x_2)} = \frac{Nr_{c1}\sigma_c\sigma_1 + Nr_{c2}\sigma_c\sigma_2}{N\sigma_c\sigma_{(x_1+x_2)}}$$

Eliminating $N\sigma_c$, and expanding the standard deviation of the sum,

$$r_{c(x_1+x_2)} = \frac{r_{c1}\sigma_1 + r_{c2}\sigma_2}{\sqrt{\sigma^2_1 + \sigma^2_2 + 2r_{12}\sigma_1\sigma_2}} \tag{A.49}$$

Let r_{cs} = correlation of the sum of n unweighted measures with C
X_i = any variable from 1 to n, inclusive
r_{ci} = correlation of C with any variable 1 to n
X_j = any variable with a greater subscript number than X_i

Extended to the general case, (A.49) becomes

$$r_{cs} = \frac{\Sigma r_{ci}\sigma_i}{\sqrt{\Sigma\sigma^2_i + 2\Sigma r_{ij}\sigma_i\sigma_j}} \qquad \text{(where } i < j) \qquad (A.50)$$

b. Correlation of one variable, C, with the sum of differentially weighted variables:

Let $w_1, w_2, \ldots, w_n$ weights be applied to measures $X_1, X_2, \ldots, X_n$, respectively. For the sum of two variables, by Pearson's formula,

$$r_{c(w_1 x_1 + w_2 x_2)} = \frac{\Sigma c(w_1 x_1 + w_2 x_2)}{N\sigma_c\sigma_{(w_1 x_1 + w_2 x_2)}}$$
$$= \frac{w_1\Sigma c x_1 + w_2\Sigma c x_2}{N\sigma_c\sigma_{(w_1 x_1 + w_2 x_2)}}$$

Making substitutions as in (A.48) above,

$$r_{c(w_1 x_1 + w_2 x_2)} = \frac{N w_1 r_{c1}\sigma_c\sigma_1 + N w_2 r_{c2}\sigma_c\sigma_2}{N\sigma_c\sigma_{(w_1 x_1 + w_2 x_2)}}$$

Eliminating $N\sigma_c$ and expanding the standard deviation of the weighted sum,

$$r_{c(w_1 x_1 + w_2 x_2)} = \frac{w_1 r_{c1}\sigma_1 + w_2 r_{c2}\sigma_2}{\sqrt{w^2_1\sigma^2_1 + w^2_2\sigma^2_2 + 2\Sigma r_{12} w_1 w_2 \sigma_1\sigma_2}} \qquad (A.51)$$

Generalizing to any number of weighted components,

$$r_{c(ws)} = \frac{\Sigma w_i r_{ci}\sigma_i}{\sqrt{\Sigma w^2_i\sigma^2_i + 2\Sigma r_{ij} w_i w_j \sigma_i\sigma_j}} \qquad \text{(where } i < j) \qquad (A.52)$$

c. Correlation of two unweighted composites:

Without presenting the proof, which is quite analogous to those just presented, two formulas will be given here for the correlation of two composite measures from information about correlations among the components.

Let X_i and X_j be any two measures in the first composite, C_1, and X_u and X_v be any two measures in the second composite, C_2. By analogy to (A.50) and (A.52), the following equations apply. (A.53) is for two unweighted composites, and (A.54) for weighted composites. (A.54) reduces to (A.53) if all weights are +1.

$$r_{c_1 c_2} = \frac{\Sigma(\sigma_i\Sigma r_{iu}\sigma_u)}{\sqrt{\Sigma\sigma^2_i + 2\Sigma r_{ij}\sigma_i\sigma_j}\sqrt{\Sigma\sigma^2_u + 2\Sigma r_{uv}\sigma_u\sigma_v}} \qquad (A.53)$$
$$\text{(where } i < j \text{ and } u < v)$$

$$r_{wc_1 wc_2} = \frac{\Sigma(w_i \sigma_i \Sigma r_{iu} w_u \sigma_u)}{\sqrt{\Sigma w^2_i \sigma^2_i + 2\Sigma r_{ij} w_i \sigma_i w_j \sigma_j} \; \sqrt{\Sigma w^2_u \sigma^2_u + 2\Sigma r_{uv} w_u \sigma_u w_v \sigma_v}} \quad (A.54)$$

$$(\text{where } i < j \text{ and } u < v)$$

14. *Linear transformation of values in one distribution to corresponding standard-score positions in another*

Problem: Given a distribution of observed values, to find a linear equation which will determine for each value one that deviates as much in terms of standard-deviation units from the mean in another distribution of similar values and in the same direction.

Let X_a = a value in distribution A

M_a = mean of values in distribution A

σ_a = standard deviation in distribution A

X_b = a value in distribution B

M_b = mean of values in distribution B

σ_b = standard deviation in distribution B

X_{ba} = a value in distribution A equivalent to one in distribution B, where equivalence is as defined above

Assume, as the problem statement requires, that standard measures or deviations in the two distributions are equal. In equation form,

$$\frac{X_{ba} - M_a}{\sigma_a} = \frac{X_b - M_b}{\sigma_b} \quad (A.55)$$

Multiplying (A.55) by σ_a,

$$X_{ba} - M_a = \frac{X_b \sigma_a - M_b \sigma_a}{\sigma_b}$$

$$= \left(\frac{\sigma_a}{\sigma_b}\right) X_b - \left(\frac{\sigma_a}{\sigma_b}\right) M_b$$

Transposing,

$$X_{ba} = \left(\frac{\sigma_a}{\sigma_b}\right) X_b - \left(\frac{\sigma_a}{\sigma_b}\right) M_b + M_a$$

$$= \left(\frac{\sigma_a}{\sigma_b}\right) X_b - \left[\left(\frac{\sigma_a}{\sigma_b}\right) M_b - M_a\right] \quad (A.56)$$

Appendix B Tables

A LIST OF BRIEF TITLES

A. *Squares, square roots, and reciprocals of numbers 1 to 1,000*
B. *Proportions of area under the normal distribution curve*
C. *Standard scores and ordinates corresponding to areas under the normal curve*
D. *Significant coefficients of correlation and t ratios*
E. *Chi square*
F. *F ratio*
G. *Functions of p, q, z, and y*
H. *Fisher's z for different values of r*
J. *Trigonometric functions*
K. *Four-place logarithms of numbers*
L. *Significance of rank-difference correlations*
M. *Values for estimation of the cosine-pi coefficient of correlation*
N. *Significant chi squares in small samples*
O. *Probabilities in tails of binomial distributions*
P. *Significant T values for ranked differences*
Q. *Significant R values for sums of ranks*

Table A   **Squares, square roots, and reciprocals of numbers 1 to 1,000**

N	N²	$\sqrt{N}$	$\sqrt{10N}$	1/N	$1/\sqrt{N}$	$1/\sqrt{10N}$
1	1	1.0000	3.1623	1.000000	1.0000	.31623
2	4	1.4142	4.4721	.500000	.7071	.22361
3	9	1.7321	5.4772	.333333	.5774	.18257
4	16	2.0000	6.3246	.250000	.5000	.15811
5	25	2.2361	7.0711	.200000	.4472	.14142
6	36	2.4495	7.7460	.166667	.4082	.12910
7	49	2.6458	8.3666	.142857	.3780	.11952
8	64	2.8284	8.9443	.125000	.3536	.11180
9	81	3.0000	9.4868	.111111	.3333	.10541
10	1 00	3.1623	10.0000	.100000	.3162	.10000
11	1 21	3.3166	10.4881	.090909	.3015	.09535
12	1 44	3.4641	10.9545	.083333	.2887	.09129
13	1 69	3.6056	11.4018	.076923	.2774	.08771
14	1 96	3.7417	11.8322	.071429	.2673	.08452
15	2 25	3.8730	12.2474	.066667	.2582	.08165
16	2 56	4.0000	12.6491	.062500	.2500	.07906
17	2 89	4.1231	13.0384	.058824	.2425	.07670
18	3 24	4.2426	13.4164	.055556	.2357	.07454
19	3 61	4.3589	13.7840	.052632	.2294	.07255
20	4 00	4.4721	14.1421	.050000	.2236	.07071
21	4 41	4.5826	14.4914	.047619	.2182	.06901
22	4 84	4.6904	14.8324	.045455	.2132	.06742
23	5 29	4.7958	15.1658	.043478	.2085	.06594
24	5 76	4.8990	15.4919	.041667	.2041	.06455
25	6 25	5.0000	15.8114	.040000	.2000	.06325
26	6 76	5.0990	16.1245	.038462	.1961	.06202
27	7 29	5.1962	16.4317	.037037	.1925	.06086
28	7 84	5.2915	16.7332	.035714	.1890	.05976
29	8 41	5.3852	17.0294	.034483	.1857	.05872
30	9 00	5.4772	17.3205	.033333	.1826	.05774
31	9 61	5.5678	17.6068	.032258	.1796	.05680
32	10 24	5.6569	17.8885	.031250	.1768	.05590
33	10 89	5.7446	18.1659	.030303	.1741	.05505
34	11 56	5.8310	18.4391	.029412	.1715	.05423
35	12 25	5.9161	18.7083	.028571	.1690	.05345
36	12 96	6.0000	18.9737	.027778	.1667	.05270
37	13 69	6.0828	19.2354	.027027	.1644	.05199
38	14 44	6.1644	19.4936	.026316	.1622	.05130
39	15 21	6.2450	19.7484	.025641	.1601	.05064
40	16 00	6.3246	20.0000	.025000	.1581	.05000
41	16 81	6.4031	20.2485	.024390	.1562	.04939
42	17 64	6.4807	20.4939	.023810	.1543	.04880
43	18 49	6.5574	20.7364	.023256	.1525	.04822
44	19 36	6.6332	20.9762	.022727	.1508	.04767
45	20 25	6.7082	21.2132	.022222	.1491	.04714
46	21 16	6.7823	21.4476	.021739	.1474	.04663
47	22 09	6.8557	21.6795	.021277	.1459	.04613
48	23 04	6.9282	21.9089	.020833	.1443	.04564
49	24 01	7.0000	22.1359	.020408	.1429	.04518
50	25 00	7.0711	22.3607	.020000	.1414	.04472

Table A **Squares, square roots, and reciprocals of numbers 1 to 1,000** *(continued)*

N	N²	√N	√10N	1/N	1/√N	1/√10N
51	26 01	7.1414	22.5832	.019608	.1400	.04428
52	27 04	7.2111	22.8035	.019231	.1387	.04385
53	28 09	7.2801	23.0217	.018868	.1374	.04344
54	29 16	7.3485	23.2379	.018519	.1361	.04303
55	30 25	7.4162	23.4521	.018182	.1348	.04264
56	31 36	7.4833	23.6643	.017857	.1336	.04226
57	32 49	7.5498	23.8747	.017544	.1325	.04189
58	33 64	7.6158	24.0832	.017241	.1313	.04152
59	34 81	7.6811	24.2899	.016949	.1302	.04117
60	36 00	7.7460	24.4949	.016667	.1291	.04082
61	37 21	7.8102	24.6982	.016393	.1280	.04049
62	38 44	7.8740	24.8998	.016129	.1270	.04016
63	39 69	7.9373	25.0998	.015873	.1260	.03984
64	40 96	8.0000	25.2982	.015625	.1250	.03953
65	42 25	8.0623	25.4951	.015385	.1240	.03922
66	43 56	8.1240	25.6905	.015152	.1231	.03892
67	44 89	8.1854	25.8844	.014925	.1222	.03863
68	46 24	8.2462	26.0768	.014706	.1213	.03835
69	47 61	8.3066	26.2679	.014493	.1204	.03807
70	49 00	8.3666	26.4575	.014286	.1195	.03780
71	50 41	8.4261	26.6458	.014085	.1187	.03753
72	51 84	8.4853	26.8328	.013889	.1179	.03727
73	53 29	8.5440	27.0185	.013699	.1170	.03701
74	54 76	8.6023	27.2029	.013514	.1162	.03676
75	56 25	8.6603	27.3861	.013333	.1155	.03651
76	57 76	8.7178	27.5681	.013158	.1147	.03627
77	59 29	8.7750	27.7489	.012987	.1140	.03604
78	60 84	8.8318	27.9285	.012821	.1132	.03581
79	62 41	8.8882	28.1069	.012658	.1125	.03558
80	64 00	8.9443	28.2843	.012500	.1118	.03536
81	65 61	9.0000	28.4605	.012346	.1111	.03514
82	67 24	9.0554	28.6356	.012195	.1104	.03492
83	68 89	9.1104	28.8097	.012048	.1098	.03471
84	70 56	9.1652	28.9828	.011905	.1091	.03450
85	72 25	9.2195	29.1548	.011765	.1085	.03430
86	73 96	9.2736	29.3258	.011628	.1078	.03410
87	75 69	9.3274	29.4958	.011494	.1072	.03390
88	77 44	9.3808	29.6648	.011364	.1066	.03371
89	79 21	9.4340	29.8329	.011236	.1060	.03352
90	81 00	9.4868	30.0000	.011111	.1054	.03333
91	82 81	9.5394	30.1662	.010989	.1048	.03315
92	84 64	9.5917	30.3315	.010870	.1043	.03297
93	86 49	9.6437	30.4959	.010753	.1037	.03279
94	88 36	9.6954	30.6594	.010638	.1031	.03262
95	90 25	9.7468	30.8221	.010526	.1026	.03244
96	92 16	9.7980	30.9839	.010417	.1021	.03227
97	94 09	9.8489	31.1448	.010309	.1015	.03211
98	96 04	9.8995	31.3050	.010204	.1010	.03194
99	98 01	9.9499	31.4643	.010101	.1005	.03178
100	1 00 00	10.0000	31.6228	.010000	.1000	.03162

N	N²	$\sqrt{N}$	$\sqrt{10N}$	1/N	$1/\sqrt{N}$	$1/\sqrt{10N}$
101	1 02 01	10.0499	31.7805	.009901	.0995	.03147
102	1 04 04	10.0995	31.9374	.009804	.0990	.03131
103	1 06 09	10.1489	32.0936	.009709	.0985	.03116
104	1 08 16	10.1980	32.2490	.009615	.0981	.03101
105	1 10 25	10.2470	32.4037	.009524	.0976	.03086
106	1 12 36	10.2956	32.5576	.009434	.0971	.03071
107	1 14 49	10.3441	32.7109	.009346	.0967	.03057
108	1 16 64	10.3923	32.8634	.009259	.0962	.03043
109	1 18 81	10.4403	33.0151	.009174	.0958	.03029
110	1 21 00	10.4881	33.1662	.009091	.0953	.03015
111	1 23 21	10.5357	33.3167	.009009	.0949	.03002
112	1 25 44	10.5830	33.4664	.008929	.0945	.02988
113	1 27 69	10.6301	33.6155	.008850	.0941	.02975
114	1 29 96	10.6771	33.7639	.008772	.0937	.02962
115	1 32 25	10.7238	33.9116	.008696	.0933	.02949
116	1 34 56	10.7703	34.0588	.008621	.0928	.02936
117	1 36 89	10.8167	34.2053	.008547	.0925	.02924
118	1 39 24	10.8628	34.3511	.008475	.0921	.02911
119	1 41 61	10.9087	34.4964	.008403	.0917	.02899
120	1 44 00	10.9545	34.6410	.008333	.0913	.02887
121	1 46 41	11.0000	34.7851	.008264	.0909	.02875
122	1 48 84	11.0454	34.9285	.008197	.0905	.02863
123	1 51 29	11.0905	35.0714	.008130	.0902	.02851
124	1 53 76	11.1355	35.2136	.008065	.0898	.02840
125	1 56 25	11.1803	35.3553	.008000	.0894	.02828
126	1 58 76	11.2250	35.4965	.007937	.0891	.02817
127	1 61 29	11.2694	35.6371	.007874	.0887	.02806
128	1 63 84	11.3137	35.7771	.007813	.0884	.02795
129	1 66 41	11.3578	35.9166	.007752	.0880	.02784
130	1 69 00	11.4018	36.0555	.007692	.0877	.02774
131	1 71 61	11.4455	36.1939	.007634	.0874	.02763
132	1 74 24	11.4891	36.3318	.007576	.0870	.02752
133	1 76 89	11.5326	36.4692	.007519	.0867	.02742
134	1 79 56	11.5758	36.6060	.007463	.0864	.02732
135	1 82 25	11.6190	36.7423	.007407	.0861	.02722
136	1 84 69	11.6619	36.8782	.007353	.0857	.02712
137	1 87 69	11.7047	37.0135	.007299	.0854	.02702
138	1 90 44	11.7473	37.1484	.007246	.0851	.02692
139	1 93 21	11.7898	37.2827	.007194	.0848	.02682
140	1 96 00	11.8322	37.4166	.007143	.0845	.02673
141	1 98 81	11.8743	37.5500	.007092	.0842	.02663
142	2 01 64	11.9164	37.6829	.007042	.0839	.02654
143	2 04 49	11.9583	37.8153	.006993	.0836	.02644
144	2 07 36	12.0000	37.9473	.006944	.0833	.02635
145	2 10 25	12.0416	38.0789	.006897	.0830	.02626
146	2 13 16	12.0830	38.2099	.006849	.0828	.02617
147	2 16 09	12.1244	38.3406	.006803	.0825	.02608
148	2 19 04	12.1655	38.4708	.006757	.0822	.02599
149	2 22 01	12.2066	38.6005	.006711	.0819	.02591
150	2 25 00	12.2474	38.7298	.006667	.0816	.02582

N	N²	$\sqrt{N}$	$\sqrt{10N}$	1/N	$1/\sqrt{N}$	$1/\sqrt{10N}$
151	2 28 01	12.2882	38.8587	.006623	.0814	.02573
152	2 31 04	12.3288	38.9872	.006579	.0811	.02565
153	2 34 09	12.3693	39.1152	.006536	.0808	.02557
154	2 37 16	12.4097	39.2428	.006494	.0806	.02548
155	2 40 25	12.4499	39.3700	.006452	.0803	.02540
156	2 43 36	12.4900	39.4968	.006410	.0801	.02532
157	2 46 49	12.5300	39.6232	.006369	.0798	.02524
158	2 49 64	12.5698	39.7492	.006329	.0796	.02516
159	2 52 81	12.6095	39.8748	.006289	.0793	.02508
160	2 56 00	12.6491	40.0000	.006250	.0791	.02500
161	2 59 21	12.6886	40.1248	.006211	.0788	.02492
162	2 62 44	12.7279	40.2492	.006173	.0786	.02485
163	2 65 69	12.7671	40.3733	.006135	.0783	.02477
164	2 68 96	12.8062	40.4969	.006098	.0781	.02469
165	2 72 25	12.8452	40.6202	.006061	.0778	.02462
166	2 75 56	12.8841	40.7431	.006024	.0776	.02454
167	2 78 89	12.9228	40.8656	.005988	.0774	.02447
168	2 82 24	12.9615	40.9878	.005952	.0772	.02440
169	2 85 61	13.0000	41.1096	.005917	.0769	.02433
170	2 89 00	13.0384	41.2311	.005882	.0767	.02425
171	2 92 41	13.0767	41.3521	.005848	.0765	.02418
172	2 95 84	13.1149	41.4729	.005814	.0762	.02411
173	2 99 29	13.1529	41.5933	.005780	.0760	.02404
174	3 02 76	13.1909	41.7133	.005747	.0758	.02397
175	3 06 25	13.2288	41.8330	.005714	.0756	.02390
176	3 09 76	13.2665	41.9524	.005682	.0754	.02384
177	3 13 29	13.3041	42.0714	.005650	.0752	.02377
178	3 16 84	13.3417	42.1900	.005618	.0750	.02370
179	3 20 41	13.3791	42.3084	.005587	.0747	.02364
180	3 24 00	13.4164	42.4264	.005556	.0745	.02357
181	3 27 61	13.4536	42.5441	.005525	.0743	.02351
182	3 31 24	13.4907	42.6615	.005495	.0741	.02344
183	3 34 89	13.5277	42.7785	.005464	.0739	.02338
184	3 38 56	13.5647	42.8952	.005435	.0737	.02331
185	3 42 25	13.6015	43.0116	.005405	.0735	.02325
186	3 45 96	13.6382	43.1277	.005376	.0733	.02319
187	3 49 69	13.6748	43.2435	.005348	.0731	.02312
188	3 53 44	13.7113	43.3590	.005319	.0729	.02306
189	3 57 21	13.7477	43.4741	.005291	.0727	.02300
190	3 61 00	13.7840	43.5890	.005263	.0725	.02294
191	3 64 81	13.8203	43.7035	.005236	.0724	.02288
192	3 68 64	13.8564	43.8178	.005208	.0722	.02282
193	3 72 49	13.8924	43.9318	.005181	.0720	.02276
194	3 76 36	13.9284	44.0454	.005155	.0718	.02270
195	3 80 25	13.9642	44.1588	.005128	.0716	.02265
196	3 84 16	14.0000	44.2719	.005102	.0714	.02259
197	3 88 09	14.0357	44.3847	.005076	.0712	.02253
198	3 92 04	14.0712	44.4972	.005051	.0711	.02247
199	3 96 01	14.1067	44.6094	.005025	.0709	.02242
200	4 00 00	14.1421	44.7214	.005000	.0707	.02236

Table A Squares, square roots, and reciprocals of numbers 1 to 1,000 (continued)

N	N²	$\sqrt{N}$	$\sqrt{10N}$	1/N	$1/\sqrt{N}$	$1/\sqrt{10N}$
201	4 04 01	14.1774	44.8330	.004975	.0705	.02230
202	4 08 04	14.2127	44.9444	.004950	.0704	.02225
203	4 12 09	14.2478	45.0555	.004926	.0702	.02219
204	4 16 16	14.2829	45.1664	.004902	.0700	.02214
205	4 20 25	14.3178	45.2769	.004878	.0698	.02209
206	4 24 36	14.3527	45.3872	.004854	.0697	.02203
207	4 28 49	14.3875	45.4973	.004831	.0695	.02198
208	4 32 64	14.4222	45.6070	.004081	.0693	.02193
209	4 36 81	14.4568	45.7165	.004785	.0692	.02187
210	4 41 00	14.4914	45.8258	.004762	.0690	.02182
211	4 45 21	14.5258	45.9347	.004739	.0688	.02177
212	4 49 44	14.5602	46.0435	.004717	.0687	.02172
213	4 53 69	14.5945	46.1519	.004695	.0685	.02167
214	4 57 96	14.6287	46.2601	.004673	.0684	.02162
215	4 62 25	14.6629	46.3681	.004651	.0682	.02157
216	4 66 56	14.6969	46.4758	.004630	.0680	.02152
217	4 70 89	14.7309	46.5833	.004608	.0679	.02147
218	4 75 24	14.7648	46.6905	.004587	.0677	.02142
219	4 79 61	14.7986	46.7974	.004566	.0676	.02137
220	4 84 00	14.8324	46.9042	.004545	.0674	.02132
221	4 88 41	14.8661	47.0106	.004525	.0673	.02127
222	4 92 84	14.8997	47.1169	.004505	.0671	.02122
223	4 97 29	14.9332	47.2229	.004484	.0670	.02118
224	5 01 76	14.9666	47.3286	.004464	.0668	.02113
225	5 06 25	15.0000	47.4342	.004444	.0667	.02108
226	5 10 76	15.0333	47.5395	.004425	.0665	.02104
227	5 15 29	15.0665	47.6445	.004405	.0664	.02099
228	5 19 84	15.0997	47.7493	.004386	.0662	.02094
229	5 24 41	15.1327	47.8539	.004367	.0661	.02090
230	5 29 00	15.1658	47.9583	.004348	.0659	.02085
231	5 33 61	15.1987	48.0625	.004329	.0658	.02081
232	5 38 24	15.2315	48.1664	.004310	.0657	.02076
233	5 42 89	15.2643	48.2701	.004292	.0655	.02072
234	5 47 56	15.2971	48.3735	.004274	.0654	.02067
235	5 52 25	15.3297	48.4768	.004255	.0652	.02063
236	5 56 96	15.3623	48.5798	.004237	.0651	.02058
237	5 61 69	15.3948	48.6826	.004219	.0650	.02054
238	5 66 44	15.4272	48.7852	.004202	.0648	.02050
239	5 71 21	15.4596	48.8876	.004184	.0647	.02046
240	5 76 00	15.4919	48.9898	.004167	.0645	.02041
241	5 80 81	15.5242	49.0918	.004149	.0644	.02037
242	5 85 64	15.5563	49.1935	.004132	.0643	.02033
243	5 90 49	15.5885	49.2950	.004115	.0642	.02029
244	5 95 36	15.6205	49.3964	.004098	.0640	.02024
245	6 00 25	15.6525	49.4975	.004082	.0639	.02020
246	6 05 16	15.6844	49.5984	.004065	.0638	.02016
247	6 10 09	15.7162	49.6991	.004049	.0636	.02012
248	6 15 04	15.7480	49.7996	.004032	.0635	.02008
249	6 20 01	15.7797	49.8999	.004016	.0634	.02004
250	6 25 00	15.8114	50.0000	.004000	.0632	.02000

N	N²	√N	√10N	1/N	1/√N	1/√10N
251	6 30 01	15.8430	50.0999	.003984	.0631	.01996
252	6 35 04	15.8745	50.1996	.003968	.0630	.01992
253	6 40 09	15.9060	50.2991	.003953	.0629	.01988
254	6 45 16	15.9374	50.3984	.003937	.0627	.01984
255	6 50 25	15.9687	50.4975	.003922	.0626	.01980
256	6 55 36	16.0000	50.5964	.003906	.0625	.01976
257	6 60 49	16.0312	50.6952	.003891	.0624	.01973
258	6 65 64	16.0624	50.7937	.003876	.0623	.01969
259	6 70 81	16.0935	50.8920	.003861	.0621	.01965
260	6 76 00	16.1245	50.9902	.003846	.0620	.01961
261	6 81 21	16.1555	51.0882	.003831	.0619	.01957
262	6 86 44	16.1864	51.1859	.003817	.0618	.01954
263	6 91 69	16.2173	51.2835	.003802	.0617	.01950
264	6 96 96	16.2481	51.3809	.003788	.0615	.01946
265	7 02 25	16.2788	51.4782	.003774	.0614	.01943
266	7 07 56	16.3095	51.5752	.003759	.0613	.01939
267	7 12 89	16.3401	51.6720	.003745	.0612	.01935
268	7 18 24	16.3707	51.7687	.003731	.0611	.01932
269	7 23 61	16.4012	51.8652	.003717	.0610	.01928
270	7 29 00	16.4317	51.9615	.003704	.0609	.01925
271	7 34 41	16.4621	52.0577	.003690	.0607	.01921
272	7 39 84	16.4924	52.1536	.003676	.0606	.01917
273	7 45 29	16.5227	52.2494	.003663	.0605	.01914
274	7 50 76	16.5529	52.3450	.003650	.0604	.01910
275	7 56 25	16.5831	52.4404	.003636	.0603	.01907
276	7 61 76	16.6132	52.5357	.003623	.0602	.01903
277	7 67 29	16.6433	52.6308	.003610	.0601	.01900
278	7 72 84	16.6733	52.7257	.003597	.0600	.01897
279	7 78 41	16.7033	52.8205	.003584	.0599	.01893
280	7 84 00	16.7332	52.9150	.003571	.0598	.01890
281	7 89 61	16.7631	53.0094	.003559	.0597	.01886
282	7 95 24	16.7929	53.1037	.003546	.0595	.01883
283	8 00 89	16.8226	53.1977	.003534	.0594	.01880
284	8 06 56	16.8523	53.2917	.003521	.0593	.01876
285	8 12 25	16.8819	53.3854	.003509	.0592	.01873
286	8 17 96	16.9115	53.4790	.003497	.0591	.01870
287	8 23 69	16.9411	53.5724	.003484	.0590	.01867
288	8 29 44	16.9706	53.6656	.003472	.0589	.01863
289	8 35 21	17.0000	53.7587	.003460	.0588	.01860
290	8 41 00	17.0294	53.8516	.003448	.0587	.01857
291	8 46 81	17.0587	53.9444	.003436	.0586	.01854
292	8 52 64	17.0880	54.0370	.003425	.0585	.01851
293	8 58 49	17.1172	54.1295	.003413	.0584	.01847
294	8 64 36	17.1464	54.2218	.003401	.0583	.01844
295	8 70 25	17.1756	54.3139	.003390	.0582	.01841
296	8 76 16	17.2047	54.4059	.003378	.0581	.01838
297	8 82 09	17.2337	54.4977	.003367	.0580	.01835
298	8 88 04	17.2627	54.5894	.003356	.0579	.01832
299	8 94 01	17.2916	54.6809	.003344	.0578	.01829
300	9 00 00	17.3205	54.7723	.003333	.0577	.01826

N	N²	√N	√10N	1/N	1/√N	1/√10N
301	9 06 01	17.3494	54.8635	.003322	.0576	.01823
302	9 12 04	17.3781	54.9545	.003311	.0575	.01820
303	9 18 09	17.4069	55.0454	.003300	.0574	.01817
304	9 24 16	17.4356	55.1362	.003289	.0574	.01814
305	9 30 25	17.4642	55.2268	.003279	.0573	.01811
306	9 36 36	17.4929	55.3173	.003268	.0572	.01808
307	9 42 49	17.5214	55.4076	.003257	.0571	.01805
308	9 48 64	17.5499	55.4977	.003247	.0570	.01802
309	9 54 81	17.5784	55.5878	.003236	.0569	.01799
310	9 61 00	17.6068	55.6776	.003226	.0568	.01796
311	9 67 21	17.6352	55.7674	.003215	.0567	.01793
312	9 73 44	17.6635	55.8570	.003205	.0566	.01790
313	9 79 69	17.6918	55.9464	.003195	.0565	.01787
314	9 85 96	17.7200	56.0357	.003185	.0564	.01785
315	9 92 25	17.7482	56.1249	.003175	.0563	.01782
316	9 98 56	17.7764	56.2139	.003165	.0563	.01779
317	10 04 89	17.8045	56.3028	.003155	.0562	.01776
318	10 11 24	17.8326	56.3915	.003145	.0561	.01773
319	10 17 61	17.8606	56.4801	.003135	.0560	.01771
320	10 24 00	17.8885	56.5685	.003125	.0559	.01768
321	10 30 41	17.9165	56.6569	.003115	.0558	.01765
322	10 36 84	17.9444	56.7450	.003106	.0557	.01762
323	10 43 29	17.9722	56.8331	.003096	.0556	.01760
324	10 49 76	18.0000	56.9210	.003086	.0556	.01757
325	10 56 25	18.0278	57.0088	.003077	.0555	.01754
326	10 62 76	18.0555	57.0964	.003067	.0554	.01751
327	10 69 29	18.0831	57.1839	.003058	.0553	.01749
328	10 75 84	18.1108	57.2713	.003049	.0552	.01746
329	10 82 41	18.1384	57.3585	.003040	.0551	.01743
330	10 89 00	18.1659	57.4456	.003030	.0550	.01741
331	10 95 61	18.1934	57.5326	.003021	.0550	.01738
332	11 02 24	18.2209	57.6194	.003012	.0549	.01736
333	11 08 89	18.2483	57.7062	.003003	.0548	.01733
334	11 15 56	18.2757	57.7927	.002994	.0547	.01730
335	11 22 25	18.3030	57.8792	.002985	.0546	.01728
336	11 28 96	18.3303	57.9655	.002976	.0546	.01725
337	11 35 69	18.3576	58.0517	.002967	.0545	.01723
338	11 42 44	18.3848	58.1378	.002959	.0544	.01720
339	11 49 21	18.4120	58.2237	.002950	.0543	.01718
340	11 56 00	18.4391	58.3095	.002941	.0542	.01715
341	11 62 81	18.4662	58.3952	.002933	.0542	.01712
342	11 69 64	18.4932	58.4808	.002924	.0541	.01710
343	11 76 49	18.5203	58.5662	.002915	.0540	.01707
344	11 83 36	18.5472	58.6515	.002907	.0539	.01705
345	11 90 25	18.5742	58.7367	.002899	.0538	.01703
346	11 97 16	18.6011	58.8218	.002890	.0538	.01700
347	12 04 09	18.6279	58.9067	.002882	.0537	.01698
348	12 11 04	18.6548	58.9915	.002874	.0536	.01695
349	12 18 01	18.6815	59.0762	.002865	.0535	.01693
350	12 25 00	18.7083	59.1608	.002857	.0535	.01690

N	N²	√N	√10N	1/N	1/√N	1/√10N
351	12 32 01	18.7350	59.2453	.002849	.0534	.01688
352	12 39 04	18.7617	59.3296	.002841	.0533	.01685
353	12 46 09	18.7883	59.4138	.002833	.0532	.01683
354	12 53 16	18.8149	59.4979	.002825	.0531	.01681
355	12 60 25	18.8414	59.5819	.002817	.0531	.01678
356	12 67 36	18.8680	59.6657	.002809	.0530	.01676
357	12 74 49	18.8944	59.7495	.002801	.0529	.01674
358	12 81 64	18.9209	59.8331	.002793	.0529	.01671
359	12 88 81	18.9473	59.9166	.002786	.0528	.01669
360	12 96 00	18.9737	60.0000	.002778	.0527	.01667
361	13 03 21	19.0000	60.0833	.002770	.0526	.01664
362	13 10 44	19.0263	60.1664	.002762	.0526	.01662
363	13 17 69	19.0526	60.2495	.002755	.0525	.01660
364	13 24 96	19.0788	60.3324	.002747	.0524	.01657
365	13 32 25	19.1050	60.4152	.002740	.0523	.01655
366	13 39 56	19.1311	60.4979	.002732	.0523	.01653
367	13 46 89	19.1572	60.5805	.002725	.0522	.01651
368	13 54 24	19.1833	60.6630	.002717	.0521	.01648
369	13 61 61	19.2094	60.7454	.002710	.0521	.01646
370	13 69 00	19.2354	60.8276	.002703	.0520	.01644
371	13 76 41	19.2614	60.9098	.002695	.0519	.01642
372	13 83 84	19.2873	60.9918	.002688	.0518	.01640
373	13 91 29	19.3132	61.0737	.002681	.0518	.01637
374	13 98 76	19.3391	61.1555	.002674	.0517	.01635
375	14 06 25	19.3649	61.2372	.002667	.0516	.01633
376	14 13 76	19.3907	61.3188	.002660	.0516	.01631
377	14 21 29	19.4165	61.4003	.002653	.0515	.01629
378	14 28 84	19.4422	61.4817	.002646	.0514	.01627
379	14 36 41	19.4679	61.5630	.002639	.0514	.01624
380	14 44 00	19.4936	61.6441	.002632	.0513	.01622
381	14 51 61	19.5192	61.7252	.002625	.0512	.01620
382	14 59 24	19.5448	61.8061	.002618	.0512	.01618
383	14 66 89	19.5704	61.8870	.002611	.0511	.01616
384	14 74 56	19.5959	61.9677	.002604	.0510	.01614
385	14 82 25	19.6214	62.0484	.002597	.0510	.01612
386	14 89 96	19.6469	62.1289	.002591	.0509	.01610
387	14 97 69	19.6723	62.2093	.002584	.0508	.01607
388	15 05 44	19.6977	62.2896	.002577	.0508	.01605
389	15 13 21	19.7231	62.3699	.002571	.0507	.01603
390	15 21 00	19.7484	62.4500	.002564	.0506	.01601
391	15 28 81	19.7737	62.5300	.002558	.0506	.01599
392	15 36 64	19.7990	62.6099	.002551	.0505	.01597
393	15 44 49	19.8242	62.6897	.002545	.0504	.01595
394	15 52 36	19.8494	62.7694	.002538	.0504	.01593
395	15 60 25	19.8746	62.8490	.002532	.0503	.01591
396	15 68 16	19.8997	62.9285	.002525	.0503	.01589
397	15 76 09	19.9249	63.0079	.002519	.0502	.01587
398	15 84 04	19.9499	63.0872	.002513	.0501	.01585
399	15 92 01	19.9750	63.1664	.002506	.0501	.01583
400	16 00 00	20.0000	63.2456	.002500	.0500	.01581

N	N^2	$\sqrt{N}$	$\sqrt{10N}$	$1/N$	$1/\sqrt{N}$	$1/\sqrt{10N}$
401	16 08 01	20.0250	63.3246	.002494	.0499	.01579
402	16 16 04	20.0499	63.4035	.002488	.0499	.01577
403	16 24 09	20.0749	63.4823	.002481	.0498	.01575
404	16 32 16	20.0998	63.5610	.002475	.0498	.01573
405	16 40 25	20.1246	63.6396	.002469	.0497	.01571
406	16 48 36	20.1494	63.7181	.002463	.0496	.01569
407	16 56 49	20.1742	63.7966	.002457	.0496	.01567
408	16 64 64	20.1990	63.8749	.002451	.0495	.01566
409	16 72 81	20.2237	63.9531	.002445	.0494	.01564
410	16 81 00	20.2485	64.0312	.002439	.0494	.01562
411	16 89 21	20.2731	64.1093	.002433	.0493	.01560
412	16 97 44	20.2978	64.1872	.002427	.0493	.01558
413	17 05 69	20.3224	64.2651	.002421	.0492	.01556
414	17 13 96	20.3470	64.3428	.002415	.0491	.01554
415	17 22 25	20.3715	64.4205	.002410	.0491	.01552
416	17 30 56	20.3961	64.4981	.002404	.0490	.01550
417	17 38 89	20.4206	64.5755	.002398	.0490	.01549
418	17 47 24	20.4450	64.6529	.002392	.0489	.01547
419	17 55 61	20.4695	64.7302	.002387	.0489	.01545
420	17 64 00	20.4939	64.8074	.002381	.0488	.01543
421	17 72 41	20.5183	64.8845	.002375	.0487	.01541
422	17 80 84	20.5426	64.9615	.002370	.0487	.01539
423	17 89 29	20.5670	65.0385	.002364	.0486	.01538
424	17 97 76	20.5913	65.1153	.002358	.0486	.01536
425	18 06 25	20.6155	65.1920	.002353	.0485	.01534
426	18 14 76	20.6398	65.2687	.002347	.0485	.01532
427	18 23 29	20.6640	65.3452	.002342	.0484	.01530
428	18 31 84	20.6882	65.4217	.002336	.0483	.01529
429	18 40 41	20.7123	65.4981	.002331	.0483	.01527
430	18 49 00	20.7364	65.5744	.002326	.0482	.01525
431	18 57 61	20.7605	65.6506	.002320	.0482	.01523
432	18 66 24	20.7846	65.7267	.002315	.0481	.01521
433	18 74 89	20.8087	65.8027	.002309	.0481	.01520
434	18 83 56	20.8327	65.8787	.002304	.0480	.01518
435	18 92 25	20.8567	65.9545	.002299	.0479	.01516
436	19 00 06	20.8806	66.0303	.002294	.0479	.01514
437	19 09 69	20.9045	66.1060	.002288	.0478	.01513
438	19 18 44	20.9284	66.1816	.002283	.0478	.01511
439	19 27 21	20.9523	66.2571	.002278	.0477	.01509
440	19 36 00	20.9762	66.3325	.002273	.0477	.01508
441	19 44 81	21.0000	66.4078	.002268	.0476	.01506
442	19 53 64	21.0238	66.4831	.002262	.0476	.01504
443	19 62 49	21.0476	66.5582	.002257	.0475	.01502
444	19 71 36	21.0713	66.6333	.002252	.0475	.01501
445	19 80 25	21.0950	66.7083	.002247	.0474	.01499
446	19 89 16	21.1187	66.7832	.002242	.0474	.01497
447	19 98 09	21.1424	66.8581	.002237	.0473	.01496
448	20 07 04	21.1660	66.9328	.002232	.0472	.01494
449	20 16 01	21.1896	67.0075	.002227	.0472	.01492
450	20 25 00	21.2132	67.0820	.002222	.0471	.01491

N	N²	√N	√10N	1/N	1/√N	1/√10N
451	20 34 01	21.2368	67.1565	.002217	.0471	.01489
452	20 43 04	21.2603	67.2309	.002212	.0470	.01487
453	20 52 09	21.2838	67.3053	.002208	.0470	.01486
454	20 61 16	21.3073	67.3795	.002203	.0469	.01484
455	20 70 25	21.3307	67.4537	.002198	.0469	.01482
456	20 79 36	21.3542	67.5278	.002193	.0468	.01481
457	20 88 49	21.3776	67.6018	.002188	.0468	.01479
458	20 97 64	21.4009	67.6757	.002183	.0467	.01478
459	21 06 81	21.4243	67.7495	.002179	.0467	.01476
460	21 16 00	21.4476	67.8233	.002174	.0466	.01474
461	21 25 21	21.4709	67.8970	.002169	.0466	.01473
462	21 34 44	21.4942	67.9706	.002165	.0465	.01471
463	21 43 69	21.5174	68.0441	.002160	.0465	.01470
464	21 52 96	21.5407	68.1175	.002155	.0464	.01468
465	21 62 25	21.5639	68.1909	.002151	.0464	.01466
466	21 71 56	21.5870	68.2642	.002146	.0463	.01465
467	21 80 89	21.6102	68.3374	.002141	.0463	.01463
468	21 90 24	21.6333	68.4105	.002137	.0462	.01462
469	21 99 61	21.6564	68.4836	.002132	.0462	.01460
470	22 09 00	21.6795	68.5565	.002128	.0461	.01459
471	22 18 41	21.7025	68.6294	.002123	.0461	.01457
472	22 27 84	21.7256	68.7023	.002119	.0460	.01456
473	22 37 29	21.7486	68.7750	.002114	.0460	.01454
474	22 46 76	21.7715	68.8477	.002110	.0459	.01452
475	22 56 25	21.7945	68.9202	.002105	.0459	.01451
476	22 65 76	21.8174	68.9928	.002101	.0458	.01449
477	22 75 29	21.8403	69.0652	.002096	.0458	.01448
478	22 84 84	21.8632	69.1375	.002092	.0457	.01446
479	22 94 41	21.8861	69.2098	.002088	.0457	.01445
480	23 04 00	21.9089	69.2820	.002083	.0456	.01443
481	23 13 61	21.9317	69.3542	.002079	.0456	.01442
482	23 23 24	21.9545	69.4262	.002075	.0455	.01440
483	23 32 89	21.9773	69.4982	.002070	.0455	.01439
484	23 42 56	22.0000	69.5701	.002066	.0455	.01437
485	23 52 25	22.0227	69.6419	.002062	.0454	.01436
486	23 61 96	22.0454	69.7137	.002058	.0454	.01434
487	23 71 69	22.0681	69.7854	.002053	.0453	.01433
488	23 81 44	22.0907	69.8570	.002049	.0453	.01431
489	23 91 21	22.1133	69.9285	.002045	.0452	.01430
490	24 01 00	22.1359	70.0000	.002041	.0452	.01429
491	24 10 81	22.1585	70.0714	.002037	.0451	.01427
492	24 20 64	22.1811	70.1427	.002033	.0451	.01426
493	24 30 49	22.2036	70.2140	.002028	.0450	.01424
494	24 40 36	22.2261	70.2851	.002024	.0450	.01423
495	24 50 25	22.2486	70.3562	.002020	.0449	.01421
496	24 60 16	22.2711	70.4273	.002016	.0449	.01420
497	24 70 09	22.2935	70.4982	.002012	.0449	.01418
498	24 80 04	22.3159	70.5691	.002008	.0448	.01417
499	24 90 01	22.3383	70.6399	.002004	.0448	.01416
500	25 00 00	22.3607	70.7107	.002000	.0447	.01414

Table A　Squares, square roots, and reciprocals of numbers 1 to 1,000 (continued)

N	N²	$\sqrt{N}$	$\sqrt{10N}$	1/N	$1/\sqrt{N}$	$1/\sqrt{10N}$
501	25 10 01	22.3830	70.7814	.001996	.0447	.01413
502	25 20 04	22.4054	70.8520	.001992	.0446	.01411
503	25 30 09	22.4277	70.9225	.001988	.0446	.01410
504	25 40 16	22.4499	70.9930	.001984	.0445	.01409
505	25 50 25	22.4722	71.0634	.001980	.0445	.01407
506	25 60 36	22.4944	71.1337	.001976	.0445	.01406
507	25 70 49	22.5167	71.2039	.001972	.0444	.01404
508	25 80 64	22.5389	71.2741	.001969	.0444	.01403
509	25 90 81	22.5610	71.3442	.001965	.0443	.01402
510	26 01 00	22.5832	71.4143	.001961	.0443	.01400
511	26 11 21	22.6053	71.4843	.001957	.0442	.01399
512	26 21 44	22.6274	71.5542	.001953	.0442	.01398
513	26 31 69	22.6495	71.6240	.001949	.0442	.01396
514	26 41 96	22.6716	71.6938	.001946	.0441	.01395
515	26 52 25	22.6936	71.7635	.001942	.0441	.01393
516	26 62 56	22.7156	71.8331	.001938	.0440	.01392
517	26 72 89	22.7376	71.9027	.001934	.0440	.01391
518	26 83 24	22.7596	71.9722	.001931	.0439	.01389
519	26 93 61	22.7816	72.0417	.001927	.0439	.01388
520	27 04 00	22.8035	72.1110	.001923	.0439	.01387
521	27 14 41	22.8254	72.1803	.001919	.0438	.01385
522	27 24 84	22.8473	72.2496	.001916	.0438	.01384
523	27 35 29	22.8692	72.3187	.001912	.0437	.01383
524	27 45 76	22.8910	72.3878	.001908	.0437	.01381
525	27 56 25	22.9129	72.4569	.001905	.0436	.01380
526	27 66 76	22.9347	72.5259	.001901	.0436	.01379
527	27 77 29	22.9565	72.5948	.001898	.0436	.01378
528	27 87 84	22.9783	72.6636	.001894	.0435	.01376
529	27 98 41	23.0000	72.7324	.001890	.0435	.01375
530	28 09 00	23.0217	72.8011	.001887	.0434	.01374
531	28 19 61	23.0434	72.8697	.001883	.0434	.01372
532	28 30 24	23.0651	72.9383	.001880	.0434	.01371
533	28 40 89	23.0868	73.0068	.001876	.0433	.01370
534	28 51 56	23.1084	73.0753	.001873	.0433	.01368
535	28 62 25	23.1301	73.1437	.001869	.0432	.01367
536	28 72 96	23.1517	73.2120	.001866	.0432	.01366
537	28 83 69	23.1733	73.2803	.001862	.0432	.01365
538	28 94 44	23.1948	73.3485	.001859	.0431	.01363
539	29 05 21	23.2164	73.4166	.001855	.0431	.01362
540	29 16 00	23.2379	73.4847	.001852	.0430	.01361
541	29 26 81	23.2594	73.5527	.001848	.0430	.01360
542	29 37 64	23.2809	73.6206	.001845	.0430	.01358
543	29 48 49	23.3024	73.6885	.001842	.0429	.01357
544	29 59 36	23.3238	73.7564	.001838	.0429	.01356
545	29 70 25	23.3452	73.8241	.001835	.0428	.01355
546	29 81 16	23.3666	73.8918	.001832	.0428	.01353
547	29 92 09	23.3880	73.9594	.001828	.0428	.01352
548	30 03 04	23.4094	74.0270	.001825	.0427	.01351
549	30 14 01	23.4307	74.0945	.001821	.0427	.01350
550	30 25 00	23.4521	74.1620	.001818	.0426	.01348

N	N²	$\sqrt{N}$	$\sqrt{10N}$	1/N	$1/\sqrt{N}$	$1/\sqrt{10N}$
551	30 36 01	23.4734	74.2294	.001815	.0426	.01347
552	30 47 04	23.4947	74.2967	.001812	.0426	.01346
553	30 58 09	23.5160	74.3640	.001808	.0425	.01345
554	30 69 16	23.5372	74.4312	.001805	.0425	.01344
555	30 80 25	23.5584	74.4983	.001802	.0424	.01342
556	30 91 36	23.5797	74.5654	.001799	.0424	.01341
557	31 02 49	23.6008	74.6324	.001795	.0424	.01340
558	31 13 64	23.6220	74.6994	.001792	.0423	.01339
559	31 24 81	23.6432	74.7663	.001789	.0423	.01338
560	31 36 00	23.6643	74.8331	.001786	.0423	.01336
561	31 47 21	23.6854	74.8999	.001783	.0422	.01335
562	31 58 44	23.7065	74.9667	.001779	.0422	.01334
563	31 69 69	23.7276	75.0333	.001776	.0421	.01333
564	31 80 96	23.7487	75.0999	.001773	.0421	.01332
565	31 92 25	23.7697	75.1665	.001770	.0421	.01330
566	32 03 56	23.7908	75.2330	.001767	.0420	.01329
567	32 14 89	23.8118	75.2994	.001764	.0420	.01328
568	32 26 24	23.8328	75.3658	.001761	.0420	.01327
569	32 37 61	23.8537	75.4321	.001757	.0419	.01326
570	32 49 00	23.8747	75.4983	.001754	.0419	.01325
571	32 60 41	23.8956	75.5645	.001751	.0418	.01323
572	32 71 84	23.9165	75.6307	.001748	.0418	.01322
573	32 83 29	23.9374	75.6968	.001745	.0418	.01321
574	32 94 76	23.9583	75.7628	.001742	.0417	.01320
575	30 06 25	23.9792	75.8288	.001739	.0417	.01319
576	33 17 76	24.0000	75.8947	.001736	.0417	.01318
577	33 29 29	24.0208	75.9605	.001733	.0416	.01316
578	33 40 84	24.0416	76.0263	.001730	.0416	.01315
579	33 52 41	24.0624	76.0920	.001727	.0416	.01314
580	33 64 00	24.0832	76.1577	.001724	.0415	.01313
581	33 75 61	24.1039	76.2234	.001721	.0415	.01312
582	33 87 24	24.1247	76.2889	.001718	.0415	.01311
583	33 98 89	24.1454	76.3544	.001715	.0414	.01310
584	34 10 56	24.1661	76.4199	.001712	.0414	.01309
585	34 22 25	24.1868	76.4853	.001709	.0413	.01307
586	34 33 96	24.2074	76.5506	.001706	.0413	.01306
587	34 45 69	24.2281	76.6159	.001704	.0413	.01305
588	34 57 44	24.2487	76.6812	.001701	.0412	.01304
589	34 69 21	24.2693	76.7463	.001698	.0412	.01303
590	34 81 00	24.2899	76.8115	.001695	.0412	.01302
591	34 92 81	24.3105	76.8765	.001692	.0411	.01301
592	35 04 64	24.3311	76.9415	.001689	.0411	.01300
593	35 16 49	24.3516	77.0065	.001686	.0411	.01299
594	35 28 36	24.3721	77.0714	.001684	.0410	.01297
595	35 40 25	24.3926	77.1362	.001681	.0410	.01296
596	35 52 16	24.4131	77.2010	.001678	.0410	.01295
597	35 64 09	24.4336	77.2658	.001675	.0409	.01294
598	35 76 04	24.4540	77.3305	.001672	.0409	.01293
599	35 88 01	24.4745	77.3951	.001669	.0409	.01292
600	36 00 00	24.4949	77.4597	.001667	.0408	.01291

N	N^2	$\sqrt{N}$	$\sqrt{10N}$	$1/N$	$1/\sqrt{N}$	$1/\sqrt{10N}$
601	36 12 01	24.5153	77.5242	.001664	.0408	.01290
602	36 24 04	24.5357	77.5887	.001661	.0408	.01289
603	36 36 09	24.5561	77.6531	.001658	.0407	.01288
604	36 48 16	24.5764	77.7174	.001656	.0407	.01287
605	36 60 25	24.5967	77.7817	.001653	.0407	.01286
606	36 72 36	24.6171	77.8460	.001650	.0406	.01285
607	36 84 49	24.6374	77.9102	.001647	.0406	.01284
608	36 96 64	24.6577	77.9744	.001645	.0406	.01282
609	37 08 81	24.6779	78.0385	.001642	.0405	.01281
610	37 21 00	24.6982	78.1025	.001639	.0405	.01280
611	37 33 21	24.7184	78.1665	.001637	.0405	.01279
612	37 45 44	24.7386	78.2304	.001634	.0404	.01278
613	37 57 69	24.7588	78.2943	.001631	.0404	.01277
614	37 69 96	24.7790	78.3582	.001629	.0404	.01276
615	37 82 25	24.7992	78.4219	.001626	.0403	.01275
616	37 94 56	24.8193	78.4857	.001623	.0403	.01274
617	38 06 89	24.8395	78.5493	.001621	.0403	.01273
618	38 19 24	24.8596	78.6130	.001618	.0402	.01272
619	38 31 61	24.8797	78.6766	.001616	.0402	.01271
620	38 44 00	24.8998	78.7401	.001613	.0402	.01270
621	38 56 41	24.9199	78.8036	.001610	.0401	.01269
622	38 68 84	24.9399	78.8670	.001608	.0401	.01268
623	38 81 29	24.9600	78.9303	.001605	.0401	.01267
624	38 93 76	24.9800	78.9937	.001603	.0400	.01266
625	39 06 25	25.0000	79.0569	.001600	.0400	.01265
626	39 18 76	25.0200	79.1202	.001597	.0400	.01264
627	39 31 29	25.0400	79.1833	.001595	.0399	.01263
628	39 43 84	25.0599	79.2465	.001592	.0399	.01262
629	39 56 41	25.0799	79.3095	.001590	.0399	.01261
630	39 69 00	25.0998	79.3725	.001587	.0398	.01260
631	39 81 61	25.1197	79.4355	.001585	.0398	.01259
632	39 94 24	25.1396	79.4984	.001582	.0398	.01258
633	40 06 89	25.1595	79.5613	.001580	.0397	.01257
634	40 19 56	25.1794	79.6241	.001577	.0397	.01256
635	40 32 25	25.1992	79.6869	.001575	.0397	.01255
636	40 44 96	25.2190	79.7496	.001572	.0397	.01254
637	40 57 69	25.2389	79.8123	.001570	.0396	.01253
638	40 70 44	25.2587	79.8749	.001567	.0396	.01252
639	40 83 21	25.2784	79.9375	.001565	.0396	.01251
640	40 96 00	25.2982	80.0000	.001562	.0395	.01250
641	41 08 81	25.3180	80.0625	.001560	.0395	.01249
642	41 21 64	25.3377	80.1249	.001558	.0395	.01248
643	41 34 49	25.3574	80.1873	.001555	.0394	.01247
644	41 47 36	25.3772	80.2496	.001553	.0394	.01246
645	41 60 25	25.3969	80.3119	.001550	.0394	.01245
646	41 73 16	25.4165	80.3714	.001548	.0393	.01244
647	41 86 09	25.4362	80.4363	.001546	.0393	.01243
648	41 99 04	25.4558	80.4984	.001543	.0393	.01242
649	42 12 01	25.4775	80.5605	.001541	.0393	.01241
650	42 25 00	25.4951	80.6226	.001538	.0392	.01240

N	N²	√N	√10N	1/N	1/√N	1/√10N
651	42 38 01	25.5147	80.6846	.001536	.0392	.01239
652	42 51 04	25.5343	80.7465	.001534	.0392	.01238
653	42 64 09	25.5539	80.8084	.001531	.0391	.01237
654	42 77 16	25.5734	80.8703	.001529	.0391	.01237
655	42 90 25	25.5930	80.9321	.001527	.0391	.01236
656	43 03 36	25.6125	80.9938	.001524	.0390	.01235
657	43 16 49	25.6320	81.0555	.001522	.0390	.01234
658	43 29 64	25.6515	81.1172	.001520	.0390	.01233
659	43 42 81	25.6710	81.1788	.001517	.0390	.01232
660	43 56 00	25.6905	81.2404	.001515	.0389	.01231
661	43 69 21	25.7099	81.3019	.001513	.0389	.01230
662	43 82 44	25.7294	81.3634	.001511	.0389	.01229
663	43 95 69	25.7488	81.4248	.001508	.0388	.01228
664	44 08 96	25.7682	81.4862	.001506	.0388	.01227
665	44 22 25	25.7876	81.5475	.001504	.0388	.01226
666	44 35 56	25.8070	81.6088	.001502	.0387	.01225
667	44 48 89	25.8263	81.6701	.001499	.0387	.01224
668	44 62 24	25.8457	81.7313	.001497	.0387	.01224
669	44 75 61	25.8650	81.7924	.001495	.0387	.01223
670	44 89 00	25.8844	81.8535	.001493	.0386	.01222
671	45 02 41	25.9037	81.9146	.001490	.0386	.01221
672	45 15 84	25.9230	81.9756	.001488	.0386	.01220
673	45 29 29	25.9422	82.0366	.001486	.0385	.01219
674	45 42 76	25.9615	82.0975	.001484	.0385	.01218
675	45 56 25	25.9808	82.1584	.001481	.0385	.01217
676	45 69 76	26.0000	82.2192	.001479	.0385	.01216
677	45 83 29	26.0192	82.2800	.001477	.0384	.01215
678	45 96 84	26.0384	82.3408	.001475	.0384	.01214
679	46 10 41	26.0576	82.4015	.001473	.0384	.01214
680	46 24 00	26.0768	82.4621	.001471	.0383	.01213
681	46 37 61	26.0960	82.5227	.001468	.0383	.01212
682	46 51 24	26.1151	82.5833	.001466	.0383	.01211
683	46 64 89	26.1343	82.6438	.001464	.0383	.01210
684	46 78 56	26.1534	82.7043	.001462	.0382	.01209
685	46 92 25	26.1725	82.7647	.001460	.0382	.01208
686	47 05 96	26.1916	82.8251	.001458	.0382	.01207
687	47 19 69	26.2107	82.8855	.001456	.0382	.01206
688	47 33 44	26.2298	82.9458	.001453	.0381	.01206
689	47 47 21	26.2488	83.0060	.001451	.0381	.01205
690	47 61 00	26.2679	83.0662	.001449	.0381	.01204
691	47 74 81	26.2869	83.1264	.001447	.0380	.01203
692	47 88 64	26.3059	83.1865	.001445	.0380	.01202
693	48 02 49	26.3249	83.2466	.001443	.0380	.01201
694	48 16 36	26.3439	83.3067	.001441	.0380	.01200
695	48 30 25	26.3629	83.3667	.001439	.0379	.01200
696	48 44 16	26.3818	83.4266	.001437	.0379	.01199
697	48 58 09	26.4008	83.4865	.001435	.0379	.01198
698	48 72 04	26.4197	83.5464	.001433	.0379	.01197
699	48 86 01	26.4386	83.6062	.001431	.0378	.01196
700	49 00 00	26.4575	83.6660	.001429	.0378	.01195

N	N²	√N	√10N	1/N	1/√N	1/√10N
701	49 14 01	26.4764	83.7257	.001427	.0378	.01194
702	49 28 04	26.4953	83.7854	.001425	.0377	.01194
703	49 42 09	26.5141	83.8451	.001422	.0377	.01193
704	49 56 16	26.5330	83.9047	.001420	.0377	.01192
705	49 70 25	26.5518	83.9643	.001418	.0377	.01191
706	49 84 36	26.5707	84.0238	.001416	.0376	.01190
707	49 98 49	26.5895	84.0833	.001414	.0376	.01189
708	50 12 64	26.6083	84.1427	.001412	.0376	.01188
709	50 26 81	26.6271	84.2021	.001410	.0376	.01188
710	50 41 00	26.6458	84.2615	.001408	.0375	.01187
711	50 55 21	26.6646	84.3208	.001406	.0375	.01186
712	50 69 44	26.6833	84.3801	.001404	.0375	.01185
713	50 83 69	26.7021	84.4393	.001403	.0375	.01184
714	50 97 96	26.7208	84.4985	.001401	.0374	.01183
715	51 12 25	26.7395	84.5577	.001399	.0374	.01183
716	51 26 56	26.7582	84.6168	.001397	.0374	.01182
717	51 40 89	26.7769	84.6759	.001395	.0373	.01181
718	51 55 24	26.7955	84.7349	.001393	.0373	.01180
719	51 69 61	26.8142	84.7939	.001391	.0373	.01179
720	51 84 00	26.8328	84.8528	.001389	.0373	.01179
721	51 98 41	26.8514	84.9117	.001387	.0372	.01178
722	52 12 84	26.8701	84.9706	.001385	.0372	.01177
723	52 27 29	26.8887	85.0294	.001383	.0372	.01176
724	52 41 76	26.9072	85.0882	.001381	.0372	.01175
725	52 56 25	26.9258	85.1469	.001379	.0371	.01174
726	52 70 76	26.9444	85.2056	.001377	.0371	.01174
727	52 85 29	26.9629	85.2643	.001376	.0371	.01173
728	52 99 84	26.9815	85.3229	.001374	.0371	.01172
729	53 14 41	27.0000	85.3815	.001372	.0370	.01171
730	53 29 00	27.0185	85.4400	.001370	.0370	.01170
731	53 43 61	27.0370	85.4985	.001368	.0370	.01170
732	53 58 24	27.0555	85.5570	.001366	.0370	.01169
733	53 72 89	27.0740	85.6154	.001364	.0369	.01168
734	53 87 56	27.0924	85.6738	.001362	.0369	.01167
735	54 02 25	27.1109	85.7321	.001361	.0369	.01166
736	54 16 96	27.1293	85.7904	.001359	.0369	.01166
737	54 31 69	27.1477	85.8487	.001357	.0368	.01165
738	54 46 44	27.1662	85.9069	.001355	.0368	.01164
739	54 61 21	27.1846	85.9651	.001353	.0368	.01163
740	54 76 00	27.2029	86.0233	.001351	.0368	.01162
741	54 90 81	27.2213	86.0814	.001350	.0367	.01162
742	55 05 64	27.2397	86.1394	.001348	.0367	.01161
743	55 20 49	27.2580	86.1974	.001346	.0367	.01160
744	55 35 36	27.2764	86.2554	.001344	.0367	.01159
745	55 50 25	27.2947	86.3134	.001342	.0366	.01159
746	55 65 16	27.3130	86.3713	.001340	.0366	.01158
747	55 80 09	27.3313	86.4292	.001339	.0366	.01157
748	55 95 04	27.3496	86.4870	.001337	.0366	.01156
749	56 10 01	27.3679	86.5448	.001335	.0365	.01155
750	56 25 00	27.3861	86.6025	.001333	.0365	.01155

N	N^2	$\sqrt{N}$	$\sqrt{10N}$	$1/N$	$1/\sqrt{N}$	$1/\sqrt{10N}$
751	56 40 01	27.4044	86.6603	.001332	.0365	.01154
752	56 55 04	27.4226	86.7179	.001330	.0365	.01153
753	56 70 09	27.4408	86.7756	.001328	.0364	.01152
754	56 85 16	27.4591	86.8332	.001326	.0364	.01152
755	57 00 25	27.4773	86.8907	.001325	.0364	.01151
756	57 15 36	27.4955	86.9483	.001323	.0364	.01150
757	57 30 49	27.5136	87.0057	.001321	.0363	.01149
758	57 45 64	27.5318	87.0632	.001319	.0363	.01149
759	57 60 81	27.5500	87.1206	.001318	.0363	.01148
760	57 76 00	27.5681	87.1780	.001316	.0363	.01147
761	57 91 21	27.5862	87.2353	.001314	.0362	.01146
762	58 06 44	27.6043	87.2926	.001312	.0362	.01146
763	58 21 69	27.6225	87.3499	.001311	.0362	.01145
764	58 36 96	27.6405	87.4071	.001309	.0362	.01144
765	58 52 25	27.6586	87.4643	.001307	.0362	.01143
766	58 67 56	27.6767	87.5214	.001305	.0361	.01143
767	58 82 89	27.6948	87.5785	.001304	.0361	.01142
768	58 98 24	27.7128	87.6356	.001302	.0361	.01141
769	59 13 61	27.7308	87.6926	.001300	.0361	.01140
770	59 29 00	27.7489	87.7496	.001299	.0360	.01140
771	59 44 41	27.7669	87.8066	.001297	.0360	.01139
772	59 59 84	27.7849	87.8635	.001295	.0360	.01138
773	59 75 29	27.8029	87.9204	.001294	.0360	.01137
774	59 90 76	27.8209	87.9773	.001292	.0359	.01137
775	60 06 25	27.8388	88.0341	.001290	.0359	.01136
776	60 21 76	27.8568	88.0909	.001289	.0359	.01135
777	60 37 29	27.8747	88.1476	.001287	.0359	.01134
778	60 52 84	27.8927	88.2043	.001285	.0359	.01134
779	60 68 41	27.9106	88.2610	.001284	.0358	.01133
780	60 84 00	27.9285	88.3176	.001282	.0358	.01132
781	60 99 61	27.9464	88.3742	.001280	.0358	.01132
782	61 15 24	27.9643	88.4308	.001279	.0358	.01131
783	61 30 89	27.9821	88.4873	.001277	.0357	.01130
784	61 46 56	28.0000	88.5438	.001276	.0357	.01129
785	61 62 25	28.0179	88.6002	.001274	.0357	.01129
786	61 77 96	28.0357	88.6566	.001272	.0357	.01128
787	61 93 69	28.0535	88.7130	.001271	.0356	.01127
788	62 09 44	28.0713	88.7694	.001269	.0356	.01127
789	62 25 21	28.0891	88.8257	.001267	.0356	.01126
790	62 41 00	28.1069	88.8819	.001266	.0356	.01125
791	62 56 81	28.1247	88.9382	.001264	.0356	.01124
792	62 72 64	28.1425	88.9944	.001263	.0355	.01124
793	62 88 49	28.1603	89.0505	.001261	.0355	.01123
794	63 04 36	28.1780	89.1067	.001259	.0355	.01122
795	63 20 25	28.1957	89.1628	.001258	.0355	.01122
796	63 36 16	28.2135	89.2188	.001256	.0354	.01121
797	63 52 09	28.2312	89.2749	.001255	.0354	.01120
798	63 68 04	28.2489	89.3308	.001253	.0354	.01119
799	63 84 01	28.2666	89.3868	.001252	.0354	.01119
800	64 00 00	28.2843	89.4427	.001250	.0354	.01118

N	N²	√N	√10N	1/N	1/√N	1/√10N
801	64 16 01	28.3019	89.4986	.001248	.0353	.01117
802	64 32 04	28.3196	89.5545	.001247	.0353	.01117
803	64 48 09	28.3373	89.6103	.001245	.0353	.01116
804	64 64 16	28.3549	89.6660	.001244	.0353	.01115
805	64 80 25	28.3725	89.7218	.001242	.0352	.01115
806	64 96 36	28.3901	89.7775	.001241	.0352	.01114
807	65 12 49	28.4077	89.8332	.001239	.0352	.01113
808	65 28 64	28.4253	89.8888	.001238	.0352	.01112
809	65 44 81	28.4429	89.9444	.001236	.0352	.01112
810	65 61 00	28.4605	90.0000	.001235	.0351	.01111
811	65 77 21	28.4781	90.0555	.001233	.0351	.01110
812	65 93 44	28.4956	90.1110	.001232	.0351	.01110
813	66 09 69	28.5132	90.1665	.001230	.0351	.01109
814	66 25 96	28.5307	90.2219	.001229	.0350	.01108
815	66 42 25	28.5482	90.2774	.001227	.0350	.01108
816	66 58 56	28.5657	90.3327	.001225	.0350	.01107
817	66 74 89	28.5832	90.3881	.001224	.0350	.01106
818	66 91 24	28.6007	90.4434	.001222	.0350	.01106
819	67 07 61	28.6182	90.4986	.001221	.0349	.01105
820	67 24 00	28.6356	90.5539	.001220	.0349	.01104
821	67 40 41	28.6531	90.6091	.001218	.0349	.01104
822	67 56 84	28.6705	90.6642	.001217	.0349	.01103
823	67 73 29	28.6880	90.7193	.001215	.0349	.01102
824	67 89 76	28.7054	90.7744	.001214	.0348	.01102
825	68 06 25	28.7228	90.8295	.001212	.0348	.01101
826	68 22 76	28.7402	90.8845	.001211	.0348	.01100
827	68 39 29	28.7576	90.9395	.001209	.0348	.01100
828	68 55 84	28.7750	90.9945	.001208	.0348	.01099
829	68 72 41	28.7924	91.0494	.001206	.0347	.01098
830	68 89 00	28.8097	91.1043	.001205	.0347	.01098
831	69 05 61	28.8271	91.1592	.001203	.0347	.01097
832	69 22 24	28.8444	91.2140	.001202	.0347	.01096
833	69 38 89	28.8617	91.2688	.001200	.0346	.01096
834	69 55 56	28.8791	91.3236	.001199	.0346	.01095
835	69 72 25	28.8964	91.3783	.001198	.0346	.01094
836	69 88 96	28.9137	91.4330	.001196	.0346	.01094
837	70 05 69	28.9310	91.4877	.001195	.0346	.01093
838	70 22 44	28.9482	91.5423	.001193	.0345	.01092
839	70 39 21	28.9655	91.5969	.001192	.0345	.01092
840	70 56 00	28.9828	91.6515	.001190	.0345	.01091
841	70 72 81	29.0000	91.7061	.001189	.0345	.01090
842	70 89 64	29.0172	91.7606	.001188	.0345	.01090
843	71 06 49	29.0345	91.8150	.001186	.0344	.01089
844	71 23 36	29.0517	91.8695	.001185	.0344	.01089
845	71 40 25	29.0689	91.9239	.001183	.0344	.01088
846	71 57 16	29.0861	91.9783	.001182	.0344	.01087
847	71 74 09	29.1033	92.0326	.001181	.0344	.01087
848	71 91 04	29.1204	92.0869	.001179	.0343	.01086
849	72 08 01	29.1376	92.1412	.001178	.0343	.01085
850	72 25 00	29.1548	92.1954	.001176	.0343	.01085

N	N²	$\sqrt{N}$	$\sqrt{10N}$	1/N	$1/\sqrt{N}$	$1/\sqrt{10N}$
851	72 42 01	29.1719	92.2497	.001175	.0343	.01084
852	72 59 04	29.1890	92.3038	.001174	.0343	.01083
853	72 76 09	29.2062	92.3580	.001172	.0342	.01083
854	72 93 16	29.2233	92.4121	.001171	.0342	.01082
855	73 10 25	29.2404	92.4662	.001170	.0342	.01081
856	73 27 36	29.2575	92.5203	.001168	.0342	.01081
857	73 44 49	29.2746	92.5743	.001167	.0342	.01080
858	73 61 64	29.2916	92.6283	.001166	.0341	.01080
859	73 78 81	29.3087	92.6823	.001164	.0341	.01079
860	73 96 00	29.3258	92.7362	.001163	.0341	.01078
861	74 13 21	29.3428	92.7901	.001161	.0341	.01078
862	74 30 44	29.3598	92.8440	.001160	.0341	.01077
863	74 47 69	29.3769	92.8978	.001159	.0340	.01076
864	74 64 96	29.3939	92.9516	.001157	.0340	.01076
865	74 82 25	29.4109	93.0054	.001156	.0340	.01075
866	74 99 56	29.4279	93.0591	.001155	.0340	.01075
867	75 16 89	29.4449	93.1128	.001153	.0340	.01074
868	75 34 24	29.4618	93.1665	.001152	.0339	.01073
869	75 51 61	29.4788	93.2202	.001151	.0339	.01073
870	75 69 00	29.4958	93.2738	.001149	.0339	.01072
871	75 86 41	29.5127	93.3274	.001148	.0339	.01071
872	76 03 84	29.5296	93.3809	.001147	.0339	.01071
873	76 21 29	29.5466	93.4345	.001145	.0338	.01070
874	76 38 76	29.5635	93.4880	.001144	.0338	.01070
875	76 56 25	29.5804	93.5414	.001143	.0338	.01069
876	76 73 76	29.5973	93.5949	.001142	.0338	.01068
877	76 91 29	29.6142	93.6483	.001140	.0338	.01068
878	77 08 84	29.6311	93.7017	.001139	.0337	.01067
879	77 26 41	29.6479	93.7550	.001138	.0337	.01067
880	77 44 00	29.6648	93.8083	.001136	.0337	.01066
881	77 61 61	29.6816	93.8616	.001135	.0337	.01065
882	77 79 24	29.6985	93.9149	.001134	.0337	.01065
883	77 96 89	29.7153	93.9681	.001133	.0337	.01064
884	78 14 56	29.7321	94.0213	.001131	.0336	.01064
885	78 32 25	29.7489	94.0744	.001130	.0336	.01063
886	78 49 96	29.7658	94.1276	.001129	.0336	.01062
887	78 67 69	29.7825	94.1807	.001127	.0336	.01062
888	78 85 44	29.7993	94.2338	.001126	.0336	.01061
889	79 03 21	29.8161	94.2868	.001125	.0335	.01061
890	79 21 00	29.8329	94.3398	.001124	.0335	.01060
891	79 38 81	29.8496	94.3928	.001122	.0335	.01059
892	79 56 64	29.8664	94.4458	.001121	.0335	.01059
893	79 74 49	29.8831	94.4987	.001120	.0335	.01058
894	79 92 36	29.8998	94.5516	.001119	.0334	.01058
895	80 10 25	29.9166	94.6044	.001117	.0334	.01057
896	80 28 16	29.9333	94.6573	.001116	.0334	.01056
897	80 46 09	29.9500	94.7101	.001115	.0334	.01056
898	80 64 04	29.9666	94.7629	.001114	.0334	.01055
899	80 82 01	29.9833	94.8156	.001112	.0334	.01055
900	81 00 00	30.0000	94.8683	.001111	.0333	.01054

N	N²	√N	√10N	1/N	1/√N	1/√10N
901	81 18 01	30.0167	94.9210	.001110	.0333	.01054
902	81 36 04	30.0333	94.9737	.001109	.0333	.01053
903	81 54 09	30.0500	95.0263	.001107	.0333	.01052
904	81 72 16	30.0666	95.0789	.001106	.0333	.01052
905	81 90 25	30.0832	95.1315	.001105	.0332	.01051
906	82 08 36	30.0998	95.1840	.001104	.0332	.01051
907	82 26 49	30.1164	95.2365	.001103	.0332	.01050
908	82 44 64	30.1330	95.2890	.001101	.0332	.01049
909	82 62 81	30.1496	95.3415	.001100	.0332	.01049
910	82 81 00	30.1662	95.3939	.001099	.0331	.01048
911	82 99 21	30.1828	95.4463	.001098	.0331	.01048
912	83 17 44	30.1993	95.4987	.001096	.0331	.01047
913	83 35 69	30.2159	95.5510	.001095	.0331	.01047
914	83 53 96	30.2324	95.6033	.001094	.0331	.01046
915	83 72 25	30.2490	95.6556	.001093	.0331	.01045
916	83 90 56	30.2655	95.7079	.001092	.0330	.01045
917	84 08 89	30.2820	95.7601	.001091	.0330	.01044
918	84 27 24	30.2985	95.8123	.001089	.0330	.01044
919	84 45 61	30.3150	95.8645	.001088	.0330	.01043
920	84 64 00	30.3315	95.9166	.001087	.0330	.01043
921	84 82 41	30.3480	95.9687	.001086	.0330	.01042
922	85 00 84	30.3645	96.0208	.001085	.0329	.01041
923	85 19 29	30.3809	96.0729	.001083	.0329	.01041
924	85 37 76	30.3974	96.1249	.001082	.0329	.01040
925	85 56 25	30.4138	96.1769	.001081	.0329	.01040
926	85 74 76	30.4302	96.2289	.001080	.0329	.01039
927	85 93 29	30.4467	96.2808	.001079	.0328	.01039
928	86 11 84	30.4631	96.3328	.001078	.0328	.01038
929	86 30 41	30 4795	96.3846	.001076	.0328	.01038
930	86 49 00	30.4959	96.4365	.001075	.0328	.01037
931	86 67 61	30.5123	96.4883	.001074	.0328	.01036
932	86 86 24	30.5287	96.5401	.001073	.0328	.01036
933	87 04 89	30.5450	96.5919	.001072	.0327	.01035
934	87 23 56	30.5614	96.6437	.001071	.0327	.01055
935	87 42 25	30.5778	96.6954	.001070	.0327	.01034
936	87 60 96	30.5941	96.7471	.001068	.0327	.01034
937	87 79 69	30.6105	96.7988	.001067	.0327	.01033
938	87 98 44	30.6268	96.8504	.001066	.0327	.01033
939	88 17 21	30.6431	96.9020	.001065	.0326	.01032
940	88 36 00	30.6594	96.9536	.001064	.0326	.01031
941	88 54 81	30.6757	97.0052	.001063	.0326	.01031
942	88 73 64	30.6920	97.0567	.001062	.0326	.01030
943	88 92 49	30.7083	97.1082	.001060	.0326	.01030
944	89 11 36	30.7246	97.1597	.001059	.0325	.01029
945	89 30 25	30.7409	97.2111	.001058	.0325	.01029
946	89 49 16	30.7571	97.2625	.001057	.0325	.01028
947	89 68 09	30.7734	97.3139	.001056	.0325	.01028
958	89 87 04	30.7896	97.3653	.001055	.0325	.01027
949	90 06 01	30.8058	97.4166	.001054	.0325	.01027
950	90 25 00	30.8221	97.4679	.001053	.0324	.01026

N	N^2	$\sqrt{N}$	$\sqrt{10N}$	$1/N$	$1/\sqrt{N}$	$1/\sqrt{10N}$
951	90 44 01	30.8383	97.5192	.001052	.0324	.01025
952	90 63 04	30.8545	97.5705	.001050	.0324	.01025
953	90 82 09	30.8707	97.6217	.001049	.0324	.01024
954	91 01 16	30.8869	97.6729	.001048	.0324	.01024
955	91 20 25	30.9031	97.7241	.001047	.0324	.01023
956	91 39 36	30.9192	97.7753	.001046	.0323	.01023
957	91 58 49	30.9354	97.8264	.001045	.0323	.01022
958	91 77 64	30.9516	97.8775	.001044	.0323	.01022
959	91 96 81	30.9677	97.9285	.001043	.0323	.01021
960	92 16 00	30.9839	97.9796	.001042	.0323	.01021
961	92 35 21	31.0000	98.0306	.001041	.0323	.01020
962	92 54 44	31.0161	98.0816	.001040	.0322	.01020
963	92 73 69	31.0322	98.1326	.001038	.0322	.01019
964	92 92 96	31.0483	98.1835	.001037	.0322	.01019
965	93 12 25	31.0644	98.2344	.001036	.0322	.01018
966	93 31 56	31.0805	98.2853	.001035	.0322	.01017
967	93 50 89	31.0966	98.3362	.001034	.0322	.01017
968	93 70 24	31.1127	98.3870	.001033	.0321	.01016
969	93 89 61	31.1288	98.4378	.001032	.0321	.01016
970	94 09 00	31.1448	98.4886	.001031	.0321	.01015
971	94 28 41	31.1609	98.5393	.001030	.0321	.01015
972	94 47 84	31.1769	98.5901	.001029	.0321	.01014
973	94 67 29	31.1929	98.6408	.001028	.0321	.01014
974	94 86 76	31.2090	98.6914	.001027	.0320	.01013
975	95 06 25	31.2250	98.7421	.001026	.0320	.01013
976	95 25 76	31.2410	98.7927	.001025	.0320	.01012
977	95 45 29	31.2570	98.8433	.001024	.0320	.01012
978	95 64 84	31.2730	98.8939	.001022	.0320	.01011
979	95 84 41	31.2890	98.9444	.001021	.0320	.01011
980	96 04 00	31.3050	98.9949	.001020	.0319	.01010
981	96 23 61	31.3209	99.0454	.001019	.0319	.01010
982	96 43 24	31.3369	99.0959	.001018	.0319	.01009
983	96 62 89	31.3528	99.1464	.001017	.0319	.01009
984	96 82 56	31.3688	99.1968	.001016	.0319	.01008
985	97 02 25	31.3847	99.2472	.001015	.0319	.01008
986	97 21 96	31.4006	99.2975	.001014	.0318	.01007
987	97 41 69	31.4166	99.3479	.001013	.0318	.01007
988	97 61 44	31.4325	99.3982	.001012	.0318	.01006
989	97 81 21	31.4484	99.4485	.001011	.0318	.01006
990	98 01 00	31.4643	99.4987	.001010	.0318	.01005
991	98 20 81	31.4802	99.5490	.001009	.0318	.01005
992	98 40 64	31.4960	99.5992	.001008	.0318	.01004
993	98 60 49	31.5119	99.6494	.001007	.0317	.01004
994	98 80 36	31.5278	99.6995	.001006	.0317	.01003
995	99 00 25	31.5436	99.7497	.001005	.0317	.01003
996	99 20 16	31.5595	99.7998	.001004	.0317	.01002
997	99 40 09	31.5753	99.8499	.001003	.0317	.01002
998	99 60 04	31.5911	99.8999	.001002	.0317	.01001
999	99 80 01	31.6070	99.9500	.001001	.0316	.01001
1,000	1 00 00 00	31.6228	100.0000	.001000	.0316	.01000

Tables B and C assume a normal distribution whose standard deviation is equal to 1.00 and whose total area (or N) also equals 1.00. Under these conditions, there are fixed mathematical relationships between values on the base line (as measured in σ units) and areas under the curve (A, B, and C) and also ordinate values (y).

The use of Tables B and C is explained in Chap. 7. Figures $A.1$, $A.2$, $B.1$, and $B.2$ may help to relate the symbols to the normal curve.

Table B is best used when we know a z and want to find a corresponding A, B, or C area, or the ordinate y. Table C is best used when we know any one of the areas A, B, or C and want to find the corresponding z or y. In case any one of these areas is known, it can be readily used to find a corresponding area by means of the following relationships:

$A = B - .50$
$A = .50 - C \qquad (A + C = .50)$
$B = A + .50$
$B = 1.00 - C \qquad (B + C = 1.00)$
$C = .50 - A$
$C = 1.00 - B$

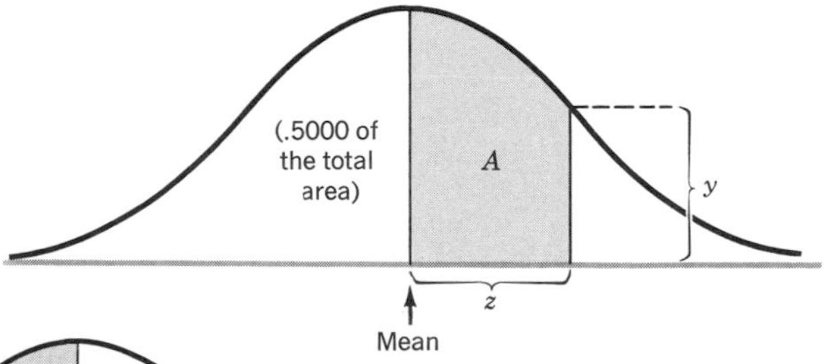

Fig. A.1

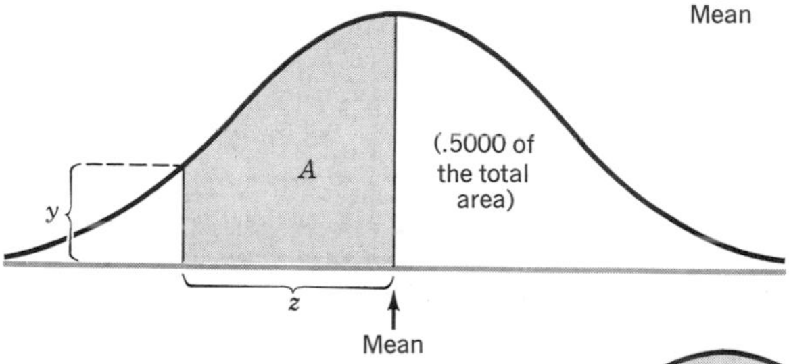

(.5000 of the total area)

A

y

z

Mean

A

(.5000 of the total area)

y

z

Mean

Fig. A.2

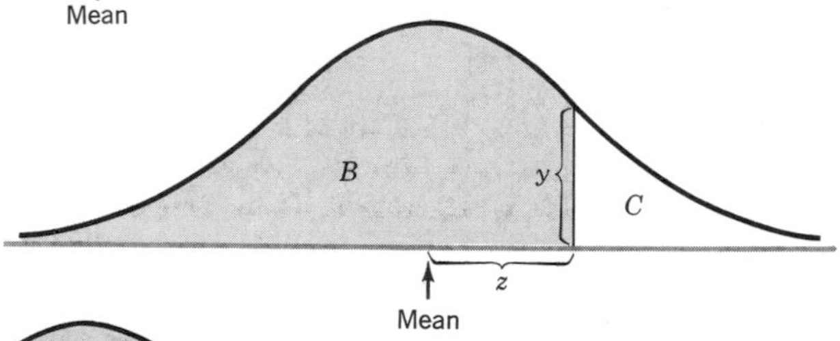

Fig. B.1

B

y

C

z

Mean

C

y

B

z

Mean

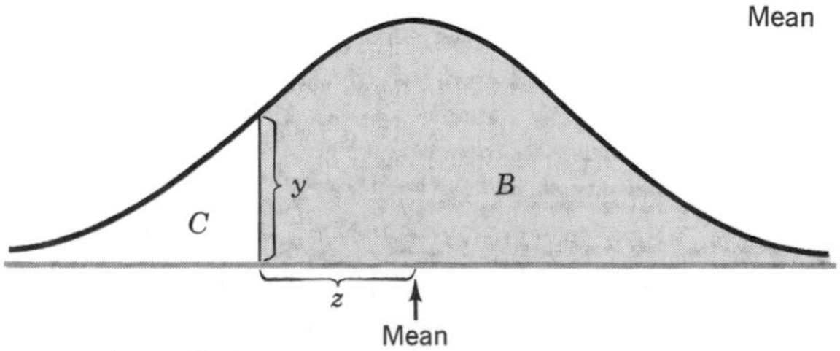

Fig. B.2

Table B   *Areas and ordinates of the normal curve in terms of* x/σ

(1)	(2)	(3)	(4)	(5)
z	A	B	C	y
Standard	Area from	Area in	Area in	Ordinate
score $\left(\dfrac{x}{\sigma}\right)$	mean to $\dfrac{x}{\sigma}$	larger portion	smaller portion	at $\dfrac{x}{\sigma}$
0.00	.0000	.5000	.5000	.3989
0.01	.0040	.5040	.4960	.3989
0.02	.0080	.5080	.4920	.3989
0.03	.0120	.5120	.4880	.3988
0.04	.0160	.5160	.4840	.3986
0.05	.0199	.5199	.4801	.3984
0.06	.0239	.5239	.4761	.3982
0.07	.0279	.5279	.4721	.3980
0.08	.0319	.5319	.4681	.3977
0.09	.0359	.5359	.4641	.3973
0.10	.0398	.5398	.4602	.3970
0.11	.0438	.5438	.4562	.3965
0.12	.0478	.5478	.4522	.3961
0.13	.0517	.5517	.4483	.3956
0.14	.0557	.5557	.4443	.3951
0.15	.0596	.5596	.4404	.3945
0.16	.0636	.5636	.4364	.3939
0.17	.0675	.5675	.4325	.3932
0.18	.0714	.5714	.4286	.3925
0.19	.0753	.5753	.4247	.3918
0.20	.0793	.5793	.4207	.3910
0.21	.0832	.5832	.4168	.3902
0.22	.0871	.5871	.4129	.3894
0.23	.0910	.5910	.4090	.3885
0.24	.0948	.5948	.4052	.3876
0.25	.0987	.5987	.4013	.3867
0.26	.1026	.6026	.3974	.3857
0.27	.1064	.6064	.3936	.3847
0.28	.1103	.6103	.3897	.3836
0.29	.1141	.6141	.3859	.3825
0.30	.1179	.6179	.3821	.3814
0.31	.1217	.6217	.3783	.3802
0.32	.1255	.6255	.3745	.3790
0.33	.1293	.6293	.3707	.3778
0.34	.1331	.6331	.3669	.3765
0.35	.1368	.6368	.3632	.3752
0.36	.1406	.6406	.3594	.3739
0.37	.1443	.6443	.3557	.3725
0.38	.1480	.6480	.3520	.3712
0.39	.1517	.6517	.3483	.3697
0.40	.1554	.6554	.3446	.3683

Source: A. L. Edwards. *Statistical Methods for the Behavioral Sciences.* New York: Holt, 1954. Reprinted by permission of author and publisher.

(1)	(2)	(3)	(4)	(5)
z	A	B	C	y
Standard	Area from	Area in	Area in	Ordinate
score $\left(\dfrac{x}{\sigma}\right)$	mean to $\dfrac{x}{\sigma}$	larger portion	smaller portion	at $\dfrac{x}{\sigma}$
0.41	.1591	.6591	.3409	.3668
0.42	.1628	.6628	.3372	.3653
0.43	.1664	.6664	.3336	.3637
0.44	.1700	.6700	.3300	.3621
0.45	.1736	.6736	.3264	.3605
0.46	.1772	.6772	.3228	.3589
0.47	.1808	.6808	.3192	.3572
0.48	.1844	.6844	.3156	.3555
0.49	.1879	.6879	.3121	.3538
0.50	.1915	.6915	.3085	.3521
0.51	.1950	.6950	.3050	.3503
0.52	.1985	.6985	.3015	.3485
0.53	.2019	.7019	.2981	.3467
0.54	.2054	.7054	.2946	.3448
0.55	.2088	.7088	.2912	.3429
0.56	.2123	.7123	.2877	.3410
0.57	.2157	.7157	.2843	.3391
0.58	.2190	.7190	.2810	.3372
0.59	.2224	.7224	.2776	.3352
0.60	.2257	.7257	.2743	.3332
0.61	.2291	.7291	.2709	.3312
0.62	.2324	.7324	.2676	.3292
0.63	.2357	.7357	.2643	.3271
0.64	.2389	.7389	.2611	.3251
0.65	.2422	.7422	.2578	.3230
0.66	.2454	.7454	.2546	.3209
0.67	.2486	.7486	.2514	.3187
0.68	.2517	.7517	.2483	.3166
0.69	.2549	.7549	.2451	.3144
0.70	.2580	.7580	.2420	.3123
0.71	.2611	.7611	.2389	.3101
0.72	.2642	.7642	.2358	.3079
0.73	.2673	.7673	.2327	.3056
0.74	.2704	.7704	.2296	.3034
0.75	.2734	.7734	.2266	.3011
0.76	.2764	.7764	.2236	.2989
0.77	.2794	.7794	.2206	.2966
0.78	.2823	.7823	.2177	.2943
0.79	.2852	.7852	.2148	.2920
0.80	.2881	.7881	.2119	.2897
0.81	.2910	.7910	.2090	.2874
0.82	.2939	.7939	.2061	.2850
0.83	.2967	.7967	.2033	.2827

(1)	(2)	(3)	(4)	(5)
z	*A*	*B*	*C*	*y*
Standard	*Area from*	*Area in*	*Area in*	*Ordinate*
score $\left(\dfrac{x}{\sigma}\right)$	*mean to* $\dfrac{x}{\sigma}$	*larger portion*	*smaller portion*	*at* $\dfrac{x}{\sigma}$
0.84	.2995	.7995	.2005	.2803
0.85	.3023	.8023	.1977	.2780
0.86	.3051	.8051	.1949	.2756
0.87	.3078	.8078	.1922	.2732
0.88	.3106	.8106	.1894	.2709
0.89	.3133	.8133	.1867	.2685
0.90	.3159	.8159	.1841	.2661
0.91	.3186	.8186	.1814	.2637
0.92	.3212	.8212	.1788	.2613
0.93	.3238	.8238	.1762	.2589
0.94	.3264	.8264	.1736	.2565
0.95	.3289	.8289	.1711	.2541
0.96	.3315	.8315	.1685	.2516
0.97	.3340	.8340	.1660	.2492
0.98	.3365	.8365	.1635	.2468
0.99	.3389	.8389	.1611	.2444
1.00	.3413	.8413	.1587	.2420
1.01	.3438	.8438	.1562	.2396
1.02	.3461	.8461	.1539	.2371
1.03	.3485	.8485	.1515	.2347
1.04	.3508	.8508	.1492	.2323
1.05	.3531	.8531	.1469	.2299
1.06	.3554	.8554	.1446	.2275
1.07	.3577	.8577	.1423	.2251
1.08	.3599	.8599	.1401	.2227
1.09	.3621	.8621	.1379	.2203
1.10	.3643	.8643	.1357	.2179
1.11	.3665	.8665	.1335	.2155
1.12	.3686	.8686	.1314	.2131
1.13	.3708	.8708	.1292	.2107
1.14	.3729	.8729	.1271	.2083
1.15	.3749	.8749	.1251	.2059
1.16	.3770	.8770	.1230	.2036
1.17	.3790	.8790	.1210	.2012
1.18	.3810	.8810	.1190	.1989
1.19	.3830	.8830	.1170	.1965
1.20	.3849	.8849	.1151	.1942
1.21	.3869	.8869	.1131	.1919
1.22	.3888	.8888	.1112	.1895
1.23	.3907	.8907	.1093	.1872
1.24	.3925	.8925	.1075	.1849
1.25	.3944	.8944	.1056	.1826
1.26	.3962	.8962	.1038	.1804

Table B   Areas and ordinates of the normal curve in terms of x/σ (continued)

(1) z Standard score $\left(\dfrac{x}{\sigma}\right)$	(2) A Area from mean to $\dfrac{x}{\sigma}$	(3) B Area in larger portion	(4) C Area in smaller portion	(5) y Ordinate at $\dfrac{x}{\sigma}$
1.27	.3980	.8980	.1020	.1781
1.28	.3997	.8997	.1003	.1758
1.29	.4015	.9015	.0985	.1736
1.30	.4032	.9032	.0968	.1714
1.31	.4049	.9049	.0951	.1691
1.32	.4066	.9066	.0934	.1669
1.33	.4082	.9082	.0918	.1647
1.34	.4099	.9099	.0901	.1626
1.35	.4115	.9115	.0885	.1604
1.36	.4131	.9131	.0869	.1582
1.37	.4147	.9147	.0853	.1561
1.38	.4162	.9162	.0838	.1539
1.39	.4177	.9177	.0823	.1518
1.40	.4192	.9192	.0808	.1497
1.41	.4207	.9207	.0793	.1476
1.42	.4222	.9222	.0778	.1456
1.43	.4236	.9236	.0764	.1435
1.44	.4251	.9251	.0749	.1415
1.45	.4265	.9265	.0735	.1394
1.46	.4279	.9279	.0721	.1374
1.47	.4292	.9292	.0708	.1354
1.48	.4306	.9306	.0694	.1334
1.49	.4319	.9319	.0681	.1315
1.50	.4332	.9332	.0668	.1295
1.51	.4345	.9345	.0655	.1276
1.52	.4357	.9357	.0643	.1257
1.53	.4370	.9370	.0630	.1238
1.54	.4382	.9382	.0618	.1219
1.55	.4394	.9394	.0606	.1200
1.56	.4406	.9406	.0594	.1182
1.57	.4418	.9418	.0582	.1163
1.58	.4429	.9429	.0571	.1145
1.59	.4441	.9441	.0559	.1127
1.60	.4452	.9452	.0548	.1109
1.61	.4463	.9463	.0537	.1092
1.62	.4474	.9474	.0526	.1074
1.63	.4484	.9484	.0516	.1057
1.64	.4495	.9495	.0505	.1040
1.65	.4505	.9505	.0495	.1023
1.66	.4515	.9515	.0485	.1006
1.67	.4525	.9525	.0475	.0989
1.68	.4535	.9535	.0465	.0973
1.69	.4545	.9545	.0455	.0957

(1)	(2)	(3)	(4)	(5)
z	A	B	C	y
Standard score $\left(\dfrac{x}{\sigma}\right)$	Area from mean to $\dfrac{x}{\sigma}$	Area in larger portion	Area in smaller portion	Ordinate at $\dfrac{x}{\sigma}$
1.70	.4554	.9554	.0446	.0940
1.71	.4564	.9564	.0436	.0925
1.72	.4573	.9573	.0427	.0909
1.73	.4582	.9582	.0418	.0893
1.74	.4591	.9591	.0409	.0878
1.75	.4599	.9599	.0401	.0863
1.76	.4608	.9608	.0392	.0848
1.77	.4616	.9616	.0384	.0833
1.78	.4625	.9625	.0375	.0818
1.79	.4633	.9633	.0367	.0804
1.80	.4641	.9641	.0359	.0790
1.81	.4649	.9649	.0351	.0775
1.82	.4656	.9656	.0344	.0761
1.83	.4664	.9664	.0336	.0748
1.84	.4671	.9671	.0329	.0734
1.85	.4678	.9678	.0322	.0721
1.86	.4686	.9686	.0314	.0707
1.87	.4693	.9693	.0307	.0694
1.88	.4699	.9699	.0301	.0681
1.89	.4706	.9706	.0294	.0669
1.90	.4713	.9713	.0287	.0656
1.91	.4719	.9719	.0281	.0644
1.92	.4726	.9726	.0274	.0632
1.93	.4732	.9732	.0268	.0620
1.94	.4738	.9738	.0262	.0608
1.95	.4744	.9744	.0256	.0596
1.96	.4750	.9750	.0250	.0584
1.97	.4756	.9756	.0244	.0573
1.98	.4761	.9761	.0239	.0562
1.99	.4767	.9767	.0233	.0551
2.00	.4772	.9772	.0228	.0540
2.01	.4778	.9778	.0222	.0529
2.02	.4783	.9783	.0217	.0519
2.03	.4788	.9788	.0212	.0508
2.04	.4793	.9793	.0207	.0498
2.05	.4798	.9798	.0202	.0488
2.06	.4803	.9803	.0197	.0478
2.07	.4808	.9808	.0192	.0468
2.08	.4812	.9812	.0188	.0459
2.09	.4817	.9817	.0183	.0449
2.10	.4821	.9821	.0179	.0440
2.11	.4826	.9826	.0174	.0431
2.12	.4830	.9830	.0170	.0422

Table B   Areas and ordinates of the normal curve in terms of x/σ (continued)

(1) z Standard score $\left(\frac{x}{\sigma}\right)$	(2) A Area from mean to $\frac{x}{\sigma}$	(3) B Area in larger portion	(4) C Area in smaller portion	(5) y Ordinate at $\frac{x}{\sigma}$
2.13	.4834	.9834	.0166	.0413
2.14	.4838	.9838	.0162	.0404
2.15	.4842	.9842	.0158	.0396
2.16	.4846	.9846	.0154	.0387
2.17	.4850	.9850	.0150	.0379
2.18	.4854	.9854	.0146	.0371
2.19	.4857	.9857	.0143	.0363
2.20	.4861	.9861	.0139	.0355
2.21	.4864	.9864	.0136	.0347
2.22	.4868	.9868	.0132	.0339
2.23	.4871	.9871	.0129	.0332
2.24	.4875	.9875	.0125	.0325
2.25	.4878	.9878	.0122	.0317
2.26	.4881	.9881	.0119	.0310
2.27	.4884	.9884	.0116	.0303
2.28	.4887	.9887	.0113	.0297
2.29	.4890	.9890	.0110	.0290
2.30	.4893	.9893	.0107	.0283
2.31	.4896	.9896	.0104	.0277
2.32	.4898	.9898	.0102	.0270
2.33	.4901	.9901	.0099	.0264
2.34	.4904	.9904	.0096	.0258
2.35	.4906	.9906	.0094	.0252
2.36	.4909	.9909	.0091	.0246
2.37	.4911	.9911	.0089	.0241
2.38	.4913	.9913	.0087	.0235
2.39	.4916	.9916	.0084	.0229
2.40	.4918	.9918	.0082	.0224
2.41	.4920	.9920	.0080	.0219
2.42	.4922	.9922	.0078	.0213
2.43	.4925	.9925	.0075	.0208
2.44	.4927	.9927	.0073	.0203
2.45	.4929	.9929	.0071	.0198
2.46	.4931	.9931	.0069	.0194
2.47	.4932	.9932	.0068	.0189
2.48	.4934	.9934	.0066	.0184
2.49	.4936	.9936	.0064	.0180
2.50	.4938	.9938	.0062	.0175
2.51	.4940	.9940	.0060	.0171
2.52	.4941	.9941	.0059	.0167
2.53	.4943	.9943	.0057	.0163
2.54	.4945	.9945	.0055	.0158
2.55	.4946	.9946	.0054	.0154

(1)	(2)	(3)	(4)	(5)
z	A	B	C	y
Standard score $\left(\dfrac{x}{\sigma}\right)$	Area from mean to $\dfrac{x}{\sigma}$	Area in larger portion	Area in smaller portion	Ordinate at $\dfrac{x}{\sigma}$
2.56	.4948	.9948	.0052	.0151
2.57	.4949	.9949	.0051	.0147
2.58	.4951	.9951	.0049	.0143
2.59	.4952	.9952	.0048	.0139
2.60	.4953	.9953	.0047	.0136
2.61	.4955	.9955	.0045	.0132
2.62	.4956	.9956	.0044	.0129
2.63	.4957	.9957	.0043	.0126
2.64	.4959	.9959	.0041	.0122
2.65	.4960	.9960	.0040	.0119
2.66	.4961	.9961	.0039	.0116
2.67	.4962	.9962	.0038	.0113
2.68	.4963	.9963	.0037	.0110
2.69	.4964	.9964	.0036	.0107
2.70	.4965	.9965	.0035	.0104
2.71	.4966	.9966	.0034	.0101
2.72	.4967	.9967	.0033	.0099
2.73	.4968	.9968	.0032	.0096
2.74	.4969	.9969	.0031	.0093
2.75	.4970	.9970	.0030	.0091
2.76	.4971	.9971	.0029	.0088
2.77	.4972	.9972	.0028	.0086
2.78	.4973	.9973	.0027	.0084
2.79	.4974	.9974	.0026	.0081
2.80	.4974	.9974	.0026	.0079
2.81	.4975	.9975	.0025	.0077
2.82	.4976	.9976	.0024	.0075
2.83	.4977	.9977	.0023	.0073
2.84	.4977	.9977	.0023	.0071
2.85	.4978	.9978	.0022	.0069
2.86	.4979	.9979	.0021	.0067
2.87	.4979	.9979	.0021	.0065
2.88	.4980	.9980	.0020	.0063
2.89	.4981	.9981	.0019	.0061
2.90	.4981	.9981	.0019	.0060
2.91	.4982	.9982	.0018	.0058
2.92	.4982	.9982	.0018	.0056
2.93	.4983	.9983	.0017	.0055
2.94	.4984	.9984	.0016	.0053
2.95	.4984	.9984	.0016	.0051
2.96	.4985	.9985	.0015	.0050
2.97	.4985	.9985	.0015	.0048
2.98	.4986	.9986	.0014	.0047
2.99	.4986	.9986	.0014	.0046

(1) z Standard score $\left(\dfrac{x}{\sigma}\right)$	(2) A Area from mean to $\dfrac{x}{\sigma}$	(3) B Area in larger portion	(4) C Area in smaller portion	(5) y Ordinate at $\dfrac{x}{\sigma}$
3.00	.4987	.9987	.0013	.0044
3.01	.4987	.9987	.0013	.0043
3.02	.4987	.9987	.0013	.0042
3.03	.4988	.9988	.0012	.0040
3.04	.4988	.9988	.0012	.0039
3.05	.4989	.9989	.0011	.0038
3.06	.4989	.9989	.0011	.0037
3.07	.4989	.9989	.0011	.0036
3.08	.4990	.9990	.0010	.0035
3.09	.4990	.9990	.0010	.0034
2.10	.4990	.9990	.0010	.0033
3.11	.4991	.9991	.0009	.0032
3.12	.4991	.9991	.0009	.0031
3.13	.4991	.9991	.0009	.0030
3.14	.4992	.9992	.0008	.0029
3.15	.4992	.9992	.0008	.0028
3.16	.4992	.9992	.0008	.0027
3.17	.4992	.9992	.0008	.0026
3.18	.4993	.9993	.0007	.0025
3.19	.4993	.9993	.0007	.0025
3.20	.4993	.9993	.0007	.0024
3.21	.4993	.9993	.0007	.0023
3.22	.4994	.9994	.0006	.0022
3.23	.4994	.9994	.0006	.0022
3.24	.4994	.9994	.0006	.0021
3.30	.4995	.9995	.0005	.0017
3.40	.4997	.9997	.0003	.0012
3.50	.4998	.9998	.0002	.0009
3.60	.4998	.9998	.0002	.0006
3.70	.4999	.9999	.0001	.0004

Table C **Standard scores (or deviates) and ordinates corresponding to divisions of the area under the normal curve into a larger proportion (B) and a smaller proportion (C); also the value $\sqrt{BC}$**

B The larger area	z Standard score	y Ordinate	$\sqrt{BC}$	C The smaller area
.500	.0000	.3989	.5000	.500
.505	.0125	.3989	.5000	.495
.510	.0251	.3988	.4999	.490
.515	.0376	.3987	.4998	.485
.520	.0502	.3984	.4996	.480
.525	.0627	.3982	.4994	.475
.530	.0753	.3978	.4991	.470
.535	.0878	.3974	.4988	.465
.540	.1004	.3969	.4984	.460
.545	.1130	.3964	.4980	.455
.550	.1257	.3958	.4975	.450
.555	.1383	.3951	.4970	.445
.560	.1510	.3944	.4964	.440
.565	.1637	.3936	.4958	.435
.570	.1764	.3928	.4951	.430
.575	.1891	.3919	.4943	.425
.580	.2019	.3909	.4936	.420
.585	.2147	.3899	.4927	.415
.590	.2275	.3887	.4918	.410
.595	.2404	.3876	.4909	.405
.600	.2533	.3863	.4899	.400
.605	.2663	.3850	.4889	.395
.610	.2793	.3837	.4877	.390
.615	.2924	.3822	.4867	.385
.620	.3055	.3808	.4854	.380
.625	.3186	.3792	.4841	.375
.630	.3319	.3776	.4828	.370
.635	.3451	.3759	.4814	.365
.640	.3585	.3741	.4800	.360
.645	.3719	.3723	.4785	.355
.650	.3853	.3704	.4770	.350
.655	.3989	.3684	.4754	.345
.660	.4125	.3664	.4737	.340
.665	.4261	.3643	.4720	.335
.670	.4399	.3621	.4702	.330
.675	.4538	.3599	.4684	.325
.680	.4677	.3576	.4665	.320
.685	.4817	.3552	.4645	.315
.690	.4959	.3528	.4625	.310
.695	.5101	.3503	.4604	.305
.700	.5244	.3477	.4583	.300
.705	.5388	.3450	.4560	.295
.710	.5534	.3423	.4538	.290
.715	.5681	.3395	.4514	.285
.720	.5828	.3366	.4490	.280

Table C **Standard scores (or deviates) and ordinates corresponding to divisions of the area under the normal curve into a larger proportion (B) and a smaller proportion (C); also the value $\sqrt{BC}$ (continued)**

B The larger area	z Standard score	y Ordinate	$\sqrt{BC}$	C The smaller area
.725	.5978	.3337	.4465	.275
.730	.6128	.3306	.4440	.270
.735	.6280	.3275	.4413	.265
.740	.6433	.3244	.4386	.260
.745	.6588	.3211	.4359	.255
.750	.6745	.3178	.4330	.250
.755	.6903	.3144	.4301	.245
.760	.7063	.3109	.4271	.240
.765	.7225	.3073	.4240	.235
.770	.7388	.3036	.4208	.230
.775	.7554	.2999	.4176	.225
.780	.7722	.2961	.4142	.220
.785	.7892	.2922	.4108	.215
.790	.8064	.2882	.4073	.210
.795	.8239	.2841	.4037	.205
.800	.8416	.2800	.4000	.200
.805	.8596	.2757	.3962	.195
.810	.8779	.2714	.3923	.190
.815	.8965	.2669	.3883	.185
.820	.9154	.2624	.3842	.180
.825	.9346	.2578	.3800	.175
.830	.9542	.2531	.3756	.170
.835	.9741	.2482	.3712	.165
.840	.9945	.2433	.3666	.160
.845	1.0152	.2383	.3619	.155
.850	1.0364	.2332	.3571	.150
.855	1.0581	.2279	.3521	.145
.860	1.0803	.2226	.3470	.140
.865	1.1031	.2171	.3417	.135
.870	1.1264	.2115	.3363	.130
.875	1.1503	.2059	.3307	.125
.880	1.1750	.2000	.3250	.120
.885	1.2004	.1941	.3190	.115
.890	1.2265	.1880	.3129	.110
.895	1.2536	.1818	.3066	.105
.900	1.2816	.1755	.3000	.100
.905	1.3106	.1690	.2932	.095
.910	1.3408	.1624	.2862	.090
.915	1.3722	.1556	.2789	.085
.920	1.4051	.1487	.2713	.080
.925	1.4395	.1416	.2634	.075
.930	1.4757	.1343	.2551	.070
.935	1.5141	.1268	.2465	.065
.940	1.5548	.1191	.2375	.060
.945	1.5982	.1112	.2280	.055

Table C **Standard scores (or deviates) and ordinates corresponding to divisions of the area under the normal curve into a larger proportion (B) and a smaller proportion (C); also the value $\sqrt{BC}$ (continued)**

B The larger area	z Standard score	y Ordinate	$\sqrt{BC}$	C The smaller area
.950	1.6449	.1031	.2179	.050
.955	1.6954	.0948	.2073	.045
.960	1.7507	.0862	.1960	.040
.965	1.8119	.0773	.1838	.035
.970	1.8808	.0680	.1706	.030
.975	1.9600	.0584	.1561	.025
.980	2.0537	.0484	.1400	.020
.985	2.1701	.0379	.1226	.015
.990	2.3263	.0267	.0995	.010
.995	2.5758	.0145	.0705	.005
.996	2.6521	.0118	.0631	.004
.997	2.7478	.0091	.0547	.003
.998	2.8782	.0063	.0447	.002
.999	3.0902	.0034	.0316	.001
.9995	3.2905	.0018	.0224	.0005

Table D **Coefficients of correlation and t ratios significant at the .05 level (lightface type) and at the .01 level (boldface type) for varying degrees of freedom***

Degrees of freedom	Number of variables									t
	2	3	4	5	6	7	9	13	25	
1	.997	.999	.999	.999	1.000	1.000	1.000	1.000	1.000	12.706
	1.000	**1.000**	**1.000**	**1.000**	**1.000**	**1.000**	**1.000**	**1.000**	**1.000**	**63.657**
2	.950	.975	.983	.987	.990	.992	.994	.996	.998	4.303
	.990	**.995**	**.997**	**.998**	**.998**	**.998**	**.999**	**.999**	**1.000**	**9.925**
3	.878	.930	.950	.961	.968	.973	.979	.986	.993	3.182
	.959	**.976**	**.983**	**.987**	**.990**	**.991**	**.993**	**.995**	**.998**	**5.841**
4	.811	.881	.912	.930	.942	.950	.961	.973	.986	2.776
	.917	**.949**	**.962**	**.970**	**.975**	**.979**	**.984**	**.989**	**.994**	**4.604**
5	.754	.836	.874	.898	.914	.925	.941	.958	.978	2.571
	.874	**.917**	**.937**	**.949**	**.957**	**.963**	**.971**	**.980**	**.989**	**4.032**
6	.707	.795	.839	.867	.886	.900	.920	.943	.969	2.447
	.834	**.886**	**.911**	**.927**	**.938**	**.946**	**.957**	**.969**	**.983**	**3.707**
7	.666	.758	.807	.838	.860	.876	.900	.927	.960	2.365
	.798	**.855**	**.885**	**.904**	**.918**	**.928**	**.942**	**.958**	**.977**	**3.499**
8	.632	.726	.777	.811	.835	.854	.880	.912	.950	2.306
	.765	**.827**	**.860**	**.882**	**.898**	**.909**	**.926**	**.946**	**.970**	**3.355**
9	.602	.697	.750	.786	.812	.832	.861	.897	.941	2.262
	.735	**.800**	**.836**	**.861**	**.878**	**.891**	**.911**	**.934**	**.963**	**3.250**
10	.576	.671	.726	.763	.790	.812	.843	.882	.932	2.228
	.708	**.776**	**.814**	**.840**	**.859**	**.874**	**.895**	**.922**	**.955**	**3.169**
11	.553	.648	.703	.741	.770	.792	.826	.868	.922	2.201
	.684	**.753**	**.793**	**.821**	**.841**	**.857**	**.880**	**.910**	**.948**	**3.106**
12	.532	.627	.683	.722	.751	.774	.809	.854	.913	2.179
	.661	**.732**	**.773**	**.802**	**.824**	**.841**	**.866**	**.898**	**.940**	**3.055**
13	.514	.608	.664	.703	.733	.757	.794	.840	.904	2.160
	.641	**.712**	**.755**	**.785**	**.807**	**.825**	**.852**	**.886**	**.932**	**3.012**
14	.497	.590	.646	.686	.717	.741	.779	.828	.895	2.145
	.623	**.694**	**.737**	**.768**	**.792**	**.810**	**.838**	**.875**	**.924**	**2.977**
15	.482	.574	.630	.670	.701	.726	.765	.815	.886	2.131
	.606	**.677**	**.721**	**.752**	**.776**	**.796**	**.825**	**.864**	**.917**	**2.947**
16	.468	.559	.615	.655	.686	.712	.751	.803	.878	2.120
	.590	**.662**	**.706**	**.738**	**.762**	**.782**	**.813**	**.853**	**.909**	**2.921**
17	.456	.545	.601	.641	.673	.698	.738	.792	.869	2.110
	.575	**.647**	**.691**	**.724**	**.749**	**.769**	**.800**	**.842**	**.902**	**2.898**
18	.444	.532	.587	.628	.660	.686	.726	.781	.861	2.101
	.561	**.633**	**.678**	**.710**	**.736**	**.756**	**.789**	**.832**	**.894**	**2.878**
19	.433	.520	.575	.615	.647	.674	.714	.770	.853	2.093
	.549	**.620**	**.665**	**.698**	**.723**	**.744**	**.778**	**.822**	**.887**	**2.861**
20	.423	.509	.563	.604	.636	.662	.703	.760	.845	2.086
	.537	**.608**	**.652**	**.685**	**.712**	**.733**	**.767**	**.812**	**.880**	**2.845**
21	.413	.498	.552	.592	.624	.651	.693	.750	.837	2.080
	.526	**.596**	**.641**	**.674**	**.700**	**.722**	**.756**	**.803**	**.873**	**2.831**
22	.404	.488	.542	.582	.614	.640	.682	.740	.830	2.074
	.515	**.585**	**.630**	**.663**	**.690**	**.712**	**.746**	**.794**	**.866**	**2.819**
23	.396	.479	.532	.572	.604	.630	.673	.731	.823	2.069
	.505	**.574**	**.619**	**.652**	**.679**	**.701**	**.736**	**.785**	**.859**	**2.807**

*Adapted from Wallace, H. A., and Snedecor, G. W. *Correlation and Machine Calculation*. Ames, Iowa: Iowa State College, 1931, by courtesy of the authors.

Degrees of freedom	Number of variables									*t*
	2	3	4	5	6	7	9	13	25	
24	.388	.470	.523	.562	.594	.621	.663	.722	.815	2.064
	.496	**.565**	**.609**	**.642**	**.669**	**.692**	**.727**	**.776**	**.852**	**2.797**
25	.381	.462	.514	.553	.585	.612	.654	.714	.808	2.060
	.487	**.555**	**.600**	**.633**	**.660**	**.682**	**.718**	**.768**	**.846**	**2.787**
26	.374	.454	.506	.545	.576	.603	.645	.706	.802	2.056
	.478	**.546**	**.590**	**.624**	**.651**	**.673**	**.709**	**.760**	**.839**	**2.779**
27	.367	.446	.498	.536	.568	.594	.637	.698	.795	2.052
	.470	**.538**	**.582**	**.615**	**.642**	**.664**	**.701**	**.752**	**.833**	**2.771**
28	.361	.439	.490	.529	.560	.586	.629	.690	.788	2.048
	.463	**.530**	**.573**	**.606**	**.634**	**.656**	**.692**	**.744**	**.827**	**2.763**
29	.355	.432	.482	.521	.552	.579	.621	.682	.782	2.045
	.456	**.522**	**.565**	**.598**	**.625**	**.648**	**.685**	**.737**	**.821**	**2.756**
30	.349	.426	.476	.514	.545	.571	.614	.675	.776	2.042
	.449	**.514**	**.558**	**.591**	**.618**	**.640**	**.677**	**.729**	**.815**	**2.750**
35	.325	.397	.445	.482	.512	.538	.580	.642	.746	2.030
	.418	**.481**	**.523**	**.556**	**.582**	**.605**	**.642**	**.696**	**.786**	**2.724**
40	.304	.373	.419	.455	.484	.509	.551	.613	.720	2.021
	.393	**.454**	**.494**	**.526**	**.552**	**.575**	**.612**	**.667**	**.761**	**2.704**
45	.288	.353	.397	.432	.460	.485	.526	.587	.696	2.014
	.372	**.430**	**.470**	**.501**	**.527**	**.549**	**.586**	**.640**	**.737**	**2.690**
50	.273	.336	.379	.412	.440	.464	.504	.565	.674	2.008
	.354	**.410**	**.449**	**.479**	**.504**	**.526**	**.562**	**.617**	**.715**	**2.678**
60	.250	.308	.348	.380	.406	.429	.467	.526	.636	2.000
	.325	**.377**	**.414**	**.442**	**.466**	**.488**	**.523**	**.577**	**.677**	**2.660**
70	.233	.286	.324	.354	.379	.401	.438	.495	.604	1.994
	.302	**.351**	**.386**	**.413**	**.436**	**.456**	**.491**	**.544**	**.644**	**2.648**
80	.217	.269	.304	.332	.356	.377	.413	.469	.576	1.990
	.283	**.330**	**.362**	**.389**	**.411**	**.431**	**.464**	**.516**	**.615**	**2.638**
90	.205	.254	.288	.315	.338	.358	.392	.446	.552	1.987
	.267	**.312**	**.343**	**.368**	**.390**	**.409**	**.441**	**.492**	**.590**	**2.632**
100	.195	.241	.274	.300	.322	.341	.374	.426	.530	1.984
	.254	**.297**	**.327**	**.351**	**.372**	**.390**	**.421**	**.470**	**.568**	**2.626**
125	.174	.216	.246	.269	.290	.307	.338	.387	.485	1.979
	.228	**.266**	**.294**	**.316**	**.335**	**.352**	**.381**	**.428**	**.521**	**2.616**
150	.159	.198	.225	.247	.266	.282	.310	.356	.450	1.976
	.208	**.244**	**.270**	**.290**	**.308**	**.324**	**.351**	**.395**	**.484**	**2.609**
200	.138	.172	.196	.215	.231	.246	.271	.312	.398	1.972
	.181	**.212**	**.234**	**.253**	**.269**	**.283**	**.307**	**.347**	**.430**	**2.601**
300	.113	.141	.160	.176	.190	.202	.223	.258	.332	1.968
	.148	**.174**	**.192**	**.208**	**.221**	**.233**	**.253**	**.287**	**.359**	**2.592**
400	.098	.122	.139	.153	.165	.176	.194	.225	.291	1.966
	.128	**.151**	**.167**	**.180**	**.192**	**.202**	**.220**	**.250**	**.315**	**2.588**
500	.088	.109	.124	.137	.148	.157	.174	.202	.262	1.965
	.115	**.135**	**.150**	**.162**	**.172**	**.182**	**.198**	**.225**	**.284**	**2.586**
1,000	.062	.077	.088	.097	.105	.112	.124	.144	.188	1.962
	.081	**.096**	**.106**	**.115**	**.122**	**.129**	**.141**	**.160**	**.204**	**2.581**
∞										1.960
										2.576

Table E Table of chi square*

df	P = .99	.98	.95	.90	.80	.70	.50	.30	.20	.10	.05	.02	.01	.001
1	.000157	.000628	.00393	.0158	.0642	.148	.455	1.074	1.642	2.706	3.841	5.412	6.635	10.827
2	.0201	.0404	.103	.211	.446	.713	1.386	2.408	3.219	4.605	5.991	7.824	9.210	13.815
3	.115	.185	.352	.584	1.005	1.424	2.366	3.665	4.642	6.251	7.815	9.837	11.341	16.268
4	.297	.429	.711	1.064	1.649	2.195	3.357	4.878	5.989	7.779	9.488	11.668	13.277	18.465
5	.554	.752	1.145	1.610	2.343	3.000	4.351	6.064	7.289	9.236	11.070	13.388	15.086	20.517
6	.872	1.134	1.635	2.204	3.070	3.828	5.348	7.231	8.558	10.6645	12.592	15.033	16.812	22.457
7	1.239	1.564	2.167	2.833	3.822	4.671	6.346	8.383	9.803	12.017	14.067	16.622	18.475	24.322
8	1.645	2.032	2.733	3.490	4.594	5.527	7.344	9.524	11.030	13.362	15.507	18.168	20.090	26.125
9	2.088	2.532	3.325	4.168	5.380	6.393	8.343	10.656	12.242	14.684	16.919	19.679	21.666	27.877
10	2.558	3.059	3.940	4.865	6.179	7.267	9.342	11.781	13.442	15.987	18.307	21.161	23.209	29.588
11	3.053	3.609	4.575	5.578	6.989	8.148	10.341	12.899	14.631	17.275	19.675	22.618	24.725	31.264
12	3.571	4.178	5.226	6.304	7.807	9.034	11.340	14.011	15.812	18.549	21.026	24.054	26.217	32.909
13	4.107	4.765	5.892	7.042	8.634	9.926	12.340	15.119	16.985	19.812	22.362	25.472	27.688	34.528
14	4.660	5.368	6.571	7.790	9.467	10.821	13.339	16.222	18.151	21.064	23.685	26.873	29.141	36.123
15	5.229	5.985	7.261	8.547	10.307	11.721	14.339	17.322	19.311	22.307	24.996	28.259	30.578	37.697
16	5.812	6.614	7.962	9.312	11.152	12.624	15.338	18.418	20.465	23.542	26.296	29.633	32.000	39.252
17	6.408	7.255	8.672	10.085	12.002	13.531	16.338	19.511	21.615	24.769	27.587	30.995	33.409	40.790
18	7.015	7.906	9.390	10.865	12.857	14.440	17.338	20.601	22.760	25.989	28.869	32.346	34.805	42.312
19	7.633	8.567	10.117	11.651	13.716	15.352	18.338	21.689	23.900	27.204	30.144	33.687	36.191	43.820
20	8.260	9.237	10.851	12.443	14.578	16.266	19.337	22.775	25.038	28.412	31.410	35.020	37.566	45.315
21	8.897	9.915	11.591	13.240	15.445	17.182	20.337	23.858	26.171	29.615	32.671	36.343	38.932	46.797
22	9.542	10.600	12.338	14.041	16.314	18.101	21.337	24.939	27.301	30.813	33.924	37.659	40.289	48.268
23	10.196	11.293	13.091	14.848	17.187	19.021	22.337	26.018	28.429	32.007	35.172	38.968	41.638	49.728
24	10.856	11.992	13.848	15.659	18.062	19.943	23.337	27.096	29.553	33.196	36.415	40.270	42.980	51.179
25	11.524	12.697	14.611	16.473	18.940	20.867	24.337	28.172	30.675	34.382	37.652	41.566	44.314	52.620
26	12.198	13.409	15.379	17.292	19.820	21.792	25.336	29.246	31.795	35.563	38.885	42.856	45.642	54.052
27	12.879	14.125	16.151	18.114	20.703	22.719	26.336	30.319	32.912	36.741	40.113	44.140	46.963	55.476
28	13.565	14.847	16.928	18.939	21.588	23.647	27.336	31.391	34.027	37.916	41.337	45.419	48.278	56.893
29	14.256	15.574	17.708	19.768	22.475	24.577	28.336	32.461	35.139	39.087	42.557	46.693	49.588	58.302
30	14.953	16.306	18.493	20.599	23.364	25.508	29.336	33.530	36.250	40.256	43.773	47.962	50.892	59.703

*Table E is reprinted from Table III of Fisher's *Statistical Methods for Research Workers*, Oliver & Boyd, Edinburgh and London, 1932, by kind permission of the author and publishers. For df larger than 30, the value from the expression $\sqrt{2x^2} - \sqrt{2df - 1}$ may be interpreted as a t ratio.

Table F .05 (lightface type) and .01 (boldface type) points for the distribution of F*

df_1 degrees of freedom (for greater mean square)

df_2	1	2	3	4	5	6	7	8	9	10	11	12	14	16	20	24	30	40	50	75	100	200	500	∞
1	161	200	216	225	230	234	237	239	241	242	243	244	245	246	248	249	250	251	252	253	253	254	254	254
	4,052	**4,999**	**5,403**	**5,625**	**5,764**	**5,859**	**5,928**	**5,981**	**6,022**	**6,056**	**6,082**	**6,106**	**6,142**	**6,169**	**6,208**	**6,234**	**6,258**	**6,286**	**6,302**	**6,323**	**6,334**	**6,352**	**6,361**	**6,366**
2	18.51	19.00	19.16	19.25	19.30	19.33	19.36	19.37	19.38	19.39	19.40	19.41	19.42	19.43	19.44	19.45	19.46	19.47	19.47	19.48	19.49	19.49	19.50	19.50
	98.49	**99.00**	**99.17**	**99.25**	**99.30**	**99.33**	**99.34**	**99.36**	**99.38**	**99.40**	**99.41**	**99.42**	**99.43**	**99.44**	**99.45**	**99.46**	**99.47**	**99.48**	**99.48**	**99.49**	**99.49**	**99.49**	**99.50**	**99.50**
3	10.13	9.55	9.28	9.12	9.01	8.94	8.88	8.84	8.81	8.78	8.76	8.74	8.71	8.69	8.66	8.64	8.62	8.60	8.58	8.57	8.56	8.54	8.54	8.53
	34.12	**30.82**	**29.46**	**28.71**	**28.24**	**27.91**	**27.67**	**27.49**	**27.34**	**27.23**	**27.13**	**27.05**	**26.92**	**26.83**	**26.69**	**26.60**	**26.50**	**26.41**	**26.35**	**26.27**	**26.23**	**26.18**	**26.14**	**26.12**
4	7.71	6.94	6.59	6.39	6.26	6.16	6.09	6.04	6.00	5.96	5.93	5.91	5.87	5.84	5.80	5.77	5.74	5.71	5.70	5.68	5.66	5.65	5.64	5.63
	21.20	**18.00**	**16.69**	**15.98**	**15.52**	**15.21**	**14.98**	**14.80**	**14.66**	**14.54**	**14.45**	**14.37**	**14.24**	**14.15**	**14.02**	**13.93**	**13.83**	**13.74**	**13.69**	**13.61**	**13.57**	**13.52**	**13.48**	**13.46**
5	6.61	5.79	5.41	5.19	5.05	4.95	4.88	4.82	4.78	4.74	4.70	4.68	4.64	4.60	4.56	4.53	4.50	4.46	4.44	4.42	4.40	4.38	4.37	4.36
	16.26	**13.27**	**12.06**	**11.39**	**10.97**	**10.67**	**10.45**	**10.27**	**10.15**	**10.05**	**9.96**	**9.89**	**9.77**	**9.68**	**9.55**	**9.47**	**9.38**	**9.29**	**9.24**	**9.17**	**9.13**	**9.07**	**9.04**	**9.02**
6	5.99	5.14	4.76	4.53	4.39	4.28	4.21	4.15	4.10	4.06	4.03	4.00	3.96	3.92	3.87	3.84	3.81	3.77	3.75	3.72	3.71	3.69	3.68	3.67
	13.74	**10.92**	**9.78**	**9.15**	**8.75**	**8.47**	**8.26**	**8.10**	**7.98**	**7.87**	**7.79**	**7.72**	**7.60**	**7.52**	**7.39**	**7.31**	**7.23**	**7.14**	**7.09**	**7.02**	**6.99**	**6.94**	**6.90**	**6.88**
7	5.59	4.74	4.35	4.12	3.97	3.87	3.79	3.73	3.68	3.63	3.60	3.57	3.52	3.49	3.44	3.41	3.38	3.34	3.32	3.29	3.28	3.25	3.24	3.23
	12.25	**9.55**	**8.45**	**7.85**	**7.46**	**7.19**	**7.00**	**6.84**	**6.71**	**6.62**	**6.54**	**6.47**	**6.35**	**6.27**	**6.15**	**6.07**	**5.98**	**5.90**	**5.85**	**5.78**	**5.75**	**5.70**	**5.67**	**5.65**
8	5.32	4.46	4.07	3.84	3.69	3.58	3.50	3.44	3.39	3.34	3.31	3.28	3.23	3.20	3.15	3.12	3.08	3.05	3.03	3.00	2.98	2.96	2.94	2.93
	11.26	**8.65**	**7.59**	**7.01**	**6.63**	**6.37**	**6.19**	**6.03**	**5.91**	**5.82**	**5.74**	**5.67**	**5.56**	**5.48**	**5.36**	**5.28**	**5.20**	**5.11**	**5.06**	**5.00**	**4.96**	**4.91**	**4.88**	**4.86**
9	5.12	4.26	3.86	3.63	3.48	3.37	3.29	3.23	3.18	3.13	3.10	3.07	3.02	2.98	2.93	2.90	2.86	2.82	2.80	2.77	2.76	2.73	2.72	2.71
	10.56	**8.02**	**6.99**	**6.42**	**6.06**	**5.80**	**5.62**	**5.47**	**5.35**	**5.26**	**5.18**	**5.11**	**5.00**	**4.92**	**4.80**	**4.73**	**4.64**	**4.56**	**4.51**	**4.45**	**4.41**	**4.36**	**4.33**	**4.31**
10	4.96	4.10	3.71	3.48	3.33	3.22	3.14	3.07	3.02	2.97	2.94	2.91	2.86	2.82	2.77	2.74	2.70	2.67	2.64	2.61	2.59	2.56	2.55	2.54
	10.04	**7.56**	**6.55**	**5.99**	**5.64**	**5.39**	**5.21**	**5.06**	**4.95**	**4.85**	**4.78**	**4.71**	**4.60**	**4.52**	**4.41**	**4.33**	**4.25**	**4.17**	**4.12**	**4.05**	**4.01**	**3.96**	**3.93**	**3.91**
11	4.84	3.98	3.59	3.36	3.20	3.09	3.01	2.95	2.90	2.86	2.82	2.79	2.74	2.70	2.65	2.61	2.57	2.53	2.50	2.47	2.45	2.42	2.41	2.40
	9.65	**7.20**	**6.22**	**5.67**	**5.32**	**5.07**	**4.88**	**4.74**	**4.63**	**4.54**	**4.46**	**4.40**	**4.29**	**4.21**	**4.10**	**4.02**	**3.94**	**3.86**	**3.80**	**3.74**	**3.70**	**3.66**	**3.62**	**3.60**
12	4.75	3.88	3.49	3.26	3.11	3.00	2.92	2.85	2.80	2.76	2.72	2.69	2.64	2.60	2.54	2.50	2.46	2.42	2.40	2.36	2.35	2.32	2.31	2.30
	9.33	**6.93**	**5.95**	**5.41**	**5.06**	**4.82**	**4.65**	**4.50**	**4.39**	**4.30**	**4.22**	**4.16**	**4.05**	**3.98**	**3.86**	**3.78**	**3.70**	**3.61**	**3.56**	**3.49**	**3.46**	**3.41**	**3.38**	**3.36**
13	4.67	3.80	3.41	3.18	3.02	2.92	2.84	2.77	2.72	2.67	2.63	2.60	2.55	2.51	2.46	2.42	2.38	2.34	2.32	2.28	2.26	2.24	2.22	2.21
	9.07	**6.70**	**5.74**	**5.20**	**4.86**	**4.62**	**4.44**	**4.30**	**4.19**	**4.10**	**4.02**	**3.96**	**3.85**	**3.78**	**3.67**	**3.59**	**3.51**	**3.42**	**3.37**	**3.30**	**3.27**	**3.21**	**3.18**	**3.16**

*Reproduced from C. W. Snedecor, *Statistical Methods*. Ames, Iowa: Collegiate, 1937. By permission of the author.

Table F   .05 (lightface type) and .01 (boldface type) points for the distribution of F (continued)

df_1 degrees of freedom (for greater mean square)

df_2	1	2	3	4	5	6	7	8	9	10	11	12	14	16	20	24	30	40	50	75	100	200	500	∞	df_2
14	4.60 / 8.86	3.74 / 6.51	3.34 / 5.56	3.11 / 5.03	2.96 / 4.69	2.85 / 4.46	2.77 / 4.28	2.70 / 4.14	2.65 / 4.03	2.60 / 3.94	2.56 / 3.86	2.53 / 3.80	2.48 / 3.70	2.44 / 3.62	2.39 / 3.51	2.35 / 3.43	2.31 / 3.34	2.27 / 3.26	2.24 / 3.21	2.21 / 3.14	2.19 / 3.11	2.16 / 3.06	2.14 / 3.02	2.13 / 3.00	14
15	4.54 / 8.68	3.68 / 6.36	3.29 / 5.42	3.06 / 4.89	2.90 / 4.56	2.79 / 4.32	2.70 / 4.14	2.64 / 4.00	2.59 / 3.89	2.55 / 3.80	2.51 / 3.73	2.48 / 3.67	2.43 / 3.56	2.39 / 3.48	2.33 / 3.36	2.29 / 3.29	2.25 / 3.20	2.21 / 3.12	2.18 / 3.07	2.15 / 3.00	2.12 / 2.97	2.10 / 2.92	2.08 / 2.89	2.07 / 2.87	15
16	4.49 / 8.53	3.63 / 6.23	3.24 / 5.29	3.01 / 4.77	2.85 / 4.44	2.74 / 4.20	2.66 / 4.03	2.59 / 3.89	2.54 / 3.78	2.49 / 3.69	2.45 / 3.61	2.42 / 3.55	2.37 / 3.45	2.33 / 3.37	2.28 / 3.25	2.24 / 3.18	2.20 / 3.10	2.16 / 3.01	2.13 / 2.96	2.09 / 2.89	2.07 / 2.86	2.04 / 2.80	2.02 / 2.77	2.01 / 2.75	16
17	4.45 / 8.40	3.59 / 6.11	3.20 / 5.18	2.96 / 4.67	2.81 / 4.34	2.70 / 4.10	2.62 / 3.93	2.55 / 3.79	2.50 / 3.68	2.45 / 3.59	2.41 / 3.52	2.38 / 3.45	2.33 / 3.35	2.29 / 3.27	2.23 / 3.16	2.19 / 3.08	2.15 / 3.00	2.11 / 2.92	2.08 / 2.86	2.04 / 2.79	2.02 / 2.76	1.99 / 2.70	1.97 / 2.67	1.96 / 2.65	17
18	4.41 / 8.28	3.55 / 6.01	3.16 / 5.09	2.93 / 4.58	2.77 / 4.25	2.66 / 4.01	2.58 / 3.85	2.51 / 3.71	2.46 / 3.60	2.41 / 3.51	2.37 / 3.44	2.34 / 3.37	2.29 / 3.27	2.25 / 3.19	2.19 / 3.07	2.15 / 3.00	2.11 / 2.91	2.07 / 2.83	2.04 / 2.78	2.00 / 2.71	1.98 / 2.68	1.95 / 2.62	1.93 / 2.59	1.92 / 2.57	18
19	4.38 / 8.18	3.52 / 5.93	3.13 / 5.01	2.90 / 4.50	2.74 / 4.17	2.63 / 3.94	2.55 / 3.77	2.48 / 3.63	2.43 / 3.52	2.38 / 3.43	2.34 / 3.36	2.31 / 3.30	2.26 / 3.19	2.21 / 3.12	2.15 / 3.00	2.11 / 2.92	2.07 / 2.84	2.02 / 2.76	2.00 / 2.70	1.96 / 2.63	1.94 / 2.60	1.91 / 2.54	1.90 / 2.51	1.88 / 2.49	19
20	4.35 / 8.10	3.49 / 5.85	3.10 / 4.94	2.87 / 4.43	2.71 / 4.10	2.60 / 3.87	2.52 / 3.71	2.45 / 3.56	2.40 / 3.45	2.35 / 3.37	2.31 / 3.30	2.28 / 3.23	2.23 / 3.13	2.18 / 3.05	2.12 / 2.94	2.08 / 2.86	2.04 / 2.77	1.99 / 2.69	1.96 / 2.63	1.92 / 2.56	1.90 / 2.53	1.87 / 2.47	1.85 / 2.44	1.84 / 2.42	20
21	4.32 / 8.02	3.47 / 5.78	3.07 / 4.87	2.84 / 4.37	2.68 / 4.04	2.57 / 3.81	2.49 / 3.65	2.42 / 3.51	2.37 / 3.40	2.32 / 3.31	2.28 / 3.24	2.25 / 3.17	2.20 / 3.07	2.15 / 2.99	2.09 / 2.88	2.05 / 2.80	2.00 / 2.72	1.96 / 2.63	1.93 / 2.58	1.89 / 2.51	1.87 / 2.47	1.84 / 2.42	1.82 / 2.38	1.81 / 2.36	21
22	4.30 / 7.94	3.44 / 5.72	3.05 / 4.82	2.82 / 4.31	2.66 / 3.99	2.55 / 3.76	2.47 / 3.59	2.40 / 3.45	2.35 / 3.35	2.30 / 3.26	2.26 / 3.18	2.23 / 3.12	2.18 / 3.02	2.13 / 2.94	2.07 / 2.83	2.03 / 2.75	1.98 / 2.67	1.93 / 2.58	1.91 / 2.53	1.87 / 2.46	1.84 / 2.42	1.81 / 2.37	1.80 / 2.33	1.78 / 2.31	22
23	4.28 / 7.88	3.42 / 5.66	3.03 / 4.76	2.80 / 4.26	2.64 / 3.94	2.53 / 3.71	2.45 / 3.54	2.38 / 3.41	2.32 / 3.30	2.28 / 3.21	2.24 / 3.14	2.20 / 3.07	2.14 / 2.97	2.10 / 2.89	2.04 / 2.78	2.00 / 2.70	1.96 / 2.62	1.91 / 2.53	1.88 / 2.48	1.84 / 2.41	1.82 / 2.37	1.79 / 2.32	1.77 / 2.28	1.76 / 2.26	23
24	4.26 / 7.82	3.40 / 5.61	3.01 / 4.72	2.78 / 4.22	2.62 / 3.90	2.51 / 3.67	2.43 / 3.50	2.36 / 3.36	2.30 / 3.25	2.26 / 3.17	2.22 / 3.09	2.18 / 3.03	2.13 / 2.93	2.09 / 2.85	2.02 / 2.74	1.98 / 2.66	1.94 / 2.58	1.89 / 2.49	1.86 / 2.44	1.82 / 2.36	1.80 / 2.33	1.76 / 2.27	1.74 / 2.23	1.73 / 2.21	24
25	4.24 / 7.77	3.38 / 5.57	2.99 / 4.63	2.76 / 4.13	2.60 / 3.86	2.49 / 3.63	2.41 / 3.46	2.34 / 3.32	2.28 / 3.21	2.24 / 3.13	2.20 / 3.05	2.16 / 2.99	2.11 / 2.89	2.06 / 2.81	2.00 / 2.70	1.96 / 2.62	1.92 / 2.54	1.87 / 2.45	1.84 / 2.40	1.80 / 2.32	1.77 / 2.29	1.74 / 2.23	1.72 / 2.19	1.71 / 2.17	25
26	4.22 / 7.72	3.37 / 5.53	2.98 / 4.64	2.74 / 4.14	2.59 / 3.82	2.47 / 3.59	2.39 / 3.42	2.32 / 3.29	2.28 / 3.17	2.22 / 3.09	2.18 / 3.02	2.15 / 2.96	2.10 / 2.86	2.05 / 2.77	1.99 / 2.66	1.95 / 2.58	1.90 / 2.50	1.85 / 2.50	1.82 / 2.36	1.78 / 2.28	1.76 / 2.25	1.72 / 2.19	1.70 / 2.15	1.69 / 2.13	26

Table F *.05 (lightface type) and .01 (boldface type) points for the distribution of F (continued)*

df_1 degrees of freedom (for greater mean square)

df_2	1	2	3	4	5	6	7	8	9	10	11	12	14	16	20	24	30	40	50	75	100	200	500	∞	df_2
27	4.21 / 7.68	3.35 / 5.49	2.96 / 4.60	2.73 / 4.11	2.57 / 3.79	2.46 / 3.56	2.37 / 3.39	2.30 / 3.26	2.25 / 3.14	2.20 / 3.06	2.16 / 2.98	2.13 / 2.93	2.08 / 2.83	2.03 / 2.74	1.97 / 2.63	1.93 / 2.55	1.88 / 2.47	1.84 / 2.38	1.80 / 2.33	1.76 / 2.25	1.74 / 2.21	1.71 / 2.16	1.68 / 2.12	1.67 / 2.10	27
28	4.20 / 7.64	3.34 / 5.45	2.95 / 4.57	2.71 / 4.07	2.56 / 3.76	2.44 / 3.53	2.36 / 3.36	2.29 / 3.23	2.24 / 3.11	2.19 / 3.03	2.15 / 2.95	2.12 / 2.90	2.06 / 2.80	2.02 / 2.71	1.96 / 2.60	1.91 / 2.52	1.87 / 2.44	1.81 / 2.35	1.78 / 2.30	1.75 / 2.22	1.72 / 2.18	1.69 / 2.13	1.67 / 2.09	1.65 / 2.06	28
29	4.18 / 7.60	3.33 / 5.42	2.93 / 4.54	2.70 / 4.04	2.54 / 3.73	2.43 / 3.50	2.35 / 3.33	2.28 / 3.20	2.22 / 3.08	2.18 / 3.00	2.14 / 2.92	2.10 / 2.87	2.05 / 2.77	2.00 / 2.68	1.94 / 2.57	1.90 / 2.49	1.85 / 2.41	1.80 / 2.32	1.77 / 2.27	1.73 / 2.19	1.71 / 2.15	1.68 / 2.10	1.65 / 2.06	1.64 / 2.03	29
30	4.17 / 7.56	3.32 / 5.39	2.92 / 4.51	2.69 / 4.02	2.53 / 3.70	2.42 / 3.47	2.34 / 3.30	2.27 / 3.17	2.21 / 3.06	2.16 / 2.98	2.12 / 2.90	2.09 / 2.84	2.04 / 2.74	1.99 / 2.66	1.93 / 2.55	1.89 / 2.47	1.84 / 2.38	1.79 / 2.29	1.76 / 2.24	1.72 / 2.16	1.69 / 2.13	1.66 / 2.07	1.64 / 2.03	1.62 / 2.01	30
32	4.15 / 7.50	3.30 / 5.34	2.90 / 4.46	2.67 / 3.97	2.51 / 3.66	2.40 / 3.42	2.32 / 3.25	2.25 / 3.12	2.19 / 3.01	2.14 / 2.94	2.10 / 2.86	2.07 / 2.80	2.02 / 2.70	1.97 / 2.62	1.91 / 2.51	1.86 / 2.42	1.82 / 2.34	1.76 / 2.25	1.74 / 2.20	1.69 / 2.12	1.67 / 2.08	1.64 / 2.02	1.61 / 1.98	1.59 / 1.96	32
34	4.13 / 7.44	3.28 / 5.29	2.88 / 4.42	2.65 / 3.93	2.49 / 3.61	2.38 / 3.38	2.30 / 3.21	2.23 / 3.08	2.17 / 2.97	2.12 / 2.89	2.08 / 2.82	2.05 / 2.76	2.00 / 2.66	1.95 / 2.58	1.89 / 2.47	1.84 / 2.38	1.80 / 2.30	1.74 / 2.21	1.71 / 2.15	1.67 / 2.08	1.64 / 2.04	1.61 / 1.98	1.59 / 1.94	1.57 / 1.91	34
36	4.11 / 7.39	3.26 / 5.25	2.86 / 4.38	2.63 / 3.89	2.48 / 3.58	2.36 / 3.35	2.28 / 3.18	2.21 / 3.04	2.15 / 2.94	2.10 / 2.86	2.06 / 2.78	2.03 / 2.72	1.98 / 2.62	1.93 / 2.54	1.87 / 2.43	1.82 / 2.35	1.78 / 2.26	1.72 / 2.17	1.69 / 2.12	1.65 / 2.04	1.62 / 2.00	1.59 / 1.94	1.56 / 1.90	1.55 / 1.87	36
38	4.10 / 7.35	3.25 / 5.21	2.85 / 4.34	2.62 / 3.86	2.46 / 3.54	2.35 / 3.32	2.26 / 3.15	2.19 / 3.02	2.14 / 2.91	2.09 / 2.82	2.05 / 2.75	2.02 / 2.69	1.96 / 2.59	1.92 / 2.51	1.85 / 2.40	1.80 / 2.32	1.76 / 2.22	1.71 / 2.14	1.67 / 2.08	1.63 / 2.00	1.60 / 1.97	1.57 / 1.90	1.54 / 1.86	1.53 / 1.84	38
40	4.08 / 7.31	3.23 / 5.18	2.84 / 4.31	2.61 / 3.83	2.45 / 3.51	2.34 / 3.29	2.25 / 3.12	2.18 / 2.99	2.12 / 2.88	2.07 / 2.80	2.04 / 2.73	2.00 / 2.66	1.95 / 2.56	1.90 / 2.49	1.84 / 2.37	1.79 / 2.29	1.74 / 2.20	1.69 / 2.11	1.66 / 2.05	1.61 / 1.97	1.59 / 1.94	1.55 / 1.88	1.53 / 1.84	1.51 / 1.81	40
42	4.07 / 7.27	3.22 / 5.15	2.83 / 4.29	2.59 / 3.80	2.44 / 3.49	2.32 / 3.26	2.24 / 3.10	2.17 / 2.96	2.11 / 2.86	2.06 / 2.77	2.02 / 2.70	1.99 / 2.64	1.94 / 2.54	1.89 / 2.46	1.82 / 2.35	1.78 / 2.26	1.73 / 2.17	1.68 / 2.08	1.64 / 2.02	1.60 / 1.94	1.57 / 1.91	1.54 / 1.85	1.51 / 1.80	1.49 / 1.78	42
44	4.06 / 7.24	3.21 / 5.12	2.82 / 4.26	2.58 / 3.78	2.43 / 3.46	2.31 / 3.24	2.23 / 3.07	2.16 / 2.94	2.10 / 2.84	2.05 / 2.75	2.01 / 2.68	1.98 / 2.62	1.92 / 2.52	1.88 / 2.44	1.81 / 2.32	1.76 / 2.24	1.72 / 2.15	1.66 / 2.06	1.63 / 2.00	1.58 / 1.92	1.56 / 1.88	1.52 / 1.82	1.50 / 1.78	1.48 / 1.75	44
46	4.05 / 7.21	3.20 / 5.10	2.81 / 4.24	2.57 / 3.76	2.42 / 3.44	2.30 / 3.22	2.22 / 3.05	2.14 / 2.92	2.09 / 2.82	2.04 / 2.73	2.00 / 2.66	1.97 / 2.60	1.91 / 2.50	1.87 / 2.42	1.80 / 2.30	1.75 / 2.22	1.71 / 2.13	1.65 / 2.04	1.62 / 1.98	1.57 / 1.90	1.54 / 1.86	1.51 / 1.80	1.48 / 1.76	1.46 / 1.72	46
48	4.04 / 7.19	3.19 / 5.08	2.80 / 4.22	2.56 / 3.74	2.41 / 3.42	2.30 / 3.20	2.21 / 3.04	2.14 / 2.90	2.08 / 2.80	2.03 / 2.71	1.99 / 2.64	1.96 / 2.58	1.90 / 2.48	1.86 / 2.40	1.79 / 2.28	1.74 / 2.20	1.70 / 2.11	1.64 / 2.02	1.61 / 1.96	1.56 / 1.88	1.53 / 1.84	1.50 / 1.78	1.47 / 1.73	1.45 / 1.70	48

Table F   .05 (lightface type) and .01 (boldface type) points for the distribution of F (continued)

df_1 degrees of freedom (for greater mean square)

df_2	1	2	3	4	5	6	7	8	9	10	11	12	14	16	20	24	30	40	50	75	100	200	500	∞
50	4.03	3.18	2.79	2.56	2.40	2.29	2.20	2.13	2.07	2.02	1.98	1.95	1.90	1.85	1.78	1.74	1.69	1.63	1.60	1.55	1.52	1.48	1.46	1.44
	7.17	**5.06**	**4.20**	**3.72**	**3.41**	**3.18**	**3.02**	**2.88**	**2.78**	**2.70**	**2.62**	**2.56**	**2.46**	**2.39**	**2.26**	**2.18**	**2.10**	**2.00**	**1.94**	**1.86**	**1.82**	**1.76**	**1.71**	**1.68**
55	4.02	3.17	2.78	2.54	2.38	2.27	2.18	2.11	2.05	2.00	1.97	1.93	1.88	1.83	1.76	1.72	1.67	1.61	1.58	1.52	1.50	1.46	1.43	1.41
	7.12	**5.01**	**4.16**	**3.68**	**3.37**	**3.15**	**2.98**	**2.85**	**2.75**	**2.66**	**2.59**	**2.53**	**2.43**	**2.35**	**2.23**	**2.15**	**2.06**	**1.96**	**1.90**	**1.82**	**1.78**	**1.71**	**1.66**	**1.64**
60	4.00	3.15	2.76	2.52	2.37	2.25	2.17	2.10	2.04	1.99	1.95	1.92	1.86	1.81	1.75	1.68	1.65	1.59	1.56	1.50	1.48	1.44	1.41	1.39
	7.08	**4.98**	**4.13**	**3.65**	**3.34**	**3.12**	**2.95**	**2.82**	**2.72**	**2.63**	**2.56**	**2.50**	**2.40**	**2.32**	**2.20**	**2.12**	**2.03**	**1.93**	**1.87**	**1.79**	**1.74**	**1.68**	**1.63**	**1.60**
65	3.99	3.14	2.75	2.51	2.36	2.24	2.15	2.08	2.02	1.98	1.94	1.90	1.85	1.80	1.73	1.68	1.63	1.57	1.54	1.49	1.46	1.42	1.39	1.37
	7.04	**4.95**	**4.10**	**3.62**	**3.31**	**3.09**	**2.93**	**2.79**	**2.70**	**2.61**	**2.54**	**2.47**	**2.37**	**2.30**	**2.18**	**2.09**	**2.00**	**1.90**	**1.84**	**1.76**	**1.71**	**1.64**	**1.60**	**1.56**
70	3.98	3.13	2.74	2.50	2.35	2.23	2.14	2.07	2.01	1.97	1.93	1.89	1.84	1.79	1.72	1.67	1.62	1.56	1.53	1.47	1.45	1.40	1.37	1.35
	7.01	**4.92**	**4.08**	**3.60**	**3.29**	**3.07**	**2.91**	**2.77**	**2.67**	**2.59**	**2.51**	**2.45**	**2.35**	**2.28**	**2.15**	**2.07**	**1.98**	**1.88**	**1.82**	**1.74**	**1.69**	**1.62**	**1.56**	**1.53**
80	3.96	3.11	2.72	2.48	2.33	2.21	2.12	2.05	1.99	1.95	1.91	1.88	1.82	1.77	1.70	1.65	1.60	1.54	1.51	1.45	1.42	1.38	1.35	1.32
	6.96	**4.88**	**4.04**	**3.56**	**3.25**	**3.04**	**2.87**	**2.74**	**2.64**	**2.55**	**2.48**	**2.41**	**2.32**	**2.24**	**2.11**	**2.03**	**1.94**	**1.84**	**1.78**	**1.70**	**1.65**	**1.57**	**1.52**	**1.49**
100	3.94	3.09	2.70	2.46	2.30	2.19	2.10	2.03	1.97	1.92	1.88	1.85	1.79	1.75	1.68	1.63	1.57	1.51	1.48	1.42	1.39	1.34	1.30	1.28
	6.90	**4.82**	**3.98**	**3.51**	**3.20**	**2.99**	**2.82**	**2.69**	**2.59**	**2.51**	**2.43**	**2.36**	**2.26**	**2.19**	**2.06**	**1.98**	**1.89**	**1.79**	**1.73**	**1.64**	**1.59**	**1.51**	**1.46**	**1.43**
125	3.92	3.07	2.68	2.44	2.29	2.17	2.08	2.01	1.95	1.90	1.86	1.83	1.77	1.72	1.65	1.60	1.55	1.49	1.45	1.39	1.36	1.31	1.27	1.25
	6.84	**4.78**	**3.94**	**3.47**	**3.17**	**2.95**	**2.79**	**2.65**	**2.56**	**2.47**	**2.40**	**2.33**	**2.23**	**2.15**	**2.03**	**1.94**	**1.85**	**1.75**	**1.68**	**1.59**	**1.54**	**1.46**	**1.40**	**1.37**
150	3.91	3.06	2.67	2.43	2.27	2.16	2.07	2.00	1.94	1.89	1.85	1.82	1.76	1.71	1.64	1.59	1.54	1.47	1.44	1.37	1.34	1.29	1.25	1.22
	6.81	**4.75**	**3.91**	**3.44**	**3.14**	**2.92**	**2.76**	**2.62**	**2.53**	**2.44**	**2.37**	**2.30**	**2.20**	**2.12**	**2.00**	**1.91**	**1.83**	**1.72**	**1.66**	**1.56**	**1.51**	**1.43**	**1.37**	**1.33**
200	3.89	3.04	2.65	2.41	2.26	2.14	2.05	1.98	1.92	1.87	1.83	1.80	1.74	1.69	1.62	1.57	1.52	1.45	1.42	1.35	1.32	1.26	1.22	1.19
	6.76	**4.71**	**3.88**	**3.41**	**3.11**	**2.90**	**2.73**	**2.60**	**2.50**	**2.41**	**2.34**	**2.28**	**2.17**	**2.09**	**1.97**	**1.88**	**1.79**	**1.69**	**1.62**	**1.53**	**1.48**	**1.39**	**1.33**	**1.28**
400	3.86	3.02	2.62	2.39	2.23	2.12	2.03	1.96	1.90	1.85	1.81	1.78	1.72	1.67	1.60	1.54	1.49	1.42	1.38	1.32	1.28	1.22	1.16	1.13
	6.70	**4.66**	**3.83**	**3.36**	**3.06**	**2.85**	**2.69**	**2.55**	**2.46**	**2.37**	**2.29**	**2.23**	**2.12**	**2.04**	**1.92**	**1.84**	**1.74**	**1.64**	**1.57**	**1.47**	**1.42**	**1.32**	**1.24**	**1.19**
1,000	3.85	3.00	2.61	2.38	2.22	2.10	2.02	1.95	1.89	1.84	1.80	1.76	1.70	1.65	1.58	1.53	1.47	1.41	1.36	1.30	1.26	1.19	1.13	1.08
	6.66	**4.62**	**3.80**	**3.34**	**3.04**	**2.82**	**2.66**	**2.53**	**2.43**	**2.34**	**2.26**	**2.20**	**2.09**	**2.01**	**1.89**	**1.81**	**1.71**	**1.61**	**1.54**	**1.44**	**1.38**	**1.28**	**1.19**	**1.11**
∞	3.84	2.99	2.60	2.37	2.21	2.09	2.01	1.94	1.88	1.83	1.79	1.75	1.69	1.64	1.57	1.52	1.46	1.40	1.35	1.28	1.24	1.17	1.11	1.00
	6.64	**4.60**	**3.78**	**3.32**	**3.02**	**2.80**	**2.64**	**2.51**	**2.41**	**2.32**	**2.24**	**2.18**	**2.07**	**1.99**	**1.87**	**1.79**	**1.69**	**1.59**	**1.52**	**1.41**	**1.36**	**1.25**	**1.15**	**1.00**

Table G Functions of p, q, z, and y, where p and q are proportions $(p + q = 1.00)$ and z and y are constants of the unit normal distribution curve*

p (or q)	A pq	B $\sqrt{pq}$	C pq/y	D $\sqrt{pq}/y$	E p/y	F y/p	G zy/p	H y	I zy/q	J y/q	K q/y	L $\sqrt{p/q}$	M $\sqrt{q/p}$	q (or p)
.99	.0099	.0995−	.3715	3.733	37.15−	.02692	−.06262	.02665	6.2002	2.665	.3752	9.950	.1005	.01
.98	.0196	.1400	.4048	2.892	20.24	.04941	−.1015	.04842	4.9719	2.421	.4131	7.000	.1429	.02
.97	.0291	.1706	.4277	2.507	14.26	.07015	−.1319	.06804	4.2657	2.268	.4409	5.686	.1759	.03
.96	.0384	.1960	.4456	2.274	11.14	.08976	−.1571	.08617	3.7717	2.154	.4642	4.899	.2041	.04
.95	.0475	.2179	.4605	2.113	9.211	.1086	−.1786	.1031	3.3928	2.063	.4848	4.359	.2294	.05
.94	.0564	.2375−	.4735	1.994	7.891	.1267	−.1970	.1191	3.0868	1.985	.5037	3.958	.2526	.06
.93	.0651	.2551	.4848	1.900	6.926	.1444	−.2131	.1343	2.8307	1.918	.5213	3.645	.2743	.07
.92	.0736	.2713	.4951	1.825	6.188	.1616	−.2271	.1487	2.6110	1.858	.5381	3.391	.2949	.08
.91	.0819	.2862	.5043	1.762	5.604	.1785	−.2393	.1624	2.4191	1.804	.5542	3.180	.3145	.09
.90	.0900	.3000	.5128	1.709	5.128	.1950	−.2499	.1755	2.2491	1.755	.5698	3.000	.3333	.10
.89	.0979	.3129	.5206	1.664	4.733	.2113	−.2591	.1880	2.0966	1.709	.5850	2.844	.3516	.11
.88	.1056	.3250	.5279	1.625	4.399	.2273	−.2671	.2000	1.9587	1.667	.5999	2.708	.3693	.12
.87	.1131	.3363	.5346	1.590	4.112	.2432	−.2739	.2115	1.8330	1.627	.6145	2.587	.3865	.13
.86	.1204	.3470	.5409	1.559	3.864	.2588	−.2796	.2226	1.7175	1.590	.6290	2.478	.4035	.14
.85	.1275	.3571	.5468	1.532	3.646	.2743	−.2843	.2332	1.6110	1.554	.6433	2.380	.4201	.15
.84	.1344	.3666	.5524	1.507	3.452	.2896	−.2880	.2433	1.5123	1.521	.6576	2.291	.4365	.16
.83	.1411	.3756	.5576	1.484	3.280	.3049	−.2909	.2531	1.4203	1.489	.6718	2.210	.4525	.17
.82	.1476	.3842	.5625	1.464	3.125	.3200	−.2929	.2624	1.3344	1.458	.6860	2.134	.4685	.18
.81	.1539	.3923	.5671	1.446	2.985	.3350	−.2941	.2714	1.2538	1.428	.7002	2.065	.4844	.19
.80	.1600	.4000	.5715	1.429	2.858	.3500	−.2946	.2800	1.1781	1.400	.7144	2.000	.5000	.20
.79	.1659	.4073	.5756	1.413	2.741	.3648	−.2942	.2882	1.1067	1.372	.7287	1.940	.5156	.21
.78	.1716	.4142	.5796	1.399	2.634	.3796	−.2931	.2961	1.0393	1.346	.7430	1.883	.5311	.22
.77	.1771	.4208	.5832	1.386	2.536	.3943	−.2913	.3036	.9754	1.320	.7575	1.830	.5465	.23
.76	.1824	.4271	.5867	1.374	2.445	.4090	−.2889	.3109	.9149	1.295	.7720	1.780	.5620	.24
.75	.1875	.4330	.5900	1.363	2.360	.4237	−.2858	.3178	.8573	1.271	.7867	1.732	.5774	.25

*When p is less than .50, interchange p and q, as headings of the first and last columns indicate.

Table G Functions of p, q, z, and y, where p and q are proportions (p + q = 1.00) and z and y are constants of the unit normal distribution curve (continued)

p (or q)	A pq	B √pq	C pq/y	D √pq/y	E p/y	F y/p	G zy/p	H y	I zy/q	J y/q	K q/y	L √p/q	M √q/p	q (or p)
.74	.1924	.4386	.5931	1.352	2.281	.4384	−.2820	.3244	.8026	1.248	.8016	1.687	.5928	.26
.73	.1971	.4440	.5961	1.343	2.208	.4529	−.2775	.3306	.7504	1.225	.8166	1.644	.6082	.27
.72	.2016	.4490	.5989	1.334	2.139	.4675	−.2725	.3366	.7006	1.202	.8318	1.604	.6236	.28
.71	.2059	.4538	.6015	1.326	2.074	.4822	−.2668	.3423	.6532	1.180	.8472	1.565	.6391	.29
.70	.2100	.4583	.6040	1.318	2.013	.4967	−.2605	.3477	.6078	1.159	.8628	1.528	.6547	.30
.69	.2139	.4625−	.6063	1.311	1.956	.5113	−.2535	.3528	.5643	1.138	.8787	1.492	.6703	.31
.68	.2176	.4665−	.6085	1.304	1.902	.5259	−.2460	.3576	.5227	1.118	.8949	1.458	.6860	.32
.67	.2211	.4702	.6106	1.298	1.850	.5405	−.2378	.3621	.4828	1.097	.9112	1.425	.7018	.33
.66	.2244	.4737	.6124	1.293	1.801	.5552	−.2290	.3664	.4445	1.078	.9279	1.393	.7178	.34
.65	.2275	.4770	.6142	1.288	1.755	.5698	−.2196	.3704	.4078	1.058	.9449	1.363	.7338	.35
.64	.2304	.4800	.6158	1.283	1.711	.5845	−.2095	.3741	.3725	1.039	.9623	1.333	.7500	.36
.63	.2331	.4828	.6174	1.279	1.669	.5993	−.1989	.3776	.3387	1.020	.9800	1.305	.7663	.37
.62	.2356	.4854	.6188	1.275	1.628	.6141	−.1876	.3808	.3061	1.002	.9980	1.277	.7829	.38
.61	.2379	.4877	.6200	1.271	1.590	.6290	−.1757	.3837	.2748	.9938	1.016	1.251	.7996	.39
.60	.2400	.4899	.6212	1.268	1.553	.6439	−.1631	.3863	.2447	.9659	1.035	1.225	.8165	.40
.59	.2419	.4918	.6223	1.265	1.518	.6589	−.1499	.3888	.2158	.9482	1.055	1.200	.8336	.41
.58	.2436	.4936	.6232	1.263	1.484	.6739	−.1361	.3909	.1879	.9307	1.074	1.175	.8510	.42
.57	.2451	.4951	.6240	1.260	1.451	.6891	−.1215	.3928	.1611	.9134	1.095	1.151	.8686	.43
.56	.2464	.4964	.6247	1.259	1.420	.7043	−.1063	.3944	.1353	.8964	1.116	1.128	.8864	.44
.55	.2475	.4975−	.6253	1.257	1.390	.7196	−.09043	.3958	.1105	.8796	1.137	1.106	.9045	.45
.54	.2484	.4984	.6258	1.256	1.360	.7351	−.07382	.3969	.0867	.8629	1.159	1.083	.9229	.46
.53	.2491	.4991	.6262	1.255	1.332	.7506	−.05650	.3978	.0637	.8464	1.181	1.062	.9417	.47
.52	.2496	.4996	.6264	1.254	1.305	.7662	−.03843	.3984	.0416	.8301	1.205	1.041	.9608	.48
.51	.2499	.4999	.6266	×1.253	1.279	.7820	−.01960	.3988	.0204	.8139	1.229	1.020	.9802	.49
.50	.2500	.5000	.6267	1.253	1.253	.7979	−.00000	.3989	.0000	.7979	1.253	1.000	1.0000	.50

Table H *Conversion of a Pearson r into a corresponding Fisher's z coefficient**

r	z	r	z	r	z	r	z	r	z	r	z
.25†	.26	.40	.42	.55	.62	.70	.87	.85	1.26	.950	1.83
.26	.27	.41	.44	.56	.63	.71	.89	.86	1.29	.955	1.89
.27	.28	.42	.45	.57	.65	.72	.91	.87	1.33	.960	1.95
.28	.29	.43	.46	.58	.66	.73	.93	.88	1.38	.965	2.01
.29	.30	.44	.47	.59	.68	.74	.95	.89	1.42	.970	2.09
.30	.31	.45	.48	.60	.69	.75	.97	.90	1.47	.975	2.18
.31	.32	.46	.50	.61	.71	.76	1.00	.905	1.50	.980	2.30
.32	.33	.47	.51	.62	.73	.77	1.02	.910	1.53	.985	2.44
.33	.34	.48	.52	.63	.74	.78	1.05	.915	1.56	.990	2.65
.34	.35	.49	.54	.64	.76	.79	1.07	.920	1.59	.995	2.99
.35	.37	.50	.55	.65	.78	.80	1.10	.925	1.62		
.36	.38	.51	.56	.66	.79	.81	1.13	.930	1.66		
.37	.39	.52	.58	.67	.81	.82	1.16	.935	1.70		
.38	.40	.53	.59	.68	.83	.83	1.19	.940	1.74		
.39	.41	.54	.60	.69	.85	.84	1.22	.945	1.78		

*The values in this table were derived by interpolation from Table VB in Fisher's *Statistical Method for Research Workers* and are published by permission of the publisher, Oliver & Boyd, Edinburgh and London, 1932.
†For all values of r below .25, r = z to two decimal places.

Table J **Trigonometric functions***

Angle	Sin	Cos	Tan	Angle	Sin	Cos	Tan
0°	.000	1.000	.000	45°	.707	.707	1.000
1°	.018	.999	.018	46°	.719	.695	1.036
2°	.035	.999	.035	47°	.731	.682	1.072
3°	.052	.998	.052	48°	.743	.669	1.111
4°	.070	.997	.070	49°	.755	.656	1.150
5°	.087	.996	.087	50°	.766	.643	1.192
6°	.105	.994	.105	51°	.777	.629	1.235
7°	.122	.992	.123	52°	.788	.616	1.280
8°	.139	.990	.141	53°	.799	.602	1.327
9°	.156	.988	.158	54°	.809	.588	1.376
10°	.174	.985	.176	55°	.819	.574	1.428
11°	.191	.982	.194	56°	.829	.559	1.483
12°	.208	.978	.213	57°	.839	.545	1.540
13°	.225	.974	.231	58°	.848	.530	1.600
14°	.242	.970	.249	59°	.857	.515	1.664
15°	.259	.966	.268	60°	.866	.500	1.732
16°	.276	.961	.287	61°	.875	.485	1.804
17°	.292	.956	.306	62°	.883	.469	1.881
18°	.309	.951	.325	63°	.891	.454	1.963
19°	.326	.946	.344	64°	.899	.438	2.050
20°	.342	.940	.364	65°	.906	.423	2.144
21°	.358	.934	.384	66°	.914	.407	2.246
22°	.375	.927	.404	67°	.921	.391	2.356
23°	.391	.921	.424	68°	.927	.375	2.475
24°	.407	.914	.445	69°	.934	.358	2.605
25°	.423	.906	.466	70°	.940	.342	2.747
26°	.438	.899	.488	71°	.946	.326	2.904
27°	.454	.891	.510	72°	.951	.309	3.078
28°	.469	.883	.532	73°	.956	.292	3.271
29°	.485	.875	.554	74°	.961	.276	3.487
30°	.500	.866	.577	75°	.966	.259	3.732
31°	.515	.857	.601	76°	.970	.242	4.011
32°	.530	.848	.625	77°	.974	.225	4.331
33°	.545	.839	.649	78°	.978	.208	4.705
34°	.559	.829	.675	79°	.982	.191	5.145
35°	.574	.819	.700	80°	.985	.174	5.671
36°	.588	.809	.727	81°	.988	.156	6.314
37°	.602	.799	.754	82°	.990	.139	7.115
38°	.616	.788	.781	83°	.992	.122	8.144
39°	.629	.777	.810	84°	.994	.105	9.514
40°	.643	.766	.839	85°	.996	.087	11.430
41°	.656	.755	.869	86°	.997	.070	14.300
42°	.669	.743	.900	87°	.998	.052	19.081
43°	.682	.731	.933	88°	.999	.035	28.636
44°	.695	.719	.966	89°	.999	.018	57.290

*From Smail, *College Algebra*. New York: McGraw-Hill, 1931.

Table K   Four-place logarithms of numbers*

N	0	1	2	3	4	5	6	7	8	9
0		0000	3010	4771	6021	6990	7782	8451	9031	9542
1	0000	0414	0792	1139	1461	1761	2041	2304	2553	2788
2	3010	3222	3424	3617	3802	3979	4150	4314	4472	4624
3	4771	4914	5051	5185	5315	5441	5563	5682	5798	5911
4	6021	6128	6232	6335	6435	6532	6628	6721	6812	6902
5	6990	7076	7160	7243	7324	7404	7482	7559	7634	7709
6	7782	7853	7924	7993	8062	8129	8195	8261	8325	8388
7	8451	8513	8573	8633	8692	8751	8808	8865	8921	8976
8	9031	9085	9138	9191	9243	9294	9345	9395	9445	9494
9	9542	9590	9638	9685	9731	9777	9823	9868	9912	9956
10	0000	0043	0086	0128	0170	0212	0253	0294	0334	0374
11	0414	0453	0492	0531	0569	0607	0645	0682	0719	0755
12	0792	0828	0864	0899	0934	0969	1004	1038	1072	1106
13	1139	1173	1206	1239	1271	1303	1335	1367	1399	1430
14	1461	1492	1523	1553	1584	1614	1644	1673	1703	1732
15	1761	1790	1818	1847	1875	1903	1931	1959	1987	2014
16	2041	2068	2095	2122	2148	2175	2201	2227	2253	2279
17	2304	2330	2355	2380	2405	2430	2455	2480	2504	2529
18	2553	2577	2601	2625	2648	2672	2605	2718	2742	2765
19	2788	2810	2833	2856	2878	2900	2934	2945	2967	2989
20	3010	3032	3054	3075	3096	3118	3139	3160	3181	3201
21	3222	3243	3263	3284	3304	3324	3345	3365	3385	3404
22	3424	3444	3464	3483	3502	3522	3541	3560	3579	3598
23	3617	3636	3655	3674	3692	3711	3729	3747	3766	3784
24	3802	3820	3838	3856	3874	3892	3909	3927	3945	3962
25	3979	3997	4014	4031	4048	4065	4082	4099	4116	4133
26	4150	4166	4183	4200	4216	4232	4249	4265	4281	4298
27	4314	4330	4346	4362	4378	4393	4409	4425	4440	4456
28	4472	4487	4502	4518	4533	4548	4564	4579	4594	4609
29	4624	4639	4654	4669	4683	4698	4713	4728	4742	4757
30	4771	4786	4800	4814	4829	4843	4857	4871	4886	4900
31	4914	4928	4942	4955	4969	4983	4997	5011	5024	5038
32	5051	5065	5079	5092	5105	5119	5132	5145	5159	5172
33	5185	5198	5211	5224	5237	5250	5263	5276	5289	5302
34	5315	5328	5340	5353	5366	5378	5391	5403	5416	5428
35	5441	5453	5465	5478	5490	5502	5514	5527	5539	5551
36	5563	5575	5587	5599	5611	5623	5635	5647	5658	5670
37	5682	5694	5705	5717	5729	5740	5752	5763	5775	5786
38	5798	5809	5821	5832	5843	5855	5866	5877	5888	5899
39	5911	5922	5933	5944	5955	5966	5977	5988	5999	6010
40	6021	6031	6042	6053	6064	6075	6085	6096	6107	6117
41	6128	6138	6149	6160	6170	6180	6191	6201	6212	6222
42	6232	6243	6253	6263	6274	6284	6294	6304	6314	6325
43	6335	6345	6355	6365	6375	6385	6395	6405	6415	6425
44	6435	6444	6454	6464	6474	6484	6493	6503	6513	6522
45	6532	6542	6551	6561	6571	6580	6590	6599	6609	6618
46	6628	6637	6646	6656	6665	6675	6684	6693	6702	6712
47	6721	6730	6739	6749	6758	6767	6776	6785	6794	6803
48	6812	6821	6830	6839	6848	6857	6866	6875	6884	6893
49	6902	6911	6920	6928	6937	6946	6955	6964	6972	6981
50	6990	6998	7007	7016	7024	7033	7042	7050	7059	7067
N	0	1	2	3	4	5	6	7	8	9

Prop. Parts

	22	21
1	2.2	2.1
2	4.4	4.2
3	6.6	6.3
4	8.8	8.4
5	11.0	10.5
6	13.2	12.6
7	15.4	14.7
8	17.6	16.8
9	19.8	18.9

	20	19
1	2.0	1.9
2	4.0	3.8
3	6.0	5.7
4	8.0	7.6
5	10.0	9.5
6	12.0	11.4
7	14.0	13.3
8	16.0	15.2
9	18.0	17.1

	18	17
1	1.8	1.7
2	3.6	3.4
3	5.4	5.1
4	7.2	6.8
5	9.0	8.5
6	10.8	10.2
7	12.6	11.9
8	14.4	13.6
9	16.2	15.3

	16	15
1	1.6	1.5
2	3.2	3.0
3	4.8	4.5
4	6.4	6.0
5	8.0	7.5
6	9.6	9.0
7	11.2	10.5
8	12.8	12.0
9	14.4	13.5

	14	13
1	1.4	1.3
2	2.8	2.6
3	4.2	3.9
4	5.6	5.2
5	7.0	6.5
6	8.4	7.8
7	9.8	9.1
8	11.2	10.4
9	12.6	11.7

	12	11
1	1.2	1.1
2	2.4	2.2
3	3.6	3.3
4	4.8	4.4
5	6.0	5.5
6	7.2	6.6
7	8.4	7.7
8	9.6	8.8
9	10.8	9.9

	9	8
1	0.9	0.8
2	1.8	1.6
3	2.7	2.4
4	3.6	3.2
5	4.5	4.0
6	5.4	4.8
7	6.3	5.6
8	7.2	6.4
9	8.1	7.2

*From Smail, *College Algebra*. New York: McGraw-Hill, 1931.

N	0	1	2	3	4	5	6	7	8	9	Prop. Parts	
50	6990	6998	7007	7016	7024	7033	7042	7050	7059	7067		**9**
51	7076	7084	7093	7101	7110	7118	7126	7135	7143	7152	1	0.9
52	7160	7168	7177	7185	7193	7202	7210	7218	7226	7235	2	1.8
53	7243	7251	7259	7267	7275	7284	7292	7300	7308	7316	3	2.7
54	7324	7332	7340	7348	7356	7364	7372	7380	7388	7396	4	3.6
55	7404	7412	7419	7427	7435	7443	7451	7459	7466	7474	5	4.5
56	7482	7490	7497	7505	7513	7520	7528	7536	7543	7551	6	5.4
57	7559	7566	7574	7582	7589	7597	7604	7612	7619	7627	7	6.3
58	7634	7642	7649	7657	7664	7672	7679	7686	7694	7701	8	7.2
59	7709	7716	7723	7731	7738	7745	7752	7760	7767	7774	9	8.1
60	7782	7789	7796	7803	7810	7818	7825	7832	7839	7846		**8**
61	7853	7860	7868	7875	7882	7889	7896	7903	7910	7917	1	0.8
62	7924	7931	7938	7945	7952	7959	7966	7973	7980	7987	2	1.6
63	7993	8000	8007	8014	8021	8028	8035	8041	8048	8055	3	2.4
64	8062	8069	8075	8082	8089	8096	8102	8109	8116	8122	4	3.2
65	8129	8136	8142	8149	8156	8162	8169	8176	8182	8189	5	4.0
66	8195	8202	8209	8215	8222	8228	8235	8241	8248	8254	6	4.8
67	8261	8267	8274	8280	8287	8293	8299	8306	8312	8319	7	5.6
68	8325	8331	8338	8344	8351	8357	8363	8370	8376	8382	8	6.4
69	8388	8395	8401	8407	8414	8420	8426	8432	8439	8445	9	7.2
70	8451	8457	8463	8470	8476	8482	8488	8494	8500	8506		**7**
71	8513	8519	8525	8531	8537	8543	8549	8555	8561	8567	1	0.7
72	8573	8579	8585	8591	8597	8603	8609	8615	8621	8627	2	1.4
73	8633	8639	8645	8651	8657	8663	8669	8675	8681	8686	3	2.1
74	8692	8698	8704	8710	8716	8722	8727	8733	8739	8745	4	2.8
75	8751	8756	8762	8768	8774	8779	8785	8791	8797	8802	5	3.5
76	8808	8814	8820	8825	8831	8837	8842	8848	8854	8859	6	4.2
77	8865	8871	8876	8882	8887	8893	8899	8904	8910	8915	7	4.9
78	8921	8927	8932	8938	8943	8949	8954	8960	8965	8971	8	5.6
79	8976	8982	8987	8993	8998	9004	9009	9015	9020	9025	9	6.3
80	9031	9036	9042	9047	9053	9058	9063	9069	9074	9079		**6**
81	9085	9090	9096	9101	9106	9112	9117	9122	9128	9133	1	0.6
82	9138	9143	9149	9154	9159	9165	9170	9175	9180	9186	2	1.2
83	9191	9196	9201	9206	9212	9217	9222	9227	9232	9238	3	1.8
84	9243	9248	9253	9258	9263	9269	9274	9279	9284	9289	4	2.4
85	9294	9299	9304	9309	9315	9320	9325	9330	9335	9340	5	3.0
86	9345	9350	9355	9360	9365	9370	9375	9380	9385	9390	6	3.6
87	9395	9400	9405	9410	9415	9420	9425	9430	9435	9440	7	4.2
88	9445	9450	9455	9460	9465	9469	9474	9479	9484	9489	8	4.8
89	9494	9499	9504	9509	9513	9518	9523	9528	9533	9538	9	5.4
90	9542	9547	9552	9557	9562	9566	9571	9576	9581	9586		**5**
91	9590	9595	9600	9605	9609	9614	9619	9624	9628	9633	1	0.5
92	9638	9643	9647	9652	9657	9661	9666	9671	9675	9680	2	1.0
93	9685	9689	9694	9699	9703	9708	9713	9717	9722	9727	3	1.5
94	9731	9736	9741	9745	9750	9754	9759	9763	9768	9773	4	2.0
95	9777	9782	9786	9791	9795	9800	9805	9809	9814	9818	5	2.5
96	9823	9827	9832	9836	9841	9845	9850	9854	9859	9863	6	3.0
97	9868	9872	9877	9881	9886	9890	9894	9899	9903	9908	7	3.5
98	9912	9917	9921	9926	9930	9934	9939	9943	9948	9952	8	4.0
99	9956	9961	9965	9969	9974	9978	9983	9987	9991	9996	9	4.5
100	0000	0004	0009	0013	0017	0022	0026	0030	0035	0039		

N	0	1	2	3	4	5	6	7	8	9		

Proportional Parts (additional columns):

4
1 0.4
2 0.8
3 1.2
4 1.6
5 2.0
6 2.4
7 2.8
8 3.2
9 3.6

Table L **Values of rank-difference coefficients of correlation that are significant at the .05 and .01 levels (one-tail test)***

N	.05	.01	N	.05	.01
5	.900	1.000	16	.425	.601
6	.829	.943	18	.399	.564
7	.714	.893	20	.377	.534
8	.643	.833	22	.359	.508
9	.600	.783	24	.343	.485
10	.564	.746	26	.329	.465
12	.506	.712	28	.317	.448
14	.456	.645	30	.306	.432

*Reproduced by permission from Dixon, W. J., and Massey, F. J., Jr. *Introduction to Statistical Analysis.* New York: McGraw-Hill, 1951. Table 17-6, p. 261. This table had been derived from Olds, E. G. The 5 per cent significance levels of sums of squares of rank differences and a correction. *Ann. math. Statist.*, 1949, **20**, 117–118. For a two-tail test, double the probabilities to .10 and .02.

$\dfrac{ad}{bc}$	$r_{\text{cos-pi}}$	$\dfrac{ad}{bc}$	$r_{\text{cos-pi}}$	$\dfrac{ad}{bc}$	$r_{\text{cos-pi}}$	$\dfrac{ad}{bc}$	$r_{\text{cos-pi}}$
1.013	.005†	1.940	.255	4.067	.505	11.512	.755
1.039	.015	1.993	.265	4.205	.515	12.177	.765
1.066	.025	2.048	.275	4.351	.525	12.906	.775
1.093	.035	2.105	.285	4.503	.535	13.702	.785
1.122	.045	2.164	.295	4.662	.545	14.592	.795
1.150	.055	2.225	.305	4.830	.555	15.573	.805
1.180	.065	2.288	.315	5.007	.565	16.670	.815
1.211	075	2.353	.325	5.192	.575	17.900	.825
1.242	.085	2.421	.335	5.388	.585	19.288	.835
1.275	.095	2.490	.345	5.595	.595	20.866	.845
1.308	.105	2.563	.355	5.813	.605	22.675	.855
1.342	.115	2.638	.365	6.043	.615	24.768	.865
1.377	.125	2.716	.375	6.288	.625	27.212	.875
1.413	.135	2.797	.385	6.547	.635	30.106	.885
1.450	.145	2.881	.395	6.822	.645	33.578	.895
1.488	.155	2.957	.405	7.115	.655	37.818	.905
1.528	.165	3.095	.415	7.428	.665	43.100	.915
1.568	.175	3.153	.425	7.761	.675	49.851	.925
1.610	.185	3.251	.435	8.117	.685	58.765	.935
1.653	.195	3.353	.445	8.499	.695	71.046	.945
1.697	.205	3.460	.455	8.910	.705	88.984	.955
1.743	.215	3.571	.465	9.351	.715	117.52	.965
1.790	.225	3.690	.475	9.828	.725	169.60	.975
1.838	.235	3.808	.485	10.344	.735	293.28	.985
1.888	.245	3.935	.495	10.903	.745	934.06	.995

*Based upon a more detailed tabluation of the same values by Perry, N. C.,
Kettner, N. W., Hertzka, A. F., and Bouvier, E. A. Estimating the tetrachoric
correlation coefficient via a cosine-pi table. Technical Memorandum No. 2.
Los Angeles: University of Southern California, 1953.
†Example: If an obtained ratio ad/bc equals 3.472, we find that this value
lies between tabled values of 3.460 and 3.571. The cosine-pi coefficient is
therefore between .455 and .465; that is to say, it is .46. If bc is greater than
ad, find the ratio bc/ad and attach a negative sign to $r_{\text{cos-pi}}$

Table N Cell frequencies required to achieve significant chi squares at the .05 point (lightface) and at the .01 point (boldface) when each is parallel to the smallest cell frequency in a fourfold table*

Smallest cell frequency

N_i	0	1	2	3	4	5	6	7	8	9	10	11	12	13	14	15	16	17	18	19	20	21	22	23	24	25
4	4	—	—																							
	—	—	—																							
5	4	5	—	—																						
	5	—	—																							
6	5	6	—	—																						
	6	—	—																							
7	5	6	7	—																						
	6	7	—	—																						
8	5	6	7	8																						
	6	8	8	—	—																					
9	5	6	8	8	9																					
	6	8	9	9	—																					
10	5	7	8	9	10	10																				
	7	8	9	10	—	—																				
11	5	7	8	9	10	11																				
	7	8	9	10	11	—																				
12	5	7	8	9	10	11	12																			
	7	8	10	11	11	12	—																			
13	5	7	8	9	10	11	12																			
	7	9	10	11	12	13	13																			
14	5	7	8	10	11	12	12	13																		
	7	9	10	11	12	13	14	14																		
15	5	7	9	10	11	12	13	14																		
	7	9	10	11	12	13	14	15																		
16	5	7	9	10	11	12	13	14	15																	
	7	9	10	12	13	14	14	15	16																	
17	5	7	9	10	11	12	13	14	15																	
	7	9	11	12	13	14	15	16	16																	
18	5	7	9	10	11	12	13	14	15	16																
	7	9	11	12	13	14	15	16	17	17																
19	5	7	9	10	11	12	14	14	15	16																
	7	9	11	12	13	14	15	16	17	18																
20	5	7	9	10	11	13	14	15	16	16	17															
	7	9	11	12	13	15	16	16	17	18	19															
30	6	8	9	11	12	13	15	16	17	18	19	20	21	22	23	24										
	8	10	12	13	15	16	17	18	19	20	21	22	23	24	25	26										
40	6	8	9	11	12	14	15	16	18	19	20	21	22	23	24	25	26	27	28	29	30					
	8	10	12	14	15	17	18	19	20	22	23	24	25	26	27	28	29	30	31	32	32					
50	6	8	10	11	13	14	15	17	18	19	20	22	23	24	25	26	27	28	29	30	31	32	33	34	35	36
	8	10	12	14	15	17	18	20	21	22	24	25	26	27	28	29	30	31	32	33	34	35	36	37	38	39
N_i	0	1	2	3	4	5	6	7	8	9	10	11	12	13	14	15	16	17	18	19	20	21	22	23	24	25

*Adapted by permission from Mainland, D., and Murray, I. M. Tables for use in fourfold contingency tables. *Science*, 1952, **116**, 591–594.

INSTRUCTIONS   Table N was designed for use in comparing frequencies in two corresponding categories, for two groups of equal size (N_i cases in each group), by means of a chi-square test of significance. For example, suppose that 10 men and 10 women were asked whether or not they liked to watch wrestling on television. Of the men, 8 said "Yes" and 2 said "No." Of the women, 4 said "Yes" and 6 said "No."

N_i is 10, so we use the row of Table N that has 10 at the left. The smallest of the four frequencies is 2, so we use the column with 2 at the top. At the intersection of the row for 10 and the column for 2, we see number 8 (in lightface) and number 9 (in boldface). These numbers mean that with 2 out of 10 men saying "No," for a chi square to be significant at the .05 level we should need to find that 8 women also said "No." Only 6 women actually said "No," so the chi square that would be computed from this fourfold table would fail to reach the value that would equal any of the highest .05 of all chance-generated chi squares when there is one degree of freedom. Therefore, we should not reject the null hypothesis.

Had there been as many as 9 women saying "No," we could have rejected the null hypothesis at the .01 level. Had there been no men who said "No," it would require only 5 No's from the women to indicate a significant χ^2 at the .05 level and only 7 No's from the women to indicate a significant χ^2 at the .01 level. The reader should verify the last two statements by referring to the appropriate cell (intersection of row 10 and column 0) in Table N.

Table O   Cumulative proportions from the tail categories of binomial distributions for $(\frac{1}{2} + \frac{1}{2})^N$, with N varying from 6 to 25

Categories (C)

C / N	C0 / N	C1 / (N − 1)	C2 / (N − 2)	C3 / (N − 3)	C4 / (N − 4)	C5 / (N − 5)	C6 / (N − 6)	C7 / (N − 7)	C8 / (N − 8)	C9 / (N − 9)
6	.016	.109								
7	.008	.062	.227							
8	.004	.035	.145							
9	.002	.020	.090	.254						
10	.001	.011	.055	.172						
11		.006	.033	.113						
12		.003	.019	.073	.194					
13		.002	.011	.046	.133					
14		.001	.006	.029	.090					
15			.004	.018	.059	.151				
16			.002	.011	.038	.105				
17			.001	.006	.025	.072	.166			
18			.001	.004	.015	.048	.119			
19				.002	.010	.032	.084	.180		
20				.001	.006	.021	.058	.132		
21				.001	.004	.013	.039	.095	.192	
22					.002	.008	.026	.067	.143	
23					.001	.005	.017	.047	.105	
24					.001	.003	.011	.032	.076	.154
25						.002	.007	.022	.054	.115

COMMENT   Each entry is the probability of an outcome as extreme as the last category (0 heads or N heads, as in coin tossing), the next-to-the-last category (1 head or N − 1 heads), and so on (i.e., the probabilities are cumulative). Each probability is for one tail only. For a two-tail test, double the probability given.

Table P *T values at the .05, .02, and .01 levels for different*
numbers of ranked differences. T is the smaller sum of ranks
*associated with differences all of the same sign**

N	P = .05	P = .02	P = .01	N	P = .05	P = .02	P = .01
6	0			31	148	129	116
7	2	0		32	159	139	126
8	4	2	0	33	171	150	136
9	6	3	2	34	183	161	147
10	8	5	3	35	195	173	158
11	11	7	5	36	208	185	169
12	14	10	7	37	222	197	181
13	17	13	10	38	235	210	193
14	21	16	13	39	249	223	205
15	25	20	16	40	264	237	218
16	30	24	20	41	279	251	231
17	35	28	23	42	295	265	245
18	40	33	28	43	311	280	259
19	46	38	32	44	327	295	274
20	52	43	38	45	344	311	289
21	59	49	43	46	361	327	304
22	66	56	49	47	379	344	320
23	73	62	55	48	397	361	336
24	81	69	61	49	416	379	353
25	89	77	68	50	435	397	370
26	98	84	74				
27	107	92	82				
28	117	101	90				
29	127	110	98				
30	137	119	107				

*Reproduced by permission from Wilcoxon, F. *Some Rapid Approximate Statistical Procedures*. Stamford, Conn.: American Cyanamid Co., 1949, with addition of cases with N 26–50.

Table Q **Significant R values at the**
.05, .02, and .01 levels for different

numbers of N_i cases in two samples
of equal size. R is the smaller sum
of ranks*

N_i	$P = .05$	$P = .02$	$P = .01$
5	18	16	15
6	27	24	23
7	37	34	32
8	49	46	44
9	63	59	56
10	79	74	71
11	97	91	87
12	116	110	105
13	137	130	125
14	160	152	147
15	185	176	170
16	212	202	196
17	241	230	223
18	271	259	252
19	303	291	282
20	338	324	315

*Reproduced by permission from Wilcoxon, F. *Some Rapid Approximate Statistical Procedures*. Stamford, Conn.: American Cyanamid Co., 1949.

INDEX

Additivity, defined, 20
Alienation, coefficient of, 376–377
Alpha, as confidence level, 205–206
  and type-I error, 206–207
Analysis of variance (*see* Variance, analysis of)
Arithmetic mean (*see* Mean, arithmetic)
Attenuation, correction for, 486–488
  in criterion, 487–488
  and factor theory, 486–487
  limitations to, 488
Average deviation, 71–72
Averages, kinds of, 43–44
  uses of, 43

b coefficient, formulas for, 396
  standard error of, 402
Baller, W. R., contingency data, 234
Beta, probability of, determination of, 208–212
  and type-II error, 206–210
Beta coefficient, formulas for, 396
  solution for, 411–412
  standard error of, 402
Binomial distribution, 118–121, 161
  applications of, 223–224
  in hypothesis testing, 220–224
  and normal-curve approximation, 124–126, 221–223
  tail probabilities, table for, 596
  uses of, 123–125
Binomial expansion, 120–121
Biographical data, reliability of, 450
Biserial correlation (*see* Correlation, biserial)
Boneau, C. A., t-test assumptions, 185n.
Bouvier, E. A., cosine-pi estimates, 329n., 594n.
Brogden, H. J., personnel classification, 434n.
Brown, S. W., chi-square formulas, 240n.

C, 338, 339
C scale, defined, 524
  evaluation of, 527–528
C scaling, procedures for, 526–527
Cantril, H., polling data, 237n.
Categories, data in, 12–15
  qualitative and quantitative, 14
Cattell, R. B., factor analysis, 474n.
Centile point, 54–55
  standard error of, 159

Centile rank, 54–55
Centile scale, 529
Chace, C. I., variance in multiple correlation, 400n.
Chance, games of, 116
Changes, significance tests for, 188, 194–196
Chesire, L., tetrachoric chart, 330n.
Chi square, for combined probabilities, 248–249
  computing formulas, 239–240
  and contingency coefficient, 338
  in contingency tables, 234–236
  in correlated data, 242–243
  and correlation, 235–236
  defined, 227
  general formula for, 231
  interpretation of, 232
  in Kolmogorov-Smirnov test, 265
  and phi coefficient, 334
  from probabilities, 238–239
  sampling distribution of, 232–233
  as sampling statistic, 228
  in small samples, table for, 595
  table for interpretation, 582
  test, for combined probabilities, 248–249
    of goodness of fit, 243–247
  Yates's correction for, 237
  and $\bar{z}$ ratio, 227–230
Class interval, 26–30
  choice of, 27
  limits of, 28–29
Classification, general, 12–15
  of personnel, 433–435
  through selection, 434
Cobb, M. V., correlation data, 331
Cochran, W. G., experimental design, 302n.
  t test with unequal variances, 185n.
Code method, for correlation coefficient, 98–103
  for mean, 46–49
  for standard deviation, 78–82
Coefficients of determination, 379–380, 399
Combinations, formula for, 121
Common factor, defined, 474
Communality, defined, 475
Composite-rank test, 258–259
Confidence intervals, 149–152
Confidence levels, 151–152
Confidence limits, 149–152
Confounding in experiments, 285
Contingency coefficient, 338
  and chi square, 338
  maximal, 339

Contingency coefficient, and prediction, 388
Contingency tables, chi square for, 234–236
  condensing, 241
Continuity, correction for, 187, 221–222
Correlation, assumptions for, 107–108
  average, 299–300
  of averages, 347–348
  biserial, 317–321
    computation of, 317–320
    conversion formulas for, 324
    evaluation of, 320–321
    formulas for, 318–319
    and Pearson r, 321
    and point-biserial r, 324
  and chi square, 235–236
  cosine-pi, 328–329
    table for, 594
  formulas, derivations of, 108–109
  and goodness of fit, 315
  graphic representation of, 106–107
  and grouping errors, 352–353
  in heterogeneous samples, 345–347
  of index numbers, 351–352
  intraclass, 299–300
  of IQ's, 351–352
  item-total, correction for, 502–503
  meaning of, 92–95
  between means, 177
  multiple, coefficient, 394
    correction for bias, 400–401
    factors in, 478–479
    formula for, 394, 398
    and intercorrelations, 404–408
    principles of, 403–408
    solution for, 413
  nonlinear, 308–312
  part with whole, 350–351
  partial, 339–341
  Pearson formula, 95
  phi coefficient (*see* Phi coefficient)
  point-biserial, 322–325
    accuracy of, 323
    and biserial r, 324–325
    derivation for, 537–538
    evaluation of, 324–325
    formulas for, 322–324
    limitations to, 324–325
    and Pearson r, 324
    and phi coefficient, 500
    and tetrachoric r, 500
  rank-difference, 305–308
    evaluation of, 307–308
    and Pearson r, 307–308
    significance of, 593
  and restriction of range, 341–345
  within sets, 346–347
  significance levels of, 580–581
  spurious, 351
  of sums, 426–428
    derivations for, 542–545
  tetrachoric, 326–332
    abac for, 500
    assumptions for, 326–327
    equation for, 327
    estimation of, 328–329
    graphic estimates of, 330
    limitations of, 332
  in unrestricted ranges, estimations of, 343–344
  and variability, 341–345
Correlation coefficient(s), average of, 348–349
  computation of, 95–103
  defined, 91

Correlation coefficient(s), interpretation of, 103–105
  origin of, 369–370
  from original measurements, 97–98
  relativity of, 105
  from scatter diagram, 98–103
  standard error, 162
  t ratio for, 163
Correlation ratio, 108, 308–312
  and analysis of variance, 313–314
  computation of, 310–312
  evaluation of, 315–316
  standard error of, 312
Covariance, analysis of, 301
  defined, 418
  symbols for, 418
  of test items, 453–454
Cox, G. M., experimental design, 302n.
  t test with unequal variances, 185n.
Critical region, defined, 201–203
Critical score in categorical prediction, 383–384
Cronbach, L. J., varieties of reliability, 446
Cross validation, need for, 506
Cureton, E. E., chi square, 249n.

D, Kolmogorov-Smirnov, 260–262
Dailey, J. T., test reliability, 482n.
Darwin, C., and correlation, 369
  and statistics, 1
Data, defined, 12
  numerical, 11
  and statistics, 11–12
Datum (*see* Data)
Decisions, statistical, 200–207
Degrees of freedom, in analysis of variance, 273–274, 291–292
  in contingency tables, 235–236
  in curve fitting, 246
  defined, 146–147
Determination, coefficient of, 379–380
  multiple, 399
Deviation, average, 71–72
  defined, 71
Difference, between correlation coefficients, 189–191
  between frequencies, 185–189
  between means, 173–185
  between proportions, 185–189
Dingman, H. F., tetrachoric r, 500
Discriminant function, 434–435
  multiple, 435
Distribution(s), combined, 536–537
  cumulative, 36–39
  dichotomizing, 321
  leptokurtic, 182
  mesokurtic, 181
  normalizing, 522–523
  platykurtic, 182
  sampling, 142–144
  skewed, 36
    central values in, 60–61
  of test scores and item statistics, 456–457
Dixon, W. J., table of significant rho coefficients, 593n.
Doolittle solution of multiple regression, 409–412
Dunlap, J. W., biserial r, 319n.

Edwards, A. L., analysis of variance, 301n.
  correlation in heterogeneous groups, 346n.
  experimental designs, 282n., 284n.

Edwards, A. L., normal-curve table, 569–576n.
Epsilon coefficient, 317
Equal likelihood, principle of, 383
Equivalence (*see* Reliability, alternate-forms)
Error term in analysis of variance, 275
Errors, types I and II, 206–207
  probabilities of, 205–207
ESP experiment, 114–115
Eta coefficient, algebraic sign of, 316
  formulas for, 310
  and number of class intervals, 316–317
Experiments, design of, 114–115, 302

F ratio, in analysis of variance, 273–274, 292–293
  for correlation ratio, 313
  defined, 191–192
  for difference in multiple R's, 403
  formation of, 275
  relation to t, 278
  without replications, 298–299
  sampling distributions of, 192
  tables for, 583–586
  for test of linear regression, 314
Factor loading, defined, 476
  and factorial validity, 471
Factor theory, 473–480
  and attenuation, 486–487
Factorial, defined, 122
Factorial designs, 282–284
  models for, 282–284
Ferguson, G. A., maximal phi, 336n.
Festinger, L., t tests in non-normal distributions, 184–185
Finite population, sampling in, 167–168
Fisher, R. A., discriminant function, 434n.
  F ratio, 191
  population correlation, 185
  t for correlations, 162
  t for difference in means, 183
  table, of chi square, 582n.
    for z, 589n.
  z, 253
Flanagan, J. S., test scaling, 512
Forecasting efficiency, index of, 377–378
  in predicting attributes, 387
Fourfold table from scatter diagram, 331
Frequency, cumulative, 36–39
  defined, 15
  expected, computation of, 236
  in normal distribution, 243–244
  polygon, 30–33
Frequency distributions, 29–40
  graphic, 30–36
Fruchter, B., factor analysis, 474n.
  factors in error scores, 492–493
Function fluctuations, of individuals, 451–452
  of tests, 452

Gaddis, L. W., restriction of range, abac for, 344n.
Gains, significance of, 196–197
Galton, F., and correlation coefficient, 369–370
  and regression, 369
  and statistics, 1
Goodfellow, L. D., random sampling, 224
Gordon, M. H., chi square, 249n.
Grouping error, in correlations, 352–353
  in means, 46
  in standard deviations, 84–85

Guilford, J. P., alternate-forms reliability, 448n.
  Aptitude Survey, 110–111, 528–529
  error scores, 492n.
  factor analysis, 471–472
  introversion analysis, 471n.
  item correlations, 500n.
  item difficulty, 497n.
  item-total correlations, 350n., 503–504n.
  item weights, 506n.
  phi coefficient, 354n.
  point-biserial r, 354n.
  prediction of categories, 384–385n.
  predictive validity, 485n.
  standard error of tetrachoric r, 330n.
  structure of intellect, 471n.
  test development, 415n.
  test standards, 104n., 408n.
Guilford, R. B., introversion analysis, 471n.
  predictive validity, 485n.
Guilford-Zimmerman Aptitude Survey, data, 110–111
  profile chart, 528–529
Guttman, L., prediction, cases of, 383

Hammond, K. R., least-squares proof, 60n.
Harman, H. H., factor analysis, 474n.
Harrell, M. E., Army General Classification Test data, 68, 153
Harrell, T. W., Army General Classification Test data, 68, 153
Hays, S. P., tetrachoric-r chart, 330n.
Henry, F. M., cluster sampling, 158n.
Henrysson, S., item-total correlations, 503
Hertzka, A. F., cosine-pi estimates, 329n., 594n.
Histogram, 33–34
  cumulative, 38
Hoel, P. G., statistical proofs, 10n.
Homoscedasticity and standard error of estimate, 360
Horst, P., differential prediction, 435n.
  reliability formula, 461
Hotelling, H., t formula for correlation, 190
Householder, J. E., least-squares proof, 60n.
Hull, C. L., U-shaped distributions, 456
  validity standards, 104
Hypothesis testing, basic logic in, 204–205

Inferences, statistical, 142–152
Isomorphism, defined, 20, 114
Item, correlations, 497–505
  difficulty, and chance success, 497
  function, 495–496
  indices of, 494–497
  discrimination value, 498
  statistics, 453–455, 494
  weighting in tests, 505–506
Item analysis, 493–505

Jarrett, R. F., cluster sampling, 158n.
Johnson, P. O., analysis of variance, 301n.
  degrees of freedom, 147
Jones, R. A., r restricted for range, abac for, 344n.

Kaiser, H. F., r restricted for range, abac for, 344n.
Kaplan, O. J., item-analyses data, 495
Kelley, T. L., standard error of C, 339n.
  test statistics, standards for, 104

Kendall, M. G., tau coefficient, 308
Kettner, N. W., table for cosine-pi, 594n.
Kolmogorov, A., D test, 260–267
Kolmogorov-Smirnov, tests, 260–267
Kreuter, R. P., example of profile, 433
Kuder, G. F., reliability formula, 459–461
Kuder-Richardson formulas (*see* Reliability)
Kurtosis of sampling distributions, 181–182

Lacey, J. I., error scores, 492n.
  item correlations, 504n.
Laird, D. A., C2 test, 471
Least squares, in prediction, 357–358
  proof for, 539–540
Leptokurtic distribution (*see* Distribution)
Lev, J., chi square, 239n.
  point-biserial r, 323n.
  Student's distribution, 249n.
  t formula for correlations, 194n.
Lewis, D., chi-square distributions, 233
  correlation ratio, 317n.
  derivation of chi square, 227n.
  statistical proofs, 10n.
Lindquist, E. F., within correlation, 346–347
  educational measurement, 512n.
  experimental designs, 284n., 302n.
  Norton study, 300
  random numbers, tables of, 139n.
  sampling distributions of means, 143
Linear transformation, in coding, 48
  derivation for, 545
  equation, 517
Literary Digest poll, 140
Logarithms, tables for, 591–592
Logic of statistics, 9
Loveland, E. H., chi square, 249n.
Lyon, T. C., standard error of tetrachoric r, 330n.

McNemar, Q., chi square from correlated data, 243
  models in analysis of variance, 284n.
  standard error of phi, 335n.
  Stanford Binet, scaling in, 512n.
  z̄ test, in correlated data, 188
Mainland, D., table for chi square, 595n.
Mann, H. B., 259–260
Mann-Whitney U-test, 259–260
Marks, E. S., cluster sampling, 158n.
  Stanford-Binet, scaling in, 512n.
Massey, F. J., Jr., table of significant rho's, 593n.
Matched samples, sampling statistics in, 165–166
Mathematical functions, use of, 317
Mathematical models, 113–114
Mathematics, need for, 113–114
Maxwell, A. E., experimental design, 302
Mean, arithmetic, 43–49
  from coded data, 46–49
  effect, of adding constant on, 534
    of constant multiplier on, 534
  formulas for, 44–49
  from grouped data, 45–49
  of linear function, 535
  of means, formula for, 63
  properties of, 57–62
  from ungrouped data, 44–45
  use of, 56, 61–62
 of binomial distribution, 123

Mean, of percentages, 63–64 population, 138
  of proportions, 63–64
  of sum, 417
    control of, 423
    derivation for, 540–541
  of ranks, 256
  weighted, 63
Mean square, for between sets, 271
  defined, 73
  from original measurements, 278–281
  for within sets, 271
Measurement, defined, 20
  educational, 19–20
  meaning of, 18–19
  psychological, 18–19
  scales, kinds of, 20–23
Median, computation of, 49–54
  defined, 49
  formulas for, 51
  in grouped data, 49–53
  properties of, 57–61
  as quartile, 69
  test of significance for, 257–258
  in ungrouped data, 53–54
  uses of, 61–62
Mesokurtic distribution (*see* Distribution)
Michael, W. B., cosine-pi estimates, 329n.
  point-biserial r, 323n., 354n.
  prediction of categories, 384–385n.
  r restricted for range, abac for, 344n.
Mode, defined, 55
  estimated, 55–56
  formula for, 56
  use of, 61–63
Moments, defined, 58
Montemagni, G., test data, 285–286n.
Mosier, C. I., neurotic-tendency analysis, 471n.
  reliability of test battery, 482n.
Mueller, C. G., transformations, 253
Multiple correlation (*see* Correlation, multiple)
Multiple-cutoff method, 428–430
  and multiple regression, 428–430
Murray, I. M., table for chi square, 595n.

Nondetermination, coefficient of, 379
  multiple, 399
Normal distribution, and binomial distribution, 124–126
  constants for, 587–588
  cumulative, 126–127
    equation for, 127
  curve, area under, 127–131
  equation for, 125
  as model, 114
  nature of, 7
  tables for, 568–579
  tests of fit to, 243–247, 260–262
  unit, 127
Normal equations, 409
Norms, test, 528–530
Null hypothesis, for correlation, 171
  defined, 171
  for difference between means, 172–173
Numbers, limits to, 23–24
  properties of, 20

Ogive, defined, 40, 498
Olds, E. G., table of significant rho's, 593n.
One-tail test, 187, 201–202
  defined, 180

Parameter, defined, 137
Partial correlation, 339–341
Pascal triangle, 122
Pearson, K., r, assumptions for, 107–108
  preference for, 304
  in restricted range, 342
Percentage(s), cumulative, 39–40
  use of, 15–17
  weighted mean of, 64
  frequencies, 35–36
Perry, N. C., cosine-pi estimates, 329n., 594n.
  phi coefficient, 354n.
  point-biserial r, 323n.
Personnel selection, restriction of range in, 342–345
Peters, C. C., correction in r, 352–353
  correlation ratio, 317
  standard errors, 167
  statistical proofs, 10
Phi coefficient, 333–338
  abac for, 501
  and chi square, 334
  corrected for coarse grouping, 353–354
  derivation of, 538–539
  evaluation of, 335–336
  formulas for, 333–334
  for item correlations, 499
  maximal, 336–337
  minimal, 338
  and Pearson r, 354
  and prediction, 388
  statistical significance of, 335
Platykurtic distribution (*see* Distribution)
Point-biserial r (*see* Correlation)
Population, defined, 5, 137
  mean of, hypotheses concerning, 148–151
Power of statistical tests, 180, 210–213
  increasing, 213–214
Prediction, accuracy of, 357, 382
  actuarial, 7
  in artificial dichotomies, 385–386
  of attributes, from attributes, 386–387
    from measurements, 380–385
  common factors in, 477–478
  and correlation, 376
  differential, 434
  errors of, 358–359
  in genuine dichotomies, 381–382
  of measurements, from attributes, 357–365
    from measurements, 362–374
  multiple, graphic, 397–398
  from regression equations, 372
  and statistics, 7–8
  test battery for, 414–416
  types of, 356–357
Primary mental abilities, 471
Probabilities, 18
  combining, 203
Probability, defined, 116–117
  maximum, principle of, 386–387
  principles of, 115–118
  requirements for, 117
  theorems for, 116–118
Profile chart, 529
  interpretation, 431–433
  for personnel selection, 431–432
Profile methods, 431–432
Proportions, cumulative, 39–40
  uses of, 17
  weighted mean of, 64, 185

Q, 69–71

Q, preference for, 88–89
Quartile, defined, 69
  interpolation of, 69–70

R in nonparametric test, tables for, 598
Random numbers, tables of, 139
Random sampling, 189, 223–224
Range as measure of variability, 68–69
Rank, centile, 54–55
Ranking, steps in, 306
Ratings, analysis of variance from, 297–299
Ratios as indices, 18
Regression, of averages, 107
  examples of, 315–316
  filial, law of, 369
  linear, 366–367
    attributes and, 381–382
    F test for, 314
  multiple, equation, 395–397, 412–414
    and multiple cutoff, 428–430
    weighting of factors in, 478–479
  nonlinear, 308–309
  origin of, 369
Regression coefficients, 366–367, 369
  from ungrouped data, 371
Regression equations, 366–368, 370–371
Regression line as mean, 375
Regression lines, 309–310, 370
Regression weights, derivation of, 539–540
  substitutes for, 423–426
Reliability, alternate-forms, 446–449
    meaning of, 452
  basic methods for, 445–453
  coefficient, basic formulas for, 441
    of determination, 443
    expected, 104
  and common factors, 475
  defined, 439
  for heterogeneous tests, 449–450
  for homogeneous tests, 449–450
  index of, 442–443
  internal-consistency, meaning, 452
    methods, 453–464
    theory, 453–457
  and item difficulty, 455
  and item intercorrelations, 455–456, 463
  Kuder-Richardson formulas, 458–462
    Horst modification, 461
  methods, preference for, 449–452
  odd-even, 458
  of power tests, 450–451
  and range, of item difficulty, 456
    of scores, 464–465
  of ratings, 466
  retest, 447–449
    changes with lapse of time, 448
    meaning of, 451–452
  Rulon formula for, 462–463
  of speed tests, 451
  of test battery, 482–483
  and test length, 465–466
  theory of, 438–445
Research, statistics in, 3–4
Residual term in analysis of variance, 275
Rho coefficient, 305–306
  formula for, 306
  standard error of estimate of, 307
Richardson, M. W., item theory, 463n.
  item validity, 484
  reliability formulas, 459–461
Root-mean-square deviation, 73
Rulon, P. J., reliability formula, 445, 462–463

Saffir, M., tetrachoric-r chart, 330n.
Sample size, and alpha, 214–216
 and beta, 216–220
 required, for significance, 214–220
Sampling, biased, 138–139, 157–158
 examples of, 154–155
 in finite populations, 167–168
 incidental, 142
 principles of, 137–142
 purposive, 141–142
 random, 223–224
  requirements for, 139
 stratification in, 140–141
 in stratified populations, 164–165
 stratified-random, 141
Sampling distribution, 142–144
 of chi square, 232–233
 of correlation coefficients, 156, 162
 of F ratio, 192
 of Fisher's z, 163
 of means, 156
 of t ratio, 182
 of $\bar{z}$ ratio, 175–176
Scale, interval, 21–22
 nominal, 20–21
 ordinal, 21
 ratio, 22–23
 standard-score, 513–516
Scatter diagram, 98–99
Scoring formulas, 489–493
 a priori, 489–490
 empirical, 490–493
 factors and, 492–493
Semi-interquartile range (*see* Q)
Shartle, C. L., Wherry-Doolittle method, 415n.
Sheppard's correction, 85, 352, 364
Siegel, S., chi-square table, 239n.
 nonparametric methods, 260n., 266n.
Sign-rank test, 255–256
Sign test, 253–254
Significance, of combined tests, 248–249
 level of, choice of, 205–207
Simultaneous equations, solution for, 409–412
Skewness, defined, 36
 and quartiles, 71
Smail, L. L., table, of logarithms, 591–592n.
 trigonometric, 590n.
Small-sample statistics, 181–185
Smirnov, N. V., D test, 260–267
Snedecor, G. W., F ratio, 191
 range and standard deviation, 81n.
 table, of F, 583–586n.
 of r and t, 580–581n.
Spearman, C., rank-difference correlation, 305–308
Spearman-Brown formula, 457–459
 derivation of, 466–467
Spurious correlation (*see* Correlation, spurious)
Stability (*see* Reliability, retest)
Standard deviation, basic formula, 72
 by code method, 78–82
 of combined distributions, 536–537
 computation of, 76–84
 corrected, 84–85
 derivation of formula, 83–84
 effect of adding constant, 535
  of constant multiplier, 535–536
 interpretation, 76–78
 of linear function, 536
 from original measurements, 82–83
 preference for, 88–89
 and range, 80–81

Standard deviation, of sum, 417–422
 control of, 422
 derivation of, 541–543
 use of, 85–89
Standard error, of b coefficient, 402
 of beta coefficient, 402
 of biserial r, 319
 of centile point, 159
 of correlation coefficient, 162
 of correlation ratio, 312
 of difference, between correlated means, 177–178
  between Fisher's z's, 190
  between means, from differences, 181
   in matched samples, 195
  between uncorrelated means, 173–174
 of estimate, 360–361
  computation of, 363–364
  corrected for bias, 362, 375, 401
  formulas for, 373
  interpretation of, 373–374
  multiple, 400
 of Fisher's z, 164
 of frequency, 160
 of mean, 136
  biased, 154–155
  in finite population, 168
  formulas for, 144–145, 147
  interpretation of, 148–155
  in matched samples, 166
  in stratified samples, 164
  use of, 153
 of measurement, 443–445
  from differences, 445
 of median, 158
 of multiple R, 402
 of obtained score, 444
 of partial correlation, 341
 of percentage, 161
 of proportion, 161
  in finite population, 168
  in matched samples, 167
  in stratified samples, 165
 of rho coefficient, 307
 of standard deviation, 159
 of tetrachoric r, 330
Standard measure (*see* Standard score)
Standard score(s), equation for, 128
 for tests, 512–514
Stanine scale, 528
Statistical decisions, errors in, 205–207
 rules for, 200–205
Statistics, defined, 12
 descriptive vs. sampling, 5–6, 136
 mathematics of, 10
 and research, 3–4
 student aims in, 8–10
 student needs for, 1–3
Stead, W. H., Wherry-Doolittle method, 415n.
Stratified population, sampling in, 164–165
Student's t, 152
Sum of squares, in analysis of variance, 270–271, 289–291
 defined, 73
 from measurements, 296–297
 without replications, 298
 from unequal samples, 280–281

T, for ranked differences, table of, 597
t ratio, for correlation coefficient, 163
 for difference, between correlation coefficients, 190–191

t ratio, for difference, between means, 183–184
  between variances, 193
  limitations to, 184–185
  relation to *F*, 278
  sampling distribution of, 181–183
  significant, 182–183
  table for, 580–581
T scale, 518–524
  defined, 518
  evaluation of, 522–524
T scaling, graphic, 521–522
  procedures for, 519–522
t test following *F* test, 275–278
Taguiri, R., test data, 285–286*n*.
Tau, Kendall's, 308
Tesi, G., test data, 285–286*n*.
Test(s), as composite of items, 453–456
  development, philosophy of, 415, 481, 493–494
  homogeneous, need for, 481–482
  items, discrimination value of, 483–485
  scales, need for, 510–513
  speed vs. power, 450
  of statistical significance (*see* Chi square; *F* ratio; *t* ratio)
Test batteries, heterogeneous, need for, 481–482
Thorndike, E. L., *T* scale, 518*n*.
Thorndike, R. L., data, on multiple correlation, 407*n*.
  on restriction of range, 344–345*n*.
  personnel classification, 434*n*.
  regression effects, 375*n*.
Thurstone, L. L., error scores, 490*n*.
  primary abilities, 471*n*.
  tetrachoric-*r* chart, 330
Tippett, L. H. C., table of random numbers, 139*n*.
Transformation of measurements, 252–253
Transition zone in test-item function, 484
Trigonometric functions, table for, 590
True scores, correlation between, 486
  (*See also* Reliability)
Tucker, L. R., validity of tests, 481
Tukey, J. W., *t* test after *F* test, 275–278

Universe (*see* Population)

Validity, coefficient, expected, 104
  and factor loadings, 477
  factorial, 471–472
  and item difficulty, range of, 484
  predictive, 472–473
  and reliability, 480–483
  of right and wrong responses, 489–493
  of test items, 498
  and test length, 485
  types of, 470–472
Van Voorhis, W. R., correction in *r*, 352–353*n*.
  correlation ratio, 317*n*.
  standard errors, 167*n*.
  statistical proofs, 10*n*.
Variability, choice of measure of, 88–89
  measures of, 68
  relations between measures of, 89
Variable, defined, 13
  dependent and independent, 392
  independent, contribution of, 399–400

Variable, suppression, 405–406
Variance(s), analysis of, assumptions for, 274, 300–301
  and correlation ratio, 313–314
  evaluation of, 300–302
  one-way, 269–275
  without replications, 297–299
  sum of squares, 270–271, 289–291
  two-way, 281–293
  of binomial distribution, 123
  components of, 440
  defined, 74–75
  of differences, 174
  differences between, significance of, 191–194
  error, 439
    contributions to, 446–449
  interaction, 285–287
    source of, 294
  population, estimate of, 269–271
  predicted, 380
  sources of, 284–287
    main effects, 285
  of sum, 174, 417–421
    derivation for, 541–543
  of test item, 453
  true, 439
    contributors to, 446–449
  unpredicted, 380
Variation, removal of sources of, 294–295
Vocational guidance as classification, 433–434

Walker, H. M., chi square, 239*n*.
  degrees of freedom, 147*n*.
  point-biserial *r*, 323*n*.
  Student's distribution, 249*n*.
  t formula for correlation, 194*n*.
Wallace, H. A., table of *r* and *t*, 580–581*n*.
Weighting, components of battery, 423–426
  of test items, 505–506
Wherry, R. J., discriminant function, 435
Wherry-Doolittle method, 414–415
Whitney, D. R., U test 259–260
Wilcoxon, F., nonparametric methods, 255–256*n*., 259
  table, of significant *R*'s, 598*n*.
  of significant *T*'s, 597*n*.
Winer, B. J., experimental designs, 302*n*.
Woodworth, R. S., inventory, 471
  transition zone, 484*n*.
Wrongs score, factors in, 492–493

Yates, F., correction, in chi square, 237, 243
Young, H. B., test data, 285–286*n*.
Yule, G. U., phi coefficient, 333*n*.

z, Fisher's, 163
  in averaging *r*'s, 348–349
  conversion table for, 589*n*.
  equation for, 128
$\bar{z}$ ratio, and chi square, 227–230
  distribution of, 175–176
  formula for, 175
Zimmerman, W. S., Aptitude Survey, 110–111, 528–529